active MATHS 4

BOOK 1

G000229693

LEAVING CERTIFICATE MATHS HIGHER LEVEL

PAPER 1

Velocity = $\frac{dh}{dt}$

$C = 2\pi r$

$V \approx \frac{4}{3}\pi r^3$

$h(t) = \frac{t^3(120-t)^3}{10^8}$,

$0 \le t \le 120$

FREE eBook
See inside cover

Michael Keating, Derek Mulvany and James O'Loughlin
Special Advisors: Oliver Murphy, Colin Townsend and Jim McElroy

FOLENS

First published in 2016 by Folens Publishers

Hibernian Industrial Estate, Greenhills Road, Tallaght, Dublin 24

Illustrations: Oxford Designers and Illustrators

ISBN 978-1-78090-638-6

Acknowledgements

Answers were checked by Síobhán Allen, Tim Allen and Jonathan Webley.

The authors and publisher are grateful to the following for permission to reproduce photographs: Alamy, Bridgeman Images, Corbis, iStock, Science Photo Library, Shutterstock and Thinkstock.

The authors and publisher wish to think Bank of Ireland for permission to reproduce copyright material on p.254.

The publisher has made every effort to contact all copyright holders but if any have been overlooked, we will be pleased to make any necessary arrangements.

Contents

Introduction

Active Maths 4, 2nd edition, is a comprehensive revision of our two-book series to cover the complete Leaving Certificate Higher Level Maths course. This programme maintains all the benefits of the previous books, while introducing a range of new and improved features. As before:

- Book 1 corresponds to Paper 1 and therefore contains Strands 3 (Number), 4 (Algebra) and 5 (Functions).

- Book 2 corresponds to Paper 2 and therefore contains Strands 1 (Statistics and Probability) and 2 (Geometry and Trigonometry).

Active Maths 4, 2nd edition, allows teachers to meet the challenge of the Higher Level Maths syllabus, and encourages students to discover for themselves that maths can be enjoyable and relevant to everyday life while preparing for their exams.

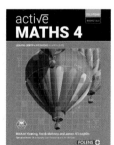

- Revised and current: Following a number of years of examination of Project Maths, additional worked examples, real-life examples, context questions and revised content reflect the reality of the curriculum.

- Exam-focused: End-of-chapter revision exercises, improved exam-focused questions and the inclusion of new past exam questions enable students to better self-assess and prepare for the Leaving Certificate.

- Digital resources: An improved bank of interactive digital resources, including chapter summaries, topic PowerPoints and constructions are available for use in the classroom, and for student revision.

- Worked solutions for students: To support independent learning in preparation for the exam.

- Differentiated learning: Comprehensive, carefully graded exercises facilitate progressive learning in mixed-ability classrooms.

- Improved layout: 'Handy Hints' boxes providing concept tips, and simplified, straightforward diagrams and graphs to help students learn effectively.

- Learning outcomes: A 'You Should Remember' section and a list of 'Key Words' are presented at the beginning of each chapter to inform students what they can expect to learn.

We believe we have improved the quality of these new books and hope that those who use them will achieve the best mark possible in the Leaving Cert Maths examinations.

Michael Keating, Jim McElroy, Derek Mulvany, Oliver Murphy, James O'Loughlin and Colin Townsend

March 2016

Key to icons used in this book

 Learning outcomes

 You should remember...

 Key words

 Formula

 Handy tips

 Digital resource available

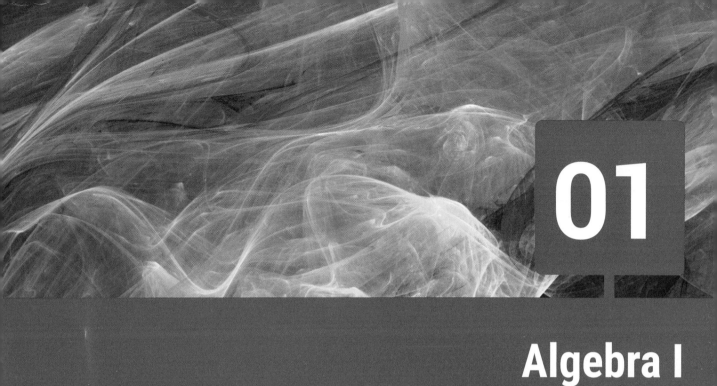

01

Algebra I

In this chapter you will learn to:

- Add, subtract, multiply and divide algebraic terms
- Apply the binomial theorem to expand expressions of the form $(a + b)^n$
- Factorise quadratic expressions
- Factorise certain cubic expressions
- Divide algebraic expressions using long division

You should remember...

- How to add, subtract, multiply and divide algebraic expressions

Key words

- Expression
- Term
- Polynomial
- Coefficient
- Pascal's triangle
- Highest common factor (HCF)
- Difference of two squares
- Quadratic trinomial
- Lowest common denominator (LCD)
- Factors

1.1 Expressions

Algebra has many uses, from the design of computer games to the modelling of weather patterns.

To be able to use algebra, we must first understand the rules involved in the basic operations of adding, subtracting, multiplying and dividing algebraic terms and expressions.

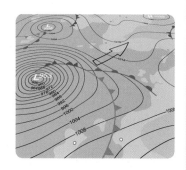

Notation in Algebra

A **variable** is a letter (usually x or y) that represents a number. This number may change or be unknown.

- In $5x$, the **variable** is x.
- In $20y$, the variable is y.

A **coefficient** is a number or symbol that is multiplying a variable.

- In $5x$, the **coefficient** is 5.
- In $20y$, the coefficient is 20.
- In x, the coefficient is 1.

A **constant** is a quantity that does not change in value, i.e. a number by itself.

In $10x + 2$, the **constant** is 2.

A constant, a variable or a constant multiplied by a variable are all considered **terms**, as are products of variables and powers of variables.

$12(x)$ is an example of a **term**.

It means '12 times x'.

This is written as $12x$.

$x + 5y - 7$ contains three terms:

- x (a variable)
- $5y$ (a constant times a variable)
- -7 (a constant)

An **algebraic expression** is an expression that contains one or more numbers, one or more variables, and one or more arithmetic operations.

$5x + 2$ is an **expression**. Other examples of expressions include $x + 3y$, $8y^2$ and $4pr^3 - 7$.

Polynomials have variables that have only non-negative whole number powers.

A **polynomial** in x has the form $a_n x^n + a_{n-1} x^{n-1} + a_{n-2} x^{n-2} + ... + a_2 x^2 + a_1 x^1 + a_0$, where all the coefficients ($a_0, a_1, a_2, ..., a_{n-1}, a_n$) are constants and the powers are non-negative whole numbers.

The **degree** (or order) of the polynomial is equal to the highest power.

- A polynomial of degree 1 is called **linear**.
- A polynomial of degree 2 is called **quadratic**.
- A polynomial of degree 3 is called **cubic**.
- A polynomial of degree 4 is called **quartic**.

For example, $5x^6 + 2x^2 - 3x + 7$ is a polynomial in x of degree 6. It has four terms. The coefficient of x is -3 and the constant is 7.

Substitution

We need to be able to evaluate expressions and formulae when given certain conditions. We replace the variables with the numerical values given.

For example, if we are given the formula for the volume of a cylinder, $V = \pi r^2 h$, and are asked to evaluate the volume of the cylinder given that $\pi = 3.14$, $r = 10$ cm and $h = 12$ cm:

$$V = \pi r^2 h$$

$$V = (3.14)(10)^2(12)$$

$$V = 3768 \text{ cm}^3$$

Worked Example 1.1

If $a = 4$, $b = -3$ and $c = -6$, evaluate the following expressions:

(i) $a^2 + 2b^3 - 3c$ (ii) $\dfrac{\sqrt[a]{3b^4 - 2c + 1}}{c}$

Solution

We rewrite the expression, using brackets to replace the variables, and insert the given values of a, b and c.

(i) $a^2 + 2b^3 - 3c$

$= (4)^2 + 2(-3)^3 - 3(-6)$

$= 16 + 2(-27) + 18$

$= 16 - 54 + 18$

$= -20$

(ii) $\dfrac{\sqrt[a]{3b^4 - 2c + 1}}{c}$

$= \dfrac{\sqrt[4]{3(-3)^4 - 2(-6) + 1}}{-6}$

$= \dfrac{\sqrt[4]{243 + 12 + 1}}{-6}$

$= \dfrac{\sqrt[4]{256}}{-6}$

$= \dfrac{4}{-6}$

$= -\dfrac{2}{3}$

Addition/Subtraction

When adding or subtracting algebraic terms, we must always remember the following rules:

Algebra Rule: Only terms that have the exact same letter(s) raised to the same power(s) (like terms) can be added or subtracted.

Examples:

$5x + 6y + 4x - 3y = 9x + 3y$

$p + 2q + 3p - 4q = 4p - 2q$

Algebra Rule: When adding or subtracting like terms, the powers of the variables do not change but the coefficients do.

Examples:

$20y^2 + 8y^2 = 28y^2$

$xy - 3w^2 + 5xy + 2w^2 = 6xy - w^2$

Multiplying

Unlike when adding or subtracting, in algebra any term may be multiplied by any other term. When we multiply terms, we encounter another set of rules that are important to understand.

Algebra Rule: To multiply terms:
coefficient × coefficient, variable × variable.

Example: $(4x)(5y)$

$= (4)(x)(5)(y)$

$= (4(x)(5))y$ (associative)

$= (4((5)(x)))y$ (commutative)

$= 20xy$

Algebra Rule: When multiplying terms that contain the same variable, we **add** the powers or indices of that variable.

This rule is also written as $a^p a^q = a^{p+q}$.

We could have written $(4x^3)(3x^5) = (4)(3)(x^3)(x^5)$

$= 12x^8$

Example: $(4x^3)(3x^5)$

$= (4)(x)(x)(x)(3)(x)(x)(x)(x)(x)$

$= (4)(3)(x)(x)(x)(x)(x)(x)(x)(x)$
(Following repeated application of the associative and commutative properties)

$= 12x^8$

ALGEBRA I

The multiplication examples above made use of the associative and commutative properties. We can also use the distributive property.

Example: $4x(x^2 + 3y)$

$$= 4x(x^2) + 4x(3y)$$

$$= 4x^3 + 12xy$$

In algebra we can be asked to expand and simplify an expression. This means we have to rewrite the expression as a sum of terms, in their simplest form. To do this we add, subtract, multiply, divide or use another method depending on the question.

Important Products

$x(y + z) = xy + xz$

$(a + b)(x + y) = ax + ay + bx + by$

$(a + b)(a - b) = a^2 - b^2$

$(a + b)^2 = a^2 + 2ab + b^2$

$(a - b)^2 = a^2 - 2ab + b^2$

$(a + b)^3 = a^3 + 3a^2b + 3ab^2 + b^3$

$(a - b)^3 = a^3 - 3a^2b + 3ab^2 - b^3$

You should verify each of the above products by manually expanding and simplifying each left-hand side (LHS).

Worked Example 1.2

Expand and simplify:

(i) $4(2a - b)(a - 5b)$ (ii) $23x - x(2x + 3)^2$ (iii) $(4x - 5)^3$ (iv) $(3a - 4)(2a + b)^3$

Solution

(i) $4(2a - b)(a - 5b)$

$$= 4[2a(a - 5b) - b(a - 5b)] \qquad \text{(distributive property)}$$

$$= 4[2a^2 - 10ab - ab + 5b^2] \qquad (ba = ab, \text{ by the commutative property)}$$

$$= 4[2a^2 - 11ab + 5b^2] \qquad \text{(subtracting like terms)}$$

$$= 8a^2 - 44ab + 20b^2$$

(ii) $23x - x(2x + 3)^2$

$$= 23x - x[(2x)^2 + 2(2x)(3) + (3)^2]$$

$$= 23x - x[4x^2 + 12x + 9]$$

$$= 23x - 4x^3 - 12x^2 - 9x$$

$$= -4x^3 - 12x^2 + 14x$$

> This is a polynomial of degree 3.

(iii) $(4x - 5)^3$

$$= (4x)^3 - 3(4x)^2(5) + 3(4x)(5)^2 - (5)^3$$

$$= 64x^3 - 240x^2 + 300x - 125$$

> You should memorise the expansions for $(a \pm b)^2$ and $(a \pm b)^3$.
>
> It will save time in an exam situation.

(iv) $(3a - 4)(2a + b)^3$

$$(2a + b)^3 = (2a)^3 + 3(2a)^2b + 3(2a)b^2 + b^3$$

$$= 8a^3 + 12a^2b + 6ab^2 + b^3$$

$$\therefore (3a - 4)(8a^3 + 12a^2b + 6ab^2 + b^3) = 3a(8a^3 + 12a^2b + 6ab^2 + b^3) - 4(8a^3 + 12a^2b + 6ab^2 + b^3)$$

$$= 24a^4 + 36a^3b + 18a^2b^2 + 3ab^3 - 32a^3 - 48a^2b - 24ab^2 - 4b^3$$

Worked Example 1.3

A rectangular playing field has length $4x$ metres and width $(3x - 5)$ metres.

Write down an expression in x for:

(i) The area of the field

(ii) The perimeter of the field

Solution

(i) Area = $l \times b$

We know that $l = 4x$ and $b = (3x - 5)$.

∴ Area = $(4x)(3x - 5)$

$= (12x^2 - 20x)$ m^2

(ii) Perimeter of a rectangle = $2l + 2b$

$= 2(4x) + 2(3x - 5)$

$= 8x + 6x - 10$

$= (14x - 10)$ m

Units of measurement should always be included in your answers.

Pascal's Triangle

$(a + b)^5$ would take a long time to expand and simplify using the methods previously employed. However, there is another method that we can employ.

A binomial expansion is where an expression of two terms is multiplied by itself a number of times.

By looking at the expansion of the binomial $(a + b)^n$ we can spot a pattern that we may be able to use for such expressions ($n \in N$ or $n = 0$).

$(a + b)^0 = 1$ (assuming $a + b \neq 0$)

$(a + b)^1 = a^1 + b^1$

$(a + b)^2 = a^2 + 2a^1b^1 + b^2$

$(a + b)^3 = a^3 + 3a^2b^1 + 3a^1b^2 + b^3$

$(a + b)^4 = a^4 + 4a^3b^1 + 6a^2b^2 + 4a^1b^3 + b^4$

$(a + b)^5 = a^5 + 5a^4b^1 + 10a^3b^2 + 10a^2b^3 + 5a^1b^4 + b^5$

If we highlight $(a + b)^5$

$(a + b)^5 = a^5b^0 + 5a^4b^1 + 10a^3b^2 + 10a^2b^3 + 5a^1b^4 + a^0b^5$

we notice that the first term is a^5 and then the powers of a decrease by 1 each term and eventually reach zero. Also, the powers of b start at zero and increase by 1 each term.

Examining the coefficients in each expansion, we notice another pattern.

The next row of coefficients can be calculated by adding the pairs of coefficients from the row above.

This pattern was described by the French mathematician Blaise Pascal (1623–1662) and is named in his honour.

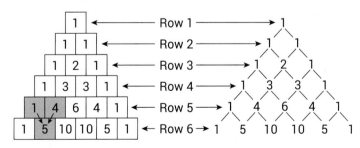

There are many interesting patterns present within Pascal's triangle. In expanding a binomial of the form $(a + b)^n$, the most important ones for us to use are:

- The first and last coefficient entries in any row are 1.

- Entries that are not 1 are found by adding together two adjacent entries in the row above.

- If the power is n, then there will be $(n + 1)$ terms in our expansion. In other words, if the power is n, use row $(n + 1)$ for the coefficients.

ALGEBRA I

Furthermore:

- In any term within the expansion of $(a + b)^n$, the powers of a and of b add up to n. This property provides us with a useful check.

In practice, when multiplying out binomial expressions, we use the binomial theorem.

We will deal with the binomial theorem later in the chapter.

Worked Example 1.4

Use Pascal's triangle to expand $(x - 2)^3$.

Solution

The power is 3 so we use row 4.

From Pascal's triangle we can determine the initial coefficients as:

$$(x - 2)^3 = (x + (-2))^3$$

1   3   3   1

We next fill in the powers of each term.

The x term will start with a power of 3 and decrease to zero.

The (-2) term will start with a power of zero and increase to 3.

$\therefore (x - 2)^3 = (x + (-2))^3 = 1x^3(-2)^0 + 3x^2(-2)^1 + 3x^1(-2)^2 + 1x^0(-2)^3 = x^3 - 6x^2 + 12x - 8$

Worked Example 1.5

Use Pascal's triangle to expand $(2p + 3)^4$.

Solution

The power is 4 so we use row 5.

From Pascal's triangle we can determine the coefficients as:

1   4   6   4   1

The $2p$ term will start with a power of 4 and decrease to zero.

The 3 term will start with a power of zero and increase to 4.

$\therefore (2p + 3)^4 = 1(2p)^4(3)^0 + 4(2p)^3(3)^1 + 6(2p)^2(3)^2 + 4(2p)^1(3)^3 + 1(2p)^0(3)^4$

$$= 16p^4 + 96p^3 + 216p^2 + 216p + 81$$

Exercise 1.1

1. If $p = 3$, $q = -4$ and $r = 7$, find the value of:

    (i) $2pq$

    (ii) $(q + r)^p$

    (iii) $\dfrac{q + p}{2r}$

    (iv) $pqr - q^2$

    (v) $\sqrt{\dfrac{q^2 + rp + r + 4}{\frac{-q}{p}}}$

2. Simplify each of the following:

    (i) $2x - 3y + 4x - 2y + 3y + 4x$

    (ii) $2xy + 3xy - 7xy$

    (iii) $4pq + 4qr + 5pq - 7qr - 8qp$

    (iv) $p^2 + p^2 + 2p^3$

    (v) $xy^2 - 2yx^2 + y^2 x$

    (vi) $5nm^2 + 2mn^2 - 2m^2n - 3mn^2$

3. Expand and simplify:

   (i) $3x(x + 4) + 5(3x - 2)$

   (ii) $3(a^2 - b) - (a - 3b)$

   (iii) $12x(3x^2 + 2x + 1) + 5x(2x - 4)$

   (iv) $-y(2y - 3x) - y(xy + 3x)$

   (v) $b(b^2 + 4b + c) - 4c(a^2 + b)$

4. Expand and simplify each of the following expressions. For each polynomial, state:

  (a) The degree

  (b) The value of the constant term

  (c) The number of terms

  (d) The coefficient of the x term

    (i) $(x + 2)(x - 3)$

    (ii) $(2x - 5)(3x + 4)$

    (iii) $-x(5x^2 - 3)(2x^2 - 3)$

    (iv) $(x^3 - 4)(2x^2 - 8x + 3)$

    (v) $(11x^4 - 3x^3 + x^2 - 3x + 1)(4x - 7)$

5. Expand and simplify:

   (i) $(5x + 1)(7x + 1)$

   (ii) $(p - q)(p + q)$

   (iii) $5(3s - t)(2t - 1)$

   (iv) $(p - q)^2$

   (v) $2x(4x + 3)^2$

   (vi) $(x^2 - y^2)(x - y)$

   (vii) $(y - 3)^3$

  (viii) $(2a + 5b)^3$

   (ix) $(9x - 2y)^3$

6. Using Pascal's triangle, expand the following binomials:

   (i) $(a + 1)^4$

   (ii) $(b - 3)^3$

   (iii) $(x + y)^5$

   (iv) $(2a + 3b)^3$

   (v) $(3y - 4x)^4$

   (vi) $(3x - 2y)^5$

7. Express as a polynomial the area and perimeter of each of the following shapes:

  (i)

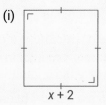

$x + 2$

  (ii)

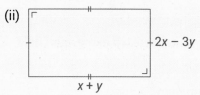

$2x - 3y$

$x + y$

8. An open-topped tank is in the shape of a cuboid. The length of the tank is $(x + 7)$ cm. Its breadth is 3 cm less than its length and its height is 1 cm more than its breadth.

Write expressions in terms of x for the volume and surface area of the tank.

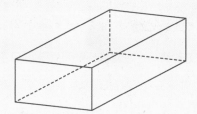

9. In a maths competition, a student gets 8 marks for a correct answer, and 3 marks are deducted if the answer is incorrect. One mark is awarded for any question not attempted. If there are 20 questions on the test, write an expression for a student's total mark if the student got x questions correct from a total of y questions attempted.

10. Mark is y years old. In five years' time, Aoife will be twice as old as Mark and Daniel will be two years younger than Aoife is now. Write an expression in y for the sum of their three ages now.

11. Expand:

   (i) $(a + b)(x + 5)^2$

   (ii) $3p(p + q)(p - q)$

   (iii) $(z + x)^2(z - x)^2$

   (iv) $(3a - 1)(a + 3b)(2a + b)$

   (v) $5(x + y)(x + 4y)(y + x)$

12. The middle term of the expansion of $(ax + ay)^n$ is $14{,}580x^3y^3$. Find the value of a and the value of n, where $a, n \in N$.

1.2 Factorising

Another important skill is that of finding the factors of an expression. This is called **factorising**.

To factorise an expression we rewrite the expression as a product, a product being two or more terms that when multiplied together will give the original expression.

Factorising is the reverse of expanding. We turn the given expression into a **product**.

For example, the factors of 35 are 5 and 7 because 5 × 7 will give us 35.

If we consider the expression $5x + 10$, then its factors would be 5 and $(x + 2)$ as $5(x + 2) = 5x + 10$.

Remember to factorise each expression fully.

We met the following methods of factorising at Junior Certificate level:

- **Highest Common Factor**

  $x^2 - 3x = x(x - 3)$

- **Grouping**

  $ax - bx + ay - by$

  $= x(a - b) + y(a - b)$

  $= (x + y)(a - b)$

- **Difference of Two Squares**

  $4x^2 - 25y^2$

  $= (2x)^2 - (5y)^2$ (writing each term as a square)

  $= (2x - 5y)(2x + 5y)$

- **Quadratic Trinomials**

  $2x^2 + 13x + 15 = (2x + 3)(x + 5)$

Worked Example 1.6

Factorise:

(i) $21xy^2 + 35x^3y^2$

(ii) $mx + 24by - 2my - 12bx$

(iii) $49x^2 - 225y^2$

(iv) $3x^2 + 11x - 20$

(v) $8x^2 - 18x + 9$

Solution

(i) $21xy^2 + 35x^3y^2$

    $= 7xy^2(3 - 5x^2)$ (as $7xy^2$ is the HCF)

(ii) $mx + 24by - 2my - 12bx$

    $= mx - 2my - 12bx + 24by$ (rearranging the terms)

    $= m(x - 2y) - 12b(x - 2y)$ (m and $-12b$ are HCFs)

    $= (m - 12b)(x - 2y)$

(iii) $49x^2 - 225y^2$

    Write each term as a square:

    $(7x)^2 - (15y)^2$

    $= (7x - 15y)(7x + 15y)$

(iv) $3x^2 + 11x - 20$

If the constant term is negative, then one factor of –20 is positive and the other is negative.

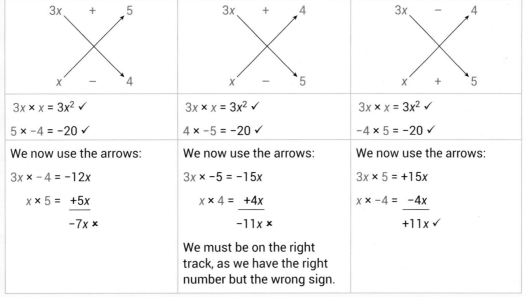

$3x \times x = 3x^2$ ✓	$3x \times x = 3x^2$ ✓	$3x \times x = 3x^2$ ✓
$5 \times -4 = -20$ ✓	$4 \times -5 = -20$ ✓	$-4 \times 5 = -20$ ✓
We now use the arrows:	We now use the arrows:	We now use the arrows:
$3x \times -4 = -12x$	$3x \times -5 = -15x$	$3x \times 5 = +15x$
$\underline{x \times 5 = \;\;+5x}$	$\underline{x \times 4 = \;\;+4x}$	$\underline{x \times -4 = \;\;-4x}$
$-7x$ ✗	$-11x$ ✗	$+11x$ ✓
	We must be on the right track, as we have the right number but the wrong sign.	

So $3x^2 + 11x - 20 = (3x - 4)(x + 5)$.

(v) We can also use the **Guide Number Method** to factorise quadratic trinomials.

$8x^2 - 18x + 9$

Step 1 Multiply the coefficient of x^2 by the constant.

$8x^2 - 18x + 9$

$8 \times 9 = 72$

Step 2 Find two factors of 72 that multiply to give 72 and add to give the coefficient of the middle term, i.e. –18.

-12 and -6

Step 3 Use the answers from Step 2 to rewrite $8x^2 - 18x + 9$ as follows:

$8x^2 - 12x - 6x + 9$

$= 4x(2x - 3) - 3(2x - 3)$ (factorise by grouping)

$= (4x - 3)(2x - 3)$ (distributive property)

So $8x^2 - 18x + 9 = (4x - 3)(2x - 3)$.

Sum and Difference of Two Cubes

We may also be asked to factorise certain cubic expressions. If we are asked to factorise $a^3 + b^3$, consider what happens when we expand and simplify $(a + b)(a^2 - ab + b^2)$.

$(a + b)(a^2 - ab + b^2)$

$= a(a^2 - ab + b^2) + b(a^2 - ab + b^2)$

$= a^3 - a^2b + ab^2 + a^2b - ab^2 + b^3$

$= a^3 - a^2b + a^2b + ab^2 - ab^2 + b^3$

$= a^3 + b^3$

$a^3 + b^3 = (a + b)(a^2 - ab + b^2)$	Sum of two cubes
$a^3 - b^3 = (a - b)(a^2 + ab + b^2)$	Difference of two cubes

> Make sure to memorise these two important rules.

We can also factorise $a^3 - b^3$ by considering $(a - b)(a^2 + ab + b^2)$.

ALGEBRA I

Worked Example 1.7

Factorise:

(i) $64p^3 - 27q^3$ (ii) $1 + 216w^3$

Solution

(i) $64p^3 - 27q^3$

Write each term as a cube:

$(4p)^3 - (3q)^3$

$= (4p - 3q)[(4p)^2 + (4p)(3q) + (3q)^2]$

$= (4p - 3q)(16p^2 + 12pq + 9q^2)$

(ii) $1 + 216w^2$

Write each term as a cube:

$(1)^3 + (6w)^3$

$= (1 + 6w)[(1)^2 - (1)(6w) + (6w)^2]$

$= (1 + 6w)(1 - 6w + 36w^2)$

Worked Example 1.8

Factorise fully:

(i) $9px^2 + 24px - 9p$ (ii) $5x^3 - 625y^3$

Solution

(i) $9px^2 + 24px - 9p$

First find the highest common factor.

$3p[3x^2 + 8x - 3]$

Now factorise the quadratic:

$3p(3x - 1)(x + 3)$

(ii) $5x^3 - 625y^3$

First, find the highest common factor.

$5[x^3 - 125y^3]$

Now factorise the expression inside the brackets:

$5(x - 5y)(x^2 + 5xy + 25y^2)$

Exercise 1.2

Factorise fully the following expressions:

1. $4ab^2 - 12ab^3$

2. $7x^2 + 9x + 2$

3. $3y^2 - 4y - 7$

4. $5x^2 + 12x + 4$

5. $x^2 - 3x - 18$

6. $3x^2 + 10x - 8$

7. $2y^2 + 11y - 63$

8. $7x^2 + 2x - 57$

9. $25a^2 - 1$

10. $2x^2 - 9x + 4$

11. $12xy - 21x - 8y + 14$

12. $5x^2 + 52x + 96$

13. $64a^2 - 81b^2$

14. $2x^2 - 23x - 12$

15. $4x^2 + 7x + 3$

16. $6a^2 - 10bc + 4ac - 15ab$

17. $10y^2 + 27y + 17$

18. $9x^2 + 3x - 2$

19. $9x^2 - 21x + 10$

20. $4y^2 + 23y + 19$

21. $x(y - z) + z - y$

22. $6x^2 + 37x + 45$

23. $36p^2 - 100q^2$

24. $12x^2 + 11x - 56$

25. $8x^2 - 22x + 15$

26. $10x^2 - 4x - 6$

27. $12x^2 - 18x - 12$

28. $48y^3 + 48y^2 + 12y$

29. $16x^2 - 100$

30. $2x^3 - 8x$

31. $6pq^2 + 11pq + 4p$

32. $x^4 - 36x^2$

Factorise fully the following expressions:

33. $x^3 - 27$

34. $p^3 + 8$

35. $x^3 - y^3$

36. $64a^3 - 1$

37. $8a^3 + 27b^3$

38. $125p^3 + 512q^3$

39. $1{,}000x^3 - 729$

40. $343c^3 + d^3$

41. $3x^3 - 648$

42. $128 + 16x^3$

43. $54a^4 + 432ab^3$

Factorise fully the following expressions:

44. $(x + 2)^2 - (x + 3)^2$

45. $x^2 + 2px + p^2$

46. $a^2c^2 - b^2$

47. $x^4 - 25$

48. $a^2b^2 - 2ab + 1$

49. $x^4 - y^4$

50. $(x - y)^2 - 9$

51. $8x^2 - 18xy + 9y^2$

52. $a^4 + a$

53. $a^2 - (b + c)^2$

54. $ab^5 - ab^2$

55. $x^4 - 7x^2 - 18$

1.3 Algebraic Fractions I: Addition and Subtraction

When asked to add or subtract two algebraic fractions, we must first find the lowest common denominator (LCD).

We then apply a similar method to that of adding/subtracting numerical fractions.

For example, consider the case where we are asked to simplify $\dfrac{3}{4} + \dfrac{2}{5}$.

Step 1 Find the LCM of 4 and 5.

$$LCM\,(4, 5) = 20$$

We now refer to 20 as the LCD.

Step 2 Now write as equivalent fractions using the LCD.

$$\frac{3}{4} + \frac{2}{5}$$

$$= \frac{15}{20} + \frac{8}{20}$$

Step 3 Add and simplify.

$$\frac{15 + 8}{20} = \frac{23}{20}$$

Worked Example 1.9

Write $\dfrac{2x + 5}{2} - \dfrac{x - 1}{9} - 2$ as a single fraction.

Solution

$$\frac{2x + 5}{2} - \frac{x - 1}{9} - \frac{2}{1}$$

Step 1 Find the LCM of 2 and 9.

$$LCM\,(2, 9) = 18$$

Step 2 Write the expression as a single fraction using the LCD.

$$= \frac{9(2x + 5)}{18} - \frac{2(x - 1)}{18} - \frac{18(2)}{18}$$

$$= \frac{9(2x + 5) - 2(x - 1) - 18(2)}{18}$$

Step 3 Expand and simplify the expression.

$$= \frac{18x + 45 - 2x + 2 - 36}{18} = \frac{16x + 11}{18}$$

Worked Example 1.10

(i) Write $\dfrac{5}{3x-5} - \dfrac{2}{4x-1}$ as a single fraction.

(ii) Write $\dfrac{1}{x-2} - \dfrac{1}{x+2}$ as a single fraction in the form $\dfrac{b}{x^a - b}$, where $a, b \in N$.

Solution

(i) $\dfrac{5}{3x-5} - \dfrac{2}{4x-1}$

Step 1 Find the LCD of $(3x-5)$ and $(4x-1)$.

LCD $= (3x-5)(4x-1)$

Step 2 Write the expression as a single fraction using the LCD.

$$= \frac{5(4x-1)}{(3x-5)(4x-1)} - \frac{2(3x-5)}{(3x-5)(4x-1)}$$

$$= \frac{5(4x-1) - 2(3x-5)}{(3x-5)(4x-1)}$$

> Do not expand the denominator unless required to do so.

Step 3 Expand and simplify the expression.

$$= \frac{20x - 5 - 6x + 10}{(3x-5)(4x-1)} = \frac{14x + 5}{(3x-5)(4x-1)}$$

(ii) $\dfrac{1}{x-2} - \dfrac{1}{x+2} = \dfrac{1(x+2) - 1(x-2)}{(x-2)(x+2)}$

> Here, the question requires that we expand the denominator.

$$= \frac{x + 2 - x + 2}{x^2 - 4}$$

$$= \frac{4}{x^2 - 4}$$

Worked Example 1.11

Simplify $\dfrac{5x-10}{x^2-4}$.

Solution

Factorise both numerator and denominator.

$5x - 10 = 5(x - 2)$

$x^2 - 4 = (x - 2)(x + 2)$

$\therefore \dfrac{5x-10}{x^2-4} = \dfrac{5(x-2)^1}{(x-2)(x+2)}$

$$= \frac{5}{x+2}$$

Worked Example 1.12

Simplify $\dfrac{3a^2 - 6a}{2 - a}$.

Solution

$\dfrac{3a^2 - 6a}{2-a} = \dfrac{3a\,\overset{1}{(a-2)}}{-1(a-2)}$

$$= \frac{3a}{-1}$$

$$= -3a$$

Numerator HCF $= 3a$

We need to rearrange the denominator so that $(a-2)$ will divide into the numerator and denominator. To do this we use -1 as the HCF of the denominator.

Worked Example 1.13

Simplify $\dfrac{12x^2 - 7x + 1}{3x - 1}$.

Solution

Factorise the numerator: $12x^2 - 7x + 1 = (4x - 1)(3x - 1)$

$$\therefore \quad \frac{12x^2 - 7x + 1}{3x - 1} = \frac{(4x - 1)(3x - 1)^1}{3x - 1_1}$$

$$= 4x - 1$$

Worked Example 1.14

(i) Express as a single fraction in its simplest form:

$$\frac{2}{x - 1} - \frac{3x - 1}{x^2 - 4x + 3} + \frac{4}{x - 3}$$

(ii) Express as a single fraction in its simplest form:

$$\frac{3}{x - 2} + \frac{2}{2 - x}$$

Solution

(i) $\dfrac{2}{x - 1} - \dfrac{3x - 1}{x^2 - 4x + 3} + \dfrac{4}{x - 3}$

Step 1 $= \dfrac{2}{x - 1} - \dfrac{3x - 1}{(x - 1)(x - 3)} + \dfrac{4}{x - 3}$ (factorising $x^2 - 4x + 3$)

Step 2 LCD $= (x - 1)(x - 3)$; which is the lowest (smallest) expression that is divisible by **all three** denominators. We write the expression as a single fraction using the LCD.

$$= \frac{(2)(x - 3) - (3x - 1)(1) + 4(x - 1)}{(x - 1)(x - 3)}$$

Step 3 Expand and simplify the expression.

$$= \frac{2x - 6 - 3x + 1 + 4x - 4}{(x - 1)(x - 3)}$$

$$= \frac{3x - 9}{(x - 1)(x - 3)}$$

$$= \frac{3(x - 3)^1}{(x - 1)(x - 3)^1}$$

$$= \frac{3}{x - 1}$$

> Not expanding the denominator can allow for reducing of fractions to occur.

(ii) $\dfrac{3}{x - 2} + \dfrac{2}{2 - x}$

$$= \frac{3}{x - 2} + \frac{2}{2 - x} \cdot \frac{-1}{-1}$$

$$= \frac{3}{x - 2} - \frac{2}{x - 2}$$

$$= \frac{3 - 2}{x - 2}$$

$$= \frac{1}{x - 2}$$

> Multiply $\dfrac{2}{2 - x}$ by $\dfrac{-1}{-1}$, giving $\dfrac{-2}{x - 2}$.
>
> This results in both fractions having the same denominator.

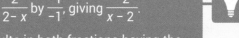

ALGEBRA I

Exercise 1.3

For questions 1 to 30, express as single fractions in their simplest form:

1. $\dfrac{4x-1}{4} + \dfrac{2x-5}{2}$

2. $\dfrac{3x-7}{12} - \dfrac{5x-3}{4}$

3. $\dfrac{7}{4x-5} + 2$

4. $\dfrac{1}{5x} - \dfrac{2}{7x}$

5. $\dfrac{8}{x+1} + x$

6. $\dfrac{3}{x+5} - \dfrac{1}{x}$

7. $\dfrac{5}{x-2} + \dfrac{2}{3x-1}$

8. $\dfrac{1}{3x+5} + \dfrac{3}{2x-1}$

9. $\dfrac{ab^3}{a^2 b}$

10. $\dfrac{x+y}{x^2-y^2}$

11. $\dfrac{ab+b^2}{a^2-b^2}$

12. $\dfrac{p-q}{q-p}$

13. $\dfrac{x^2-2x}{x-2}$

14. $\dfrac{15x^2+5x}{15x^2+20x+5}$

15. $\dfrac{x^3-8}{x^2+2x+4}$

16. $\dfrac{2x^4-250x}{4x^2-20x}$

17. $\dfrac{x^3+y^3}{x^2-y^2}$

18. $\dfrac{x^4-y^4}{x^2-y^2}$

19. $\dfrac{(p-q)^3}{p^2-q^2}$

20. $\dfrac{x^2-8x+16}{x^2-16} - \dfrac{16x}{16-x^2}$

21. $\dfrac{2x}{x-1} - \dfrac{x}{1-x}$

22. $\dfrac{x+4}{x^2-16} + \dfrac{x-5}{x^2-25}$

23. $\dfrac{1}{x+2} - \dfrac{3}{x-3} + \dfrac{4}{x^2-x-6}$

24. $\dfrac{1}{x^2+3x+2} + \dfrac{4}{x+2} - \dfrac{3}{x+1}$

25. $\dfrac{3}{a-1} - \dfrac{a+1}{a^2-1} + \dfrac{a-1}{a+1}$

26. $\dfrac{a}{a+b} + \dfrac{a}{a-b}$

27. $\dfrac{a+2}{a-2} + \dfrac{a-3}{a+3}$

28. $\dfrac{1}{n+1} + \dfrac{1}{n} + \dfrac{1}{n+2}$

29. $\dfrac{a+b}{a^2-b^2} - \dfrac{a-b}{b^2-a^2}$

30. $\dfrac{a-b}{a^2-2ab+b^2} - \dfrac{a+b}{a^2+2ab+b^2}$

31. Write as a single fraction in the form $\dfrac{a}{x^b-c}$, where a, b and $c \in N$:

   (i) $\dfrac{5}{x^2-1} + \dfrac{1}{1-x^2}$

   (ii) $\dfrac{3x}{x^2+3x-18} - \dfrac{18}{18-3x-x^2}$

1.4 Algebraic Fractions II: Multiplication and Division

We can apply the same method to multiply and divide numerical fractions.

To multiply two (or more) fractions (proper or improper) we simply do the following

$$\dfrac{\text{numerator} \times \text{numerator}}{\text{denominator} \times \text{denominator}}$$

and simplify the answer.

For example: $\dfrac{3}{4} \times \dfrac{2}{5} = \dfrac{3 \times 2}{4 \times 5} = \dfrac{6}{20} = \dfrac{3}{10}$

Of course it is usually easier to divide any numerator and denominator by any **common factors** before multiplying.

$\dfrac{3}{{}_2 4} \times \dfrac{2^1}{5} = \dfrac{3}{10}$

To divide one fraction by another we multiply by the reciprocal of the divisor.

For example: $\dfrac{3}{4} \div \dfrac{2}{5} = \dfrac{3}{4} \times \dfrac{5}{2} = \dfrac{15}{8}$

Worked Example 1.15

Simplify $\dfrac{3x^2 - 27}{4x^2 - 15x + 9} \times \dfrac{4x - 3}{x^2 + 3x}$.

Solution

$\dfrac{3x^2 - 27}{4x^2 - 15x + 9} \times \dfrac{4x - 3}{x^2 + 3x}$

$= \dfrac{3(x^2 - 9)}{(4x - 3)(x - 3)} \cdot \dfrac{(4x - 3)}{x(x + 3)}$ (Factorise numerator and denominator.)

$= \dfrac{3(x + 3)\overset{1}{(x - 3)}\overset{1}{(4x - 3)}}{(4x - 3)(x - 3)(x)(x + 3)}$

$= \dfrac{3}{x}$

Worked Example 1.16

Simplify $\dfrac{x - 5}{x + 1} \div \dfrac{x^2 - 25}{x^2 + 4x + 3}$.

Solution

$\dfrac{x - 5}{x + 1} \div \dfrac{x^2 - 25}{x^2 + 4x + 3}$

$= \dfrac{x - 5}{x + 1} \times \dfrac{x^2 + 4x + 3}{x^2 - 25}$ (Dividing by $\dfrac{a}{b}$ is the same as multiplying by $\dfrac{b}{a}$.)

$= \dfrac{\overset{1}{(x - 5)}}{(x + 1)} \cdot \dfrac{(x + 3)\overset{1}{(x + 1)}}{(x + 5)(x - 5)}$ (Factorise numerator and denominator.)

$= \dfrac{x + 3}{x + 5}$

Complex Fractions

A complex fraction is a fraction where the numerator, denominator or both contain a fraction.

For example, $\dfrac{1 + \frac{1}{3}}{\frac{2}{5} + \frac{3}{7}}$ is a complex fraction.

Worked Example 1.17

Simplify $\dfrac{1 - \dfrac{9}{x^2}}{2 + \dfrac{6}{x}}$.

Solution

Numerator: $1 - \dfrac{9}{x^2} = \dfrac{x^2 - 9}{x^2}$

$= \dfrac{(x - 3)(x + 3)}{x^2}$

Denominator: $2 + \dfrac{6}{x} = \dfrac{2x + 6}{x}$

$= \dfrac{2(x + 3)}{x}$

$\therefore \dfrac{1 - \dfrac{9}{x^2}}{2 + \dfrac{6}{x}} = \dfrac{(x - 3)(x + 3)}{x^2} \div \dfrac{2(x + 3)}{x}$

$= \dfrac{(x - 3)(x + 3)}{x^2} \cdot \dfrac{x^1}{2(x + 3)_1}$

$= \dfrac{x - 3}{2x}$

Alternative Method

Multiply the numerator **and** the denominator by x^2.

$= \dfrac{\left(1 - \dfrac{9}{x^2}\right)x^2}{\left(2 + \dfrac{6}{x}\right)x^2}$

$= \dfrac{x^2 - 9}{2x^2 + 6x}$

$= \dfrac{(x + 3)\overset{1}{(x - 3)}}{2x(x + 3)_1}$

$= \dfrac{x - 3}{2x}$

ALGEBRA I

Exercise 1.4

For Questions 1 to 19, express as single fractions in their simplest form.

1. $\dfrac{10b^2}{5a^2} \times \dfrac{25a^3}{2b}$

2. $\dfrac{4x}{2y} \div \dfrac{8x^3}{4y^2}$

3. $\dfrac{2}{2x-1} \div \dfrac{4}{4x^2-1}$

4. $\dfrac{x^2+x-2}{x^2+2x-3} \times \dfrac{2x+6}{4x-4}$

5. $\dfrac{4x-4}{x} \div \dfrac{x^2-1}{x^3}$

6. $\dfrac{y^2-64}{y^2-16} \times \dfrac{2y^2-8y}{2y-16}$

7. $\dfrac{2x^2-x-1}{2x^2+x-1} \cdot \dfrac{4x^2-1}{x^2-1}$

8. $\dfrac{8x^2-34x-9}{4x+1} \times \dfrac{3x}{4x^2-81}$

9. $\dfrac{6x^2-20x+16}{4x^2-16x+16} \div \dfrac{9x^2-16}{2x^2+2x-12}$

10. $\dfrac{\dfrac{4x+3}{x^2-49}}{\dfrac{16x^2-9}{x-7}}$

11. $\dfrac{\dfrac{x-y}{xy}}{\dfrac{5}{xy}}$

12. $\dfrac{\dfrac{x-5}{x+5}}{\dfrac{1}{x^2-25}}$

13. $\dfrac{\dfrac{x}{x+1}+1}{\dfrac{3}{x+1}}$

14. $\dfrac{1-\dfrac{1}{x}}{2-\dfrac{2}{x^2}}$

15. $\dfrac{\dfrac{x}{x^2-6x+9}}{\dfrac{5}{(3-x)(x-3)}}$

16. $\dfrac{a-\dfrac{1}{b}}{1-\dfrac{1}{b}}$

17. $\dfrac{\dfrac{p+q}{1}}{\dfrac{1}{p}+\dfrac{1}{q}}$

18. $\dfrac{\dfrac{x+3}{y-x}}{\dfrac{x^2+3x}{x^2-y^2}}$

19. $\dfrac{\dfrac{x^2-y^2}{x^2}}{\dfrac{x^2+2xy+y^2}{x}}$

20. The combined resistance (R_T) of two resistors R_1 and R_2 (in parallel) is given by the following formula:

$$R_T = \dfrac{1}{\dfrac{1}{R_1} + \dfrac{1}{R_2}}$$

Simplify this formula.

21. If $u = x - \dfrac{1}{x}$ and $v = x^2 - \dfrac{1}{x^2}$, show that $u^2(u^2 + 4) = v^2$.

22. If $x = \dfrac{a^3 - b^3}{a^3 + ab^2}$ and $y = \dfrac{a^3 - ab^2}{a^2b + b^3}$, show that $\dfrac{x}{y} = \dfrac{b(a^2 + ab + b^2)}{a^2(a + b)}$.

1.5 Binomial Expansions

A **binomial expansion** is where an expression of two terms is multiplied by itself a number of times. Here are some examples, where the right-hand side is worked out by repeated multiplications:

$(x + y)^2 = x^2 + 2xy + y^2$

$(x + y)^3 = x^3 + 3x^2y + 3xy^2 + y^3$

Before we work out $(x + y)^4$, which will take a considerable number of calculations and additions, we ask ourselves, 'Is there an easy way?' The answer is 'Yes, there is!' And here it is:

$(x + y)^n = \binom{n}{0}x^n + \binom{n}{1}x^{n-1}y + \binom{n}{2}x^{n-2}y^2 + \binom{n}{3}x^{n-3}y^3 + \dots + \binom{n}{r}x^{n-r}y^r + \dots + \binom{n}{n}y^n$

(where n is a natural number)

This formula appears on p20 of *Formulae and Tables*.

ALGEBRA I

This result is called the **binomial theorem**. Its proof is not part of this course.

$\binom{n}{0}$, $\binom{n}{1}$, etc is pronounced 'n C 0', 'n C 1' or 'n choose 0', 'n choose 1', and so on.

To find out, for example, the value of $\binom{8}{3}$, we can use a calculator.

On the calculator, we would press:

> We will explore combinatorial numbers (^nC_r) in much greater depth in Book 2, Chapters 2 and 3.

Worked Example 1.18

Write out the binomial expansion of $(x + y)^4$.

Solution

$$(x + y)^4 = \binom{4}{0}x^4 + \binom{4}{1}x^3y + \binom{4}{2}x^2y^2 + \binom{4}{3}xy^3 + \binom{4}{4}y^4$$

$$= x^4 + 4x^3y + 6x^2y^2 + 4xy^3 + y^4$$

Worked Example 1.19

Show that $(1 + x)^6 + (1 - x)^6 = 2 + 30x^2 + 30x^4 + 2x^6$, and hence, evaluate $(1 + \sqrt{2})^6 + (1 - \sqrt{2})^6$.

Solution

$$(1 + x)^6 = \binom{6}{0}(1)^6 + \binom{6}{1}(1)^5x + \binom{6}{2}(1)^4x^2 + \binom{6}{3}(1)^3x^3 + \binom{6}{4}(1)^2x^4 + \binom{6}{5}(1)x^5 + \binom{6}{6}x^6$$

$$= 1 + 6x + 15x^2 + 20x^3 + 15x^4 + 6x^5 + x^6$$

$(1 - x)^6 = (1 + (-x))^6$

$$= \binom{6}{0}(1)^6 + \binom{6}{1}(1)^5(-x) + \binom{6}{2}(1)^4(-x)^2 + \binom{6}{3}(1)^3(-x)^3 + \binom{6}{4}(1)^2(-x)^4 + \binom{6}{5}(1)(-x)^5 + \binom{6}{6}(-x)^6$$

$$= 1 + 6(1)(-x) + 15(1)(x^2) + 20(1)(-x^3) + 15(1)(x^4) + 6(1)(-x^5) + 1x^6$$

$$= 1 - 6x + 15x^2 - 20x^3 + 15x^4 - 6x^5 + x^6 \quad \text{(Note how the signs of the terms alternate here.)}$$

Adding these results gives:

$(1 + x)^6 \qquad = 1 + 6x + 15x^2 + 20x^3 + 15x^4 + 6x^5 + x^6$

$(1 - x)^6 \qquad = 1 - 6x + 15x^2 - 20x^3 + 15x^4 - 6x^5 + x^6$

$(1 + x)^6 + (1 - x)^6 = 2 \qquad + 30x^2 \qquad + 30x^4 \qquad + 2x^6$ **QED**

Letting $x = \sqrt{2}$ on both sides, we get:

$$(1 + \sqrt{2})^6 + (1 - \sqrt{2})^6 = 2 + 30(\sqrt{2})^2 + 30(\sqrt{2})^4 + 2(\sqrt{2})^6$$

$$= 2 + 30(2) + 30(4) + 2(8)$$

$$= 198$$

ALGEBRA I

Worked Example 1.20

Write out the binomial expansion of $\left(2x^2 + \dfrac{3}{x}\right)^3$.

Show that one of the terms is independent of x.

Solution

$$\left(2x^2 + \frac{3}{x}\right)^3 = \binom{3}{0}(2x^2)^3 + \binom{3}{1}(2x^2)^2\left(\frac{3}{x}\right) + \binom{3}{2}(2x^2)\left(\frac{3}{x}\right)^2 + \binom{3}{3}\left(\frac{3}{x}\right)^3$$

$$= (1)(8x^6) + (3)(4x^4)\left(\frac{3}{x}\right) + (3)(2x^2)\left(\frac{9}{x^2}\right) + (1)\left(\frac{27}{x^3}\right)$$

$$= 8x^6 + 36x^3 + 54 + \frac{27}{x^3}$$

The third term is independent of x. In other words, its value does not depend on the value of x.

Exercise 1.5

1. Write out the binomial expansion of:

    (i) $(x + y)^5$ (v) $(1 + 2x)^3$

    (ii) $(x + y)^6$ (vi) $(1 - 3x)^4$

    (iii) $(x + y)^7$ (vii) $(1 + 2x)^6$

    (iv) $(a + b)^8$ (viii) $(1 + k)^7$

2. (i) Write out the binomial expansion for $(1 + x)^4$.

    (ii) Show that $(1 + x)^4 + (1 - x)^4 = 2(1 + 6x^2 + x^4)$.

    (iii) Hence, evaluate $(1 + \sqrt{3})^4 + (1 - \sqrt{3})^4$.

3. Write out the binomial expansion of $(1 + 3x)^3$. Verify your answer by putting $x = 1$ on both sides.

4. Write out the binomial expansion of $(1 - 2x)^5$. Verify your answer by putting $x = 2$ on both sides.

5. Show that $(1 + x)^7 - (1 - x)^7 = 2(7x + 35x^3 + 21x^5 + x^7)$. Hence, write $(1 + \sqrt{2})^7 - (1 - \sqrt{2})^7$ in the form $k\sqrt{2}$, where $k \in N$.

6. Write out the binomial expansion of $\left(x + \dfrac{1}{x}\right)^6$.

    Show that one term is independent of x.

7. (i) Expand $(a + b)^4 + (a - b)^4$.

    (ii) Hence, write $(x + \sqrt{x^2 + 1})^4 + (x - \sqrt{x^2 + 1})^4$ as a polynomial in x.

    (iii) Hence, evaluate $(8 + \sqrt{65})^4 + (8 - \sqrt{65})^4$.

8. (i) Expand $(a + b)^5$.

    (ii) Hence, or otherwise, expand $(1 + 2x)^5 - (1 - 2x)^5$.

    (iii) If $(1 + 2\sqrt{5})^5 - (1 - 2\sqrt{5})^5 = n\sqrt{5}$, find $n \in N$.

Terms

The $(r + 1)$th term, T_{r+1}, of the binomial expansion of $(x + y)^n$ is given by $T_{r+1} = \binom{n}{r}x^{n-r}y^r$.

This is often called the **general term**.

Worked Example 1.21

Find:

(i) The 4th term of $(1 + 2x)^{11}$

(ii) The middle term of $(x - 2y)^8$

(iii) The coefficient of x^5 in the binomial expansion of $(2 - x)^7$

Solution

(i) $T_4 = \binom{11}{3}(1)^{11-3}(2x)^3$ \hspace{1cm} (Term 4 implies $r + 1 = 4$, so $r = 3$.)

$= \binom{11}{3}(1)^8(2x)^3$

$= (165)(1)(8x^3)$

$= 1,320x^3$

(ii) The middle term $= \binom{8}{4}(x)^4(-2y)^4$

$= 70(x^4)(16y^4)$

$= 1,120x^4y^4$

> There are 9 terms in this expansion. Therefore, the middle term is T_5.
> $\therefore r + 1 = 5 \Rightarrow r = 4$

(iii) The general term in this expansion is $\binom{7}{r}(2)^{7-r}(-x)^r$.

We require a term with x^5. Therefore $r = 5$.

$\therefore$ The term required $= \binom{7}{5}(2)^2(-x)^5$

$= (21)(4)(-x^5)$

$= -84x^5$

$\therefore$ The coefficient of x^5 is -84.

Worked Example 1.22

Find the term independent of x in the binomial expansion of $\left(2x^2 + \dfrac{3}{x}\right)^6$.

Solution

The general term of this expansion, T_{r+1}, is given by $T_{r+1} = \binom{6}{r}(2x^2)^{6-r}\left(\dfrac{3}{x}\right)^r$.

We extract from this term **only** the power of x, leaving the rest behind.

The powers of x are $\dfrac{(x^2)^{6-r}}{x^r} = \dfrac{x^{12-2r}}{x^r} = x^{12-3r}$.

We are seeking out the term where the power of x is zero.

$12 - 3r = 0$

$\therefore r = 4$

The term independent of x is the fifth term (i.e. $r + 1 = 4 + 1 = 5$).

$T_5 = \binom{6}{4}(2x^2)^2\left(\dfrac{3}{x}\right)^4 = (15)(4x^4)\dfrac{(81)}{x^4}$

$= 4,860$

$=$ the independent term

Exercise 1.6

1. Find:

(i) The 3rd term of $(1 + x)^8$

(ii) The 5th term of $(1 + 2x)^7$

(iii) The 4th term of $(x + y)^9$

(iv) The 7th term of $(2 - x)^8$

(v) The middle term of $(x + y)^6$

(vi) The 6th term of $(7x - y)^6$

(vii) The second last term of $(3 - 2x)^7$

(viii) The middle term of $(1 - 2x)^{10}$

(ix) The 5th term of $(1 + x^2)^5$

(x) The 3rd term of $(1 + 0.2)^{11}$

2. Find the coefficient of x^4 in each of these binomial expansions:

 (i) $(1 + x)^{10}$ (iv) $(1 - 3x)^8$

 (ii) $(2 + x)^5$ (v) $(2 + \sqrt{2}x^2)^3$

 (iii) $(1 + x^2)^6$

3. $(p + q)^9$ is expanded in descending powers of p.

 Evaluate the 4th term when $p = \dfrac{1}{2}$ and $q = 2$.

4. Find the sum of the first three terms of the binomial expansion of $(1 + 0.01)^{10}$.

5. Find the coefficient of a^7 in the binomial expansion of $(a + 2b)^9$.

6. Write down the middle term of $(x - 2y)^{12}$ and evaluate it if $x = \dfrac{3}{2}$ and $y = \dfrac{1}{6}$.

7. When $(1 - 5x)^7$ is expanded in ascending powers of x, find:

 (i) The coefficient of x^3

 (ii) The value of the 5th term if $x = 0.2$

8. Find the term independent of x in each of the following:

 (i) $\left(x + \dfrac{1}{x}\right)^4$

 (ii) $\left(x - \dfrac{2}{x}\right)^6$

 (iii) $\left(x^3 + \dfrac{1}{x^2}\right)^{10}$

 (iv) $\left(2x^3 - \dfrac{1}{3x}\right)^8$

      (Give your answer as a rational number.)

 (v) $\left(x^2 + \dfrac{1}{\sqrt{x}}\right)^{15}$

9. Find the coefficient of x in each of the following:

 (i) $(1 - 7x)^{10}$ (ii) $\left(3x^3 + \dfrac{2}{x^2}\right)^7$

10. Find the coefficient of x^2 in:

 (i) $(1 - 3x)^{10}$ (ii) $\left(x - \dfrac{1}{x^3}\right)^{10}$

11. The coefficient of x^3 in the binomial expansion of $(k + 2x)^6$ is 4,320. Find the value of k.

12. In the binomial expansion of $(8 + kx)^{10}$, the coefficients of x^2 and x^3 are equal. Find the value of k.

13. In the binomial expansion of $(1 + x)^6$, for what positive value of x are the second and third terms of equal value?

14. Write down the general term (T_{r+1}) of the binomial expansion of $\left(x + \dfrac{1}{x}\right)^{12}$, giving your answer as $\binom{12}{r}x^k$.

 If $T_5 > T_4$, find a condition on x, given that x is a positive real number.

15. The first three terms in the expansion of $(1 + ax)^n$ are $1 + 24x + 240x^2$. Find a and n.

16. If the first four terms in the expansion of $(1 + kx)^n$ are $1 - 20x + 180x^2 + px^3$, find the values of k, n and p.

17. By writing $(a + b + c)^8$ as $[(a + b) + c]^8$, find the coefficient of a^5bc^2 in the expansion of $(a + b + c)^8$.

18. Show that the coefficient of x^3y^2z in the expansion of $(x + y + z)^6$ is equal to $\dfrac{6!}{3!\,2!\,1!}$.

19. Show that the coefficient of a^3b^2cd in the expansion of $(a + b + c + d)^7$ is 420.

20. Write out three terms of the binomial expansion of $[1 + (2x + 3x^2)]^5$. Hence, or otherwise, find the coefficient of x^2 in $(1 + 2x + 3x^2)^5$.

21. Find the coefficient of x^3 in the expansion of $(1 + x + x^2)^6$.

22. Find the coefficient of x^4 in the expansion of $(1 + 2x + x^2)^4$.

1.6 Long Division in Algebra

We can apply the method of long division from our primary school studies to help us understand how to do long division in algebra.

Example: Divide 1064 by 19.

Solution:

$$
\begin{array}{r}
5\,6 \\
19\,\overline{)1\,0\,6\,\textcircled{4}} \\
-(9\,5)\!\downarrow \\
\hline
1\,1\,4 \\
-(1\,1\,4) \\
\hline
0
\end{array}
$$

Steps:
- $106 \div 19 = 5$ (Write 5 on top.)
- Multiply 19 by 5 and subtract from 106. Remainder = 11.
- Bring down the 4
- $114 \div 19 = 6$ (Write 6 on top.)
- Multiply 19 by 6 and subtract from 114. Remainder = 0.

$$\therefore 1064 \div 19 = 56$$

We can use similar steps when asked to do long division in algebra.

Worked Example 1.23

Simplify $\dfrac{6x^3 + 5x^2 - 10x + 3}{2x - 1}$.

The numerator is called the dividend (the 'number' being divided).

The denominator is called the divisor (the 'number' which we're dividing by).

Solution

$$
\begin{array}{r}
3x^2 + 4x - 3 \\
2x - 1\,\overline{)6x^3 + 5x^2 - 10x + 3} \\
-\,(6x^3 - 3x^2) \\
\hline
8x^2 - 10x \\
-\,(8x^2 - 4x) \\
\hline
-6x + 3 \\
-\,(-6x + 3) \\
\hline
0
\end{array}
$$

Arrange the divisor and dividend in descending powers of x.

We divide $6x^3$ by $2x$ to get $3x^2$.

We multiply $2x - 1$ by $3x^2$ to get $6x^3 - 3x^2$ and subtract to get $8x^2$.

Bring down the next term, which is $-10x$. We divide $8x^2$ by $2x$ to get $4x$.

We multiply $2x - 1$ by $4x$ to get $8x^2 - 4x$ and subtract to get $-6x$.

Bring down the next term, which is 3. We divide $-6x$ by $2x$ to get -3.

We multiply $2x - 1$ by -3 to get $-6x + 3$ and subtract.

We get a remainder of 0.

The remainder 0 tells us that $2x - 1$ is a factor of $6x^3 + 5x^2 - 10x + 3$.

$$\therefore \frac{6x^3 + 5x^2 - 10x + 3}{2x - 1} = 3x^2 + 4x - 3$$

Worked Example 1.24

Divide $x^3 - 4x^2 + 3$ by $x - 1$.

Solution

As the x term is missing, we write $0x$ into the dividend. This will make the long division easier to perform.

$$
\begin{array}{r}
x^2 - 3x - 3 \\
x - 1\,\overline{)x^3 - 4x^2 + 0x + 3} \\
-\,(x^3 - x^2) \\
\hline
-3x^2 + 0x \\
-\,(-3x^2 + 3x) \\
\hline
-3x + 3 \\
-\,(-3x + 3) \\
\hline
0
\end{array}
$$

$x^2 - 3x - 3$ is called the quotient. In mathematics, a quotient is the result of division.

$$\therefore (x^3 - 4x^2 + 3) \div (x - 1) = x^2 - 3x - 3$$

ALGEBRA I

Long division is also useful as it can be used to find the other factors of an expression.

Consider the following question: Find the prime factors of 30.

Starting with the smallest prime factor of 30, which is 2, we have:

$30 \div 2 = 15$

Continuing:

$15 \div 3 = 5$

So the prime factors of 15 are 3 and 5.

$\therefore 30 = 2(3)(5)$. Its prime factors are 2, 3 and 5.

Long division in algebra is very similar to finding the prime factors of a positive whole number.

Worked Example 1.25

Show that $x - 4$ is a factor of $12x^3 - 55x^2 + 29x - 4$ and find the other two factors.

Solution

$$
\begin{array}{r}
12x^2 - 7x + 1 \\
x - 4 \overline{\smash{\big)}\ 12x^3 - 55x^2 + 29x - 4} \\
\underline{-\ (12x^3 - 48x^2)} \\
-7x^2 + 29x \\
\underline{-\ (-7x^2 + 28x)} \\
x - 4 \\
\underline{-\ (x - 4)} \\
0
\end{array}
$$

There is no remainder, so $(x - 4)$ is a factor.

$\therefore 12x^3 - 55x^2 + 29x - 4 = (x - 4)(12x^2 - 7x + 1)$

$= (x - 4)(4x - 1)(3x - 1)$

$\therefore$ The other two factors are $(4x - 1)$ and $(3x - 1)$.

Exercise 1.7

Simplify each of the following:

1. $(x^3 + 2x^2 - 7x - 2) \div (x - 2)$

2. $(3x^3 + 13x^2 - 18x - 40) \div (3x + 4)$

3. $(6x^3 - 29x^2 + 21x - 4) \div (3x - 1)$

4. $(14x^3 + 33x^2 - 5x) \div (7x - 1)$

5. $(36x^3 - 28x + 8) \div (3x - 2)$

6. $(15x^4 - 11x^3 - 77x^2 + 31x + 42) \div (5x + 3)$

7. Divide $x^3 - 13x - 12$ by $x + 1$.
   Hence, find the other factors.

8. Show that $x - 1$ is a factor of
   $2x^4 - 14x^3 + 22x^2 - 10x$.

9. Find all four factors of $36x^4 - 289x^2 + 400$, if $4x^2 - 25$ divides evenly into the quartic expression.

10. Divide $x^5 - x^4 - 6x^3 - 8x^2 + 8x + 48$ by $x^2 - x - 6$. Hence, fully factorise $x^5 - x^4 - 6x^3 - 8x^2 + 8x + 48$.

11. Show that $2x + 1$ is not a factor of $6x^3 - 13x^2 - 19x + 12$.
    Give a reason for your answer.

12. Investigate if $g(x) = 3x + 4$ and $h(x) = 5x + 4$ are factors of the polynomial $f(x) = -6x^4 - 29x^3 - 16x^2 + 16x$.

ALGEBRA I

Revision Exercises

1. (a) Expand and simplify:

    (i) $4x(x - 3) + 2(x - 5)$

    (ii) $3a(a^2 + b - 2c) - 2b(a^2 + b - 2c)$

    (iii) $(x + 5)(x + 1)$

    (iv) $(5x - 2)(3x - 4)$

    (v) $(11p - 3q)(11p + 3q)$

  (b) Expand:

    (i) $(3x + 7)^2$ (iii) $(4x - 5)^3$

    (ii) $(2x - 1)^3$ (iv) $(4p + 3)^3(p - 2)$

  (c) Using Pascal's triangle, expand the following binomials:

    (i) $(2a + 1)^3$

    (ii) $(4b - 7c)^4$

    (iii) $(6x - 5)^5$

2. (a) Factorise the following:

    (i) $x^2 - x - 90$

    (ii) $15ac - 12ad - 10bc + 8bd$

    (iii) $4x^2 - 81$

    (iv) $4x^2 + 4x + 1$

  (b) Factorise the following:

    (i) $25x^2 - 49y^2$

    (ii) $121a^2 - 144b^2$

    (iii) $6m^2 + 15bx - 10bm - 9mx$

    (iv) $10x^2 - x - 2$

    (v) $14x^2 - 15x + 4$

  (c) Factorise:

    (i) $x^3 + 27$

    (ii) $2b^3 + 2000$

    (iii) $y^3 - 1$

    (iv) $8y^3 - 1$

3. (a) Write as a single fraction in its simplest form:

    (i) $\dfrac{3}{x - 3} + \dfrac{5}{x + 4}$

    (ii) $\dfrac{7}{2y + 1} - \dfrac{6}{2y - 1}$

    (iii) $\dfrac{2}{x + 1} - \dfrac{x}{x - 1}$

(b) Simplify:

    (i) $\dfrac{3a - 9b}{6a - 18b}$ (iv) $\dfrac{by + b - y - 1}{b^3 - 1}$

    (ii) $\dfrac{8x - 10}{16x^2 - 25}$ (v) $\dfrac{x^2 - x}{x^2 - 4x + 3}$

    (iii) $\dfrac{a^3 - b^3}{6a - 6b}$

(c) Write as single fractions in their lowest terms:

    (i) $\dfrac{5}{x - 2} + \dfrac{1}{2 - x}$ (iii) $\dfrac{2}{b - a} + \dfrac{2}{a - b}$

    (ii) $\dfrac{7}{2y - 1} + \dfrac{5}{1 - 2y}$ (iv) $\dfrac{9}{2x - 1} - \dfrac{4}{1 - 2x}$

4. (a) Simplify the following:

    (i) $\dfrac{2x^2 + 9x + 4}{2x^2 + 11x + 5}$ (iii) $\dfrac{2x - 2y}{3y - 3x}$

    (ii) $\dfrac{a^2 - b^2}{a^3 - b^3}$ (iv) $\dfrac{x - 3}{9 - x^2}$

  (b) Express as single fractions in their lowest terms:

    (i) $\dfrac{6x}{x^2 - 9} - \dfrac{1}{x + 3}$ (ii) $\dfrac{4}{3y - 2} - \dfrac{2y}{9y^2 - 4}$

  (c) Simplify the following:

    (i) $\dfrac{x^2 - 2xy + y^2 - z^2}{x^2 - y^2 - 2yz - z^2}$

    (ii) $\dfrac{x^2 - 25}{x^2 - 64} \times \dfrac{x^2 - 8x}{x - 5}$

5. (a) Find the quotient in each of the following:

    (i) $(4x^3 - 5x^2 - 2x + 3) \div (x - 1)$

    (ii) $(36x^3 - 18x^2 - 10x + 4) \div (3x - 1)$

    (iii) $(24x^4 - 22x^3 - 7x^2 + 4x + 1) \div (3x + 1)$

    (iv) $(2x^4 + 13x^3 + 19x^2 - 10x - 24) \div (2x + 3)$

  (b) (i) Show that $8x + 1$ is a factor of $48x^3 + 62x^2 - 33x - 5$ and find the other factors.

    (ii) Show that $x - 2$ is not a factor of $8x^3 + 22x^2 - 7x - 3$.

  (c) Write $\dfrac{2x}{x + 3} + \dfrac{3x}{x - 3} - \dfrac{5x^2 + 9}{x^2 - 9}$

    as a fraction in the form $\dfrac{k}{x + t}$ where $k \in Z$.

ALGEBRA I

6. (a) Factorise:

    (i) $8x^3 + 125$ (iv) $ax + by + ay + bx$

    (ii) $x^3 - 216$ (v) $9x^2 - 12xy + 4y^2$

    (iii) $(5x + 6y)^2 - (x + y)^2$

(b) Find the coefficient of x^3 in the binomial expansions:

    (i) $(3 - 2x)^7$

    (ii) $\left(x - \dfrac{2}{x^2}\right)^9$

(c) Write out the binomial expansion of $(1 + x)^4$.

    Deduce that $(1 + \sqrt{2})^4 = 17 + 12\sqrt{2}$.

(d) Simplify:

    (i) $\dfrac{ax + ay - cx - cy}{ax + ay + cx + cy}$

    (ii) $\dfrac{9y^3 - y}{3y^2 + 8y - 3}$

    (iii) $\dfrac{(a + b)^2 - c^2}{a^2 - (b + c)^2}$

7. (a) The sides of a triangle are $(m^2 + n^2)$, $(m^2 - n^2)$ and $2mn$ in length.

    (i) Prove that the triangle is right-angled.

    (ii) Deduce the three lengths of the sides if $m = 5$ and $n = 2$.

(b) Find the coefficient of x^2 in the binomial expansion of $\left(x^2 + \dfrac{3}{x}\right)^{10}$.

(c) Factorise fully:

    (i) $3x^2 - 75$ (iv) $x^4 - 81$

    (ii) $9x^3 - 25x$ (v) $ax^2 - bx^2 - ay^2 + by^2$

    (iii) $x^4 - y^4$

8. (a) Rearrange the order of the terms in these expressions and then factorise them:

    (i) $51 + x^2 + 20x$ (iii) $a^2 + b^2 - 2ab$

    (ii) $-x^2 + 169$ (iv) $a^2 + b^2 - c^2 - 2ab$

(b) (i) Show that $x - 1$ is not a factor of $4x^4 - 20x^3 - 7x^2 + 32x + 15$.
    Give a reason for your answer.

    (ii) Show that $4x^2 - 1$ is a factor of $12x^4 + 4x^3 - 59x^2 - x + 14$ and find the other factors.

    (iii) Show that $x^3 - x^2$ is a factor of $4x^5 - 7x^3 + 3x^2$ and find the other factors.

(c) (i) Factorise $x^3 + y^3$.

    (ii) Hence, write $x^3 + y^3 + 3xy(x + y)$ as a perfect cube (i.e. as (expression)^3).

    (iii) Hence, factorise $x^3 + y^3 + z^3 + 3xy(x + y)$.

9. (a) The area of a rectangle can be expressed as $2x^2 + 3x - 20$. The length of the rectangle is $x + 4$.

    (i) Find the breadth of the rectangle in terms of x.

    This rectangle is used as a base for a rectangular box. The volume of this box can be expressed as $6x^3 + 7x^2 - 63x + 20$.

    (ii) Find the height of this rectangular box in terms of x.

(b) The binomial expansion of $\left(x + \dfrac{2}{x}\right)^{11}$ is written in decreasing powers of x.

    If the 4th term is less than the 5th term, find the condition on x, where x is a positive real number.

(c) Simplify $\dfrac{\dfrac{z}{z - 1} + \dfrac{z}{z + 1}}{\dfrac{z}{z - 1} - \dfrac{z}{z + 1}}$.

10. (a) Factorise fully the following expressions:

    (i) $x^3 + y^3 + 3x + 3y$ (iv) $x^3 - y^3 + x^2 - y^2$

    (ii) $x^2 - y^2 + 5x + 5y$ (v) $a^2 - (b + c)^2$

    (iii) $x^2 - 2xy + y^2 - 4z^2$

(b) Find and simplify the 4th term of $\left(\dfrac{x}{\sqrt{y}} + \dfrac{\sqrt{y}}{2x}\right)^{12}$.

    If $x = 1$ and if $y \in N$, find the greatest value of y for which the value of this 4th term is greater than 1.

(c) Show that

$$\dfrac{x^2}{(x - y)(x - z)} + \dfrac{y^2}{(y - z)(y - x)} + \dfrac{yz}{(z - x)(z - y)}$$

simplifies to $\dfrac{x}{(x - z)}$.

Verify your answer by letting $x = 1$, $y = 2$ and $z = 3$.

Solutions and chapter summary available online

Algebra II

In this chapter you will learn to:

- Solve linear equations
- Solve simultaneous linear equations in two unknowns
- Solve simultaneous linear equations in three unknowns
- Solve quadratic equations
- Form quadratic equations given the roots
- Solve simultaneous equations: one linear, one non-linear
- Use the factor theorem for polynomials

- Solve cubic equations with at least one integer root
- Manipulate formulae
- Determine unknown coefficients
- Solve problems using:
    - Linear equations
    - Simultaneous equations
    - Quadratic equations
    - Cubic equations

You should remember...

- Algebra from the Junior Cycle
- How to find the factors of quadratic expressions
- How to plot and read graphs

Key words

- Solve
- Unknown
- Variable
- Linear equation
- Polynomial

- LCD
- Simultaneous equations
- Quadratic equation
- Quadratic trinomials
- Quadratic formula

- Solution
- Roots
- Cubic equation

2.1 Solving Linear Equations

When solving an equation, we are being asked to find the value(s) of the unknown(s) that satisfy the equation. There are many different methods that can be used to solve an equation.

A linear equation is of the form $ax + b = 0$, $a \neq 0$. There are numerous ways of solving a linear equation.

Using Trial and Error

Trial and error involves the following steps:

- Make an educated guess as to what the value of the unknown may be.
- Check to see if your guess is correct by substituting your guessed value into the equation.
- Keep guessing to try to arrive at the correct solution. It is often possible to use previous guesses to make an improved next guess.

Worked Example 2.1

$y = 10 + 9.8x$ is a linear equation representing the speed y (in ms^{-1}) of a free-falling object x seconds after it was travelling at 10 ms^{-1}.

Using trial and error, find out how long it takes for the object to be travelling at a speed of 49.2 ms^{-1} (in other words, solve for x given that $y = 49.2$).

Solution

We use trial and error to solve:

$49.2 = 10 + 9.8x$

x	$10 + 9.8x$	$= 49.2$	
2	$10 + 9.8(2)$	$= 29.6$	Too small. Try a value for x bigger than 2.
5	$10 + 9.8(5)$	$= 59$	Too big. Try a value for x smaller than 5.
4	$10 + 9.8(4)$	$= 49.2$	

∴ Solution is $x = 4$

> If the unknown is being multiplied by a negative number, then bigger guesses will lead to smaller answers.

Using Graphs

Linear equations can also be solved by using graphs. We plot graphs of the linear functions concerned and then read the required solution from the graphs. The graph of a linear function is a line.

ALGEBRA II

Worked Example 2.2

(i) Graph the line $y = 2x + 4$ and, hence, solve for x if $y = 0$.

(ii) Explain the significance of the x-intercept.

(iii) Use a graphical approach to solve $2x + 4 = 2$.

(iv) Using your graph, solve $2x + 4 = 3x + 3$.

Solution

 $y = mx + c$ is the equation of a line with slope m and y-intercept c (see page 18 of *Formulae and Tables*).

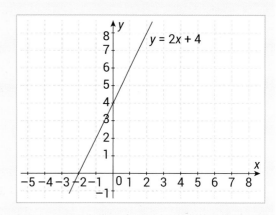

(i) We graph the line $y = 2x + 4$.

This line has a slope of 2 and a y-intercept of 4.

$y = 0$ anywhere on the x-axis.

The line crosses the x-axis at the point $(-2, 0)$.

∴ The x-intercept = -2.

∴ $x = -2$ is the solution to $y = 0$.

(ii) The x-intercept is the solution (or root) of the equation $2x + 4 = 0$.

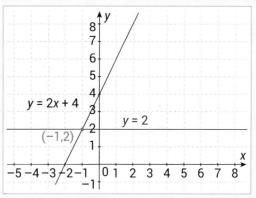

(iii) Using the same axes and scales, graph the line $y = 2$.

This line is horizontal to the x-axis and the y-intercept is 2.

The point of intersection of the two lines gives the solution to $2x + 4 = 2$.

From our graph, the point of intersection of these two lines is $(-1, 2)$.

As the x co-ordinate here is -1, $x = -1$ is the required solution.

(iv) Using the same axes and scales, graph the line $y = 3x + 3$.

This line has a slope of 3 and a y-intercept of 3.

The point of intersection of the two lines gives the solution to $2x + 4 = 3x + 3$.

From our graph, the point of intersection of these two lines is $(1, 6)$.

As the x co-ordinate here is 1, $x = 1$ is the required solution.

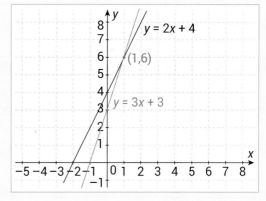

Using Algebra

Both of the previous methods have drawbacks.

● Trial and error can be time-consuming and may not even lead to an exact solution in a reasonable time if the unknown is not an integer.

● Solving by graphing can also be time-consuming and may only give us an estimate of the solution in cases where lines cannot easily be drawn accurately or where the co-ordinates of the point of intersection cannot be read exactly from the diagram.

A more accurate and systematic approach to solving an equation is to use algebra.

ALGEBRA II

Worked Example 2.3

Solve the following linear equation in *a* and verify your answer:

$3(4a - 6) + 25(a + 2) = a - 4$

Solution

Solve the equation.

$3(4a - 6) + 25(a + 2) = a - 4$

$12a - 18 + 25a + 50 = a - 4$ (Multiply through both brackets on the LHS.)

$37a + 32 = a - 4$ (Simplify the LHS.)

$36a = -36$ (Isolate the unknown on the LHS and constant terms on the RHS.)

$\therefore a = -1$

Verify the answer.

We check to see if our answer is correct. We substitute the value we got for *a* into the original equation.

LHS: $3(4a - 6) + 25(a + 2)$

$= 3(4(-1) - 6) + 25((-1) + 2)$

$= 3(-4 - 6) + 25(-1 + 2)$

$= 3(-10) + 25(1)$

$= -30 + 25$

$\therefore$ LHS $= -5$

RHS: $a - 4$

$= (-1) - 4$

$\therefore$ RHS $= -5$

LHS = RHS

$\therefore a = -1$ is the correct solution.

If asked to solve by trial and error or by graphing, you can use algebra first in rough work to help you in your answering.

Worked Example 2.4

Solve $\frac{1}{5}(x + 3) - 7 = \frac{3x}{10}$.

Solution

Rewrite the equation.

$\frac{x + 3}{5} - \frac{7}{1} = \frac{3x}{10}$

The LCD of 5, 1 and 10 is 10. We multiply the entire equation by 10.

$10\left(\frac{x + 3}{5}\right) - 10\left(\frac{7}{1}\right) = 10\left(\frac{3x}{10}\right)$

$2(x + 3) - 70 = 3x$

$2x + 6 - 70 = 3x$

$\therefore x = -64$

Exercise 2.1

Using trial and error, find the value of the unknown variable:

1. $2x + 4 = 2$ **3.** $2(x + 3) = 18$

2. $-3a + 2 = 17$ **4.** $3(2 - x) = -9$

Solve the following linear equations by graphing:

5. $2x - 9 = 0$ **7.** $3x + 10 = 2x + 5$

6. $5 - 4x = -3$ **8.** $4x + 1 = x - 7$

Solve the following equations using algebra and verify your answer in each case:

9. $2x + 3 = 4(3x - 1)$ **10.** $4(2a - 1) = -3(2a - 1)$

11. $-(x - 3) - (x + 2) = 2(x - 1)$

12. $\frac{1}{4}(x - 1) + \frac{2x}{3} = \frac{5}{2}$

13. $\frac{y + 3}{4} - \frac{1}{3}(y - 5) = 2\frac{3}{8}$

14. The expected relationship between height x (in cm) and weight y (in kg) of a group of female Leaving Certificate students is found to be $y = 0.5x - 25$. Find the expected height of a student who weighs 55 kg using:

   (i) Trial and error   (ii) A graphical approach

2.2 Solving Simultaneous Linear Equations in Two Variables

We can use various methods to solve simultaneous linear equations with two unknowns.

Using Trial and Error

Worked Example 2.5

Investigate if $x = 1$ and $y = -2$ is the correct solution for the following set of equations:

$2x - y = 4$ $5x - 3y = 1$

Solution

We substitute $x = 1$ and $y = -2$ into both equations.

$2x - y = 4$	$5x - 3y = 1$
$2(1) - (-2) = 4$	$5(1) - 3(-2) = 1$
$2 + 2 = 4$	$5 + 6 = 1$
$4 = 4$	$11 = 1$
True	False

$\therefore x = 1$ and $y = -2$ is not the correct solution to both equations.

The point $(-1,2)$ lies on the line with equation $2x - y = 4$ but does not lie on the line with equation $5x - 3y = 1$.

Using Graphs

Worked Example 2.6

Solve the following set of equations by graphing:

$2x - 4 = y$ $2x + y = 2$

Solution

We plot both lines using the same axes and scales.

$2x - 4 = y$	
This line has a slope of 2 and a y-intercept of -4.	
$2x + y = 2$	
Let $x = 0$.	Let $y = 0$.
$2(0) + y = 2$	$2x + (0) = 2$
$y = 2$	$2x = 2$
	$x = 1$
If $x = 0$ then $y = 2$.	If $y = 0$ then $x = 1$.
Point $(0,2)$	Point $(1,0)$

Mark the point of intersection of both lines.

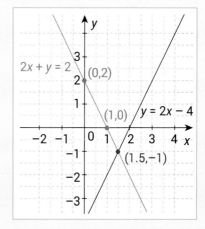

From our graph, we see that the point of intersection is $(1.5,-1)$.

$\therefore x = 1.5$ and $y = -1$

Using Elimination

Worked Example 2.7

Solve the equations:

$3x - 2y = 14$ $\quad \dfrac{2x+1}{3} - \dfrac{y+1}{9} = 2$

Solution

First, ensure that both equations are in the same format.

$$\frac{2x+1}{3} - \frac{y+1}{9} = 2$$

$$\frac{9(2x+1)}{3} - \frac{9(y+1)}{9} = 9(2)$$

$$3(2x+1) - 1(y+1) = 9(2)$$

$$6x + 3 - y - 1 = 18$$

$$6x - y = 16$$

Now work with both equations simultaneously.

$$3x - 2y = 14$$

$$6x - y = 16$$

We make the y coefficients the same in each equation.

$3x - 2y = 14$ $(\times 1)$ $\rightarrow$ $3x - 2y = 14$

$6x - y = 16$ $(\times 2)$ $\rightarrow$ $12x - 2y = 32$

> Remember we need to make the x or y term in each question have the same coefficient. We can do this by multiplying each equation by the non-negative (absolute) value of the coefficient of interest in the other equation.

As the y coefficients are of the same sign, we will subtract one equation from the other.

(If they were of the opposite sign, we would add.)

$$3x - 2y = 14$$
$$-(12x - 2y = 32)$$

$$\overline{}$$

$$3x - 2y = 14$$
$$-12x + 2y = -32$$
$$\overline{}$$
$$-9x = -18$$

$$\therefore x = 2$$

Substitute $x = 2$ into one of the equations.

$$6x - y = 16$$

$$6(2) - y = 16$$

$$12 - y = 16$$

$$\therefore -4 = y$$

Answer: $x = 2$, $y = -4$

We could also write the solution as $(x,y) = (2,-4)$ as the solution gives the co-ordinates of the point of intersection of the two lines.

Alternative Methods

We can also solve simultaneous linear equations by using substitution.

Worked Example 2.8

Solve the set of equations in Worked Example 2.7 by using substitution.

Solution

The set of equations is: $3x - 2y = 14$

$$6x - y = 16$$

Make y the subject of each equation (we could just as well have chosen to work with x).

$3x - 2y = 14$ $\Rightarrow$ $2y = 3x - 14$

$$y = \frac{3}{2}x - 7$$

$6x - y = 16$ $\Rightarrow$ $y = 6x - 16$

Equate y with itself.

$$y = y$$
$$\frac{3}{2}x - 7 = 6x - 16$$

Solve for x.

$$3x - 14 = 12x - 32$$
$$18 = 9x$$
$$x = 2$$

Use one of the equations to solve for y.

$$y = 6x - 16$$
$$y = 6(2) - 16$$
$$y = 12 - 16$$
$$y = -4$$

$\therefore (x,y) = (2,-4)$ is the solution.

Exercise 2.2

Solve using trial and error:

1. $3x + 2y = 21$
    $4x - 5y = 28$

2. $6x + 5y = 19$
    $3x - 7y = 19$

Solve by graphing:

3. $x + y = 4$
    $x - y = 10$

4. $5x - 2y = 9$
    $3x + y = 1$

Solve by elimination:

5. $7x - 8y = -1$
    $x - 4y = -23$

6. $4x + 5y = 0$
    $x + y = 1$

7. $9p - 4q + 16 = 0$
    $-p + q = -1$

8. $2x + 5y = -14$
    $2x = 3y + 18$

Solve using any method:

9. $2x + 3y = 29$
    $x - 7y = -28$

11. $\frac{x-3}{4} + \frac{5-y}{2} = \frac{1}{4}$

    $\frac{2x-1}{3} - \frac{y+3}{2} = -\frac{13}{6}$

10. $\frac{2}{3}x + \frac{3}{5}y = \frac{8}{5}$

    $\frac{1}{2}x + \frac{2}{9}y = \frac{17}{18}$

12. $p + 2(q-1) = -12$

    $q + \frac{1}{3}p = -5$

2.3 Solving Simultaneous Equations in Three Variables

To solve for three unknown quantities, we need three equations. Then one unknown at a time can be solved for.

Worked Example 2.9

Solve the equations:

$x + y + z = 6$ $5x + 3y - 2z = 5$ $3x - 7y + z = -8$

An equation of the form $Ax + By + Cz = D$ in three unknowns x, y, z (A, B, C, D constants) represents a plane (flat surface) in three dimensions. The three planes described by the system of equations in this example are shown in the diagram. The solution to such a system gives the x, y and z co-ordinates of the common point of intersection of the three planes.

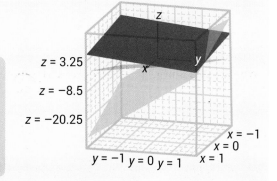

Solution

We will select one of the variables and eliminate it from a pair of equations.

The variable z looks to be the easiest to eliminate, since two of its coefficients have an absolute value of 1.

$x + y + z = 6$ $(\times 2)$ $\rightarrow 2x + 2y + 2z = 12$

$5x + 3y - 2z = 5$ $(\times 1)$ $\rightarrow 5x + 3y - 2z = 5$

As the coefficients of z have different signs, we will add the two equations.

$2x + 2y + 2z = 12$

$+(5x + 3y - 2z = 5)$

$\overline{\quad 7x + 5y = 17 \quad}$ (Equation 1)

We now pick a different pair of equations and again eliminate the z variable.

$x + y + z = 6$

$3x - 7y + z = -8$

The z coefficients are the same sign, so we will subtract the two equations.

$x + y + z = 6$

$-(3x - 7y + z = -8)$

$\overline{\quad -2x + 8y = 14 \quad}$ (Equation 2)

We now have two equations with two unknowns.

Let's eliminate x from this set of equations.

$7x + 5y = 17$ (× 2) → $14x + 10y = 34$

$-2x + 8y = 14$ (× 7) → $-14x + 56y = 98$

The coefficients of x have different signs, so we add the two equations.

$14x + 10y = 34$

$-14x + 56y = 98$

$\overline{\quad 66y = 132 \quad}$

$\therefore y = 2$

Using Equation 1, we solve for x.

$7x + 5y = 17$	$7x = 7$
$7x + 5(2) = 17$	$\therefore x = 1$
$7x + 10 = 17$	

We now have the values of x and y. We can substitute these values into any of the original equations to find the value of z.

$x + y + z = 6$	$\therefore z = 3$
$1 + 2 + z = 6$	$\therefore x = 1, y = 2$ and $z = 3$
$3 + z = 6$	

It is good practice in a question like this to verify your solution using each of the three original equations. A simple arithmetic mistake is easy to make.

ALGEBRA II

Exercise 2.3

Solve the following systems of equations:

1. $2x + y + 4z = 23$

$5x + y + 2z = 19$

$3x - 2y + z = 13$

2. $x + y + z = 9$

$2x + 3y + z = 16$

$3x - 4y + 2z = 1$

3. $2a - 2b - 5c = -4$

$2a - 4b - c = -10$

$5a - 3b + 5c = -4$

4. $x + y + z = 16$

$\frac{5}{2}x + y + 10z = 40$

$2x + \frac{1}{2}y + 4z = 21$

5. $2x + 8y - 3z = -1$

$2x - 3y + 2z = 2$

$2x + y + z = 5$

6. $3p + 4q - 2r = 8$

$9p + 8q + 2r = -13$

$6p - 12q + 14r = -59$

7. $x + y = z$

$2x + 3y = 2z$

$x + 2y = 10$

8. $x + 2y + 3z = 24$

$\frac{x}{2} + \frac{y}{3} + \frac{z}{6} = 4$

$x + 2y + 5z = 28$

9. $\frac{3}{4}x + \frac{2}{5}y - \frac{3}{10}z = 0$

$x + 2y + 3z = -1$

$\frac{3}{8}x + \frac{1}{2}y + \frac{1}{3}z = -\frac{5}{12}$

10. $x + y = z$

$3x + 2y - 4z = -1$

$x - 3y + 3z = 2$

11. Solve:

$x + y + z = 5$

$2x - y + 3z = 3$

$3x + 2y - 5z = 21$

Hence, solve:

$a^2 + b + (c + 1) = 5$

$2a^2 - b + 3(c + 1) = 3$

$3a^2 + 2b - 5(c + 1) = 21$

2.4 Solving Quadratic Equations

Quadratic equations arise in many areas of mathematical investigation, from analysing the flight of a projectile such as a kicked football, to studying the population growth behaviour of bacteria, to determining the break-even points for a commercial company. Being able to solve quadratic equations is a fundamental part of our Leaving Certificate course.

Using Graphs

To estimate the roots of a quadratic equation of the form $ax^2 + bx + c = 0$, we read off the values of x where the graph of $y = ax^2 + bx + c$ intersects the x-axis. The roots (zeros) are the input values that result in an output value of zero for the quadratic function.

For example:

The equation $x^2 = 3x$ has roots $x = 0$ or $x = 3$ as each of these values satisfies the equation.

Alternatively, rewrite the equation as $x^2 - 3x = 0$. Then define a function $y = x^2 - 3x$. This function has roots $x = 0$ or $x = 3$ as each of these input values results in an output value of zero.

Note: Roots are sometimes referred to as 'zeros'.

Worked Example 2.10

Find the roots of $-x^2 + 7x - 12 = 0$ by graphing $f(x) = -x^2 + 7x - 12$ between $x = 1$ and $x = 6$.

> $f(x)$ is pronounced 'f of x'. This notation is used when we have a function, in this case called 'f'.
>
> $f(x)$ or y ($y = f(x)$) is the outcome (output) we get when we insert (input) a value for x into the function f. We will deal with functions in more detail in Chapter 6.

Solution

We construct an input–output table and substitute x-values to calculate y-values.

x	$-x^2 + 7x - 12$	y	Point
1	$-(1)^2 + 7(1) - 12$	-6	$(1,-6)$
2	$-(2)^2 + 7(2) - 12$	-2	$(2,-2)$
3	$-(3)^2 + 7(3) - 12$	0	$(3,0)$
4	$-(4)^2 + 7(4) - 12$	0	$(4,0)$
5	$-(5)^2 + 7(5) - 12$	-2	$(5,-2)$
6	$-(6)^2 + 7(6) - 12$	-6	$(6,-6)$

We now plot our points on an x and y co-ordinate diagram and then draw a curved graph.

The roots are the x-values where the graph crosses the x-axis (i.e. that give us a y-value of zero).

$\therefore$ The roots of the equation are $x = 3$ or $x = 4$.

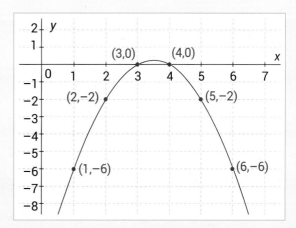

ALGEBRA II

Using Algebra

(i) Solve $3x^2 + 5x - 12 = 0$.

(ii) Hence, solve $3(y - 1)^2 + 5(y - 1) - 12 = 0$.

Solution

(i) $3x^2 + 5x - 12 = 0$

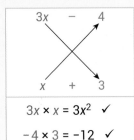

$3x \times x = 3x^2$ ✓

$-4 \times 3 = -12$ ✓

Using the arrows:

$3x \times 3 = 9x$

$\underline{x \times -4 = -4x}$

$5x$ ✓

$(3x - 4)(x + 3) = 0$

Let both factors equal 0 and solve:

$3x - 4 = 0$ **OR** $x + 3 = 0$

$3x = 4$ **OR** $x = -3$

$x = \dfrac{4}{3}$ **OR** $x = -3$

Alternatively, we can use the **Guide Number Method**.

Step 1 Multiply the coefficient of x^2 by the constant.

$3x^2 + 5x - 12$

$3 \times -12 = -36$

Step 2 Find two factors of -36 that will multiply to -36 and add up to give 5, the coefficient of x.

-4 and 9

Step 3 Use the answers from Step 2 to rewrite $3x^2 + 5x - 12 = 0$ as follows:

$3x^2 - 4x + 9x - 12 = 0$

$x(3x - 4) + 3(3x - 4) = 0$ (Factorise by grouping.)

$(x + 3)(3x - 4) = 0$ (distributive property)

$x + 3 = 0$ **OR** $3x - 4 = 0$

$x = -3$ **OR** $3x = 4$

$x = -3$ **OR** $x = \dfrac{4}{3}$

(ii) To solve $3(y - 1)^2 + 5(y - 1) - 12 = 0$, we note that this equation has the same structure as the original equation, except that each x has been replaced by $y - 1$.

$\therefore y - 1 = x$

$y - 1 = \dfrac{4}{3}$ **OR** $y - 1 = -3$

$y = \dfrac{7}{3}$ **OR** $y = -2$

Solve $\dfrac{8}{y + 2} - \dfrac{2}{y + 3} = \dfrac{8}{5}$, $y \ne -2, -3$.

Solution

The LCD is $(5)(y + 2)(y + 3)$.

$$\dfrac{8(5)(y + 2)(y + 3)}{y + 2} - \dfrac{2(5)(y + 2)(y + 3)}{y + 3} = \dfrac{8(5)(y + 2)(y + 3)}{5}$$ (Multiply the whole equation by the LCD.)

$\Rightarrow 8(5)(y + 3) - 2(5)(y + 2) = 8(y + 2)(y + 3)$

$40(y + 3) - 10(y + 2) = 8(y^2 + 5y + 6)$

$40y + 120 - 10y - 20 = 8y^2 + 40y + 48$

$30y + 100 = 8y^2 + 40y + 48$

$8y^2 + 10y - 52 = 0$

$4y^2 + 5y - 26 = 0$

$\therefore (4y + 13)(y - 2) = 0$

$4y + 13 = 0$ **OR** $y - 2 = 0$

$4y = -13$ **OR** $y = 2$

$y = -\dfrac{13}{4}$ **OR** $y = 2$

Worked Example 2.13

Solve $\dfrac{2x + 5}{3x + 1} - \dfrac{2x - 1}{5x + 4} = -4\dfrac{1}{2}$.

Solution

We first write $-4\dfrac{1}{2}$ as an improper fraction.

$$\frac{2x + 5}{3x + 1} - \frac{2x - 1}{5x + 4} = -\frac{9}{2}$$

The LCD is $2(5x + 4)(3x + 1)$.

$$\frac{2(5x + 4)(3x + 1)(2x + 5)}{(3x + 1)} - \frac{2(5x + 4)(3x + 1)(2x - 1)}{(5x + 4)} = \frac{-9(2)(5x + 4)(3x + 1)}{2}$$

(Multiply every term in the equation by the LCD.)

$$2(5x + 4)(2x + 5) - 2(3x + 1)(2x - 1) = -9(5x + 4)(3x + 1)$$

We need to be very careful when multiplying, adding and subtracting the various terms as it is easy to make a mistake.

$2(10x^2 + 8x + 25x + 20) - 2(6x^2 - 3x + 2x - 1) = -9(15x^2 + 5x + 12x + 4)$

$2(10x^2 + 33x + 20) - 2(6x^2 - x - 1) = -9(15x^2 + 17x + 4)$

$20x^2 + 66x + 40 - 12x^2 + 2x + 2 = -135x^2 - 153x - 36$

$20x^2 - 12x^2 + 135x^2 + 66x + 2x + 153x + 40 + 2 + 36 = 0$

$143x^2 + 221x + 78 = 0$

Divide the equation by the HCF, which is 13.

$11x^2 + 17x + 6 = 0.$

$\therefore (11x + 6)(x + 1) = 0$

$11x + 6 = 0$	**OR**	$x + 1 = 0$
$11x = -6$	**OR**	$x = -1$
$x = -\dfrac{6}{11}$	**OR**	$x = -1$

Solving by Using the Quadratic Formula

There are alternative methods of solving quadratic equations. One approach is to use the quadratic formula.

We can use this formula instead of factorising an equation and finding its roots.

Many quadratic equations cannot be solved by factorisation because they do not have simple factors. Using the quadratic formula will allow you to solve **any** quadratic equation.

When using the quadratic formula, it is important to note that in, for example, the equation $x^2 - 2x - 8 = 0$:

- $a = 1$ (the coefficient of x^2)
- $b = -2$ (the coefficient of x)
- $c = -8$ (the constant)

$$x = \frac{-b \pm \sqrt{b^2 - 4ac}}{2a}$$

a = coefficient of x^2

b = coefficient of x

c = constant term

This formula appears on page 20 of *Formulae and Tables*.

To use the quadratic formula, we should ensure that:

- The equation is written in the form $ax^2 + bx + c = 0$
- The a value is positive (this is just to make calculations easier)

The symbol $\pm$ requires two procedures:

(i) Add $\sqrt{b^2 - 4ac}$ to $-b$ in the numerator.

(ii) Subtract $\sqrt{b^2 - 4ac}$ from $-b$ in the numerator.

ALGEBRA II

Worked Example 2.14

Solve $5x^2 - 2x = 25$ and give your answer:

(i) In surd form   (ii) Correct to three decimal places

Solution

We must first have the equation in the correct form.

$5x^2 - 2x - 25 = 0$

Using the quadratic formula:

$a = 5$ $b = -2$ $c = -25$

$$x = \frac{-(-2) \pm \sqrt{(-2)^2 - 4(5)(-25)}}{2(5)}$$

$$x = \frac{2 \pm \sqrt{4 + 500}}{10}$$

$$x = \frac{2 \pm \sqrt{504}}{10}$$

(i) Surd form:

$$\sqrt{504} = \sqrt{36}\,\sqrt{14} = 6\sqrt{14}$$

$$\therefore x = \frac{2 \pm 6\sqrt{14}}{10}$$

This answer can be simplified further by dividing each term by the highest common factor of 2, 6 and 10 (which is 2).

$$\therefore x = \frac{1 \pm 3\sqrt{14}}{5}$$

(ii) $x = \dfrac{1 - 3\sqrt{14}}{5}$ **OR** $x = \dfrac{1 + 3\sqrt{14}}{5}$

$x = -2.044994432$ **OR** $x = 2.444994432$

Answer to three decimal places:

$x = -2.045$ **OR** $x = 2.445$

Roots of Quadratic Equations

If we are given the roots of a quadratic equation, it is possible to construct a quadratic equation with those roots. To form a quadratic equation when given the roots, we change the roots into factors and then use these factors to form the equation.

Worked Example 2.15

Form an equation from each of the following roots:

(i) $5, -\dfrac{2}{3}$ (ii) $\dfrac{1}{2}, -\dfrac{3}{4}$

Solution

(i) $5, -\dfrac{2}{3}$

Root	$x = 5$	$x = -\dfrac{2}{3}$
Factor	$x - 5 = 0$	$3x = -2$
		$3x + 2 = 0$
Equation	$(x - 5)(3x + 2) = 0$	
	$3x^2 - 13x - 10 = 0$	

Consider the equation $x^2 + bx + c = 0$, which has the roots α and β.

$\therefore (x - \alpha)$ and $(x - \beta)$ are factors of the equation $x^2 + bx + c = 0$.

$(x - \alpha)(x - \beta) = x^2 + bx + c$

$x(x - \beta) - \alpha(x - \beta) = x^2 + bx + c$

$x^2 - \beta x - \alpha x + \alpha\beta = x^2 + bx + c$

$x^2 - (\beta + \alpha)x + \alpha\beta = x^2 + bx + c$

> Given two roots α and β, there exists an infinite number of quadratic equations with such roots.

From this we can derive the formula:

> Quadratic Equation $\Rightarrow x^2 - $ (sum of the roots)$x + $ (product of the roots) $= 0$

(ii) $\frac{1}{2}, -\frac{3}{4}$

Sum = $\frac{1}{2} + \left(-\frac{3}{4}\right)$	Product = $\left(\frac{1}{2}\right)\left(-\frac{3}{4}\right)$
Sum = $-\frac{1}{4}$	Product = $-\frac{3}{8}$

$$x^2 - \left(-\frac{1}{4}\right)x + \left(-\frac{3}{8}\right) = 0$$

$$x^2 + \frac{1}{4}x - \frac{3}{8} = 0$$

Multiply by the LCD, which is 8.

$$8x^2 + 2x - 3 = 0$$

Exercise 2.4

1. Use trial and error to find one whole number root of each of the following equations:

   (i) $x^2 + 11x - 42 = 0$

   (ii) $2x^2 - 7x + 3 = 0$

   (iii) $x^2 + 2x - 63 = 0$

2. For each graph below, estimate the roots of the quadratic function graphed.

   (i)
   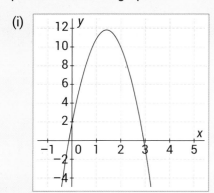

   (ii)
   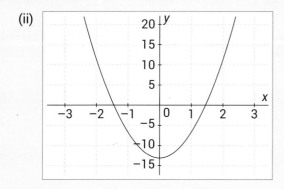

   (iii)
   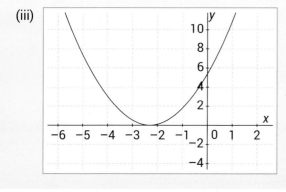

   (iv)
   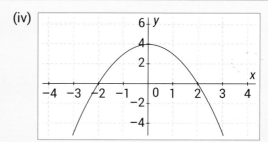

3. Solve $-x^2 + 4x - 4 = 0$ by graphing the function $y = -x^2 + 4x - 4$ between $x = -2$ and $x = 4$.

4. Graph the function $f(x) = 3x^2 - 6x - 5 = 0$ between $x = -2$ and $x = 5$.

   (i) Use your graph to find an estimate of the roots of the equation $3x^2 - 6x - 5 = 0$.

   (ii) Graph the line $g(x) = 4$. Mark the points of intersection of your two graphs.

   (iii) Explain what these points of intersection signify.

   (iv) Check your answer to part (iii) by solving $f(x) = g(x)$.

5. Solve the following equations using algebra:

   (i) $2x^2 - 13x + 18 = 0$
   (v) $7x^2 - 22x - 24 = 0$

   (ii) $3x^2 + x - 14 = 0$
   (vi) $4x^2 - 11x - 20 = 0$

   (iii) $25x^2 - 81 = 0$
   (vii) $8x^2 - 11x - 10 = 0$

   (iv) $25x^2 - 81x = 0$
   (viii) $6x^2 - 25x + 26 = 0$

6. Solve $x^2 + 7x + 12 = 0$ and, hence, solve $(y^2 + 4y)^2 + 7(y^2 + 4y) + 12 = 0$.

7. Solve $2x^2 - 17x + 35 = 0$ and, hence, solve $2\left(\frac{3}{2}t + 2t^2\right)^2 - 17\left(\frac{3}{2}t + 2t^2\right) + 35 = 0$.

8. Form a quadratic equation with each pair of roots, giving your answers in the form $ax^2 + bx + c = 0$ where $a, b, c \in Z$:

(i) 3, 2

(ii) 5, −2

(iii) 6, 0

(iv) $\dfrac{5}{2}$, −3

(v) $\dfrac{1}{2}, \dfrac{1}{5}$

(vi) $\dfrac{3}{4}, \dfrac{3}{4}$

(vii) $4 + \sqrt{3}, 4 - \sqrt{3}$

(viii) $-1 - \sqrt{2}, -1 + \sqrt{2}$

9. Use the quadratic formula to solve each of the following equations to either two decimal places (2 d.p.) or three decimal places (3 d.p.):

(i) $2x^2 + 9x - 16 = 0$ (2 d.p.)

(ii) $8x^2 + 5x - 9 = 0$ (2 d.p.)

(iii) $2x^2 - x - 17 = 0$ (3 d.p.)

(iv) $4x^2 + 9x - 5 = 0$ (2 d.p.)

(v) $3x^2 - 2x - 23 = 0$ (3 d.p.)

(vi) $7x^2 + 3x - 5 = 0$ (3 d.p.)

10. Solve the following equations, leaving your answers in surd form:

(i) $x^2 - 5 = 0$

(ii) $x^2 + 6x + 7 = 0$

(iii) $6x^2 + 8x + 1 = 0$

(iv) $3x^2 + 12x + 1 = 0$

11. Solve the following equations:

(i) $2 - \dfrac{13}{x^2} + \dfrac{20}{x} = 0, x \neq 0$

(ii) $\dfrac{3}{x^2} = \dfrac{11}{x} - 10, x \neq 0$

(iii) $\dfrac{1}{x + 1} + \dfrac{1}{x} = \dfrac{5}{6}, x \neq -1, 0$

(iv) $\dfrac{1}{x - 3} - \dfrac{1}{2x - 1} = \dfrac{1}{12}, x \neq \dfrac{1}{2}, 3$

(v) $\dfrac{5}{2x - 1} - \dfrac{4}{3x + 2} = -7, x \neq -\dfrac{2}{3}, \dfrac{1}{2}$

(vi) $\dfrac{1}{x + 2} - \dfrac{2}{x} + \dfrac{1}{x - 6} = 0, x \neq -2, 0, 6$

(vii) $\dfrac{1}{x + 1} + \dfrac{1}{x - 3} = 2, x \neq -1, 3$

(viii) $\dfrac{4}{4x - 3} + 1 = \dfrac{2}{x - 1}, x \neq \dfrac{3}{4}, 1$

12. Find the value of the constant c and the roots of the quadratic equation $x^2 - 10x + c = 0$, if one root is four times the other.

13. Find the value of the constant d and the roots of the quadratic equation $x^2 - 12x + d = 0$, if one root is two less than the other.

2.5 Simultaneous Equations: One Linear and One Non-Linear

Earlier in this chapter we outlined several methods for solving two linear equations in two unknowns simultaneously (finding the point of intersection of two lines) and a method for solving a system of three linear equations in three unknowns (finding the point of intersection of three planes). We now outline a method for solving simultaneously a set of equations where one is linear (line) and the other is non-linear (parabola, circle, ellipse, hyperbola, etc.). Solving simultaneously will give us the co-ordinates of the point(s) of intersection between the line and the non-linear curve.

Type of curve	Example equation	Graph	Type of curve	Example equation	Graph
Parabola	$y = x^2 - 6x + 9$		Ellipse	$16x^2 + 25y^2 = 400$	
Circle	$x^2 + y^2 = 25$		Hyperbola	$x^2 + 2xy - 4y^2 + 5x = 0$	

Worked Example 2.16

Solve for x and y:

$x + 4y = 1$ $2x^2 + 3xy = 35$

A non-linear equation in x and y contains terms of the form x^2 or xy or y^2, etc.

Solution

Step 1 Linear	We start with the linear equation. We make one of the variables the subject of the formula. $x + 4y = 1$ $\Rightarrow x = 1 - 4y$
Step 2 Substitution Always substitute from the linear into the non-linear.	$2x^2 + 3xy = 35$ Substitute $x = 1 - 4y$ into this equation. $2(1 - 4y)^2 + 3(1 - 4y)(y) = 35$ $2(1 - 4y)(1 - 4y) + 3(1 - 4y)(y) = 35$ $2(1 - 8y + 16y^2) + (1 - 4y)(3y) = 35$ $2 - 16y + 32y^2 + 3y - 12y^2 = 35$ $2 - 13y + 20y^2 = 35$ $20y^2 - 13y - 33 = 0$
Step 3 Solving for one variable	$20y^2 - 13y - 33 = 0$ 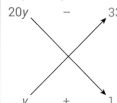 $(20y - 33)(y + 1) = 0$ $20y - 33 = 0$ **OR** $y + 1 = 0$ $20y = 33$ **OR** $y = -1$ $y = \dfrac{33}{20}$ **OR** $y = -1$
Step 4 Solving for the other variable Always substitute back into the linear. This will avoid obtaining an incorrect solution.	As we know the two values of y, we can now find the corresponding values of x. **$x = 1 - 4y$** If $y = \dfrac{33}{20}$ If $y = -1$ $x = 1 - 4\left(\dfrac{33}{20}\right)$ $x = 1 - 4(-1)$ $x = 1 - \dfrac{33}{5}$ $x = 1 + 4$ $x = -\dfrac{28}{5}$ $x = 5$
Step 5 Write answer	$x = -\dfrac{28}{5}, y = \dfrac{33}{20}$ **OR** $x = 5, y = -1$ $\left(-\dfrac{28}{5}, \dfrac{33}{20}\right)$ $(5, -1)$ These are the co-ordinates of the points of intersection between the line and the non-linear curve.

Using Graphs

We have used graphs to solve linear equations and quadratic equations. We can also use graphs to solve a system of one linear and one non-linear equation. The solution will be the co-ordinates of the point(s) of intersection between the linear and non-linear graphs. The concern with this method is that it may not be accurate.

Worked Example 2.17

Using the diagram/graphs, write down the points of intersection of $2x + 3y = 0$ and $2x^2 + y^2 = 22$.

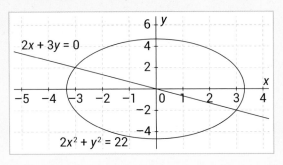

Solution

We find the points of intersection between the two curves by reading them off the graph.

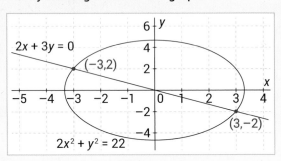

$\therefore$ $x = -3, y = 2$ **OR** $x = 3, y = -2$

      $(-3, 2)$ $(3, -2)$

Exercise 2.5

1. Estimate the points of intersection between the linear and non-linear graphs shown.

(i)

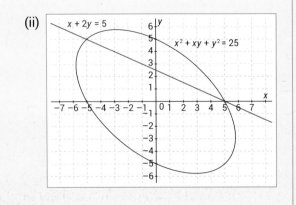

(iii)

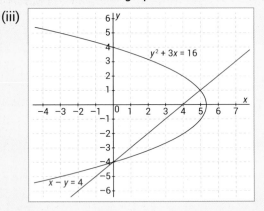

(ii)

(iv)

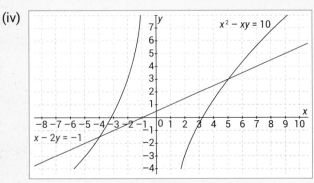

Solve the simultaneous equations:

2. $x + y = 5$

$x^2 + y^2 = 13$

3. $x - y = 2$

$2x^2 + y^2 = 36$

4. $2x + y = 9$

$xy = 10$

5. $4x - y = -3$

$x^2 - y^2 = 0$

6. $3x - y - 3 = -4$

$xy - y = -1$

7. $x = 2y$

$x^2 + y^2 - 2xy - 9 = 0$

8. $a^2 - ab + b^2 = 3$

$a + 2b + 1 = 0$

9. $x - 4y = -13$

$x^2 + 2y^2 + 6xy = 29$

10. $x - 2y = 12$

$x^2 + y^2 - 10x - 4y + 4 = 0$

11. $-\frac{1}{2}x + \frac{1}{4}y = -4$

$x^2 + y^2 - 4x - 6y = 52$

12. $4x = 3y$

$4x^2 - 6y^2 - 6xy - 2y + 5 = 0$

13. $3x + 5y = 15$

$x^2 + y^2 - 10x - 9 = 0$

14. $4x - 7y = 9$

$8x^2 - 3y^2 = -1$

2.6 The Factor Theorem

A polynomial function $f(x)$ of one variable x is of the form

$$f(x) = a_nx^n + a_{n-1}x^{n-1} + \ldots + a_2x^2 + a_1x + a_0$$

where all powers are non-negative whole numbers and each of $a_n, a_{n-1}, \ldots, a_1, a_0$ is constant.

Examples: $f(x) = 3x^2 + 5x + 7$ $g(x) = 1 + 2x^2 - 11x^3 + x^4$

The following are **not** polynomials, as they are not of the required form above:

$h(x) = x^2 - 7\sqrt{x} + 3$ (Here, $\sqrt{x} = x^{\frac{1}{2}}$, so the power is **not** a non-negative integer.)

$k(x) = 2 + \sqrt{3}x^{\frac{2}{3}} - x^2 + x^3$ (Here, the power $\frac{2}{3}$ is **not** a non-negative integer.)

The factor theorem can be used to find the roots of, or the factors of, a polynomial function.

A polynomial $f(x)$ has a factor $(x - a)$ if and only if $f(a) = 0$.

This means that if $(x - a)$ is a factor of $f(x)$, then $f(a) = 0$. Also, if $f(a) = 0$, then $(x - a)$ is a factor of $f(x)$.

The factor theorem can be very useful when finding the roots or factors of cubic polynomials (polynomials where the highest power is 3). We can use the factor theorem to find one factor and then use long division to proceed further.

Worked Example 2.18

Solve the equation $2x^3 - 3x^2 - 17x + 30 = 0$.

Solution

The constant term is 30. We investigate if one of the roots is a factor of 30.

The factors of 30 are $\pm 1, \pm 2, \pm 3, \pm 5, \pm 6, \pm 10, \pm 15, \pm 30$.

We now use trial and error.

x	$2x^3 - 3x^2 - 17x + 30$	$= 0$	
1	$2(1)^3 - 3(1)^2 - 17(1) + 30$	$= 12$	Not a root
-1	$2(-1)^3 - 3(-1)^2 - 17(-1) + 30$	$= 42$	Not a root
3	$2(3)^3 - 3(3)^2 - 17(3) + 30$	$= 6$	Not a root
-3	$2(-3)^3 - 3(-3)^2 - 17(-3) + 30$	$= 0$	Root ✓

$x = -3$ is a root.

$\therefore x + 3$ is a factor.

ALGEBRA II

We can now use long division to find the other factors and hence, the other roots.

$$\begin{array}{r} 2x^2 - 9x + 10 \\ x+3\overline{\smash{\big)}\ 2x^3 - 3x^2 - 17x + 30} \\ \underline{-(2x^3 + 6x^2)} \\ -9x^2 - 17x \\ \underline{-(-9x^2 - 27x)} \\ 10x + 30 \\ \underline{-(10x + 30)} \\ 0 \end{array}$$

$\therefore 2x^3 - 3x^2 - 17x + 30 = 0$

$\Rightarrow (x + 3)(2x^2 - 9x + 10) = 0$

$(x + 3)(2x - 5)(x - 2) = 0$

Set each factor equal to 0 and solve.

$\therefore x = -3,\ x = \dfrac{5}{2},\ x = 2$

Worked Example 2.19

Let $f(x) = ax^3 + bx^2 - 9$, where a and b are constants.

Given that $(x + 3)$ and $(x - 1)$ are factors of $f(x)$, find the value of a and the value of b.

Solution

$x + 3$ is a factor.

$\therefore x = -3$ is a root.

$f(-3) = a(-3)^3 + b(-3)^2 - 9$

$\quad \Rightarrow -27a + 9b - 9 = 0$

$\quad\quad\quad -3a + b - 1 = 0$

$\quad\quad\quad\quad -3a + b = 1$

$x - 1$ is a factor.

$\therefore x = 1$ is a root.

$f(1) = a(1)^3 + b(1)^2 - 9$

$\quad\quad a + b - 9 = 0$

$\quad\quad\quad a + b = 9$

We now solve the simultaneous equations.

$-3a + b = 1$

$\ \ a + b = 9$

As the coefficients of b are the same sign, we will subtract.

$\quad -3a + b = 1$

$\underline{-(a + b = 9)}$

$\quad\quad -4a = -8$

$\quad\quad \therefore a = 2$

$a + b = 9$

$2 + b = 9$

$\therefore b = 7$

Alternative Method

$(x + 3)(x - 1) = x^2 + 2x - 3$ is a quadratic factor. When the cubic polynomial is divided by this factor the remainder will be zero.

$$\begin{array}{r} ax + (b - 2a) \\ x^2 + 2x - 3\overline{\smash{\big)}\ ax^3 + bx^2 + 0x - 9} \\ \underline{-(ax^3 + 2ax^2 - 3ax)} \\ (b - 2a)x^2 + 3ax - 9 \\ \underline{-((b - 2a)x^2 + 2(b - 2a)x - 3(b - 2a))} \\ [3a - 2(b - 2a)]x - 9 + 3(b - 2a) \end{array}$$

$\therefore$ Remainder $= (7a - 2b)x + (3b - 6a - 9)$

Since remainder is zero *for all x*:

$7a - 2b = 0 \quad$ and $\quad 3b - 6a - 9 = 0$

$\quad\quad\quad\quad\quad\quad\quad \Rightarrow 6a - 3b = -9$

$\quad\quad\quad\quad\quad\quad\quad \Rightarrow 2a - b = -3$

Solve these two equations in a and b for $a = 2$, $b = 7$ using the same method as before.

Using a Graph to Estimate a Polynomial

A polynomial $f(x)$ has a factor $(x - a)$ if and only if its graph touches or crosses the x-axis at $x = a$ $(a \in R)$.

For example, the polynomial $y = x^4 + 6x^3 - 13x^2 - 66x + 72$ has the following factors and, hence, roots:

Factors: $x + 6 \quad x + 4 \quad x - 1 \quad x - 3$

Roots: $x = -6 \quad x = -4 \quad x = 1 \quad x = 3$

By graphing this polynomial, we notice that at a root (or zero), the graph will either cross or touch the *x*-axis.

- The values of *x* for which $f(x) = 0$ are called the **roots** or **zeros** of the function.
- The **degree** of a polynomial is the highest power within the polynomial.
- The maximum number of distinct real roots a polynomial can have is the same as its **degree**.
- The **leading coefficient** of a polynomial is the coefficient of the term with the highest power.

For example, $f(x) = x^3 - 5x^2 + 7x - 11$. The degree is 3; the leading coefficient is 1.

A polynomial may have a factor or root that occurs multiple times. This is called **multiplicity**.

For example, $(x - 2)^2$ is a factor of the polynomial $y = x^5 - 2x^4 - 23x^3 + 64x^2 + 4x - 80$.

$\therefore x = 2$ is a root that has a multiplicity 2.

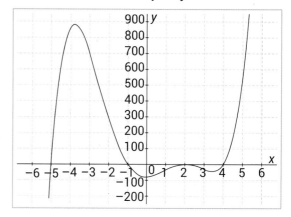

Notice how the graph of the function does not cross the *x*-axis at $x = 2$ but only touches the *x*-axis at $x = 2$. This is true for all roots with even multiplicity.

On the other hand, the multiplicity of the root $x = 4$ is 1. The graph of the function does cross the *x*-axis at $x = 4$. This is true for all roots with odd multiplicity.

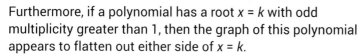

Even multiplicity $\Rightarrow$ Touching

Odd multiplicity $\Rightarrow$ Crossing

Furthermore, if a polynomial has a root $x = k$ with odd multiplicity greater than 1, then the graph of this polynomial appears to flatten out either side of $x = k$.

We can see this in the graph of $y = x^4 - x^3 - 3x^2 + 5x - 2$, which has a root $x = 1$ with multiplicity 3.

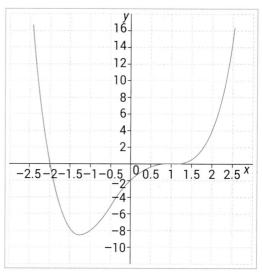

To determine the general shape of a polynomial, we consider the polynomial's end behaviour. The end behaviour is how the function's graph looks as we move further and further in either direction (left/right). The two 'end' pieces of the graph are known as the arms of the graph.

The end behaviour of a polynomial function will always follow these rules.

1. If the polynomial is of **even degree**, then the arms of the graph both point up or both point down.

2. If the polynomial is of **odd degree**, then one arm points up and one points down.

3. If the **leading coefficient is positive**, then the right arm points up.

4. If the **leading coefficient is negative**, then the right arm points down.

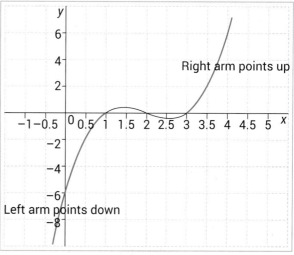

Right arm points up

Left arm points down

Example: $f(x) = x^3 - 6x^2 + 11x - 6$

Degree is 3, which is odd; leading coefficient is 1, which is positive.

$\therefore$ The left arm points down and the right arm points up.

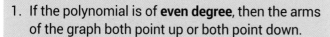

ALGEBRA II

Worked Example 2.20

Find a polynomial of degree 5 whose graph is shown below.

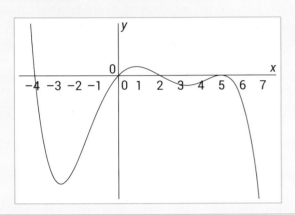

Solution

The polynomial is of degree 5, so it has a maximum of five distinct real roots. From the graph, we see that the polynomial intersects the x-axis at $x = -4, 0, 2$ and 5.

At $x = 5$, the graph touches the x-axis but does not cross it. Therefore, $(x - 5)^2$ is a factor. $x = 5$ is a repeated root.

The other factors are $x + 4$, x (i.e. $x = 0$), and $x - 2$.

Therefore, two possible polynomials are:

$$x(x + 4)(x - 2)(x - 5)^2 \quad \textbf{OR} \quad -x(x + 4)(x - 2)(x - 5)^2$$

We now test which polynomial will correctly describe the end behaviour of the graph. To do this, pick an x-value less than the smallest root or greater than the largest root. In this example, we will pick $x = 6$. From our graph, we know that when $x > 5$, the graph (y-value) is negative.

x	Polynomial	= y	y-value (positive/negative)
6	$x(x + 4)(x - 2)(x - 5)^2$	$6(6 + 4)(6 - 2)(6 - 5)^2 = 240$	+
6	$-x(x + 4)(x - 2)(x - 5)^2$	$-6(6 + 4)(6 - 2)(6 - 5)^2 = -240$	−

$\therefore -x(x + 4)(x - 2)(x - 5)^2$ is a possible answer.

Alternatively, from inspection of the graph, we can see that the right arm points down. So the leading coefficient must be negative.

$\therefore -x(x + 4)(x - 2)(x - 5)^2$ is a possible answer.

> It is usually better to use the first method, as this shows your work. Then check your answer using the second method.

Polynomials with the Same Roots

Consider the graphs of the following three polynomials:

$y = 3x^3 - 21x + 18$

$y = 2x^3 - 14x + 12$

$y = x^3 - 7x + 6$

As you can see, each of these polynomials intersects the x-axis at the same points:

$x = -3 \qquad x = 1 \qquad x = 2$

$\therefore$ Each polynomial has the same roots.

In fact there is an infinite number of polynomials for any given set of roots. What differentiates these polynomials from each other is the y-intercept of each one.

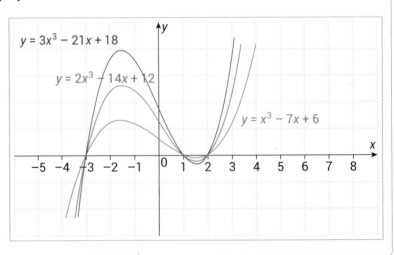

Worked Example 2.21

Sketch a graph of the polynomial $y = x(x + 3)(x - 2)^2(x - 4)$.

Solution

Factors:	x	$x + 3$	$x - 2$	$x - 4$
Roots:	$x = 0$	$x = -3$	$x = 2$	$x = 4$

The roots or zeros of the polynomial are $x = -3, 0, 2$ and 4. However, a **multiple root** occurs at $x = 2$.

∴ The graph of the polynomial crosses the x-axis at $x = -3, 0$ and 4. It touches the x-axis at $x = 2$ but does not cross it. We can mark these points in on our sketch (see below).

We next need to find the general shape of the graph.

The degree of the polynomial is 5, i.e. it has five factors – remember that $(x - 2)$ occurs twice. 5 is an odd number. This means one arm points up and one arm points down. The leading coefficient is 1 (a positive number), so the right arm points up.

Alternatively, we can substitute into the polynomial an x-value to determine the end behaviour of the graph. The smallest root occurs at $x = -3$; therefore, we test an x-value less than -3. Let us test for $x = -4$.

x	Polynomial	$= y$	y-value (positive/negative)
-4	$-4(-4 + 3)(-4 - 2)^2(-4 - 4)$	$-1,152$	Negative

As the y-value is negative, we start the graph on the left-hand side from below the x-axis.

Using either of the above approaches, we can then sketch the polynomial.

> Remember, when sketching we are looking for the general shape of the graph and where the graph crosses or touches the x-axis. For more detail, you could also calculate the y-intercept of the graph by letting $x = 0$. In this example, since x is a factor, the y-intercept happens to be 0. To find the y-intercept of a function we let $x = 0$.

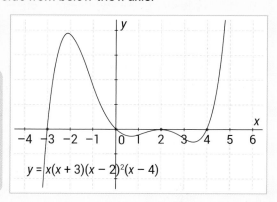
$y = |x(x + 3)(x - 2)^2(x - 4)$

Exercise 2.6

1. Show that $x - 1$ is a factor of $x^3 - 2x^2 - 5x + 6$ and find the two other factors.

2. Show that $x = -4$ is a root of the equation $2x^3 - 7x^2 - 42x + 72 = 0$ and, hence, find the other roots.

3. Show that $x = 5$ is a root of the equation $4x^3 - 32x^2 + 68x - 40 = 0$ and, hence, find the other roots.

4. Show that $x + 3$ is a factor of $x^4 + 2x^3 - 25x^2 - 26x + 120$ and find the other factors.

5. Show that $2x + 3$ is a factor of $6x^3 - 13x^2 - 13x + 30$ and, hence, find the other two factors.

6. Show that $x = \frac{1}{2}$ is a root of the equation $32x^4 - 8x^3 - 52x^2 + 42x - 9 = 0$ and, hence, find the other roots.

7. Show that $x = 3$ is a root of the equation $x^5 - 10x^4 + 35x^3 - 50x^2 + 24x = 0$ and, hence, find the other roots.

8. Write in the form $ax^3 + bx^2 + cx + d = 0$ an equation with the roots:

    (i) $-1, 2, 5$
    (ii) $3, \frac{1}{2}, -7$
    (iii) $1, -1, -\frac{1}{3}$
    (iv) $0, 5, -2$
    (v) $1, 1, 1$

9. (a) The graph of a cubic function $f(x)$ cuts the x-axis at $x = -3$, $x = -1$ and $x = 2$, and the y-axis at $(0,-6)$, as shown.

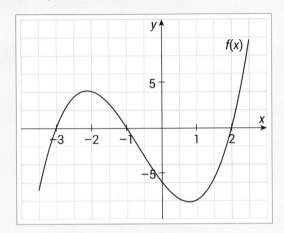

Verify that $f(x)$ can be written as $f(x) = x^3 + 2x^2 - 5x - 6$.

(b) (i) The graph of the function $g(x) = -2x - 6$ intersects the graph of the function $f(x)$ above. Let $f(x) = g(x)$ and solve the resulting equation to find the co-ordinates of the points where the graphs of $f(x)$ and $g(x)$ intersect.

(ii) Make a copy of the graph from part (a) and, on it, draw the graph of the function $g(x) = -2x - 6$.

10. Solve the following cubic equations:

(i) $x^3 - 6x^2 + 11x - 6 = 0$

(ii) $3x^3 - 19x^2 + 33x = 9$

(iii) $x^3 - 19x - 30 = 0$

(iv) $x^3 - 9x^2 + 16x + 16 = 0$

(v) $2x^3 - 9x^2 + 2x + 21 = 0$

11. Solve the equation $x^3 - 3x^2 - 9x + 11 = 0$. Write any irrational solution in the form $a + b\sqrt{c}$, where $a, b, c \in Z$.

12. Write down a polynomial function for each of the given graphs.

(i) Polynomial of degree 3

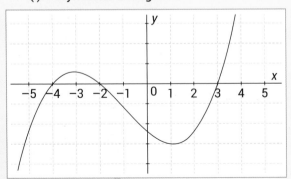

(ii) Polynomial of degree 4

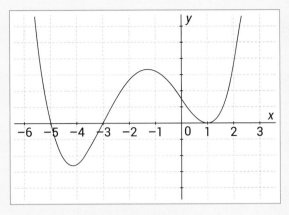

(iii) Polynomial of degree 5

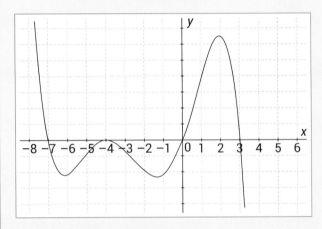

(iv) Polynomial of degree 6

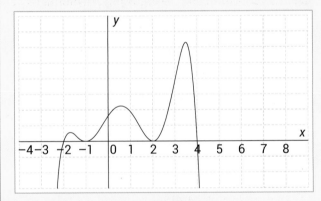

(v) Polynomial of degree 7

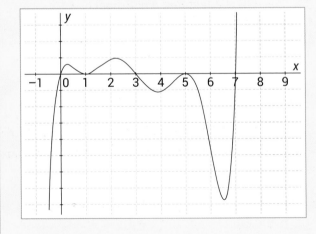

(vi) Polynomial of degree 6

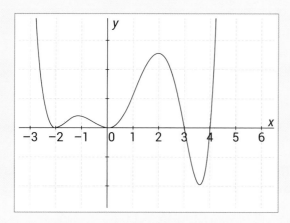

(vii) Polynomial of degree 7

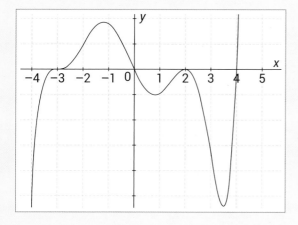

13. Sketch a graph of the following polynomials:

(i) $(x + 3)(x + 1)(x - 2)(x - 5)(x - 6)$

(ii) $(x + 2)(x - 1)^2(x - 4)$

(iii) $-x(x + 4)(x - 2)(x - 3)^2$

(iv) $-(x - 3)(x - 2)(x + 2)^2(x + 5)^2$

— (v) $x(x + 7)^2(x + 4)(x - 2)^2$

— (vi) $x^2(x - 5)(x + 2)(x + 3)$

(vii) $x^2(x - 2)^3$

(viii) $-x(x + 3)(x + 4)^2$

14. If $(x - 4)$ is a factor of $x^3 - 2x^2 - 11x + k$, find the value of k.

15. Form an equation whose roots are $(2 - \sqrt{3})$, $(2 + \sqrt{3})$ and 3.

16. $(x + 1)$ is a factor of $2x^3 + kx^2 - 10x - 3k$, $k \in R$. Find the value of k and the two other factors.

17. If $(x + 2)$ and $(x - 1)$ are factors of $x^3 - ax^2 - bx + 6 = 0$, find the value of a and the value of b.

18. If $f(x) = px^3 - qx^2 - 36x + 18 = 0$, $f(-3) = 0$ and $f\left(\frac{1}{2}\right) = 0$, find the value of p and the value of q.

19. $x^2 - 4x - 12$ is a factor of $rx^3 - sx^2 + 36$. Find the value of r and the value of s.

20. If $(x - 1)$, $(x + 3)$ and $(x - 2)$ are factors of $x^4 + ax^3 - bx^2 + cx - 6 = 0$, find the values of a, b and c.

21. A cubic function f is defined for $x \in R$ as $f: x \mapsto x^3 + (1 - k^2)x + k$, where k is a constant.

(a) Show that $-k$ is a root of f.

(b) Find, in terms of k, the other two roots of f.

22. $f(x) = x^3 + ax^2 + bx + c$ is a cubic function such that $f(3) = 0$, $f(-2) = 0$ and $f(1) = -36$. Solve for a, b and c and, hence, solve $x^3 + ax^2 + bx + c = 0$.

23. The graph of the polynomial $2x^4 - 6x^3 - 65x^2 + 120x + 225$ is shown.

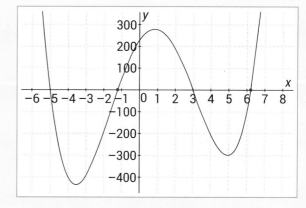

Find, correct to three decimal places, the non-integer roots of this polynomial.

2.7 Manipulation of Formulae

The volume of a cylinder is given by the formula $V = \pi r^2 h$.

However, if we wish to find the radius of a cylinder using this formula, we must rearrange or manipulate the formula:

$r = \sqrt{\dfrac{V}{\pi h}}$ $\left(\text{as } r > 0, \text{ we ignore the result } r = -\sqrt{\dfrac{V}{\pi h}}\right)$

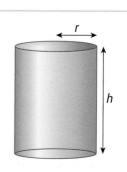

Worked Example 2.22

Given that $a = \sqrt{\dfrac{p}{1-q}}$, write q in terms of p and a.

Solution

$$a = \sqrt{\dfrac{p}{1-q}}$$

Square both sides.

$$a^2 = \dfrac{p}{1-q}$$

Multiply both sides by $1 - q$.

$$a^2(1-q) = p$$

$$a^2 - a^2 q = p$$

Isolate the q term on one side.

$$a^2 - p = a^2 q$$

$$\dfrac{a^2 - p}{a^2} = q \quad \left(\text{or } q = 1 - \dfrac{p}{a^2}\right)$$

Worked Example 2.23

The mirror equation expresses the quantitative relationship between the object distance (d_0), the image distance (d_i) and the focal length (f).

The equation is $\dfrac{1}{f} = \dfrac{1}{d_0} + \dfrac{1}{d_i}$.

Express d_0 in terms of f and d_i.

Solution

The LCD is $f d_0 d_i$. Multiply the whole equation by $f d_0 d_i$.

$$f d_0 d_i\left(\dfrac{1}{f}\right) = f d_0 d_i\left(\dfrac{1}{d_0}\right) + f d_0 d_i\left(\dfrac{1}{d_i}\right)$$

$$d_0 d_i = f d_i + f d_0$$

Isolate the d_0 terms on one side.

$$d_0 d_i - f d_0 = f d_i \qquad \textbf{OR} \qquad \dfrac{1}{f} - \dfrac{1}{d_i} = \dfrac{1}{d_0}$$

$$(d_i - f)d_0 = f d_i \qquad\qquad\qquad \dfrac{d_i - f}{f d_i} = \dfrac{1}{d_0}$$

$$\therefore d_0 = \dfrac{f d_i}{d_i - f} \qquad\qquad\qquad \therefore \dfrac{f d_i}{d_i - f} = d_0$$

Exercise 2.7

For questions 1 to 17, express the variable in the square brackets in terms of the other variables.

1. $a = 3bc - d$ [b]

2. $x = y + 3z$ [z]

3. $2p = \dfrac{q+r}{5}$ [r]

4. $s = \dfrac{a+b+c}{2}$ [c]

5. $\sqrt{\dfrac{x}{y}} = z$ [y]

6. $S = 4\pi r^2$ [r]

7. $h = \sqrt{a^2 + b^2}$ [a]

8. $s = pq^2 - r$ [q]

9. $p = \dfrac{1}{2}q + \sqrt{r}$ [r]

10. $R = \sqrt[3]{ab}$ [a]

11. $a = b\sqrt{x} + c$ [x]

12. $v = \sqrt{u^2 + 2as}$ [u]

13. $a - bc = \dfrac{1}{2}b$ [b]

14. $\dfrac{1}{u} + \dfrac{1}{v} = \dfrac{1}{f}$ [f]

15. $a = \dfrac{p}{p+b}$ [p]

16. $\sqrt{\dfrac{p}{r-q}} = p$ [r]

17. $a = \dfrac{1-x}{1+x}$ [x]

18. Show that for the equation $a + b^3 = \dfrac{c}{d}$, $b = \dfrac{\sqrt[3]{d^2(c-ad)}}{d}$.

19. The volume of a cone is given by the formula

    $$V = \frac{1}{3}\pi r^2 h$$

    where r is the radius and h is the height of the cone.

    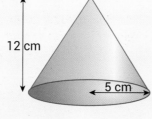

    12 cm

    5 cm

    (i) Find the volume of a cone with a radius of 5 cm and a height of 12 cm. Give your answer in terms of π.

    (ii) Express h in terms of r and V.

    (iii) Hence find the height of a cone with a radius of 9 cm and a volume of 423.9 cm³. (Use $\pi = 3.14$.)

    (iv) Express r in terms of h and V.

    (v) Hence find the radius of a cone with a height of 24.5 cm and a volume of 3,696 cm³. $\left(\text{Use } \pi = \frac{22}{7}.\right)$

20. Galileo discovered that the time it takes a pendulum to complete one full swing back and forth (one period) depends only on the length of the pendulum and the acceleration due to gravity.

    This relationship only applies when it is a simple pendulum swinging back and forth over a small distance.

    The period (T) of a simple pendulum is given by the formula

    $$T = 2\pi\sqrt{\frac{l}{g}}$$

    where:

    T = period, time taken for one complete swing back and forth, measured in seconds

    l = length of the pendulum, measured in metres

    g = acceleration due to gravity, which is 9.81 ms⁻² at sea level.

Assume that $\pi = 3.14$.

(i) What is the period, to the nearest second, of a pendulum of 25 m in length?

(ii) Express l in terms of the other variables.

(iii) What is the length, to the nearest metre, of a pendulum with a period of 35 seconds?

(iv) Express g in terms of the other variables.

(v) An astronaut is standing on Mars with a pendulum. The period of the pendulum is 2.8 seconds and the length of the pendulum is 75 cm. What is the acceleration due to gravity, to one decimal place, on Mars?

21. The distance travelled by an object can be found using the formula

    $$s = ut + \frac{1}{2}at^2$$

    where s = distance travelled in m, u = initial velocity in ms⁻¹, a = acceleration in ms⁻², and t = time taken in seconds.

    (i) A car accelerates at 12 ms⁻² for 3 seconds from an initial velocity of 10 ms⁻¹. Find the distance travelled by the car.

    (ii) Express u in terms of a and t.

    (iii) A rocket accelerates at a rate of 2.5 ms⁻². It travels a distance of 3.25 km in 50 seconds. Find the bus's initial velocity.

    (iv) Express a in terms of s and t.

    (v) A passenger plane travelling at a landing speed of 80 ms⁻¹ approaches a runway. The plane lands on the runway and travels 2.1 km in 30 seconds until it comes to a complete stop. Calculate the deceleration of the plane.

    (vi) Find the time it takes an object to travel 480 m from an initial velocity of 28 ms⁻¹ and with an acceleration of 2 ms⁻².

ALGEBRA II

2.8 Unknown Coefficients

$x^2 = 9$ is an equation. There are only two values of x for which x^2 will be equal to 9: $x = 3$ or $x = -3$. $(x - 1)^2 = x^2 - 2x + 1$ is an identity. It is true for all values of $x \in R$. This is because the LHS will always be equal to the RHS. We can use this property of identities to find the value of unknown coefficients.

Worked Example 2.24

If $c(x - a)^2 + b = 3x^2 - 6x + 5$ for all values of x, find the values of $a, b, c \in R$.

Solution

$$c(x - a)^2 + b = 3x^2 - 6x + 5$$

$$c(x^2 - 2ax + a^2) + b = 3x^2 - 6x + 5$$

$$cx^2 - 2acx + a^2c + b = 3x^2 - 6x + 5$$

LHS = RHS for all values of x. This means that we can now equate like terms from each side.

x^2 terms	x terms	Constants
$cx^2 = 3x^2$	$-2acx = -6x$	$a^2c + b = 5$
$\therefore c = 3$	$-2ac = -6$	$\Rightarrow (1)^2(3) + b = 5$
	$\Rightarrow -2a(3) = -6$	$3 + b = 5$
	$-6a = -6$	$\therefore b = 2$
	$\therefore a = 1$	

Worked Example 2.25

If $x^2 - ax + b$ is a factor of $x^3 + cx + d$, prove that:

(i) $b = a^2 + c$ (ii) $d = a^3 + ac$

Solution

$$\begin{array}{r} x + a \\ x^2 - ax + b \overline{\big)\, x^3 + 0x^2 + cx + d} \\ -\,(x^3 - ax^2 + bx) \\ \hline ax^2 + (c - b)x + d \\ -(ax^2 - a^2x + ab) \\ \hline (c - b + a^2)x + d - ab = 0 \end{array}$$

Since remainder = 0 for any value of x:

$$c - b + a^2 = 0 \quad \text{and} \quad d - ab = 0$$

(i) $c - b + a^2 = 0$

$c + a^2 = b$

$\therefore b = a^2 + c$ QED

(ii) $d - ab = 0$

$\Rightarrow d = ab$

$d = a(a^2 + c)$ (from part (i))

$\therefore d = a^3 + ac$ QED

Worked Example 2.26

If $x^2 + px + r$ is a factor of $x^3 + 2px^2 + 9x + 2r$, find the value of p and r.

Solution

Let $(x + k)$ be the other factor.

The coefficient of x in the linear factor has to be 1, since only $(x + k)(x^2 + px + r)$ gives an x^3 term with a coefficient of 1.

$$(x + k)(x^2 + px + r) = x^3 + 2px^2 + 9x + 2r$$

$$x^3 + px^2 + rx + kx^2 + kpx + kr = x^3 + 2px^2 + 9x + 2r$$

$$x^3 + px^2 + kx^2 + rx + kpx + kr = x^3 + 2px^2 + 9x + 2r$$

We now equate like terms from each side.

x^3 terms	x^2 terms	x terms	Constants
$x^3 = x^3$	$px^2 + kx^2 = 2px^2$	$rx + kpx = 9x$	$kr = 2r$
	$p + k = 2p$	$\therefore r + kp = 9$	$\therefore k = 2$
	$\therefore k = p$		

$k = 2$ $r + kp = 9$

But $k = p$ $r + (2)(2) = 9$

$\therefore p = 2$ $r + 4 = 9$

             $\therefore r = 5$

Exercise 2.8

1. If $(x + b)^2 = x^2 + 6x + q$ for all values of x, find the value of b and the value of q.

2. If $(x - 3)(x + 4) = ax^2 + bx + c$ for all values of x, solve for a, b and c.

3. If $(x - p)(qx - 4) = 3x^2 - 19x + 20$ for all values of x, solve for p and q.

4. If $(x - a)^2 - (x - b)^2 = 12 - 4x$ for all values of x, find the value of a and the value of b.

5. If $(x + a)^3 = x^3 + px^2 + qx + 64$ for all values of x, solve for p and q.

6. If $a(3x^2 + 1) + (x - 3)(bx + c) = 8x^2 - 3x - 7$ for all values of x, find the values of a, b and c.

7. Given that $p(x + 2)(x + 1) + q(x - 3)(x - 1) + r(x - 2)(x - 6) = 2x^2 + 7x - 13$ for all values of x, find the values of p, q and r.

8. If $3x^2 - 11x + r$ is a factor of $3x^3 - 14x^2 + 17x - r$, find the value of r. Hence, solve $3x^3 - 14x^2 + 17x - r = 0$.

9. $x^2 - ax + 2$ is a factor of $x^3 - x^2 + 5ax - b$.

   (i) Express a in terms of b.

   (ii) Find the value of a. Express your answer in surd form.

10. $(x - 3)$ and $(x + 4)$ are factors of $x^3 + ax^2 + bx + c$.

   (i) Express b in terms of a.

   (ii) Express c in terms of b.

11. If $x^2 + ax - b$ is a factor of $x^3 - 2bx^2 + ax - 6$, show that $a = -2b - \dfrac{6}{b}$.

12. If $x^2 + px + q$ is a factor of $x^3 + ax^2 + b$, prove that:

   (i) $b = q(a - p)$ (iii) $q^2 + bp = 0$

   (ii) $q = p(p - a)$

2.9 Problem Solving Using Algebra

One of the main uses of algebra is in problem solving. Information is given in a 'real life' context using words and/or diagrams. The student must then use the methods they have learnt (in this chapter and previous ones) to represent this information mathematically. This usually involves writing an algebraic equation that is then solved, giving us the answer required.

The following steps can be useful when approaching a problem-solving algebra question:

1. Read the question all the way through.

2. Identify an unknown value and represent it with a letter (say x).

3. Most problems will consist of several unknown values, so let your letter (say x) represent the simplest of these.

4. Express all other unknown values in terms of this simplest value.

5. Convert the word equation into a mathematical equation.

ALGEBRA II

6. Solve this mathematical equation for the variable in which it has been written (x).

7. Then, answer the question which was asked.

When answering any problem-solving question we should always:

- Be careful of the units of measurements we have used in the question, especially that of our answer.
- Make sure that we have clearly explained the meanings of any letters (variables) that we have used.
- Check that our answer makes sense in the context of the question. For example, the length of a rectangle cannot be −8 cm.

Worked Example 2.27

A manufacturer produces a calculator that sells for €12. It costs €x to manufacture each calculator.

(i) Write an expression to show the profit per calculator.

The manufacturer must sell $50 - x$ of these calculators per day to achieve a daily profit of €215.

(ii) Find the total cost of producing the required number of calculators.

Solution

(i) Profit per calculator = Selling price − cost price

$$= €(12 - x)$$

(ii) Daily profit of €215 = Profit per calculator × number of calculators sold

$$= (12 - x)(50 - x)$$

$$\therefore (12 - x)(50 - x) = 215$$

$$600 - 12x - 50x + x^2 = 215$$

$$x^2 - 62x + 385 = 0$$

$$(x - 7)(x - 55) = 0$$

$$x - 7 = 0 \ \textbf{OR} \ x - 55 = 0$$

$$x = 7 \ \textbf{OR} \qquad x = 55$$

> Double check your work in context questions, as you may need to reject an answer due to the nature of the question.

Check both solutions:

- If $x = 55$, then $50 - x = -5$. It is not possible to sell −5 calculators. Therefore, reject $x = 55$.
- $x = 7$ is acceptable, as $50 - x = 43$ and it is possible to sell 43 calculators.

$\therefore$ Cost per calculator = €7

Find the total cost of producing the required number of calculators.

= Cost per calculator × number of calculators sold

= 7 × 43

= €301

Worked Example 2.28

Seán requires an alloy of metal that is 30% copper. He has 50 g of an alloy that is 20% copper. Let x be the amount of an alloy that is 70% copper, which Seán will mix with all of the 20% alloy to produce the 30% copper alloy.

Find the value of x.

Solution

We can now write an equation for the amount of copper alloy.

$$0.2(50) + 0.7(x) = 0.3(50 + x)$$

$$10 + 0.7x = 15 + 0.3x$$

$$0.4x = 5$$

$$x = 12.5 \text{ g}$$

Copper (%)	Mass (g)	Amount of copper in alloy
0.2	50	0.2(50)
0.7	x	0.7(x)
0.3	50 + x	0.3(50 + x)

∴ 12.5 g of the 70% copper alloy must be added.

Worked Example 2.29

A company has to design a rectangular box for a new range of jellybeans. The box is to be assembled from a single piece of cardboard, cut from a rectangular sheet measuring 31 cm by 22 cm. The box is to have a capacity (volume) of 500 cm³.

The net for the box is shown below. The company is going to use the full length and width of the rectangular piece of cardboard. The shaded areas are flaps of width 1 cm, which are needed for assembly. The height of the box is h cm, as shown on the diagram.

(i) Write the dimensions of the box, in centimetres, in terms of h.

(ii) Write an expression for the capacity of the box in cubic centimetres, in terms of h.

(iii) Show that the value of h that gives a box with a square bottom will give the correct capacity.

(iv) Find, correct to one decimal place, the other value of h that gives a box of the correct capacity.

(v) The client is planning a special '10% extra free' promotion and needs to increase the capacity of the box by 10%. The company is checking whether they can make this new box from a piece of cardboard the same size as the original one (31 cm × 22 cm). They draw this graph to represent the box's capacity as a function of h. Use the graph to explain why it is *not* possible to make the larger box from such a piece of cardboard.

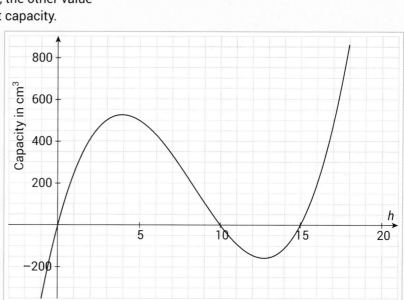

Solution

(i) Let l = length of the box.

Let h = height of the box.

Let w = width of the box.

We know that the total length of cardboard = 31 cm.

ALGEBRA II

$$1 + l + h + l + h = 31$$

$$2l + 2h = 30$$

$$l + h = 15$$

$$\therefore l = (15 - h)$$

We know that the total width of cardboard = 22 cm.

$$1 + h + w + h + 1 = 22$$

$$2h + w = 20$$

$$w = (20 - 2h)\text{ cm}$$

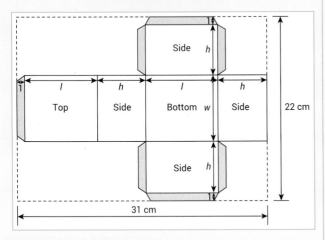

(ii) Volume = $h \times w \times l$

Volume = $h(20 - 2h)(15 - h)$

$\quad = (20h - 2h^2)(15 - h)$

$\quad = 300h - 20h^2 - 30h^2 + 2h^3$

Volume = $2h^3 - 50h^2 + 300h$

(iii) If the base is a square then the length and width must be equal to each other.

$\therefore l = w$

Square base $\Rightarrow 20 - 2h = 15 - h$

$$h = 5$$

We now have the value for h, which we can substitute into the volume formula.

Volume = $2h^3 - 50h^2 + 300h$

When $h = 5$:

Volume = $2(5)^3 - 50(5)^2 + 300(5)$

Volume = $250 - 1{,}250 + 1{,}500$

Volume = 500 cm^3, which is the correct volume.

(iv) We know that the volume = 500 cm³.

$$2h^3 - 50h^2 + 300h = 500$$

$$2h^3 - 50h^2 + 300h - 500 = 0$$

This is a cubic equation. We also know that

$h = 5$ is a solution $\therefore h - 5$ is a factor.

Using the factor theorem we can find the other value.

$$
\begin{array}{r}
2h^2 - 40h + 100 \\
h - 5 \overline{\smash{)}\, 2h^3 - 50h^2 + 300h - 500} \\
\underline{2h^3 - 10h^2} \\
-40h^2 + 300h \\
\underline{-40h^2 + 200h} \\
+100h - 500 \\
\underline{+100h - 500}
\end{array}
$$

$$\Rightarrow 2h^2 - 40h + 100 = 0$$

We now solve $2h^2 - 40h + 100 = 0$.

$$h = \frac{-b \pm \sqrt{b^2 - 4ac}}{2a}$$

$$= \frac{40 \pm \sqrt{1600 - 4(2)(100)}}{2(2)}$$

$$= \frac{40 \pm \sqrt{800}}{4}$$

$h = 17.1$ or $h = 2.9$

The length of the box is $15 - h$, but $15 - 17.1$ gives a negative value.

$\therefore h = 2.9$

It is important in our written answer that we clearly show that, in this case, we have accepted only one answer and rejected the other.

(v)

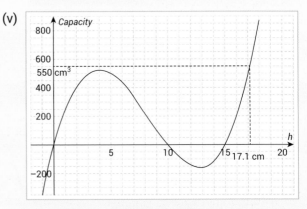

If the capacity of the box were 10% more it would give a volume of 550 cm³.

By drawing a horizontal line on the graph at volume = 550 cm², we see that the corresponding height is approximately 17.1 cm.

This is impossible as stated in part (iv). Therefore, it is not possible to make the larger box from such a piece of cardboard.

Exercise 2.9

1. A small bag of cement weighs x kg. A large bag of cement is four times as heavy as the small bag. A medium bag of cement is 5 kg lighter than the large bag. Two small bags plus a large bag of cement weigh the same as two medium bags.

   How much does each type of bag of cement weigh?

2. A company's formula for its production costs is cost (€) = 200 + 4x, where x is the number of units produced. Determine the cost if:

   (i) No units are produced.

   (ii) 3,000 units are produced.

   If the company spends €5,000 on production, how many units are produced?

3. Karl's and Eddie's ages added together are equal to 65. Ten years ago, Karl was twice as old as Eddie. How old are they now?

4. Paul is offered two different sale contracts in a goods company. The first contract has a salary of €25,000 per year with an end-of-year commission of 2% of total sales. The other contract offers a salary of €20,000 with a 3% end-of-year commission.

   (i) How much would Paul have to sell in order for him to earn the same amount of money under each contract?

   (ii) Paul expects to sell €700,000 worth of goods. Which contract should he take?

5. Two cars leave a town at the same time but travelling in opposite directions. Car A travels at a speed of 50 kmh^{-1} and car B travels at a speed of 70 kmh^{-1}. How long will it take for the cars to be 200 km apart?

6. Catherine has €3,000 to invest. She invests a sum of money at 9% per annum and the rest at 5% per annum. If the return on the higher interest rate is €95 more than the lower rate, how much did she invest at each rate?

7. A metal alloy is 30% nickel. Another metal alloy is 70% nickel. The two alloys are mixed to produce 20 kg of a metal alloy that is 48% nickel. How much of each metal alloy is used?

8. The first two sections of a bicycle race are x and y metres long. Annie cycles the first part of the race at 6 ms^{-1} and the second part at 12 ms^{-1}. Barry cycles the same sections at 10 ms^{-1} and 6 ms^{-1}. It takes Annie 30 seconds to cycle these two sections, whereas it takes Barry 46 seconds to cover the same distance.

   How long are these two sections of the race?

9. The relationship between degrees Fahrenheit (F) and degrees Celsius (C) is given by the formula $F = \frac{9}{5} C + 32$.

   (i) At what temperature will degrees Fahrenheit and degrees Celsius be the same?

   Find, to the nearest degree:

   (ii) The temperature at which degrees Celsius will be twice degrees Fahrenheit

   (iii) The temperature at which degrees Fahrenheit will be twice degrees Celsius

10. The longest side of a right-angled triangle is 31 m. Find the lengths of the other two sides, given that one of these sides is 5 m longer than the other side. Give your answers correct to the nearest centimetre.

11. A cinema contains 315 seats. It has x rows with an equal number of seats in each row. Six rows of seats are removed to create a fire escape. To ensure the same capacity, the number of seats per row must be increased by six.

    How many rows of seats did the cinema originally have?

12. When the two digits of a two-digit number are added together, the answer is 12. The two-digit number obtained by swapping the digits around is 18 more than the original number. Find the two digits.

13. The linear path of a ship is given by the equation $2x + y = 6$. The boundary of a reef is represented by the equation $x^2 + y^2 = 17$.

At what two points will the ship cross the boundary of the reef?

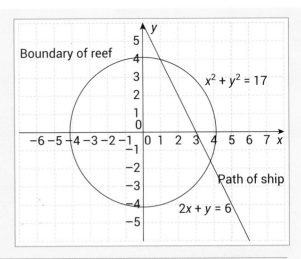

14. Harry takes 2 hours less to travel 50 km than Cara takes to travel 35 km. Cara travels at a speed that is 5 kmh^{-1} slower than that of Harry. Find the time taken by Harry and Cara to complete their respective journeys and the speed at which they each travelled.

15. A shop sells 30 LCD televisions per month at €350 each. A computer model suggests that for every €25 drop in price, two more televisions would be sold per month.

Let x represent the number of €25 drops in price.

(i) Write down an expression for the suggested price.

(ii) Write down an expression for the number sold.

(iii) Hence, what price should the televisions be sold at to ensure that the shop achieves a sales target of €9,000 per month?

16. The linear flight path of a plane is given by the equation $x + y = -3$. The airspace boundary of a certain city is given by the equation $x^2 + y^2 = 17$.

(i) At which two points does the flight of this plane cross the boundary of the airspace of the city?

The airplane control tower is situated at the point (0,0). The point (−5,1) is 5 km west and 1 km north of the tower.

(ii) Give the co-ordinates of each point of intersection as kilometres east/west and kilometres north/south.

(iii) How far are these two points from the tower? Give your answer to three significant figures.

17. The price of gold is approximately €40/g.

The price of silver is approximately €800/kg. A jeweller wishes to produce 20 g of a gold–silver alloy (mixture) worth €15/g.

(i) Write an equation that represents this alloy.

(ii) Find to two decimal places the number of grams of gold and silver used in the alloy.

18. A company produces an algebraic model that accurately predicts the number of units sold per month of a seasonal item for a certain period in time.

$$y = -x^4 + 11x^3 - 39x^2 + 45x$$

where y is the number of units (in thousands) sold per month and x is the time in months.

(a) Calculate the number of units sold per month at:

(i) 1 month   (ii) 4 months

(b) The company knows that this model is accurate for only a few months before it becomes unreliable. By sketching the above sales function, explain at what time this occurs and why.

19. A landlord rents out 30 apartments. The monthly rent of each apartment is €750. For each €75 increase in rent, the landlord expects to lose one tenant.

Let x represent each €75 increase in the rent.

Calculate the monthly rent needed to ensure that the landlord makes €30,000 in rent per month.

20. The sum of the digits of a three-digit number is 16. The second digit in the number is three times the third digit. The three-digit number obtained by reversing the order of the digits is 594 less than the original number. Find the three digits.

21. Working together, Peter and Simon can build a wall in four hours. It would take Peter 15 hours more to build the wall than Simon. How long would it take Peter and Simon to build the wall if working alone?

22. Two taps running together take 6 minutes to fill a bath. The hot tap, working by itself, takes 100 seconds longer to fill the bath than the cold tap working by itself. To the nearest second, how long would it take each tap to fill the bath by itself?

23. The minimum speed formula is used by police to calculate the minimum velocity at which a car is travelling by measuring the tyre marks formed by the car skidding to a stop. The formula assumes that the car stops at the end of the skid.

$V_0 = \sqrt{19.6\,\mu d}$, where V_0 = minimum velocity in ms^{-1}, μ = coefficient of friction and d = distance of the skid marks in metres.

(a) Calculate the minimum speed for the following tyre skid marks:

(i) 30 m on a wet road ($\mu = 0.6$)

(ii) 40 m on a dry road ($\mu = 0.8$)

(b) (i) Explain how doubling the distance of the skid marks affects the minimum velocity (assume that the coefficient of friction is constant).

(ii) Derive a formula that will find the length of the tyre skid marks when given the velocity and coefficient of friction.

(c) A car on old tyres is travelling at a velocity of 90 kmh^{-1} on a wet road ($\mu = 0.4$). The driver slams on the brakes and skids to a halt. Find the approximate length of the tyre skid marks expected at this speed.

24. The formula for the approximate velocity (V) of sound in metres per second in dry air at a temperature of T °C is given by the following formula:

$$V = 331\sqrt{1 + \frac{T}{273}}$$

(i) Find the velocity of sound when the temperature is 30°C (answer to two decimal places).

(ii) Derive a formula that shows the temperature T when given the velocity V of the sound.

(iii) Use this formula to find the temperature to the nearest degree, if the velocity of sound is 1,200 kmh^{-1}.

(iv) The formula to convert degrees Celsius into degrees Fahrenheit is $F = \frac{9}{5}C + 32$. Find the velocity of sound at a temperature of 150° F (to the nearest metre per second).

Revision Exercises

1. (a) Solve the following equations using algebra and verify your answer in each case:

(i) $2(x + 1) - 3(x + 2) + 6 = 0$

(ii) $2a - 4 - 2(a + 2) = a - 8$

(iii) $\frac{2y + 1}{6} - \frac{2y + 1}{10} = \frac{2}{5}$

(iv) $\frac{2}{3}(2x + 1) = \frac{1}{2}(3x - 1) + 2$

(b) Solve the following equations:

(i) $5x - 3y - 11 = 0$
$3x + 10y + 17 = 0$

(ii) $\frac{x + y}{5} + \frac{y - x}{2} = 5$

$\frac{x + 2y}{9} = 2$

(iii) $5x - 12y - 17 = 0$

$\frac{1}{9}(x + 2) - (y + 1) + \frac{3}{2} = 0$

ALGEBRA II

(c) Solve:

   (i) $x + y + z = 1$

     $2x + 3y + z = 4$

     $4x + 9y + z = 16$

   (ii) $2x + y + z + 7 = 0$

     $x + 2y + z + 8 = 0$

     $x + y + 2z + 9 = 0$

   (iii) $x + y = z$

     $x + z = 11$

     $y + z = 7$

   (iv) $\dfrac{2x}{5} + \dfrac{y}{8} + z = \dfrac{5}{2}$

     $\dfrac{x+1}{3} - \dfrac{y}{2} - 4z = 0$

     $\dfrac{x+y+z}{2} = 1$

2. (a) Solve:

   (i) $4x^2 - 4x + 1 = 0$

   (ii) $4x^2 - 9 = 0$

   (iii) $\dfrac{1}{2}x^2 - \dfrac{5}{2}x - 12 = 0$

   (iv) $\dfrac{1}{x-3} + \dfrac{1}{2x-1} = \dfrac{1}{2}$, $x \neq 3, \dfrac{1}{2}$

   (v) $\dfrac{2x-3}{x+1} = -\dfrac{11}{6} + \dfrac{x+7}{x-1}$, $x \neq \pm 1$

(b) (i) Solve $4x^2 - 23x + 15 = 0$.

    Hence, solve:
    $4(y^2 + y)^2 - 23(y^2 + y) + 15 = 0$

   (ii) Solve $x^2 - 6x - 2 = 0$, giving your
    answer in the form $a \pm \sqrt{b}$,
    where $a, b \in N$. Hence, solve
    $(t + 3)^2 - 6(t + 3) - 2 = 0$.

(c) Solve each of the following quadratic
equations to two decimal places:

   (i) $2x^2 - 5x - 9 = 0$

   (ii) $5x^2 - 12x + 5 = 0$

   (iii) $\dfrac{1}{x} - \dfrac{1}{x-5} = \dfrac{2}{x-1}$, $x \neq 0, 5, 1$

   (iv) $\dfrac{2x-3}{3x+2} - \dfrac{4x-1}{2x-5} = 1\dfrac{1}{3}$, $x \neq -\dfrac{2}{3}, \dfrac{5}{2}$

(d) Solve for x and y:

   (i) $x - y = 1$

     $x^2 + y^2 = 5$

   (ii) $2x + y = 7$

     $xy = 3$

   (iii) $5x - 2y = 3$

     $x^2 + y^2 - 2xy = 0$

3. (a) Find a functional form for each of the
following polynomials:

   (i) Polynomial of degree 4

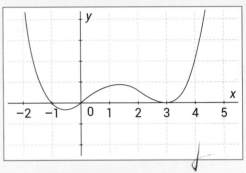

   (ii) Polynomial of degree 5

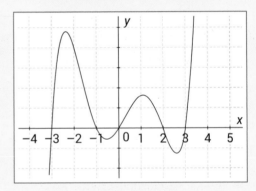

   (iii) Polynomial of degree 6

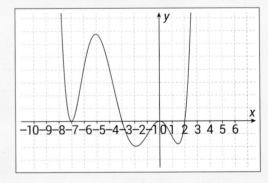

(iv) Polynomial of degree 7

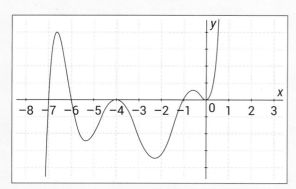

(v) Polynomial of degree 7

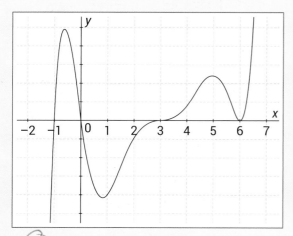

(b) Sketch a graph of the following polynomials:

   (i) $(x + 4)(x + 1)(x - 2)(x - 5)^2$

   (ii) $x(x + 2)(x - 3)^2(x - 6)^2$

   (iii) $-x(x + 1)^2(x + 4)^2(x - 3)$

   (iv) $x(x + 8)^2(x + 3)(x - 2)^2$

   (v) $-x^3(x - 3)(x - 5)^2$

(c) Solve the following equations:

   (i) $x^3 - 3x^2 - 6x + 8 = 0$

   (ii) $2x^3 + 5x^2 - 4x - 12 = 0$

   (iii) $15x^3 + 62x^2 - 32 = 0$

   (iv) $x^3 - 9x^2 + 22x - 12 = 0$

(d) (i) If $(x - 3)$ is a factor of $3x^3 - 2x^2 + kx - 6$, find the other two factors.

   (ii) $(x - 2)$ and $(x + 2)$ are factors of $x^3 + 7x^2 + ax + b$. Find the value of a and the value of b and, hence, find the third factor.

   (iii) $f(x)$ is a cubic function with roots 2, −1 and k. If $f(3) + 5f(0) = 0$, find the value of k.

4. (a) In each case, express the variable in the square brackets in terms of the other variables.

   (i) $a = b - \frac{1}{2}c$ [c]

   (ii) $a = b + c(d + 5)$ [c]

   (iii) $pq + pr = q$ [p]

   (iv) $A = \pi rl + 2\pi rh$ [r]

   (v) $y = \sqrt{\dfrac{ax^2}{1 - r}}$ [x]

   (vi) $x = \dfrac{y^3 + 1}{y^3 - 3}$ [y]

(b) (i) If $(x + a)^2 + b = x^2 + 8x + 11$ for all values of x, find the values of $a, b \in R$.

   (ii) If $(x + p)^2 - q = x^2 - 4x - 10$, for all values of x, find p and q.

   (iii) If $2x^2 + 7x + 10 = p(x + q)^2 + r$ for all values of x, find the values of $p, q, r \in Q$.

(c) If $x^2 + px + q$ is a factor of $x^3 + ax^2 + bx + c$, prove that:

   (i) $b - q = p(a - p)$

   (ii) $c = q(a - p)$

5. (a) (i) The volume of a frustum of a cone is given by the following formula:

$$V = \frac{1}{3}\pi h\{R^2 + Rr + r^2\}$$

Find the height of the frustum if $V = 33$ cm^3, $R = 2$ cm, $r = 1$ cm and $\pi = \frac{22}{7}$.

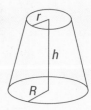

   (ii) The amount earned (F) after investing P for t years at a rate of interest (i) is given by the formula $F = P(1 + i)^t$.

Find the rate of interest if $P = $ €4,500, $t = 3$ years and $F = $ €6,000.

(b) The diagram shows two squares. The sum of their areas is 58 m^2. The sum of the lengths of their sides is 10 m as shown. Find the values of x and y. ($y > x$)

(c) One-third of a number is four more than one-half of another number.
The first number is one more than twice the second. Find the two numbers.

(d) The perimeter of this right-angled triangle is 60 units.

26 ⟋ y

x

(i) Write down two equations in x and y.

(ii) Find the values of x and y, given that $x > y$.

6. (a) $3n$ is an odd natural number. The product of this number and the next consecutive odd number is 483.
Find the two consecutive odd natural numbers.

(b) Fiona travels by train from town A to town B at a speed of 85 kmh⁻¹. At the same time, Gerry travels by train from town B to town A at a speed of 65 kmh⁻¹. If the two towns are 100 km apart:

(i) How long will it take before the trains meet?

(ii) How far will each train have travelled?

(c) The linear path of a comet is given by the equation $x - 2y = 4$. The orbit of a planet around a star is represented by the equation $x^2 + y^2 = 25$. This planet orbits the star at an average distance of 450 million km.

The star is situated at the point (0,0).
A satellite orbits this star and its orbit is represented by the equation $3x^2 + 10y^2 = 150$.

If the comet, planet and satellite all orbit the sun in the same plane, at what distances from the star will the comet cross the orbits of the planet and the satellite?

7. (a) A pet shop has rabbits and guinea pigs for sale. They have 30 in total for sale. They sell four rabbits. Two guinea pigs are also sold. The shop now has twice as many guinea pigs as rabbits. How many of each type did the shop start with?

(b) A restaurant bill that comes to €200 is to be divided equally among a group of people. However, three people leave before the bill is settled and the remainder of the group have to pay an extra €15 each.

How many people were originally in the group?

(c) The formula $s = \frac{1}{2}gt^2$ represents the distance (s) in metres a free-falling object falls from rest in a given time (t) in seconds. The gravitational acceleration (g) is the acceleration of an object caused by gravity and is measured in ms⁻².

(i) Express g in terms of s and t.

(ii) A free-falling object takes 3.5 seconds to fall 60 m from rest on Earth. Find the value of g for Earth.

(iii) The gravitational acceleration (g) value for the moon is $\frac{1}{6}$ that of the Earth. Find how long it would take an object to fall 30 m from rest on the moon's surface.

8. (a) A quadratic equation has the roots p and $4p$. Form a quadratic equation with these roots.

(b) The graphs of a linear, a quadratic and a cubic function are shown.

(i) Write down the points of intersection marked (A, B, C, D, E).

(ii) Interpret the significance of each point (note that there may be more than one interpretation).

(iii) Find the equation of the line shown. Also, write down a functional form for both the quadratic and the cubic graphs shown.

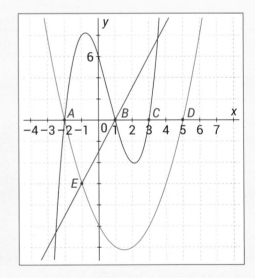

(c) Using the same axes and scales, graph $f(x) = x^3 + 7x^2 + 14x + 8$ and $g(x) = x^2 + 5x + 6$ between $x = -5$ and $x = 1$.

  (i) Mark the points of intersection of the two graphs.

  (ii) What do these points of intersection signify?

  (iii) Use another solving method to confirm your answer from part (i).

(d) If $x^2 + ax + b$ is a factor of $x^3 + 3ax^2 + c$, prove that $b + 2a^2 = 0$ and that $c + 4a^3 = 0$.

9. (a) Write $\dfrac{1}{x + 2} - \dfrac{1}{2x - 1}$ as a single fraction and, hence, solve:
$$\frac{1}{x + 2} - \frac{1}{2x - 1} = \frac{1}{2x^2 + 3x - 2}$$

(b) If $(x + a)^3 + bx^2 + cx = x^3 - 8$ for all values of x, find the values of the real numbers a, b, c.

(c) $f(x) = x^3 + ax + b$ is a function such that $f(2) = 0$ and $f(3) = -20$. Solve for a and b and, hence, solve $f(x) = 0$.

10. (a) Given that $(x + 2)$ is a factor of $x^3 + tx^2 + 3x - 10$, find the value of t and the solutions of the equation $x^3 + tx^2 + 3x - 10 = 0$.

(b) If $x^2 + ax + b$ is a factor of $x^3 + cx + d$, prove that:

  (i) $d + ab = 0$ (ii) $a^2 = b - c$

(c) (i) Show that, if $f(x) = ax^2 + bx + c$ and if $f(k) = 0$, then $(x - k)$ is a factor of $f(x)$.

  (ii) Find a quadratic function with roots $3 + \sqrt{7}$ and $3 - \sqrt{7}$.

  (iii) Find a cubic equation with roots $3 + \sqrt{7}$, $3 - \sqrt{7}$ and -1.

11. (a) If $x^2 - x - 2$ is a factor of $3x^3 + ax^2 - 10x + b$, find the value of a and the value of b.

(b) If $(x + a)^2$ is a factor of $x^3 + 6px + k$, show that:

  (i) $k + 2a^3 = 0$ (iii) $k^2 + 32p^3 = 0$

  (ii) $a^2 + 2p = 0$

(c) (i) Show that, if $f(x) = ax^3 + bx^2 + cx + d$ and if $f(k) = 0$, then $(x - k)$ is a factor of $f(x)$.

  (ii) The roots of a cubic function $g(x)$ are -1, 3 and k. If $7g(0) + 3g(2) = 0$, find the value of k.

Exam Questions

1. Gold jewellery is made from a gold alloy – that is, a mixture of pure gold and other metals. The purity of the material is measured by its 'carat rating', given by the formula

$$c = \frac{24m_g}{m_t}$$

where c = carat rating, m_g = mass of gold in the material and m_t = total mass of the material.

A jeweller is recycling old gold jewellery. He has the following old jewellery in stock:

- 147 g of 9-carat gold   ● 85 g of 18-carat gold

He can melt down this old jewellery and mix it in various proportions to make new jewellery of different carat values. The value of the old jewellery is equal to the value of its gold content only. Gold is valued at €36 per gram.

(a) What is the total value of the jeweller's stock of old jewellery?

(b) The jeweller wants to make a 15-carat gold pendant weighing 21 g. He melts down some 9-carat gold and some 18-carat gold to do this. How many grams of each should he use in order to get the 21 g of 15-carat gold?

(c) The other metals in the gold alloy are copper and silver. The colour of the alloy depends on the ratio of copper to silver. In all of the old jewellery, the amount of silver is equal to the amount of copper. The jeweller has a stock of pure silver that he can add to any mixture. He wants to make an item that:

- Weighs 48 g
- Is of 15-carat gold purity
- Has twice as much silver as copper

(i) How many grams of copper will this item contain?

(ii) How many grams of each type of stock (9-carat gold, 18-carat gold, and pure silver) should the jeweller use in order to make this item?

(d) A large jewellery business makes and sells 14-carat gold wedding rings, weighing an average of 5 g each. The cost of producing each ring is €135 plus the value of the gold. The manager has noted that the more they charge for the rings, the fewer they sell. In particular:

- If they charge €200, they sell an average of 20 per month.
- For each additional €20 charged, the number sold drops by one per month.

(i) Taking the price charged as €$(200 + 20x)$, find an expression in x for the monthly profit from these rings.

(ii) Find the range of selling prices for which the monthly profit is at least €1,600.

SEC Project Maths Leaving Certificate Higher Level, Paper 1, 2011

2. (a) Three natural numbers a, b and c, such that $a^2 + b^2 = c^2$, are called a Pythagorean triple.

(i) Let $a = 2n + 1$, $b = 2n^2 + 2n$ and $c = 2n^2 + 2n + 1$. Pick one natural number n and verify that the corresponding values of a, b and c form a Pythagorean triple.

(ii) Prove that $a = 2n + 1$, $b = 2n^2 + 2n$, and $c = 2n^2 + 2n + 1$, where $n \in N$, will always form a Pythagorean triple.

(b) $ADEC$ is a rectangle with $|AC| = 7$ m and $|AD| = 2$ m, as shown. B is a point on $[AC]$ such that $|AB| = 5$ m. P is a point on $[DE]$ such that $|DP| = x$ m.

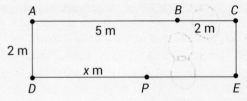

Let $f(x) = |PA|^2 + |PB|^2 + |PC|^2$. Show that $f(x) = 3x^2 - 24x + 86$, for $0 \leqslant x \leqslant 7$, $x \in R$.

SEC Leaving Certificate Higher Level, Paper 1, 2014

3. In 2011, a new footbridge was opened at Mizen Head, the most south-westerly point of Ireland.

The arch of the bridge is in the shape of a parabola, as shown. The length of the span of the arch, $[AB]$, is 48 metres.

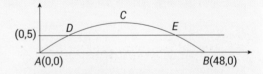

(a) Using the co-ordinate plane, with $A(0,0)$ and $B(0,48)$, the equation of the parabola is $y = -0.013x^2 + 0.624x$. Find the co-ordinates of C, the highest point of the arch.

(b) The perpendicular distance between the walking deck, $[DE]$, and $[AB]$ is 5 metres. Find the co-ordinates of D and of E. Give your answers correct to the nearest whole number.

SEC Leaving Certificate Higher Level, Paper 1, 2014

Solutions and chapter summary available online

ALGEBRA II

03

Algebra III

In this chapter you will learn to:

- Solve equations containing surds
- Select and use suitable strategies (graphic, numeric, algebraic, mental) for finding solutions to inequalities of the form

  $g(x) \le k,\ g(x) \ge k,\ g(x) < k,\ g(x) > k$

  where $g(x) = ax + bx$ or $g(x) = ax^2 + bx + c$ or $g(x) = \dfrac{ax + b}{cx + d}$ and $a, b, c, d, k \in Q, x \in R$

- Use notation $|x|$
- Solve inequalities of the form $|x - a| < b$, $|x - a| > b$ and combinations of these, where $a, b \in Q, x \in R$
- Prove algebraic inequalities
- Use discriminants to determine the nature of roots of quadratic equations

You should remember...

- How to solve equations
- How to solve inequalities
- How to work with surds

Key words

- Surd
- Square
- Inequality
- Linear
- Quadratic
- Rational
- Modulus
- Discriminant

3.1 Surd Equations

If the root of a rational number is irrational then that root is considered a surd.

For example $\sqrt{2}$ cannot be written as a rational number. So $\sqrt{2}$ is a surd. Likewise, $\sqrt{3}$ cannot be written as a rational number. So $\sqrt{3}$ is a surd.

What about $\sqrt{4}$? Since $\sqrt{4}$ can be simplified to 2, which is rational, $\sqrt{4}$ is not a surd. Other examples of roots that are not surds include $\sqrt[3]{-8} = -2$, $\sqrt[4]{16} = 2$ and $\sqrt[5]{-243} = -3$.

A number of the form $\pm\sqrt{a}$, where a is a positive rational number that is not the square of another rational number, is called a pure quadratic surd. A number of the form $a \pm \sqrt{b}$, where a is rational and $\sqrt{b}$ is a pure quadratic surd, is sometimes called a mixed quadratic surd.

Quadratic surds are sometimes also called quadratic irrationals.

In this section we will deal with equations that contain surds. These are often referred to as irrational equations.

When solving irrational equations, it is important that we check our answer, as an incorrect solution can sometimes be generated as a result of squaring.

Worked Example 3.1

(i) Solve $\sqrt{x + 1} = 5$. (ii) Solve $\sqrt{x + 2} = x - 4$.

Solution

> Square **both sides** to eliminate the square root.

(i) $(\sqrt{x + 1})^2 = 5^2$

$\qquad x + 1 = 25$

$\qquad \therefore x = 24$

Check:

$\sqrt{24 + 1} = \sqrt{25} = 5$ ✓

(ii) $\qquad (\sqrt{x + 2})^2 = (x - 4)^2$

$\qquad\qquad x + 2 = x^2 - 8x + 16$

$\qquad x^2 - 9x + 14 = 0$

$\qquad (x - 7)(x - 2) = 0$

$\qquad \therefore x = 7 \quad \textbf{OR} \quad x = 2$

Check: $\sqrt{7 + 2} = 7 - 4 \qquad \sqrt{2 + 2} = 2 - 4$

$\qquad\qquad \sqrt{9} = 3$ ✓ $\qquad\qquad \sqrt{4} = -2$ ✗

> Note: $\sqrt{\ }$ means 'the non-negative square root of'.

$\therefore x = 7$ is the only solution.

> It is necessary to check any solution as squaring can introduce an erroneous solution (as seen in part (ii)). Always check the solution in the original equation.

Worked Example 3.2

Solve $\sqrt{x + 12} - 2 = 2x - 6$.

Solution

> We leave our surd term on one side of the equation and move every other term onto the other side.

$\qquad \sqrt{x + 12} = 2x - 4$

$\qquad (\sqrt{x + 12})^2 = (2x - 4)^2$ **Square both sides.**

$\qquad\qquad x + 12 = 4x^2 - 16x + 16$

$\qquad 4x^2 - 17x + 4 = 0$

$\qquad (4x - 1)(x - 4) = 0$

$\qquad 4x - 1 = 0 \quad \textbf{OR} \quad x - 4 = 0$

$\qquad \therefore x = \dfrac{1}{4} \quad \textbf{OR} \qquad x = 4$

Check:

If $x = \dfrac{1}{4}$: $\quad$ LHS $= \sqrt{\dfrac{1}{4} + 12} - 2 = 3.5 - 2 = 1.5$

$\qquad\qquad\qquad$ RHS $= 2\left(\dfrac{1}{4}\right) - 6 = -5.5 \neq$ LHS

$\therefore x = \dfrac{1}{4}$ does **not** satisfy the equation.

If $x = 4$: $\quad$ LHS $= \sqrt{4 + 12} - 2 = 4 - 2 = 2$

$\qquad\qquad\quad$ RHS $= 2(4) - 6 = 2 =$ LHS

$\therefore x = 4$ does satisfy the equation.

$\therefore x = 4$ is the only solution.

Worked Example 3.3

Solve $\sqrt{x+7} + \sqrt{x+2} = 5$.

Solution

As we have more than one surd term, we leave one surd term on one side of the equation and move every other term onto the other side, to simplify the arithmetic.

$\sqrt{x+7} = 5 - \sqrt{x+2}$

$(\sqrt{x+7})^2 = (5 - \sqrt{x+2})^2$ Square both sides.

$x + 7 = (5 - \sqrt{x+2})(5 - \sqrt{x+2})$

$x + 7 = 25 - 5\sqrt{x+2} - 5\sqrt{x+2} + (\sqrt{x+2})^2$

$x + 7 = 25 - 10\sqrt{x+2} + x + 2$

$x + 7 = 27 - 10\sqrt{x+2} + x$

Again, isolate the surd term on one side of the equation.

$10\sqrt{x+2} = 20$

$\sqrt{x+2} = 2$

$x + 2 = 4$ Square both sides.

$\therefore x = 2$

Check (in the original equation):

If $x = 2$ LHS $= \sqrt{2+7} + \sqrt{2+2} = 3 + 2 = 5$

RHS $= 5$

$\therefore x = 2$ (as this satisfies the original equation)

Exercise 3.1

Solve the following equations:

1. $\sqrt{x+3} = 4$

2. $\sqrt{x-5} = 2$

3. $\sqrt{7x-3} = 4$

4. $x = \sqrt{x+6}$

5. $\sqrt{4x-4} = x$

6. $\sqrt{4x-3} = 2x - 1$

7. $5x - 4 = \sqrt{3x-2}$

8. $\sqrt{x+5} + 1 = x$

9. $x + \sqrt{2x} = 4$

10. $x - \sqrt{5x-1} = 5$

11. $3\sqrt{x-6} = -4 + x$

12. $(\sqrt{6x+4} - 1)^2 = \sqrt{3x+1}$

13. $\sqrt{5x+1} + \sqrt{x+1} = 6$

3.2 Linear Inequalities

Sometimes, when solving for an unknown, we are not asked for an exact value. Instead, our solution consists of a range of values.

An **inequality** gives a range of values.

$<$ means 'less than'

$\leq$ means 'less than or equal to'

$>$ means 'greater than'

$\geq$ means 'greater than or equal to'

Examples: $x < 3$ means 'x is less than 3'.

$x \geq 5$ means 'x is greater than or equal to 5'.

$x + 1 > 6$ means '$x + 1$ is greater than 6'.

We may be asked to graph a solution to an inequality. In such cases it is important that we distinguish between the different types of number we may be asked to graph.

You have dealt with the different types of numbers in your Junior Cycle course.

3

ALGEBRA III

Natural Numbers – N

A **natural number** is any positive whole number (i.e. any whole number greater than 0).

$N = \{1, 2, 3, 4, ...\}$

The set of naturals is denoted by the letter N.

> If x is a natural number we can write $x \in N$. This means that x is an element of the set of natural numbers.

As natural numbers are whole numbers, in order to graph them on the numberline we use shaded dots.

> Arrows on a numberline denote that the solution set continues indefinitely (forever) in that direction.

Integers – Z

An **integer** is any whole number; positive, negative or zero.

$Z = \{..., -3, -2, -1, 0, 1, 2, 3, ...\}$

The set of integers is denoted by the letter Z.

> If x is an integer, we can write $x \in Z$.

As integers are also whole numbers, in order to graph them on the numberline we use shaded dots.

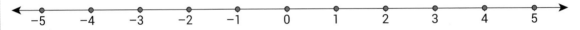

Real Numbers – R

A **real number** is any number that can be plotted on the numberline.

The set of reals is denoted by the letter R.

> If x is a real number, we can write $x \in R$.

As real numbers can be any number, in order to show them on the numberline we use solid continuous shading.

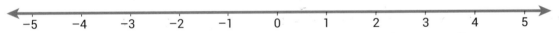

Multiplication/Division of an Inequality by a Negative Number

It is important to remember the following rule:

> When we multiply or divide both sides of an inequality by a negative number, we reverse the inequality sign, as well as changing the signs of all terms in the inequality.

Example: $-x < 5$

$\Rightarrow x > -5$

> We will explore real numbers in greater depth in Chapter 5.

Worked Example 3.4

Solve the following inequality:
$x + 5 > 12, x \in R$

Solution

We can solve this inequality using a number of techniques that we have encountered in the previous algebra chapter, Algebra II. These are:

- Trial and Error
- Using Graphs
- Using Algebra

ALGEBRA III

Trial and Error

Using this method we will make an educated guess as to what range of values (when substituted in for the variable) will ensure that $x + 5$ will always be greater than 12.

x	$x + 5$		>12
6	6 + 5	11	$11 < 12$ so the number is too small
7	7 + 5	12	12 = 12 but is still not greater than 12

From our table we can see that the solution set for this inequality will be any real number greater than 7.

$\therefore x > 7, x \in R$

Using Graphs

Using the same axes and scale, graph the line $y = x + 5$ and the line $y = 12$.

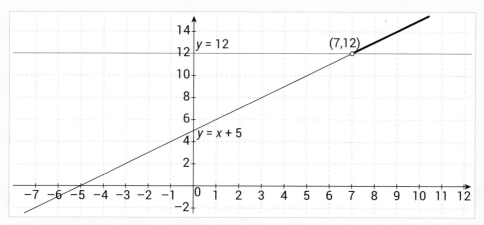

We are looking for where the line $y = x + 5$ is greater than (above) the line $y = 12$.

This happens for all values of x greater than 7.

$\therefore x > 7, x \in R$

Most times the above two methods are only practical when dealing with very simple inequalities. As stated previously, both methods have their drawbacks.

- Trial and error can be time-consuming and may not even lead to an exact solution in reasonable time if the unknown is not an integer.
- Solving by graphing is also time-consuming and may only give us an estimate of the solution where the co-ordinates of a point of intersection cannot be read exactly from the diagram.

A more accurate and usable approach to solving an inequality is to use algebra.

Using Algebra

$x + 5 > 12$

$x > 12 - 5$

$\therefore x > 7, x \in R$

Worked Example 3.5

Solve the following inequality and show the solution on the numberline:

$x - 1 > 2(x - 3) - 1, x \in N$

ALGEBRA III

Solution

$x - 1 > 2(x - 3) - 1$

$x - 1 > 2x - 6 - 1$

$x - 1 > 2x - 7$

$-x > -6$

$\therefore x < 6, x \in N$

The smallest natural number is 1; there are no further values. Therefore, we don't put an arrow on the numberline. The largest number in our solution set is 5.

When we multiply or divide an inequality by a negative number, we reverse the inequality sign.

Worked Example 3.6

Solve the following inequality and show the solution set on the numberline: $-1 \leqslant \dfrac{2x + 4}{3} < 2, x \in R$

Solution

Method 1

Multiply every expression by 3.

$-3 \leqslant 2x + 4 < 6$

Subtract 4 from each expression.

$-3 - 4 \leqslant 2x + 4 - 4 < 6 - 4$

$-7 \leqslant 2x < 2$

Divide each expression by 2.

$\therefore -3.5 \leqslant x < 1, x \in R$

Method 2

Write as two inequalities.

$-1 \leqslant \dfrac{2x + 4}{3}$ $\qquad$ $\dfrac{2x + 4}{3} < 2$

$-3 \leqslant 2x + 4$ $\qquad$ $2x + 4 < 6$

$-7 \leqslant 2x$ $\qquad$ $2x < 2$

$-3.5 \leqslant x$ $\qquad$ $x < 1$

$\therefore -3.5 \leqslant x < 1 \; x \in R$

- at $x = -3.5$ indicates that x can be equal to -3.5.

- at $x = 1$ indicates that x is not equal to 1.

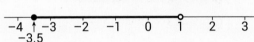

Worked Example 3.7

(i) Find the solution set E of $-4 > \dfrac{x - 6}{2}, x \in Z$.

(ii) Find the solution set F of $x \geqslant \dfrac{2x + 1}{3}, x \in Z$.

(iii) Graph the solution sets of E and F on the same numberline.

(iv) Find the solution sets of E ∩ F and E ∪ F.

Solution

(i) $-4 > \dfrac{x - 6}{2}$

$-8 > x - 6$

$-x > -6 + 8$

$-x > 2$

$\therefore x < -2, x \in Z$

$\therefore E = \{x \mid x < -2, x \in Z\}$

This is read as 'E is the set of elements x such that x is an integer less than -2'.

(ii) $x \geqslant \dfrac{2x + 1}{3}$

$3x \geqslant 2x + 1$

$\therefore x \geqslant 1, x \in Z$

$\therefore F = \{x \mid x \geqslant 1, x \in Z\}$

(iii)

The arrows on the numberline indicate that the solution set concerned continues indefinitely in that directon.

(iv) In the graph, the solution sets of E and F do not intersect/overlap.

Hence, E ∩ F = { } or ∅, the null set.

The union of E and F includes any elements in E or in F (or in both).

Hence, E ∪ F = $\{x \mid x < -2, x \geqslant 1, x \in Z\}$.

ALGEBRA III

Exercise 3.2

Solve each of the following inequalities and show each solution on a numberline:

1. $2(x - 1) < 4x, x \in Z$

2. $5(2x - 3) > 2(x - 1) + 11, x \in N$

3. $3(x - 6) \leq 4(x - 1) - 15, x \in R$

4. $2(3 - 2x) > 2(3 - x) - 6 + x, x \in R$

5. $11 < 7(x + 1) - 2(3 - 8x) - 3x, x \in R$

6. $\dfrac{2x - 1}{3} > x - 1, x \in N$

7. $\dfrac{3x - 2}{8} - \dfrac{x - 1}{2} < 0, x \in Z$

8. $\dfrac{x + 2}{3} > \dfrac{x + 1}{4} + \dfrac{1}{3}, x \in R$

9. Solve the following inequalities and graph the solution to each on a numberline:

   (i) $4 < 2x \leq 8, x \in N$

   (ii) $-7 < -x < 2, x \in Z$

   (iii) $3 \geq x - 2 > -5, x \in R$

   (iv) $0 \leq 3 - 4x < 2, x \in R$

   (v) $-4 < -\dfrac{x + 2}{3} \leq -3, x \in R$

10. (i) Graph the solution set A of:

   $$-3 < \dfrac{5x - 1}{2}, x \in R$$

(ii) Graph the solution set B of:

   $$7 \geq \dfrac{15x - 2}{4}, x \in R$$

(iii) Find the solution set of A ∩ B.

11. (i) Graph the solution set C of:
   $15 - 4x > -1, x \in N$

   (ii) Graph the solution set D of:

   $$\dfrac{2x + 1}{2} - \dfrac{x + 2}{3} \leq 1, x \in N$$

   (iii) Find the solution set of C ∩ D.

12. (i) Graph the solution set E of:
   $2x + 3 \leq 5x - 12, x \in R$

   (ii) Graph the solution set F of:

   $$\dfrac{9x - 1}{3} \leq \dfrac{2(2x - 4)}{5} + 2, x \in R$$

   (iii) Find the solution set of E ∪ F.

13. The recommended daily intake of calories for a man is 2,500 calories. Maurice usually eats within 10% of his recommended daily intake.

   What range of caloric intake does Maurice usually eat each day?

14. If 5 is added to an integer, the result is less than 15. If 3 is subtracted from the integer, the result is greater than 5. What is the number?

3.3 Quadratic and Rational Inequalities

A quadratic inequality is of the form $ax^2 + bx + c \,\square\, 0$, where the box is filled by one of the four inequality signs. ($a, b, c \in R, a \neq 0$)

When trying to solve quadratic inequalities, we must be able to sketch quadratic functions. From the graph we can then determine the solution required.

In the quadratic function $y = ax^2 + bx + c$:

- If $a > 0$ then the graph is ∪-shaped
- If $a < 0$ then the graph is ∩-shaped

> means 'above the x-axis'

≥ means 'on or above the x-axis'

< means 'below the x-axis'

≤ means 'on or below the x-axis'

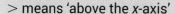

Worked Example 3.8

Solve the inequality $x^2 + 7x + 12 \leqslant 0$, $x \in R$.

Solution

Step 1 Let $x^2 + 7x + 12 = 0$ and solve.

$x^2 + 7x + 12 = 0$

$(x + 3)(x + 4) = 0$

$\quad\quad x + 3 = 0 \quad$ **OR** $\quad x + 4 = 0$

$\quad\quad\quad\quad x = -3 \quad$ **OR** $\quad\quad x = -4 \quad$ (roots)

Step 2 Sketch the quadratic function
$y = x^2 + 7x + 12$.

The coefficient of x^2 is **positive**. Therefore,
the graph is U-shaped. The roots are
$x = -3$ and $x = -4$.

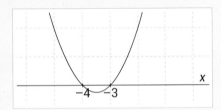

Step 3 From our graph, we can now determine
where $x^2 + 7x + 12 \leqslant 0$ (lies on or below the x-axis).

- Use shaded dots at $x = -4$ and $x = -3$ since
  these two points lie **on** the x-axis.
- Shade in the part of the graph that is
  below the x-axis.

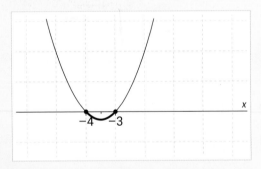

∴ The solution is $-4 \leqslant x \leqslant -3$, $x \in R$.

To sketch a quadratic function $y = ax^2 + bx + c$:

1. Check if $a > 0$ or $a < 0$ to determine the
   shape of the graph.
2. Find the roots to determine where the graph
   intersects the x-axis.

Worked Example 3.9

Solve the inequality $-3x^2 - 8x < -16$, $x \in R$.

Solution

Step 1 $-3x^2 - 8x + 16 < 0$ (Bring all terms to
one side.)

$\quad\quad\quad 3x^2 + 8x - 16 > 0$ (Multiply both
sides by -1.)

Step 2 Let $3x^2 + 8x - 16 = 0$ and solve.

$(3x - 4)(x + 4) = 0$

$3x - 4 = 0 \quad$ **OR** $\quad x + 4 = 0$

$\quad\quad x = \dfrac{4}{3} \quad$ **OR** $\quad\quad x = -4 \quad$ (roots)

Step 3 Sketch the quadratic function. (Using the
inequality $3x^2 + 8x - 16 > 0$, the quadratic function
is $y = 3x^2 + 8x - 16$.)

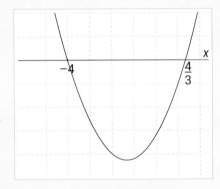

Step 4 From our graph, we can now determine
where $3x^2 + 8x - 16 > 0$ and, hence, solve the
inequality $-3x^2 - 8x < -16$.

- Use unshaded dots at $x = -4$ and $x = \dfrac{4}{3}$
  since we are only interested in those
  parts of the graph **above** the x-axis.
- Shade in those parts of the graph **above**
  the x-axis.

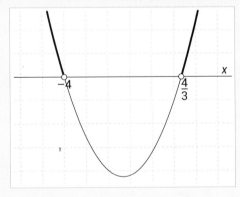

∴ The solution is $x < -4 \quad$ **OR** $\quad x > \dfrac{4}{3}$, $x \in R$.

Rational Inequalities

A complication occurs when we try to solve an inequality whose numerator and denominator are both algebraic expressions. These are referred to as **rational inequalities**.

Example: $\dfrac{4x-3}{2x-5} > 4 \ \left(x \neq \dfrac{5}{2}\right)$

In this example, we cannot be sure whether the denominator $2x - 5$ is positive or negative. Therefore, if we multiply both sides by $(2x - 5)$, we do not know whether or not to reverse the inequality sign.

So, we multiply both sides of the inequality by $(2x - 5)^2$, which we know is positive.

Worked Example 3.10

Solve the inequality $\dfrac{2x+4}{x+1} < 3, \ x \in R, \ x \neq -1.$

> Notice that $x \neq -1$ as this would lead to the denominator of the fraction being equal to zero.
>
> We should always check our solution to ensure that it is valid and amend if necessary.

Solution

$$\frac{(x+1)^2(2x+4)}{(x+1)} < 3(x+1)^2$$ Multiply both sides by $(x+1)^2$.

$(x+1)(2x+4) < 3(x+1)^2$

$2x^2 + 6x + 4 < 3(x^2 + 2x + 1)$

$2x^2 + 6x + 4 < 3x^2 + 6x + 3$

$-x^2 + 1 < 0$

$x^2 - 1 > 0$

Let $x^2 - 1 = 0$ and solve.

$x^2 - 1 = 0$

$x^2 = 1$

$x = \pm 1$ (roots)

Sketch the quadratic function. (Using the inequality $x^2 - 1 > 0$, the quadratic function is $y = x^2 - 1$.)

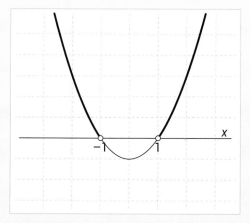

∴ The solution is $x < -1$ **OR** $x > 1, x \in R.$

Alternative Method

Consider separately the two cases where $x + 1 < 0$ and $x + 1 > 0$.

Case 1 $x + 1 < 0$

$\left(\dfrac{2x+4}{x+1}\right)(x+1) > 3(x+1)$

$2x + 4 > 3x + 3$

$1 > x$

i.e. $x < 1$

> Reverse the inequality sign since multiplication of both sides by $x + 1$ is multiplication of both sides by a negative number.

Since we are assuming $x + 1 < 0$, we are assuming $x < -1$.

So, the solution $x < 1$ is actually $x < -1$.

Case 2 $x + 1 > 0$

$\left(\dfrac{2x+4}{x+1}\right)(x+1) < 3(x+1)$

$2x + 4 < 3x + 3$

$1 < x$

i.e. $x > 1$

> Multiplication of both sides by $x + 1$ (a positive number) does not change the inequality sign.

We are assuming $x + 1 > 0$, so we are assuming $x > -1$.

So, the solution is $x > 1$.

Bringing the two cases together:

∴ The solution is $x < -1$ **OR** $x > 1, x \in R.$

Worked Example 3.11

The number (N) of a certain type of insect in a pond depends on the temperature (t) in degrees Celsius and is given by the formula $N = 120t - 3.5t^2$.

For what range of temperature (to two decimal places) will the number of insects be greater than 500?

Solution

We are being asked to find the temperature (t) at which the number of insects (N) will be **greater** than 500.

$$\text{Set } N > 500$$

$$120t - 3.5t^2 > 500$$

$$-3.5t^2 + 120t - 500 > 0$$

$$3.5t^2 - 120t + 500 < 0 \quad \text{(multiplying both sides by } -1\text{)}$$

Let $3.5t^2 - 120t + 500 = 0$.

Using the quadratic formula:

$a = 3.5, b = -120, c = 500$

$$t = \frac{-(-120) \pm \sqrt{(-120)^2 - 4(3.5)(500)}}{2(3.5)}$$

$$t = \frac{120 \pm \sqrt{7400}}{7}$$

$$t = \frac{120 + \sqrt{7400}}{7} \quad \textbf{OR} \quad t = \frac{120 - \sqrt{7400}}{7}$$

$$t = 29.43 \quad \textbf{OR} \quad t = 4.85 \quad \text{(roots)}$$

We now sketch the quadratic function $y = 3.5t^2 - 120t + 500$.

From our graph, we can then determine where $3.5t^2 - 120t + 500 < 0$ (lies below the t-axis).

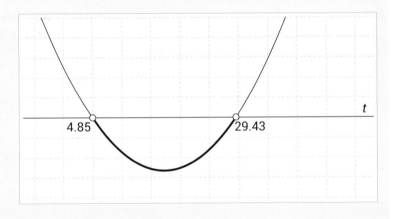

The solution to two decimal places is $4.85°C < t < 29.43°C$, $t \in R$.

Strictly between 4.85°C and 29.43°C, the number of insects in the pond will be greater than 500.

Exercise 3.3

Solve each of the following inequalities for $x \in R$:

1. $x^2 + x - 12 > 0$

2. $2x^2 + 11x + 14 < 0$

3. $3x^2 - 26x + 16 \leqslant 0$

4. $2x^2 + 3x < 0$

5. $121x^2 \leqslant 25$

6. $2x^2 + x - 15 \geqslant 0$

7. $7x^2 + 21x < -14$

8. $-72 \geqslant -5x^2 + 54x$

9. $-5x^2 - 13x - 3 \geqslant 3$

10. $\dfrac{2x + 1}{x + 3} < 1, x \neq -3$

11. $\dfrac{3x - 7}{x - 4} < 2, x \neq 4$

12. $\dfrac{x + 2}{x - 3} \leqslant 5, x \neq 3$

13. $\dfrac{x + 5}{x - 2} > 4, x \neq 2$

14. $\dfrac{x + 1}{2x + 4} \geqslant 3, x \neq -2$

15. $\dfrac{2x - 6}{3x - 5} \geqslant 2, x \neq \dfrac{5}{3}$

16. $\dfrac{2x - 5}{x - 3} \leqslant \dfrac{5}{2}, x \neq 3$

17. (i) Use the quadratic formula to find the roots of $x^2 - 13x - 13 = 0$ correct to one decimal place.

    (ii) Hence, find the least value of $n \in N$ such that $n^2 - 13n - 13 > 0$.

18. Find, in surd form, the range of values of x for which $x^2 + 6x + 4 \geqslant 0$, $x \in R$.

19. A stuntman is about to jump off a 20 m building. Once in flight, his height in metres above the ground will be given by the function $h(t) = 20 - 5t^2$, where h is his height above the ground and t is the time elapsed in seconds. The film crew want to film him when he is between 15 m and 10 m above the ground.

    (i) Form a quadratic inequality representing the above information.

    (ii) Hence, write down the time at which the film crew should start filming and the time at which they should stop filming. Give your answers correct to one decimal place.

20. A Transition Year mini-company decide to produce and sell keyrings emblazoned with their school logo. They research an idea and discover that their projected monthly costs (C) and revenues (R) in hundreds of euro will be given by the equations

    $R = 5p - p^2$ $C = 7 - p$

    where p is the price per keyring in euro.

    (i) Find the range of prices for which the mini-company will make a profit (Profit = Revenues − Costs).

    (ii) If the mini-company decide to charge €2 per keyring, what monthly percentage profit margin will they make? (Answer correct to the nearest percentage.)

    > The profit margin is the **net profit** as a percentage of the **revenue**.

21. A delivery company is designing a new rectangular box to be used for packaging fragile items prior to transit. The box's dimensions must meet the following specifications:

    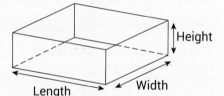

    - The length must be 60% greater than the width.
    - The surface area of the base must not exceed 300 cm².
    - The height of the box must be at least 3 cm but should not exceed one-fifth of the length.

    (i) Letting x be the width of the box in centimetres, write down an expression for the surface area of the base of the box in terms of x.

    (ii) Write down an inequality for the surface area of the base.

    (iii) Solve this inequality for x, answering correct to two decimal places.

    (iv) If the width finally chosen is the largest whole number that satisfies the inequality in part (ii), find the range of values for the box's volume in cm³.

3.4 Absolute Value (Modulus)

The **absolute value** or **modulus** of a real number x, written as $|x|$, is the magnitude of the number without regard to its sign (i.e. the non-negative value of the number). If $x < 0$, $|x| = -x$. If $x \geqslant 0$, $|x| = x$.

Examples: $|-7| = 7$ $|1.3| = 1.3$ $\left|-\dfrac{1}{2}\right| = \dfrac{1}{2}$ $|0| = 0$

Geometrically, the absolute value is how far away the number is from zero on the numberline.

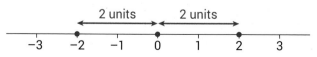

So, $|-2| = |2| = 2$.

> Let $a \geqslant 0$.
> If $|x| = a$, then $x = -a$ or $x = a$.

Example: If $|x| = 5$, then $x = -5$ **OR** $x = 5$.

Likewise, if x and y are two real numbers, then $|x - y|$ represents the distance between x and y on a numberline.

Examples: $|3 - 10| = |-7| = 7$ $|5-(-6)| = |5 + 6| = |11| = 11$

Worked Example 3.12

Find two values of x if $|x + 1| = 3$.

Solution

Method 1

$|x + 1| = 3$

$\Rightarrow x + 1 = 3$ **OR** $x + 1 = -3$

$\therefore x = 2$ **OR** $x = -4$

Method 2

$|x + 1| = 3$ means 'the non-negative value of $(x + 1)$ is 3'.

Therefore, the square of $(x + 1)$ must equal the square of 3.

$(x + 1)^2 = (3)^2$

$x^2 + 2x + 1 = 9$

$x^2 + 2x - 8 = 0$

$(x + 4)(x - 2) = 0$

$\therefore x = -4$ **OR** $x = 2$

Method 3

$|x + 1| = |x - (-1)| = 3$

What numbers x are 3 units away from -1?

Answer: $x = -4$ **OR** $x = 2$

> Note: Squaring both sides removes the modulus notation.

Graphing a Function of the Form $y = |x - a|$

Consider the function $y = |x|$, $x \in R$. To graph this function we first complete an input–output table.

x	|x|	y	(x, y)
-3	3	3	(-3,3)
-2	2	2	(-2,2)
-1	1	1	(-1,1)
0	0	0	(0,0)
1	1	1	(1,1)
2	2	2	(2,2)
3	3	3	(3,3)

Plotting these points and connecting we get the graph of $y = |x|$.

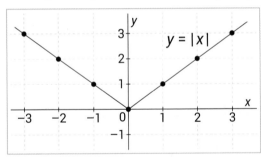

Notice how the graph of $y = |x|$ is a combination of the graph of $y = -x$ on $x < 0$, $x \in R$ and the graph of $y = x$ on $x \geqslant 0$, $x \in R$.

The graphs of other modulus functions have a similar structure:

$y = |x - 2|$

x	|x - 2|	y
-1	|-1 - 2| = |-3|	3
0	|0 - 2| = |-2|	2
1	|1 - 2| = |-1|	1
2	|2 - 2| = |0|	0
3	|3 - 2| = |1|	1
4	|4 - 2| = |2|	2
5	|5 - 2| = |3|	3

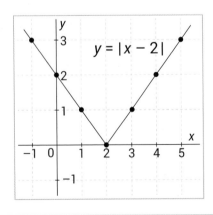

> Notice that if we let $x - 2 = 0$ and solve we get $x = 2$. This gives us the point of intersection for the graph and the x-axis.

ALGEBRA III

$y = |x + 3|$

x	|x + 3|	y
-6	|-6 + 3| = |-3|	3
-5	|-5 + 3| = |-2|	2
-4	|-4 + 3| = |-1|	1
-3	|-3 + 3| = |0|	0
-2	|-2 + 3| = |1|	1
-1	|-1 + 3| = |2|	2
0	|0 + 3| = |3|	3

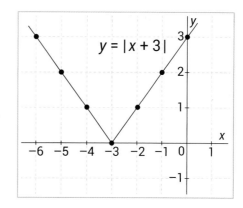

Notice the rule below from the above examples.

Let $a \geqslant 0$. The graph of $y = |x - a|$ can be constructed as follows:

- The graph contains the point $(a,0)$.
- For $x < a$, the graph is that of $y = -(x - a)$.
- For $x \geqslant a$, the graph is that of $y = x - a$.

Worked Example 3.13

Graph the functions $f(x) = |x + 2|$ and $g(x) = 4$ in the domain $-8 \leqslant x \leqslant 3, x \in R$. Hence, solve $|x + 2| = 4$.

Solution

We can use an input–output table to help graph $f(x) = |x + 2|$.

x	|x + 2|	y
-8	|-8 + 2|	6
-7	|-7 + 2|	5
-6	|-6 + 2|	4
-5	|-5 + 2|	3
-4	|-4 + 2|	2
-3	|-3 + 2|	1
-2	|-2 + 2|	0
-1	|-1 + 2|	1
0	|0 + 2|	2
1	|1 + 2|	3
2	|2 + 2|	4
3	|3 + 2|	5

The graph of $g(x) = 4$ is a horizontal line four units above the x-axis.

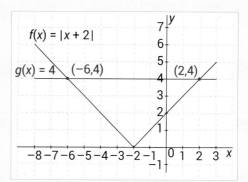

Being asked to solve $|x + 2| = 4$ is the same as being asked to solve $f(x) = g(x)$.

The graphs of f and g intersect at $(-6,4)$ and $(2,4)$.

$\therefore x = -6$ **OR** $x = 2$ are the required solutions.

ALGEBRA III

Solve for x: $|x + 1| - |x + 5| = 0$, by:

(i) Using algebra   (ii) Graphing   (iii) Some other method

Solution

(i) Using algebra

Rewrite the equation with one modulus expression on each side of the equation.

$$|x + 1| = |x + 5|$$
$$\Rightarrow \quad (x + 1)^2 = (x + 5)^2$$
$$(x + 1)^2 - (x + 5)^2 = 0$$

Apply the factorisation for the difference of two squares **OR** multiply out the equation.

$\Rightarrow \quad (x + 1 + x + 5)(x + 1 - x - 5) = 0$ **OR** $\Rightarrow (x + 1)^2 - (x + 5)^2 = 0$

$\qquad\qquad\quad (2x + 6)(-4) = 0 \qquad\qquad\qquad\qquad (x^2 + 2x + 1) - (x^2 + 10x + 25) = 0$

$\qquad\qquad\qquad\qquad 2x + 6 = 0 \qquad\qquad\qquad\qquad x^2 + 2x + 1 - x^2 - 10x - 25 = 0$

$\qquad\qquad\qquad\qquad\quad 2x = -6 \qquad\qquad\qquad\qquad\qquad\qquad -8x - 24 = 0$

$\qquad\qquad\qquad\qquad \therefore x = -3 \qquad\qquad\qquad\qquad\qquad\qquad\qquad -8x = 24$

$\qquad\qquad\qquad\qquad\qquad\qquad\qquad\qquad\qquad\qquad\qquad\qquad\qquad \therefore x = -3$

(ii) Graphing

We are really being asked to solve $|x + 1| = |x + 5|$.

Let $f(x) = |x + 1|$.

Let $g(x) = |x + 5|$.

Sketch the graphs of f and g and determine the point(s) of intersection.

From the graph, the solution is $x = -3$.

(iii) Some other method

To solve $|x + 1| = |x + 5|$:

Set $|x + 1| = 0 \quad \Rightarrow x = -1$

Set $|x + 5| = 0 \quad \Rightarrow x = -5$

Plot -1 and -5 on a numberline.

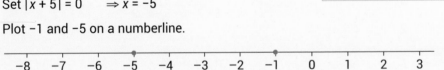

Consider the number halfway between -1 and -5 on the numberline. This number is -3.

-3 is the same distance from -1 as it is from -5.

No other number has this property.

$|x + 1|$ can be rewritten as $|x - (-1)|$, the distance between x and (-1).

Likewise, $|x + 5| = |x - (-5)|$, the distance between x and (-5).

Solving $|x + 1| = |x + 5|$ is the same as finding the number x that is the same distance from -1 as it is from -5.

$\therefore x = -3$ is the required solution.

Modulus Inequalities

If $|x| = 4$, then $x = -4$ **OR** $x = 4$.

If $|x| < 4$, then x must be less than 4 units away from 0 on the numberline.

∴ x must have a value strictly between −4 and 4.

∴ $|x| < 4 \Rightarrow -4 < x < 4$

> If $|x| < a$, then $-a < x < a$, where $a > 0$, $a \in R$.

If $|x| > 4$, then x must be more than 4 units away from 0 on the numberline.

∴ x must have a value less than −4 **OR** greater than 4.

∴ $|x| > 4 \Rightarrow x < -4$ **OR** $x > 4$

> If $|x| > a$, then $x < -a$ or $x > a$, where $a > 0$, $a \in R$.

Likewise, if $|x + 1| < 3$, $(x + 1)$ is less than 3 units away from 0.

$\Rightarrow -3 < x + 1 < 3$

$\Rightarrow -4 < x < 2$.

Similarly, if $|x - 2| > 5$, the distance between x and 2 is greater than 5 units.

$\Rightarrow x - 2 < -5$ **OR** $x - 2 > 5$

$\Rightarrow x < -3$ **OR** $x > 7$

Worked Example 3.15

Solve $|x + 3| \geqslant 5$, $x \in R$, by:

(i) Algebra

(ii) Graphing

Solution

(i) Algebra

Method 1

$|x + 3| \geqslant 5$

$(x + 3)^2 \geqslant (5)^2$

$x^2 + 6x + 9 \geqslant 25$

$x^2 + 6x - 16 \geqslant 0$

Let $x^2 + 6x - 16 = 0$

$(x - 2)(x + 8) = 0$

$x - 2 = 0$ **OR** $x + 8 = 0$

$x = 2$ **OR** $x = -8$ (roots)

We now sketch the quadratic function $y = x^2 + 6x - 16$.

We want the range of values of x for which $x^2 + 6x - 16 \geqslant 0$ (i.e. on or above the x-axis).

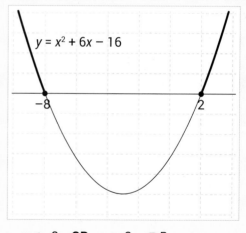

$y = x^2 + 6x - 16$

∴ $x \leqslant -8$ **OR** $x \geqslant 2$, $x \in R$

Method 2

$|x + 3| \geqslant 5$

> If $|x| \geqslant a$ (where $a > 0$) then $x \leqslant -a$ or $x \geqslant a$.

$x + 3 \leqslant -5$ **OR** $x + 3 \geqslant 5$

∴ $x \leqslant -8$ **OR** $x \geqslant 2$, $x \in R$

(ii) Graphing

We graph the functions $f(x) = |x + 3|$ and $g(x) = 5$.

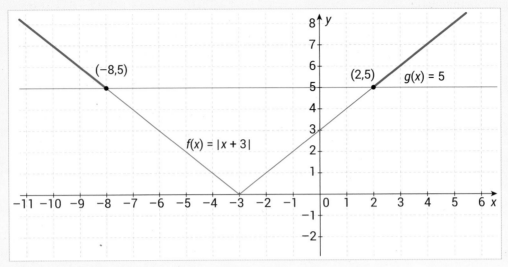

We are looking for the **range of values** for which $|x + 3| \geqslant 5$.

$\therefore x \leqslant -8$ **OR** $x \geqslant 5, x \in R$

Worked Example 3.16

Solve for x: $1 < |x - 2| \leqslant 3, x \in R$.

Solution

Method 1

Consider the inequality $1 < |x - 2|$.

This can be written as $|x - 2| > 1$.

 If $|x| > a$ (where $a > 0$), then $x < -a$ or $x > a$.

$\Rightarrow x - 2 < -1$ **OR** $x - 2 > 1$

$\qquad x < 1$ **OR** $\qquad x > 3$

Call this set of solutions set A.

Consider the inequality $|x - 2| \leqslant 3$.

 If $|x| \leqslant a$ (where $a > 0$), then $-a \leqslant x \leqslant a$.

$\Rightarrow -3 \leqslant x - 2 \leqslant 3$

$\qquad -1 \leqslant x \leqslant 5$

Call this set of solutions set B.

To solve $1 < |x - 2| \leqslant 3$ we need to find the elements of $A \cap B$.

$A \cap B$: $-1 \leqslant x < 1$ **OR** $3 < x \leqslant 5$ $\qquad (x \in R)$

Our required solution.

Method 2

Graph the functions $y = |x - 2|$, $y = 1$ and $y = 3$.

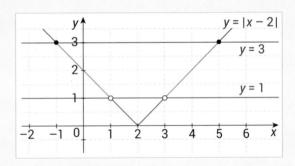

We are only interested in those parts of the graph of $y = |x - 2|$ above $y = 1$ and on or below $y = 3$.

From the graph, this yields the solution set:

$-1 \leqslant x < 1$ **OR** $3 < x \leqslant 5$ $\qquad (x \in R)$

Exercise 3.4

1. Evaluate the following:

   (i) $|8|$

   (ii) $|-3|$

   (iii) $|-8 + 3|$

   (iv) $|8 - 3|$

   (v) $|-8| + |3|$

   (vi) $|8| + |-3|$

2. If $p = 2$, $q = 5$ and $r = -4$, find the value of:

   (i) $|p + q|$

   (ii) $|r + q|$

   (iii) $|pq|$

   (iv) $5|rq|$

   (v) $2|pr| - 3|q|$

   (vi) $|p||q| + 3|q - r|$

3. The triangle inequality states that $|x + y| \leq |x| + |y|$ for any $x, y \in R$.

   Verify this inequality for each of the following cases:

   (i) $x = 3$, $y = 4$

   (ii) $x = -2$, $y = 5$

   (iii) $x = a$, $y = 2a$ ($a < 0$)

   Under what circumstances will $|x + y| < |x| + |y|$?

Solve questions 4 to 10 for $x \in R$:

4. $|x| = 5$

5. $|x| = 10$

6. $|x + 1| = 8$

7. $|x - 8| = 3$

8. $\left|x - \dfrac{1}{2}\right| = 4$

9. $|x + 3| - 4 = 9$

10. $|x - 2| - 5 = 0$

11. Using the same axes and scales, graph the functions $f(x) = |x + 1|$ and $g(x) = 3$. Using your graph, find the value of x for which $|x + 1| = 3$.

12. Using the same axes and scales, graph the functions $f(x) = |x - 4|$ and $g(x) = 2$. Using your graph, find the value of x for which $|x - 4| = 2$.

13. Solve for x: $|x + 2| - |x + 4| = 0$, by:

    (i) Algebra

    (ii) Graphing

    (iii) Another method

14. Solve for x: $|x + 5| - |x - 2| = 0$, by:

    (i) Algebra

    (ii) Graphing

    (iii) Another method

15. Solve for $x \in R$: $\left|x + \dfrac{2}{5}\right| = \left|x - \dfrac{1}{3}\right|$

16. Solve for $x \in R$: $|x + 1| < 5$

17. Solve for $x \in R$: $|x - 4| > 3$

18. The graphs of the functions $f: x \mapsto |x - 3|$ and $g: x \mapsto 2$ are shown in the diagram.

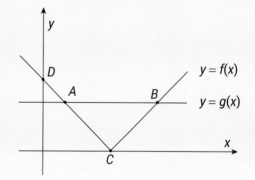

   (i) Find the co-ordinates of the points A, B, C and D.

   (ii) Hence, or otherwise, solve the inequality $|x - 3| < 2$.

19. Solve for x: $2 < |x + 3| < 6$, $x \in R$.

20. Solve for x: $3 \leq |x - 7| < 10$, $x \in R$.

21. Using the same axes and scales, graph the functions $f(x) = |x - 2|$, $g(x) = 3$ and $h(x) = 1$.

    Using your graph, find the value(s) of $x \in R$ for which:

    (i) $f(x) = g(x)$

    (ii) $f(x) = h(x)$

    (iii) $f(x) < h(x)$

    (iv) $g(x) \leq f(x)$

    (v) $h(x) < f(x) < g(x)$

    Use algebra to check each of your answers to parts (iii), (iv) and (v).

ALGEBRA III

3.5 Inequalities: Proofs

We may be asked to prove that certain inequalities are true or false. One of the more useful tools in answering such questions is the property that the square of any real number is non-negative.

Consider a real number (any number on the numberline).

Take a negative real number, such as -2. $(-2)^2 = 4 \geqslant 0$.

Take the neutral number, 0. $(0)^2 = 0 \geqslant 0$.

Take a positive real number, such as $\frac{1}{3}$. $\left(\frac{1}{3}\right)^2 = \frac{1}{9} \geqslant 0$.

What do we notice? We can see that whatever real number we consider, the following will always be true:

$$(\text{real})^2 \geqslant 0$$

Worked Example 3.17

Prove that if a and b are real numbers, then $a^2 + b^2 \geqslant 2ab$.

Solution

$$\text{Is } a^2 + b^2 \geqslant 2ab?$$

Yes, if $a^2 + b^2 - 2ab \geqslant 0$.

$$a^2 - 2ab + b^2 \geqslant 0$$

$(a - b)^2 \geqslant 0$ True (since $(\text{real})^2 \geqslant 0$)

$$\therefore a^2 + b^2 \geqslant 2ab$$

Worked Example 3.18

If $a, b \in R$, prove that $a^2 - 10a + 25 + 4b^2 \geqslant 0$.

Solution

$$\text{Is } a^2 - 10a + 25 + 4b^2 \geqslant 0?$$

Yes, if $(a - 5)(a - 5) + (2b)^2 \geqslant 0$.

$(a - 5)^2 + (2b)^2 \geqslant 0$ True (as $a, b \in R$, and $(\text{real})^2 + (\text{real})^2 \geqslant 0$)

$$\therefore a^2 - 10a + 25 - 4b^2 \geqslant 0$$

Exercise 3.5

1. Prove that for all $x, y \in R$, $x^2 + y^2 \geqslant 2xy$.

2. Prove that for all $p \in R$, $p^2 + 1 \geqslant 2p$.

3. Prove that if $b > 0$, $b \in R$, then $b + \frac{1}{b} \geqslant 2$.

4. If $x, y \in R$, prove that $(x + y)^2 \leqslant 2(x^2 + y^2)$.

5. If $x, y \in N$, prove that $(x + y)\left(\frac{1}{x} + \frac{1}{y}\right) \geqslant 4$.

6. Prove that $a^2 + b^2 - 8a + 16 \geqslant 0$, for all $a, b \in R$.

7. Prove that $x^2 + 2xy + 3y^2 \geqslant 0$, for all $x, y \in R$.

8. If $x, y \in R$, prove that $x^2 + y^2 - 6y + 9 \geqslant 0$.

9. If $a, b \in R$ such that $a > b > 0$, prove that $a^2 - b^2 > (a - b)^2$.

10. Let $a, b, x, y \in R$.

    (a) Prove that $a^2 + b^2 \geqslant 2ab$.

    (b) Complete (without proof) the following inequalities:

    $$x^2 + y^2 \geqslant$$

    $$a^2 + x^2 \geqslant$$

    $$b^2 + y^2 \geqslant$$

    (c) Deduce that, if $x^2 + y^2 = 1$ and if $a^2 + b^2 = 1$, then:

    (i) $ab + xy \leqslant 1$

    (ii) $ax + by \leqslant 1$

11. Let $w, x, y, z \in R$.

    (a) Prove that $x^2 + y^2 \geqslant 2xy$.

    (b) Deduce that $x^4 + y^4 \geqslant 2x^2y^2$.

    (c) Deduce that $x^4 + y^4 + z^4 + w^4 \geqslant 4xyzw$.

12. (i) Factorise $a^3 - a^2b - ab^2 + b^3$.

    (ii) If $a, b \in N$, show that $a^3 + b^3 \geqslant a^2b + ab^2$.

3.6 Discriminants

The formula $x = \dfrac{-b \pm \sqrt{b^2 - 4ac}}{2a}$ can be used to solve equations of the form $ax^2 + bx + c = 0$, $a \neq 0$.

$b^2 - 4ac$ is called the **discriminant**.

The value of the discriminant, $b^2 - 4ac$, can be used to determine whether the graph of the quadratic function (the parabola) intersects, touches or does not intersect the x-axis.

Discriminant			
	$b^2 - 4ac > 0$	$b^2 - 4ac = 0$	$b^2 - 4ac < 0$
Number of roots	Two distinct real roots	One repeated real root (two equal roots)	No real roots
Intersection with the x-axis	Two distinct points	Curve touches x-axis	Curve and x-axis do not intersect
Sketch for $a > 0$			
Sketch for $a < 0$			

Real roots $\Rightarrow b^2 - 4ac \geq 0$ Real and equal roots $\Rightarrow b^2 - 4ac = 0$

Real and distinct roots $\Rightarrow b^2 - 4ac > 0$ No real roots $\Rightarrow b^2 - 4ac < 0$

We will investigate situations in which $b^2 - 4ac < 0$ (no real roots) in much greater detail in Chapter 12, Complex Numbers.

Worked Example 3.19

Find the value of k if $x^2 + 6x + k = 0$ has two equal roots.

Solution

Equal roots: $b^2 - 4ac = 0$

$a = 1, b = 6, c = k$

$(6)^2 - 4(1)(k) = 0$

$36 - 4k = 0$

$36 = 4k$

$\therefore k = 9$

Worked Example 3.20

For what values of p does $2px^2 - px + 1 = x^2 + x$ have real roots?

Solution

$$2px^2 - px + 1 = x^2 + x$$

$$2px^2 - px + 1 - x^2 - x = 0$$

$$2px^2 - x^2 - px - x + 1 = 0$$

$$(2p - 1)x^2 + (-p - 1)x + 1 = 0$$

$a = 2p - 1, b = -p - 1, c = 1$

Real roots: $b^2 - 4ac \geqslant 0$

$$(-p - 1)^2 - 4(2p - 1)(1) \geqslant 0$$

$$p^2 + 2p + 1 - 8p + 4 \geqslant 0$$

$$p^2 - 6p + 5 \geqslant 0 \quad \text{(quadratic inequality)}$$

Let $p^2 - 6p + 5 = 0$.

$$(p - 1)(p - 5) = 0$$

$p - 1 = 0$ **OR** $p - 5 = 0$

$p = 1$ **OR** $p = 5$ (roots)

We sketch the quadratic function $y = p^2 - 6p + 5$.

We want the range of values of p for which $p^2 - 6p + 5 \geqslant 0$ (i.e. on or above the p-axis).

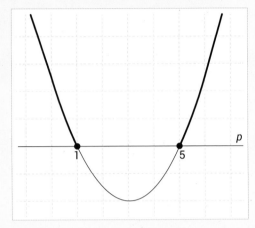

$\therefore p \leqslant 1$ **OR** $p \geqslant 5$ for real roots.

Worked Example 3.21

Prove that for all values of $p \in R$, $(p - 2)x^2 + 2x - p = 0$ has real roots.

Solution

We need to show that $b^2 - 4ac \geqslant 0$, for real roots.

$a = (p - 2), b = 2$ and $c = -p$

$$b^2 - 4ac = (2)^2 - 4(p - 2)(-p)$$

$$= 4 + 4p^2 - 8p$$

$$= 4p^2 - 8p + 4$$

$$= 4(p^2 - 2p + 1)$$

$$= 4(p - 1)(p - 1)$$

$$\therefore b^2 - 4ac = 4(p - 1)^2$$

But $(p - 1)^2 \geqslant 0$ as (any real number)$^2 \geqslant 0$.

$$\therefore b^2 - 4ac \geqslant 0$$

$\therefore (p - 2)x^2 + 2x - p = 0$ has real roots for all values of $p \in R$.

Exercise 3.6

1. The graphs of five quadratic functions are shown. In each case, comment on the nature of the roots and on whether the discriminant will be greater than, equal to or less than 0.

(i)

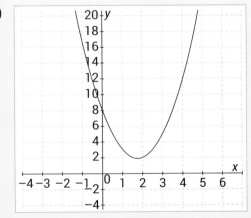

ALGEBRA III

(ii)
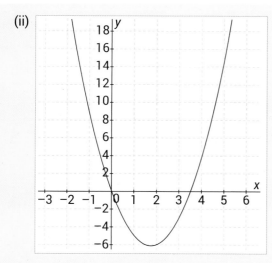

(iii)
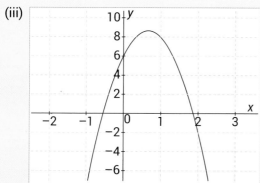

(iv)
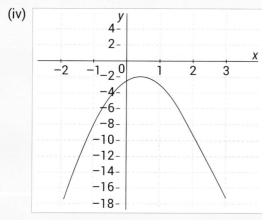

(v)
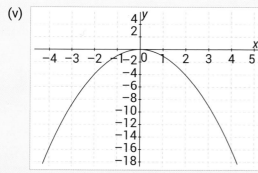

2. For each equation given below, calculate the discriminant and comment appropriately on the nature of the roots.

(i) $x^2 + 6x + 5 = 0$

(ii) $x^2 - 4x + 4 = 0$

(iii) $x^2 - 2x + 5 = 0$

(iv) $-x^2 + 6x + 9 = 0$

(v) $5x^2 + 2x - 10 = 0$

(vi) $x^2 - kx - a^2 = 0$ $(a, k, \in R)$

(vii) $x^2 + 2ax + a^2 = 0$ $(a \in R)$

(viii) $3(4x - 2)^2 + 1 = 12$

(ix) $x^2 + (a - 1)x - 9 = 0$ $(a \in R)$

3. Graph the function $f(x) = 2x^2 - 3x + 5$ in the domain $-3 \leqslant x \leqslant 3, x \in R$.
From your graph, determine the nature of the roots of $2x^2 - 3x + 5 = 0$.

4. Find the values of $a \in R$ for which $x^2 + ax + 16 = 0$ has real roots.

5. Find the value of $b \in R$ if $x^2 + 6x - b = 0$ has two equal real roots.

6. Find the range of values of $c \in R$ if $cx^2 + 4x - 2 = 0$ has no real roots.

7. For what values of $q \in R$ does the equation $x^2 + qx + q = 0$ have no real roots?

8. $(2p + 1)x^2 + (p + 2)x + 1 = 0$ has real roots. Find all possible values of $p, p \in R$.

9. $(b + 1)x^2 + bx + b + 1 = 0$ has two equal real roots. Find the values of $b, b \in R$.

10. Show that the equation $4ax^2 - 4ax + a + c^2 = 0$ has no real roots for $a \in N, c \in R, c \neq 0$.

11. Prove that the equation $kx^2 + (2k - 1)x - 2 = 0$ has real roots for all values of $k \in R$.

12. Prove that the equation $x^2 + (a - 2d)x + (ab - ad - b^2) = 0$ has real roots for all real values of a, b and d.

1. Solve (and check your answer):

   (i) $\sqrt{x + 3} = x - 3$ (iv) $x + \sqrt{x} = 2$

   (ii) $\sqrt{2x + 1} = x - 1$ (v) $\sqrt{7x + 1} - x = 1$

   (iii) $x - \sqrt{x - 3} = 5$

2. (a) Solve the following inequalities and show the solution on a numberline.

   (i) $7(2x - 1) \geqslant 3(4 - x) - 2x, x \in N$

   (ii) $2x - 1 < \dfrac{x + 7}{3}, x \in Z$

   (iii) $\dfrac{6x + 1}{5} > \dfrac{2x - 3}{3}, x \in R$

   (b) (i) Graph the solution set A of

   $-4x - 1 < 2, x \in R$.

   (ii) Graph the solution set B of

   $\dfrac{5x - 8}{6} \leqslant -\dfrac{x}{2}, x \in R$.

   (iii) Find the solution set $A \cap B$.

3. (a) (i) Solve $x^2 - 7x + 10 = 0$.

   (ii) Hence, solve $x^2 - 7x + 10 < 0$.

   (iii) Solve $x^2 - 8x + 15 = 0$.

   (iv) Hence, find the solution set of $x^2 - 8x + 15 \geqslant 0$.

   (b) Find the values of $x \in R$ that satisfy each of the following inequalities:

   (i) $x^2 - 2x - 8 < 0$ (iii) $x^2 - 3x - 10 \leqslant 0$

   (ii) $x^2 + x - 20 \geqslant 0$ (iv) $x^2 - 4 > 0$

   (c) Find the values of $x \in R$ that satisfy the following inequalities:

   (i) $2x^2 + x - 10 \leqslant 0$

   (ii) $6x^2 > x + 1$

   (iii) $(x - 3)(1 - x) > -15$

4. (a) (i) Use the quadratic formula to find the roots of $2x^2 - 11x - 22 = 0$ correct to one decimal place.

   (ii) Hence, find the greatest value of $n \in Z$, such that $2n^2 < 11(n + 2)$.

   (b) Solve the following inequalities, $x \in R$:

   (i) $\dfrac{x + 3}{x - 4} > 3, x \neq 4$ (iii) $\dfrac{2x - 1}{x - 3} \geqslant 3, x \neq 3$

   (ii) $\dfrac{x - 3}{x + 7} < 2, x \neq -7$ (iv) $\left| \dfrac{1 - x}{2} \right| \geqslant 5$

   (c) Find the least value of $n \in N$, for which

   $\dfrac{5n + 3}{7 - n} < 1, n \neq 7$.

5. (a) If $x = -2.4$ and $y = 1.8$, investigate if:

   (i) $|x + y| = |x| + |y|$

   (ii) $|xy| = |x||y|$

   (iii) $|x - y| = |x| - |y|$

   (iv) $|y - x| = |y| - |x|$

   (v) $\left| \dfrac{y}{x} \right| = \dfrac{|y|}{|x|}$

   (b) Solve for x in each case, and verify your answers:

   (i) $|x| = 5$ (iii) $|x - 1| = 10$

   (ii) $|x + 1| = 10$ (iv) $|1 - x| = 9$

   (c) Solve each of the following for x by graphing. Check your answers using algebra.

   (i) $|x + 3| = 2$ (iii) $|x + 7| = |x + 1|$

   (ii) $4 = |x - 6|$ (iv) $|x + 8| - |x - 5| = 0$

6. (a) Here are four statements that are true for any $x, y \in R$:

   (i) $|x| + |y| \geqslant |x + y|$

   (ii) $|x| - |y| \leqslant |x - y|$

   (iii) $|x||y| = |xy|$

   (iv) $\left| \dfrac{x}{y} \right| = \dfrac{|x|}{|y|}$

   Verify each statement by putting $x = 5$ and $y = -2$.

   (b) Solve each of the following for x by graphing. Check your answers using algebra.

   (i) $|x + 1| < 7$

   (ii) $|x - 5| \geqslant 2$

7. (a) If $x, y \in R$, show that $x^2 + 2xy + y^2 \geqslant 0$.

   (b) If $p > 0$ and if $x^2 - 2(p - q)x + q^2 = 0$ has real roots, prove that $p \geqslant 2q$.

   (c) (i) Factorise $q^3 - p^3$.

   (ii) If p and q are distinct positive real numbers, prove that:

   $\dfrac{q^3 - p^3}{pq^2 - qp^2} > 3$

8. (a) Find the value of $t \in R$, if $x^2 - 12x + 9t = 0$ has equal roots.

   (b) If the equation $x^2 + 8x + p = 0$ has no real roots, show that $p > 16$.

   (c) If the equation $x^2 + kx + (k + 3) = 0, k \in R$, has two equal roots, find two possible values of k. In each case, find the two roots.

   (d) Show that, for all values of $k \in R$, $x^2 - 3kx + (k^2 - 6) = 0$ has real roots.

9. (a) If $x^2 + 2kx + (k + 2) = 0$ has equal roots, find two possible values for $k, k \in R$. Find the roots in both cases.

   (b) Mohamad has just celebrated his birthday. He knows that if he doubles the age he will be in three years' time, the answer that he gets will be less than five times his age three years ago. He also knows that if he tripled his age now, he would still be younger than his older brother Saif, who is 27. Given that today is Mohamad's birthday:

      (i) Write down two inequalities representing the above information.

      (ii) Solve each inequality.

      (iii) Write down what age Mohamad is today

   (c) Solve for x: $5 < |x - 2| \leqslant 9, x \in R$, by:

      (i) Algebra

      (ii) Graphing

10. (a) $f(x) = \dfrac{100}{x + 1}$ is a function, defined for all $x \in R, x \neq -1$.

      Find the values of x for which $f(x) > 5$.

   (b) If a is the area of the rectangle and p is the perimeter, prove that $p^2 - 16a \geqslant 0$.

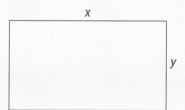

   (c) A drug is administered to a patient by injection into their left arm. The concentration (C) of the drug in the patient's bloodstream is measured in mg/ml and is given by the formula:

   $$C = \frac{0.12t}{t^2 + 2}$$

   where t is the time since injection measured in hours.

   When will the concentration of the drug in the patient's blood exceed 0.04 mg/ml?

11. (a) Solve for x: $-2 \leqslant |x + 3| < 3, x \in R$, by:

      (i) Algebra

      (ii) Graphing

   (b) Let $f(x) = (x^2 - 1)(x - 1)$.

      (i) Show why $f(x) \geqslant 0$ in each of the following cases, ($x \in R$):

         1. $x = 0$

         2. $x = 1$

         3. $x > 1$

         4. $0 < x < 1$

         5. $-1 < x < 0$

      (ii) Hence, deduce that $x^3 + 1 \geqslant x^2 + x$ for all $x > -1, x \in R$.

   (c) In August 2010, Washington Redskins NFL footballer Albert Haynesworth was reportedly suffering from rhabdomyolysis, a rare medical condition that can result from extreme physical exertion. Rhabdomyolysis causes levels of creatine kinase to rise in the blood. The levels of creatine kinase in the blood for the first six days after onset of the condition are given by the formula

   $$(0.0004)L = 3 + 11t - 2t^2$$

   where L is level in units/litre and t is time (since onset) in days.

   A patient with rhabdomyolysis requires hospitalisation when levels of creatine kinase exceed 8,000 units/litre.

   For how long would you expect Albert Haynesworth to have required hospitalisation? Answer to the nearest hour.

Solutions and chapter summary available online

ALGEBRA III

04

Length, Area and Volume

In this chapter you will learn to:

⊙ Find the area and perimeter of various 2D shapes

⊙ Find the area and circumference of circles and sectors of circles

⊙ Solve problems involving area

⊙ Investigate the nets of prisms, cylinders and cones

⊙ Find the surface area and volume of various 3D solids

⊙ Solve problems involving surface area and volume

⊙ Use the trapezoidal rule to approximate area

You should remember...

⊙ Perimeter, area and volume from your Junior Certificate course

⊙ The theorem of Pythagoras

Key words

⊙ Triangle
⊙ Rectangle
⊙ Square
⊙ Parallelogram
⊙ Trapezium

⊙ Disc (circle)
⊙ Sector of a disc
⊙ Rectangular block
⊙ Cylinder
⊙ Right cone

⊙ Right prism
⊙ Sphere
⊙ Hemisphere
⊙ Trapezoidal rule
⊙ Perimeter

⊙ Area
⊙ Surface area
⊙ Volume

4.1 Two-Dimensional (2D) Shapes

In everyday life there are many situations in which we need to know the area and perimeter of objects.

Area and Perimeter

Area is the amount of flat space that a shape occupies.

Perimeter is the sum of the length of all the sides of a shape.

Rectangle	**Square**

Area = (length × width) = lw Perimeter = $2l + 2w$ **or** $2(l + w)$	Area = (length)² = l^2 Perimeter = $4l$
Triangle	**Parallelogram**
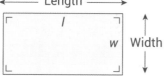 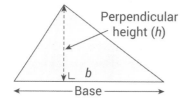 Area = $\frac{1}{2}$ × base × perpendicular height = $\frac{1}{2}bh$	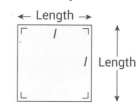 Area = base × perpendicular height = bh

Trapezium

A trapezium is a quadrilateral that has one pair of parallel sides.

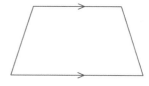

Trapezium	
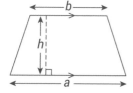	Area = Half the sum of the lengths of the parallel sides (a and b) × perpendicular height between them Area = $\frac{1}{2}(a + b)h$ **or** Area = $\left(\dfrac{a + b}{2}\right)h$ This formula appears on page 8 of *Formulae and Tables*.

Worked Example 4.1

The area of the shaded part of the trapezium shown is equal to 270 m². Calculate the value of h.

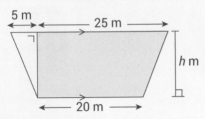

Area $= \frac{1}{2}(a+b)h$	Unshaded area (triangle):
$= \frac{1}{2}(50)(h)$	Area $= \frac{1}{2}bh$
$= 25h \text{ m}^2$	$= \frac{1}{2}(5)(h)$

$= 2.5h \text{ m}^2$

$\therefore 25h - 2.5h = 270$

$22.5h = 270$

$\therefore h = 12$

Solution

Area of shaded shape = total area − unshaded area

Total area (trapezium):

$a = 20$, $b = 30$, $h = h$

Circles

The circumference of any circle divided by the length of its diameter is always the same. This ratio is π (pronounced 'pi'). We use π to calculate the area and circumference (length) of a circle or sector of a circle.

Area and Circumference of a Circle

$$\pi = \frac{\text{Circumference of a circle}}{\text{Length of diameter}}$$

Area of a circle $= \pi \times r^2$, usually written as πr^2.

 Circumference of a circle $= 2 \times \pi \times r$, usually written as $2\pi r$.

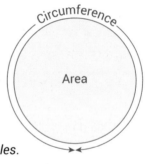

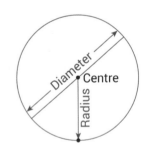

These formulae appear on page 8 of *Formulae and Tables*.

π is an irrational number. To eight decimal places, $\pi = 3.14159265$. As π is an infinite non-recurring decimal, we often use approximations of π in our calculations. In calculating the area or circumference of a circle, we may be told to use one of the following values for π:

- $\pi = 3.14$
- $\pi = \frac{22}{7}$
- The value of π from the calculator

We may also be asked to leave our answer in terms of π.

Sector of a Circle

A **sector** is a specific slice of a circle.

A sector of a circle is the portion of a circle bounded by two radii and the included arc.

Area of sector $= \pi r^2 \left(\dfrac{\theta}{360°} \right)$

Length of arc $l = 2\pi r \left(\dfrac{\theta}{360°} \right)$

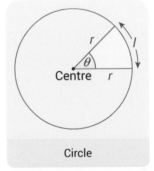

Circle

Sector

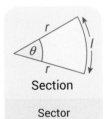

Section

Sector

Note: θ must be in degrees to use either of these two formulae.

We also have two formulae for finding the area and length when using radian measure. We will study radian measure in greater detail in Book 2, Chapter 7, Trigonometry.

Length of an arc $l = r\theta$ (θ in radians)

Area of a sector $A = \frac{1}{2}r^2\theta$ (θ in radians)

These formulae appear on page 9 of *Formulae and Tables*.

Worked Example 4.2

The area of the sector shown is $1,414\frac{2}{7}$ cm².
Find the length of the radius r.

Take π to be $\frac{22}{7}$.

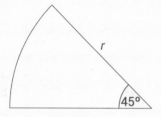

Solution

Area of sector $= \pi r^2\left(\dfrac{\theta}{360°}\right)$

$\therefore \dfrac{22}{7} \times r^2 \times \dfrac{45°}{360°} = 1,414\frac{2}{7}$

$\dfrac{11}{28}r^2 = 1,414\frac{2}{7}$

$r^2 = \dfrac{1,414\frac{2}{7}}{\frac{11}{28}}$

$r^2 = 3,600$

$r = \sqrt{3,600}$

$\therefore r = 60$ cm

Worked Example 4.3

A rectangle's width is 3 cm less than its length. The area of this rectangle is 810 cm². Find both the length and width of this rectangle.

Solution
Let x = length. ∴ width = $x - 3$

Length × Width = Area

$x(x - 3) = 810$

$x^2 - 3x = 810$

$x^2 - 3x - 810 = 0$

$(x - 30)(x + 27) = 0$

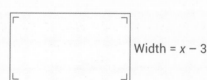

Width = $x - 3$

Length = x

$x - 30 = 0$ or $x + 27 = 0$

$x = 30$ **or** $x = -27$

∴ Length = 30 cm

Width = 27 cm

As x is a length, we discard the negative answer for x.

In a right-angled triangle, the area of the square on the hypotenuse is equal to the sum of the areas of the squares on the other two sides.

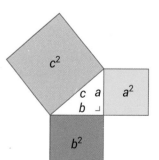

$c^2 = a^2 + b^2$

Formulae and Tables, page 16

LENGTH, AREA AND VOLUME

Exercise 4.1

1. Find the area and circumference of each of the following circles:

   (i) Radius length = 5 cm
     (π = 3.14)

  (ii) Radius length = 8 km
     $\left(\pi = \frac{22}{7}\right)$

 (iii) Radius length = 0.7 m
     (in terms of π)

 (iv) Diameter length = 2.5 mm
     (π = 3.14)

  (v) Radius length = 4.5 cm
     $\left(\pi = \frac{22}{7}\right)$

 (vi) Diameter length = 126 mm
     (in terms of π)

2. Find the area, arc length and perimeter of each of the following sectors:

   (i) π = 3.14

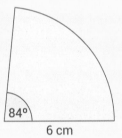

  (ii) $\pi = \frac{22}{7}$

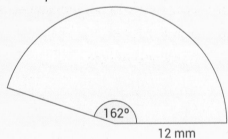

 (iii) π = 3.14

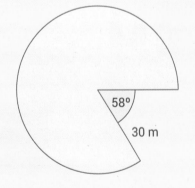

3. Fill in the table below by first finding the radius of each of the circles.

π	r	Area	Circumference
π			24π
3.14			4.71
$\frac{22}{7}$		1,386	
π		324π	
3.14		254.34	
$\frac{22}{7}$		346.5	

4. Find the area and perimeter (to two decimal places where necessary) of each of the following compound shapes (all units are in centimetres; π = 3.14):

   (i)

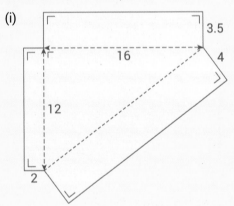

  (ii)

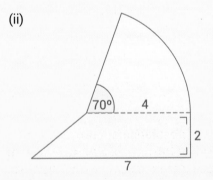

 (iii)

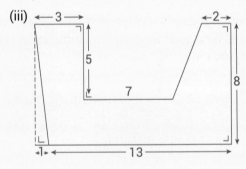

5. A circular cog has a circumference of 13.288 cm.

   (i) Find the radius of the cog $\left(\pi = \frac{22}{7}\right)$.

   (ii) This cog must be replaced after 5,000 revolutions. How far is this in metres?

6. Using the information given, find the measure of the unknown radius or angle of each of the following sectors:

   (i) Length of arc = 7π cm

   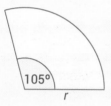

   (ii) Area = 439.6 cm² (π = 3.14)

   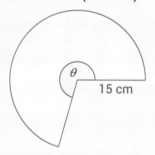

   (iii) Area = 6.16 cm² ($\pi = \frac{22}{7}$)

   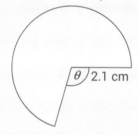

7. The area of a rectangular lawn is 204 m². The length of the lawn is 5 m more than its width. Calculate the perimeter of the lawn.

8. There is a path 5 metres wide around a small green area as shown. Together the green area and the path make up a park.

   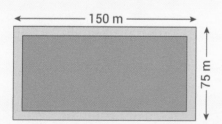

Find:

   (i) The area of the park

   (ii) The area of the path

   (iii) The cost of replacing the path if each 2 m² of path costs €7.25

9. A square plastic cover for a drain is shown. Each cover has five circular holes, each with a diameter of 15 cm. If 1 cm² of plastic weighs 0.2 g, how much does the cover weigh, correct to the nearest gram?

   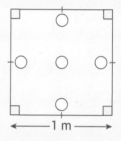

10. The perimeter of a rectangular garden is 22.5 m. The area is 12.5 m². Find the dimensions of the garden.

   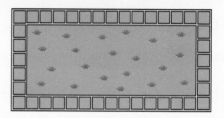

11. The points *P*, *Q*, *R*, *S* are points on two circular arcs of centre *O*. If |*OP*| = 13 cm and |*OR*| = 6 cm, find to the nearest centimetre:

   (i) The area of *PQSR*

   (ii) The perimeter of *PQSR*

   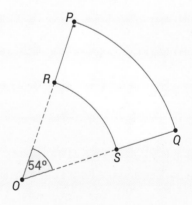

12. A design for a new metal medal is shown. Each medal initially costs €2 to make. The outer ring of the medal is then to be covered in gold leaf. Gold leaf costs €1 per 70 cm². Find the total cost of producing 125 of these medals. (Assume that both sides are identical.)

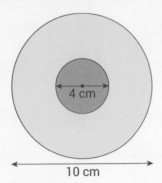

13. Find, to the nearest centimetre, the side length of a square that is inscribed in a circle of diameter 40 cm.

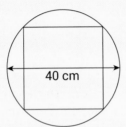

14. Find, in terms of π, the area of a circle that circumscribes a square of area 81 cm².

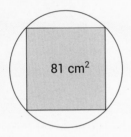

15. A design for a garden is shown. The length of the rectangular part of the garden is 21 m, and the total area of the garden is 1,336.8 m². Find the radius of the circular part of the garden (π = 3.14) to the nearest metre.

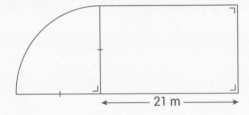

16. An office has 1,104 m² of floor space. An extension increases the length by 2 m, the width by 3 m and the floor space by 196 m².

Find the dimensions of the original office (two possible sets of dimensions).

17. A square is to be constructed with a side length the same as the diagonal of a square of side length x cm. Find, in terms of x, the side length of the larger square.

18. The diagram shows a square inscribed in a circle and another square circumscribed about the circle.

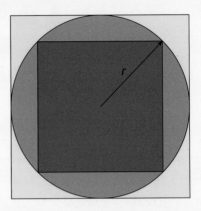

Find the area of each of the following in terms of r, to two decimal places where necessary:

(i) Red shaded region

(ii) Yellow shaded region

(iii) Green shaded region

19. A design for a construction company's new logo is shown. It consists of a square of side length y inscribed in a circle s and a circle p inscribed in the square.

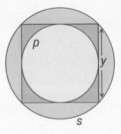

(i) Find the radius of the circle s in terms of y.

(ii) Find the radius of the circle p in terms of y.

(iii) Find the ratio of the area of the circle s to the area of the circle p.

20. The diagram below shows six circles with the same centre, each a distance x units apart. The diameter of the centre circle also measures x units.

Which has the greater area: the inner shaded region (pink) or the outer shaded region (blue)?

4.2 Rectangular Solids and Prisms

Rectangular Solids

One type of 3D object is the rectangular solid.
To find the volume of a rectangular solid (**cuboid**),
we multiply out the three dimensions given.

> Volume of a cuboid = length × breadth × height
> ∴ Volume = *lbh*

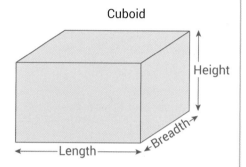
Cuboid

Height

Breadth

Length

If all sides of the rectangular solid are equal in length, then it can be referred to as a **cube**.

> Volume of a cube = length × length × length
> ∴ Volume = l^3

Cube

l

l

l

Surface Area and Nets

A cube or cuboid has six flat sides or faces.

| The line where two faces meet is called an edge. | The corner where three edges meet is called a vertex. |

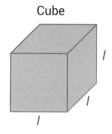
Edge

Face

Vertex

If we cut along the edges of a rectangular solid, we can create a **net** of that solid.

 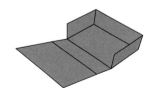 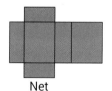

Net

> A **net** is a 2D (flat) shape that folds up along its edges to make a 3D shape.

There can be many different nets for one rectangular
solid. These are two possible nets for a cube.

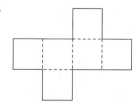 

Nets can be used to help determine the **surface area** of a 3D shape.

> **Surface area of a cuboid** = the sum of the area of all six faces of its net.

Surface area = area of (top + base + front + back + side + side).

This can also be written as:

> **Surface area of a cuboid** = $2lb + 2lh + 2bh$

> **Surface area of a cube** = $6(\text{length})^2$ or $6l^2$

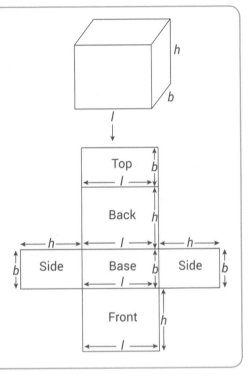

Worked Example 4.4

A cuboid has side length dimensions in the ratio 1:2:3. Find its dimensions if its volume is 2,058 cm³.

Solution

Let p = length of smallest side.

∴ Ratio of side lengths = $p:2p:3p$

Volume = 2,058 cm³

$(p)(2p)(3p) = 2{,}058$

$6p^3 = 2{,}058$

$p^3 = 343$

$p = \sqrt[3]{343}$

∴ $p = 7$

∴ The dimensions are 7 cm, 14 cm and 21 cm.

Prisms

> A **prism** is a 3D solid that has parallel congruent bases that are both polygons.

> A **right prism** is a prism in which one of the bases is directly above the other. Its side faces are therefore rectangles.

The volume of a right prism is the area of its base multiplied by the prism's length.

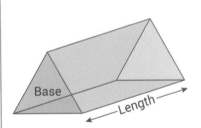

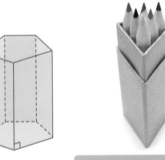

The surface area of a prism can be found by using nets.

> Volume of a prism = area of base × length

Worked Example 4.5

Find the volume and surface area of the following right prism:

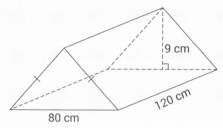

Solution
Volume

Area of triangle = $\frac{1}{2}bh$

$\qquad = \frac{1}{2}(80)(9)$

$\qquad = 360 \text{ cm}^2$

Volume = Area of base × Length

$\qquad = (360)(120)$

$\qquad = 43{,}200 \text{ cm}^3$

Surface Area

By the theorem of Pythagoras:

$\quad x^2 = (9)^2 + (40)^2$

$\quad x^2 = 1{,}681$

$\quad x = \sqrt{1{,}681}$

$\therefore x = 41$

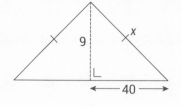

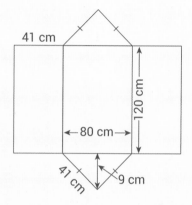

Work out the area of each face.

Surface area = 2(360) + 2(120)(41) + (80)(120)

$\qquad = 20{,}160 \text{ cm}^2$

Exercise 4.2

1. A box measuring 20 cm by 33 cm by 6 cm is gift-wrapped. What is the least amount of wrapping paper needed?

2. Find the volume and surface area of the following right prisms:

(i)
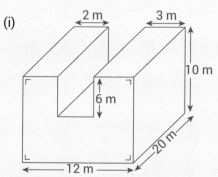

(ii)
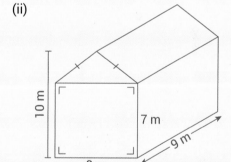

(iii)
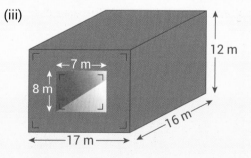

3. For each of the following prisms:

(a) Calculate the volume to the nearest whole number

(b) Draw a net of the prism

(c) Hence, or otherwise, calculate the surface area to two significant figures

(i)

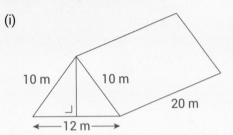

(ii)

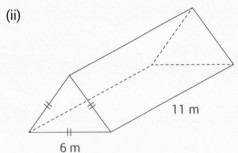

(iii)

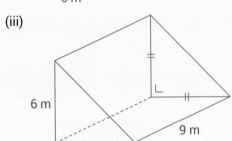

4. Draw a net for the following right prism and hence find its surface area (answer to two decimal places):

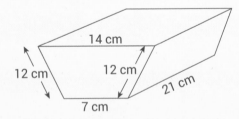

5. A podium for a medal ceremony is shown.

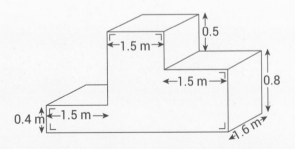

Find the volume and surface area of the podium.

6. A cuboid has a base of 30 cm by 20 cm. Water is poured into this cuboid to a depth of 12 cm. Another 2 litres of water is poured into the container. Calculate the rise in the height of the water in centimetres.

7. A rectangular tank with no lid has a surface area of 288 cm². If its length is three times its height and its width is half its height, find the volume of the tank.

8. The volume of a cube is 32 times the volume of another cube. If the side length of the smaller cube is x cm, find in terms of x the surface area of the larger cube.

9. The diagram of a swimming pool is shown. The swimming pool bottom and side walls are being re-tiled. Each square tile used has a side length of 50 cm.

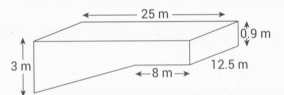

(i) Find the number of tiles needed to tile the pool.

(ii) Find the volume of water needed to fill the pool, if the water level is 10 cm below the top of the pool.

10. The diagonal length (d) of a cube is 48 cm. Find the volume and surface area of this cube.

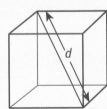

11. A cuboid with a length of x cm and a breadth of y cm is shown. ($x > y$)

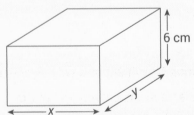

(i) Draw a labelled net of this cuboid.

(ii) Write an expression for the volume and surface area of this cuboid in terms of x and y.

(iii) If the surface area of the cuboid is 568 cm² and the volume is 840 cm³, find the value of x and the value of y.

12. A rectangular sheet of metal is 18 cm long and 16 cm wide. A square of side length x cm is cut from each corner of this sheet. The sheet is then folded to form an open rectangular box with a volume of V cm³.

   (i) Draw a labelled net of this box.

  (ii) Show that $V = 4x^3 - 68x^2 + 288x$.

 (iii) Find the possible values of x if the volume of the box is 320 cm³. (Give answers to two decimal places where necessary.)

4.3 Cylinders, Cones, Spheres and Hemispheres

There are many other types of 3D solid.

Volume of a Cylinder

Volume of cylinder = $\pi \times$ (radius)² $\times$ height
∴ Volume = $\pi r^2 h$

This formula appears on page 10 of *Formulae and Tables*.

Surface Area of a Cylinder

We can use a net to show how to calculate the two types of surface area of a cylinder.

Curved Surface Area (CSA) of a cylinder

This is the area of just the curved part of the cylinder.

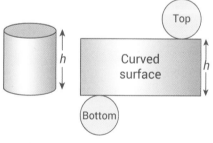

Curved surface area (CSA) of cylinder = $2\pi rh$

This formula appears on page 10 of *Formulae and Tables*.

Total Surface Area (TSA) of a solid cylinder

This is the area of the curved part of the cylinder **plus** the top and bottom circles.

(TSA = $2\pi rh + \pi r^2$ if either no top or no bottom)

Total surface area (TSA) of solid cylinder = $2\pi rh + 2\pi r^2$
∴ TSA = CSA + $2\pi r^2$ or $2\pi r(h + r)$

LENGTH, AREA AND VOLUME

Right Circular Cones

A **right circular cone** has an apex (top) directly above the centre of a circular base.

Volume of a Cone

Volume of cone = $\frac{1}{3} \times \pi \times$ (radius)$^2 \times$ height

$$\therefore \text{Volume} = \frac{1}{3}\pi r^2 h$$

This formula appears on page 10 of *Formulae and Tables*.

Surface Area of a Cone

There are two types of surface area of a cone.

Curved Surface Area (CSA) of a Cone

This is the area of just the curved part of the cone.
To calculate the CSA, we must have the slant height (l) of the cone.

Using Pythagoras' theorem, we can state that $l^2 = h^2 + r^2$.

$l^2 = h^2 + r^2$

l in the formula refers to the slant height of the cone. This is the distance from any point on the circular base to the top (apex) of the cone.

h is the perpendicular height (altitude) of the cone.

r is the radius of the circular base.

Total Surface Area (TSA) of a Cone

This is the area of the curved part of the cone **plus** the circular base.

The following diagram can help us visualise the net of a cone.

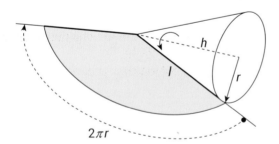

From this we can draw a net of a cone.

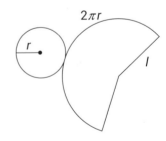

Net of a cone.

Curved surface area (CSA) of cone = $\pi r l$

This formula appears on page 10 of *Formulae and Tables*.

Total surface area (TSA) of cone = $\pi r l + \pi r^2$

$$\therefore \text{TSA} = \text{CSA} + \pi r^2 \text{ or } \pi r(l + r)$$

Volume of a Sphere

Volume of sphere = $\frac{4}{3} \times \pi \times$ (radius)^3

∴ Volume = $\frac{4}{3}\pi r^3$

These formulae appear on page 10 of *Formulae and Tables*.

Surface Area of a Sphere

A sphere has no flat parts, so we can only have one type of surface area.

Surface area of sphere = $4\pi r^2$

Volume of a Hemisphere

A hemisphere is **half** a sphere.

Volume of hemisphere = $\frac{2}{3}\pi r^3$

Surface Area of a Hemisphere

A hemisphere has a flat circular part, so two types of surface area can be found.

Curved Surface Area (CSA) of a Hemisphere

The area of the curved part of the sphere is **half** that of the surface area of a sphere.

Curved surface area (CSA) of hemisphere = $2\pi r^2$

Total Surface Area (TSA) of a Hemisphere

This is the area of the curved part of the hemisphere **plus** the circular top.

Total surface area (TSA) of hemisphere = $2\pi r^2 + \pi r^2$

∴ TSA = CSA + $\pi r^2 = 3\pi r^2$

Worked Example 4.6

A cylinder of wax of volume $426\frac{2}{3}\pi\,\text{cm}^3$ is melted down into two candles, one in the shape of a sphere of radius 4 cm and the other in the shape of a cone with a radius half its height.
Assuming no wax is wasted in the melting process, calculate the dimensions of the cone.

Solution

Volume of sphere + volume of cone = $426\frac{2}{3}\pi\,\text{cm}^3$

$\frac{4}{3}\pi r^3_{\text{sphere}} + \frac{1}{3}\pi r^2_{\text{cone}}\,h = 426\frac{2}{3}\pi$

$\frac{4}{3}r^3_{\text{sphere}} + \frac{1}{3}r^2_{\text{cone}}\,h = 426\frac{2}{3}$ (Divide both sides by π.)

Height of cone = $2r_{cone}$ and r_{sphere} = 4 cm

$$\frac{4}{3}(4)^3 + \frac{1}{3}r_{cone}^2(2r_{cone}) = 426\frac{2}{3}$$

$$85\frac{1}{3} + \frac{2}{3}r_{cone}^3 = 426\frac{2}{3}$$

$$\frac{2}{3}r_{cone}^3 = 341\frac{1}{3}$$

$$r_{cone}^3 = 512$$

$$r_{cone} = \sqrt[3]{512}$$

$$r_{cone} = 8$$

∴ Radius of cone = 8 cm; height of cone = 16 cm

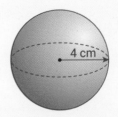

Worked Example 4.7

An experiment to measure the volume of a metal spherical ball is conducted. The ball is lowered into a cylinder of water. The cylinder has a radius of 5 cm and a height of 9 cm and is half-full of water. When the ball is lowered into the cylinder, the water level rises by 4 cm. The ball is completely submerged in the water.

Find the radius of the metal spherical ball in cm correct to one decimal place.

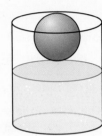

Solution

When the ball is lowered into the water, the water level rises by 4 cm.

The volume of the sphere is equal to the volume of the displaced water.

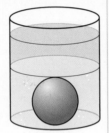

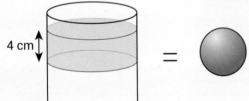

Volume of displaced water = $\pi r^2 h$

$$= \pi \times (5)^2 \times 4$$

$$= 100\pi \text{ cm}^3$$

∴ Volume of sphere = 100π cm³

$$\frac{4}{3}\pi r^3 = 100\pi$$

$$\frac{4}{3}r^3 = 100$$

$$r^3 = 75$$

$$\Rightarrow r = \sqrt[3]{75}$$

$$\Rightarrow r = 4.2172 \text{ cm}$$

∴ $r \approx 4.2$ cm

Exercise 4.3

1. Find the volume, curved surface area and total surface area of each of the following cylinders:

   (i) r = 12 cm, h = 4 cm (closed at both ends, π = 3.14)

   (ii) r = 7 mm, h = 2.8 mm $\left(\text{closed at both ends, } \pi = \frac{22}{7}\right)$

   (iii) r = 4 m, h = 20 m (open at one end, in terms of π)

   (iv) r = 6 m, h = 14 m (open at one end, π = 3.14)

2. Find the volume, curved surface area and total surface area of each of the following cones:

   (i) r = 8 cm, h = 6 cm (π = 3.14)

   (ii) r = 40 mm, l = 4.1 cm $\left(\pi = \frac{22}{7}\right)$

   (iii) h = 36 cm, l = 600 mm (in terms of π)

   (iv) r = 240 cm, l = 5.1 m $\left(\pi = \frac{22}{7}\right)$

3. Find the volume and surface area of each of the following spheres:

    (i) $r = 25$ m ($\pi = 3.14$)

    (ii) $r = 14$ mm $\left(\pi = \frac{22}{7}\right)$

    (iii) $r = 12$ cm (in terms of π)

4. Find the volume, curved surface area and total surface area of each of the following hemispheres:

    (i) $r = 25$ cm ($\pi = 3.14$)

    (ii) $r = 14.5$ mm $\left(\pi = \frac{22}{7}\right)$

    (iii) $r = 9$ m (in terms of π)

5. A cylindrical can with no top is made from metal. The cylinder has a height of 10 cm and a radius of 4 cm.

    (i) Draw a net of this shape.

    (ii) Find in terms of π the amount of metal required to make the cylinder.

6. A cylindrical tank of radius 12 cm is partly filled with water. A sphere of radius 6 cm is immersed in the water. By how much will the water rise?

7. A cone of radius 10 cm has the same volume as a cylinder with height 8 cm and radius 4 cm. Find the height of the cone to the nearest millimetre.

8. Water flows through a cylindrical pipe at a speed of 10 cm per second. The pipe has a diameter of 4 cm. How long will it take to pour out 22 litres of water? $\left(\pi = \frac{22}{7}\right)$

4 cm

9. A solid metal sphere of radius 6 cm is melted down and remoulded into a solid cone of diameter 18 cm.

    Find:

    (i) The volume of the sphere in terms of π

    (ii) The height of the cone

    (Assume no wastage in the manufacturing process.)

10. A fishing float consists of a solid hemisphere surmounted by a solid cone.

The radius of the cone is of length 3 cm. The volume of the cone is half the volume of the hemisphere.

Find:

    (i) The volume of the hemisphere in terms of π

    (ii) The height of the cone

    (iii) The overall height of the float

    (iv) The total surface area of the float

11. The volume of a sphere of radius r is double the volume of a cone of radius r and height h.

    (i) Show that $h = 2r$.

    (ii) Find the ratio of the surface area of the cone to the surface area of the sphere.

12. Three cylinders (A, B and C) have radii in the ratio 3:2:4 and heights in the ratio 4:5:2. Which cylinder has the greatest volume?

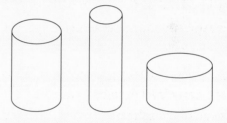

13. The radius of the base of a cylinder is x cm and its height is h cm. The radius of a sphere is $2x$ cm. The volume of the cylinder and the volume of the sphere are equal.

    Express h in terms of x.

14. A sphere has a radius of x cm. Find, in terms of x, how much the radius of the sphere increases if the sphere's surface area is increased by 50%.

15. An inflated spherical balloon has a diameter of 15 cm.

    Take $\pi = 3.14$.

    (i) What is the volume of air in the balloon?

    (ii) While retaining its spherical shape, more air is pumped into the balloon until its volume reaches 2,500 cm³. Find, to two decimal places, the radius of the balloon.

    (iii) The balloon is then placed inside a rectangular box. What are the dimensions of this box, assuming that the inflated balloon fits exactly in the box?

LENGTH, AREA AND VOLUME

16. A cylindrical tin has a radius of 4 cm and a height of 12 cm. A rectangular label is glued to the outer surface of the tin as shown.

There is a 15 mm gap between the label and the top and bottom of the tin and a 10 mm overlap. Find, to the nearest millimetre, the dimensions of this label.

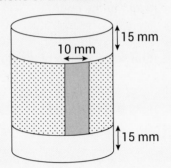

17. A closed container consists of a cylinder joined to a cone. The height of the cylinder is 10 cm and its diameter is 7 cm.

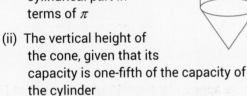

Calculate:

(i) The capacity of the cylindrical part in terms of π

(ii) The vertical height of the cone, given that its capacity is one-fifth of the capacity of the cylinder

(iii) The volume of the water (in terms of π) in the container when its depth is 13 cm

(iv) The height of the water in the cylinder if the container were inverted

(v) Draw a net of this shape.

(vi) Find, to the nearest cm, the surface area of this container.

18. A solid metal spherical ball of radius 5 cm is coated with another metal. This metal forms a spherical shell around the original metal ball. If the total volume of the sphere increases by 516π cm³, find the thickness of the metal coat applied.

19. A solid cone has a height of 20 cm and a radius of 10 cm. A small cone of height 1.5 cm is cut off the top. Calculate the volume (to two significant figures) of the remaining solid.

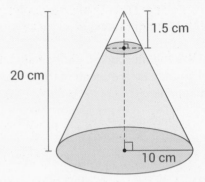

20. An inverted plastic cone of radius 12 cm and height 25 cm is shown. A cone of the same radius and with a slant height of $3\sqrt{17}$ cm is cut from the top of this plastic cone. What is the volume and surface area of the plastic that remains?

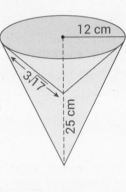

Take π = 3.14; answer to two decimal places.

21. A cube is inscribed in a sphere. Find the ratio of their volumes.

22. (a) A solid sphere of radius r is melted down and recast into a cone that has a height five times the radius of the sphere. Find in terms of r:

(i) The volume of the cone

(ii) The surface area of the cone

(b) The total surface area of a cylinder is P. If the height of the cylinder is twice the radius of the cylinder, express the volume of the cylinder in terms of P.

4.4 Trapezoidal Rule

It is difficult to measure the exact area of an irregular shape and therefore we generally approximate the area.

The **trapezoidal rule** is used to estimate the area under a curve.

The area under the curve is approximated by trapezoids of equal width, as shown in the diagram. We can then find the sum of the areas of the trapeziums. For the five trapeziums shown:

Sum of areas $= \frac{1}{2}(y_1 + y_2)h + \frac{1}{2}(y_2 + y_3)h + \frac{1}{2}(y_3 + y_4)h + \frac{1}{2}(y_4 + y_5)h + \frac{1}{2}(y_5 + y_6)h$

$\qquad = \frac{h}{2}[y_1 + 2y_2 + 2y_3 + 2y_4 + 2y_5 + y_6]$

$\qquad = \frac{h}{2}[y_1 + y_6 + 2(y_2 + y_3 + y_4 + y_5)]$

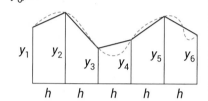

This can be generalised to the case with $(n - 1)$ trapezoids:

Sum of areas $= \frac{h}{2}[y_1 + y_n + 2(y_2 + y_3 + ... + y_{n-1})]$

When we use this rule, the shape to be measured must be divided into **segments or strips of equal width**. We then need to measure the height at the boundaries of each of these segments. In the diagram shown, h is the equal width, and $y_1, y_2, ..., y_n$ are the heights.

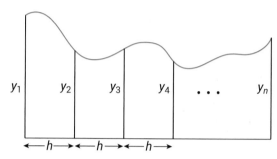

Area $\approx \frac{h}{2}$ [first height + last height + 2(the sum of the rest of the heights)]

When using the trapezoidal rule, the smaller the width of each segment, the more accurate the approximation of the area will be.

Area $\approx \frac{h}{2}[y_1 + y_n + 2(y_2 + y_3 + y_4 + ... + y_{n-1})]$
Here, y_{n-1} refers to the second-last height.

This formula appears on page 12 of *Formulae and Tables*.

The trapezoidal rule determines the area under a curve by approximating it to that of a trapezoid. Therefore the answer we calculate will only be an approximate answer. To determine the actual area under a curve we can use integration. We will study this in Chapter 15.

Worked Example 4.8

Estimate the area of the piece of land shown below. (Units are in metres.)

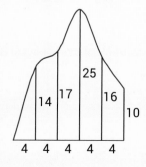

Solution

Fill in the following:

$h = 4$ m

First height $= 0$ m

Last height $= 10$ m

The first and last heights can sometimes be 0. It's important to look out for this.

Area $\approx \frac{4}{2}[0 + 10 + 2(14 + 17 + 25 + 16)]$

$\qquad = 2[10 + 2(72)]$

$\qquad = 2[154]$

$\therefore$ Area ≈ 308 m²

Worked Example 4.9

The area of this irregular shape is calculated as 40 square units by use of the trapezoidal rule. Find the value of x.

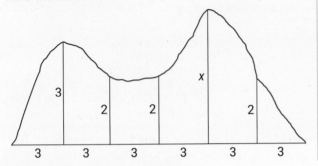

Solution

$h = 3$ First height = 0   Last height = 0

Area = 40 units²

$$\Rightarrow \frac{3}{2}[0 + 0 + 2(3 + 2 + 2 + x + 2)] = 40$$

$$\frac{3}{2}[2(x + 9)] = 40$$

$$3(x + 9) = 40$$

$$3x + 27 = 40$$

$$3x = 13$$

$$\therefore x = 4\tfrac{1}{3} \text{ units}$$

Exercise 4.4

Use the trapezoidal rule to estimate the area of each of the following:

1.

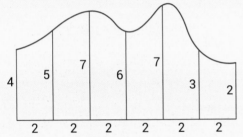

(Units are in metres.)

2.

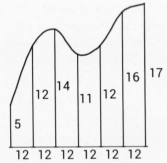

(Units are in centimetres.)

3.

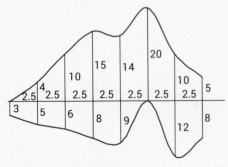

(Units are in metres.)

4. The diagram shows the plan of a lake. Use the trapezoidal rule to estimate the area of the lake, given that the offsets are a distance of 10 m apart, and all measurements are in metres.

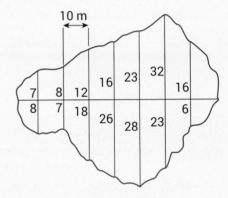

5. The diagram shows the curve $y = x^2 + 1$ in the domain $0 \leqslant x \leqslant 4$.

Use the equation of the curve to complete the following table.

x	0	1	2	3	4
y					

Hence, use the trapezoidal rule to estimate the area between the curve and the x-axis.

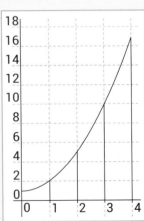

6. The speed of a runner in ms^{-1} was recorded every 10 seconds.

Time	0	10	20	30	40	50	60
Speed	1	2.5	4	3.2	2.8	3.1	2.4

The area under a speed–time graph represents the distance travelled. Use the trapezoidal rule to estimate the distance travelled by the runner.

7. An estimate for the area of this shape using the trapezoidal rule is 11,700 m². Find the value of *h*. Measurements are in metres.

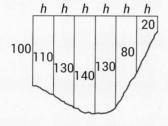

8. If $y = \sqrt{3x}$, complete the table below.

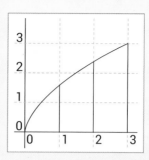

x	0	1	2	3
y				

(i) Hence, use the trapezoidal rule to estimate the area between the curve and the *x*-axis.

(ii) Explain how you could improve the accuracy of your answer.

(iii) Hence, using your method, estimate the area between the curve and the *x*-axis.

9. The area of the field below is estimated, using the trapezoidal rule, to be 6.775 hectares. Find the value of *x*. Measurements are in metres.
1 hectare = 10,000 m²

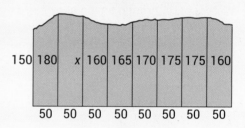

Revision Exercises

1. (a) A semicircular piece is cut from a piece of circular metal as shown. The circle has a diameter of 28 cm, and the area of the metal remaining is equal to 146 π cm². Find the radius of the semicircular piece cut.

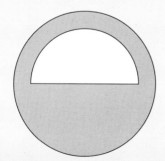

(b) The diagonal (*d*) of the cube shown is 5√7 cm. Find the volume of this cube to the nearest cm³.

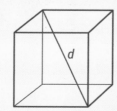

(c) The sides of a square are each of length 2*r*, as shown. Circles are drawn inside and outside the square, as shown.

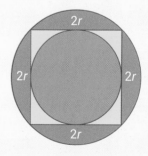

(i) Find the radius of each circle in terms of *r*.

(ii) Verify that the areas of the two circles are in the ratio 2:1.

2. (a) A machine part consists of a hemisphere and a cone cut from a single cylindrical piece of metal as shown.

The cylindrical piece of metal has a radius of 12 cm and a height of 18 cm. Find, in terms of π, the volume of this machine part.

(b) Water flows through a cylindrical pipe at a rate of 10 cm per second. The diameter of the pipe is 7 cm. The water is poured into an empty rectangular tank of length 55 cm and width 20 cm.

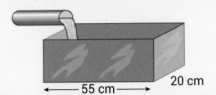

What is the depth of the water in the tank after one minute? (π = 3.14; give your answer correct to the nearest centimetre.)

(c) Water pours through a pipe of radius 3 cm at a rate of 15 cm per second. It flows into a conical tank of height 0.9 metres and radius 0.6 metres.

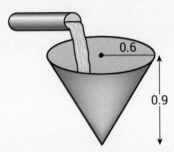

How long will it take to fill the tank?

3. (a) A sphere and a cone have equal volumes and equal radii. Find the ratio of the height of the cone to its radius.

(b) A beverage is sold in two different cylindrical jars. The height of the smaller jar is twice its radius. The larger jar has three times the radius of the smaller jar and is twice the height. A small and large jar, if filled completely, can store 1.5 litres. Find the dimensions of each jar to two significant figures.

4. (a) A sheet of metal 2 m long, 75 cm wide and 10 mm thick is melted down to form spherical ball bearings. How many spherical ball bearings of radius 5 mm can be made from this sheet, assuming no wastage? (π = 3.14)

(b) The radius r of a cone is twice its height. Express the volume and total surface area of the cone in terms of r.

5. (a) A sphere fits exactly into an open cylindrical container. Show that both have the same curved surface area.

(b) A hollow container consists of a cylinder with a cone on top.

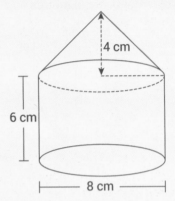

The container contains oil up to the level of the top of the cylinder.

The container is then turned upside down. Find the depth of the oil.

6. (a) Use the trapezoidal rule to estimate the area of each of the following (all measurements are in metres):

(i)
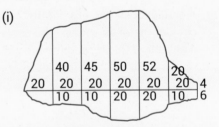

(ii)
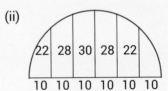

(b) (i) The area of this irregular shape is estimated by the trapezoidal rule to be 690 square units. Find the value of x.

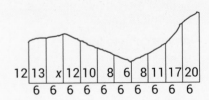

LENGTH, AREA AND VOLUME

(ii) The area of this field is estimated by the trapezoid rule as 583.15 m². Measurements are in metres. Find the value of *h*, the width of each strip.

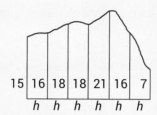

15 | 16 | 18 | 18 | 21 | 16 | 7
h | *h* | *h* | *h* | *h* | *h*

7. (a) The perimeter of the shaded region consists of three semicircles.

Find, in terms of *x* and π:

(i) The area of the region

(ii) The perimeter of the region

x

x

$\frac{3}{2}x$

$\frac{3}{2}x$

(b) The cross-section of a storage shed is shown. Beams that support the roof are marked as *p* and *q*.

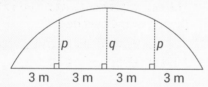

p | *q* | *p*

3 m | 3 m | 3 m | 3 m

The longer beam *q* is 1.6 times the length of the smaller beam *p*. An estimate of the cross-sectional area of the shed is 16.2 m². Find the value of *p* and the value of *q*.

8. (a) A river is 21 m wide at a certain point. Students take a depth reading every 3 metres across a cross-section of the river at this point.

Distance from bank	0	3	6	9	12	15	18	21
Depth (m)	0.5	1.25	1.7	3	5	4	2.4	0.1

(i) Estimate the cross-sectional area of the river.

(ii) If the speed of the river at this point is 7 ms⁻¹, find the number of cubic metres that flow by this point in the river each minute.

(b) The planet Mars orbits the Sun at an average distance of 227,940,000 km and at an average orbital speed of 24 kms⁻¹.

(i) Assuming the orbit of Mars to be a circle, find the length of its orbit in kilometres to five significant figures.

(ii) Calculate the time to the nearest day (Earth) that it takes Mars to complete one orbit.

The planet Neptune has an average orbital speed of 5.43 kms⁻¹ and on average takes 165 years to complete one orbit.

(iii) Find in kilometres, to three significant figures, the distance Neptune is from the Sun. Assume a circular orbit.

(iv) If light travels at a speed of 3×10^8 ms⁻¹, find to the nearest minute how long light from the Sun takes to reach Neptune.

9. A solid made from a cone and hemisphere is shown.

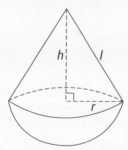

h | *l*

r

The curved surface area of the cone and the total surface area of the hemisphere are equal.

(i) Express the slant height of the cone *l* in terms of *r*.

(ii) Find *h*, the perpendicular height of the cone in terms of *r*.

(iii) Find, in surd form, the ratio of the volume of the cone to the volume of the hemisphere.

LENGTH, AREA AND VOLUME

Exam Questions

1. A company uses waterproof paper to make disposable conical drinking cups. To make each cup, a sector *AOB* is cut from a circular piece of paper of radius 9 cm. The edges *AO* and *OB* are then joined to form the cup, as shown.

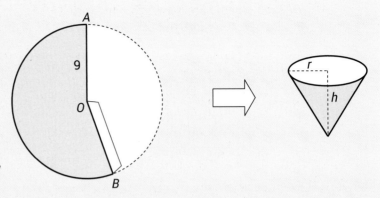

The radius of the rim of the cup is *r*, and the height of the cup is *h*.

(a) By expressing r^2 in terms of *h*, show that the capacity of the cup, in cm^3, is given by the formula:

$$V = \frac{\pi}{3}h(81 - h^2)$$

(b) There are two positive values of *h* for which the capacity of the cup is $\frac{154\pi}{3}$.

One of these values is an integer.

Find the two values.

Give the non-integer value correct to two decimal places.

SEC Project Maths Leaving Certificate Higher Level, Paper 1, 2012

2. A company has to design a rectangular box for a new range of jellybeans. The box is to be assembled from a single piece of cardboard, cut from a rectangular sheet measuring 31 cm by 22 cm. The box is to have a capacity (volume) of 500 cm^3.

The net for the box is shown on the right. The company is going to use the full length and width of the rectangular piece of cardboard.

The shaded areas are flaps of width 1 cm, which are needed for assembly. The height of the box is *h* cm, as shown on the diagram.

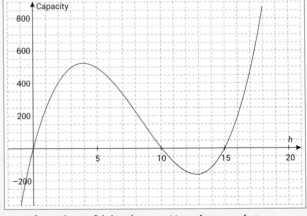

(a) Write the dimensions of the box, in centimetres, in terms of *h*.

(b) Write an expression for the capacity of the box in cubic centimetres, in terms of *h*.

(c) Show that the value of *h* that gives a box with a square bottom will give the correct capacity.

(d) Find, correct to one decimal place, the other value of *h* that gives a box of the correct capacity.

(e) The client is planning a special '10% extra free' promotion and needs to increase the capacity of the box by 10%. The company is checking whether they can make this new box from a piece of cardboard the same size as the original one (31 cm × 22 cm). A graph of the box's capacity as a function of *h* is shown. Use the graph to explain why it is not possible to make the larger box from such a piece of cardboard.

SEC Leaving Certificate Higher Level, Sample Paper 1, 2011

Solutions and chapter summary available online

05

Real Numbers

In this chapter you will learn:

- To consolidate your understanding of factors, multiples and prime numbers in N
- To express natural numbers in terms of their prime factors
- About operating on the set of integers, Z and the set of rationals, Q
- To recognise irrational numbers, $R\backslash Q$

- To prove by contradiction that $\sqrt{2}$ is not rational
- To geometrically construct $\sqrt{2}$ and $\sqrt{3}$
- About rounding and significant figures
- About scientific notation and orders of magnitude

You should remember...

- How to graph whole numbers on the number line
- Working with number systems for Junior Certificate

Key words

- Factor
- Multiple
- Prime factor
- Proof by contradiction

- Natural number
- Integer
- Rational number
- Irrational number

- Real number
- Order of magnitude
- Scientific notation

5.1 Introduction

The **real numbers** can be thought of as the set of all numbers that lie along an infinitely long number line.

$$\longleftarrow \overset{\mid}{-8} \ \overset{\mid}{-7} \ \overset{\mid}{-6} \ \overset{\mid}{-5} \ \overset{\mid}{-4} \ \overset{\mid}{-3} \ \overset{\mid}{-2} \ \overset{\mid}{-1} \ \overset{\mid}{0} \ \overset{\mid}{1} \ \overset{\mid}{2} \ \overset{\mid}{3} \ \overset{\mid}{4} \ \overset{\mid}{5} \ \overset{\mid}{6} \ \overset{\mid}{7} \ \overset{\mid}{8} \longrightarrow$$

This is not a very rigorous definition of the **real numbers**. However, it will serve our purposes. The discovery of a proper rigorous definition of the real numbers was one of the most important developments in the mathematics of the nineteenth century. The main contributors to the field were a French mathematician, Augustin-Louis Cauchy (1789–1857), and two German mathematicians, Richard Dedekind (1831–1916) and Karl Weierstrass (1815–1897).

Augustin-Louis
Cauchy (1789–1857)

Richard Dedekind
(1831–1916)

Karl Weierstrass
(1815–1897)

The natural numbers, the integers, the rational numbers and the irrational numbers are all subsets of the real number system. We will learn about these number systems during the course of this chapter.

5.2 Factors, Multiples and Prime Factors

Natural Numbers

The **natural numbers** are the ordinary counting numbers. The set of natural numbers is an infinite set. This means that the set is never-ending. The letter N is used to label the set of natural numbers.

$N = \{1, 2, 3, 4...\}$

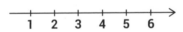

Factors

For example, all the **factors** of 24 are $\{1, 2, 3, 4, 6, 8, 12, 24\}$.

As you can see, 1 is a factor of 24 and 24 is a factor of 24.

> A **factor** of a natural number is any natural number that divides evenly into the given number.

- 1 is a factor of every natural number.
- Every natural number is a factor of itself.
- A factor divides evenly into a number leaving zero remainder.

Multiples

The **multiples** of a natural number are its products with the natural numbers.

For example, the multiples of 6 are $\{6(1), 6(2), 6(3), ...\} = \{6, 12, 18, ...\}$.

As you can see, the set of multiples is an infinite set, i.e. it goes on forever.

> A **multiple** of a natural number is itself a natural number, into which the natural number divides, leaving no remainder.

Prime Numbers

- 7 is a **prime number** as it has two factors only: 1 and 7.
- 2 is the only even prime number. Its two factors are 1 and 2.

> **Prime numbers** are natural numbers that have exactly **two** factors.

- 11 is the first two-figure prime. Its two factors are 1 and 11.
- 1 is **not** a prime as it has one factor only, itself.
- 0 is **not** a prime as it is not a natural number.
- There are infinitely many primes. The largest one currently known is $2^{57,885,161} - 1$.
- Natural numbers greater than 1 that are not prime are called composite numbers.

> A composite number is a natural number with more than two factors.

The Fundamental Theorem of Arithmetic

> Every natural number greater than 1 is either prime or can be written as a unique product of primes.

The **Fundamental Theorem of Arithmetic** is an important result that shows that the primes are the building blocks of the natural numbers. For example, $12 = 2^2 \times 3$. Apart from rearranging the order of multiplication, there is no other prime factorisation of 12.

Highest Common Factor

> The highest common factor (HCF) of two natural numbers, n_1 and n_2, is the largest natural number that divides evenly into both n_1 and n_2.

The **highest common factor** of 12 and 20 is 4, as 4 is the largest natural number that divides evenly into both 12 and 20. Numbers that do not share any common factor other than 1 are said to be relatively prime. For example, 15 and 28 are relatively prime.

Lowest Common Multiple

> The lowest common multiple (LCM) of two numbers is the smallest multiple that both numbers share.

The **lowest common multiple** of 3 and 4 is 12, as 12 is the smallest number that both 3 and 4 divide evenly into.

Worked Example 5.1

Express 240 as a product of prime numbers.

Solution

Start with the lowest prime that is a factor.

2	240
2	120
2	60
2	30
3	15
5	5
	1

$240 = 2 \times 2 \times 2 \times 2 \times 3 \times 5$

$\therefore 240 = 2^4 \times 3 \times 5$

Worked Example 5.2

Find (i) the HCF and (ii) the LCM of 512 and 280.

Solution

Express both numbers as a product of primes.

2	512
2	256
2	128
2	64
2	32
2	16
2	8
2	4
2	2
	1

2	280
2	140
2	70
5	35
7	7
	1

$512 = 2^9$ and $280 = 2^3 \times 5 \times 7$

We can use a Venn diagram to help calculate the HCF and LCM.

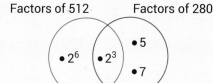

Factors of 512   Factors of 280

(i) HCF: Intersection of the sets: $2^3 = 8$

(ii) LCM: Union of the sets: $2^6 \times 2^3 \times 5 \times 7 = 17{,}920$

Worked Example 5.3

Two cylindrical tanks contain 850 litres and 680 litres of oil respectively.

Find the maximum capacity of a container that can measure the amount of oil in both tanks when used an exact number of times.

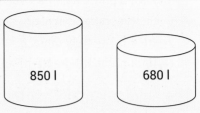

850 l   680 l

Solution

We need the largest possible container that can divide the oil in both containers exactly.

Thus we need to find the HCF of 850 and 680.

2	850
5	425
5	85
17	17
	1

2	680
2	340
2	170
5	85
17	17
	1

$850 = 2 \times 5^2 \times 17$

$680 = 2^3 \times 5 \times 17$

$\text{HCF} = 2 \times 5 \times 17$

$\quad = 170$

The capacity of the largest possible container is 170 litres.

Factors of 850   Factors of 680

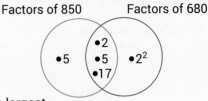

The capacity of the largest possible container is 170 litres.

Let n be a natural number. Then $n!$, read as n factorial, is the product of the natural numbers 1, 2, 3 ... n. Factorials and their applications are dealt with in more detail in Book 2, Chapter 2 in 2.1 The Fundamental Principle of Counting.

Worked Example 5.4

(i) Evaluate $5!$ and $5 \times 4!$ (ii) By considering the sequence $5!$, $4!$, $3!$, etc., calculate the value of $0!$

Solution

(i) $5! = 5 \times 4 \times 3 \times 2 \times 1$

$\therefore 5! = 120$

$5 \times 4! = 5 \times (4 \times 3 \times 2 \times 1)$

$\quad = 120$

(ii) $5! = 120$

$\left.\vphantom{\begin{array}{c}a\\b\end{array}}\right\}$ $120 \div 24 = 5$

$4! = 24$

$\left.\vphantom{\begin{array}{c}a\\b\end{array}}\right\}$ $24 \div 6 = 4$

$3! = 6$

$\left.\vphantom{\begin{array}{c}a\\b\end{array}}\right\}$ $6 \div 2 = 3$

$2! = 2$

$\left.\vphantom{\begin{array}{c}a\\b\end{array}}\right\}$ $2 \div 1 = 2$

$1! = 1$

$\left.\vphantom{\begin{array}{c}a\\b\end{array}}\right\}$ $1 \div x = ①$ ← to continue the pattern

$0! = x$

$\Rightarrow \dfrac{1}{x} = 1$

$x = 1$

$\therefore 0!$ is defined as being $= 1$.

Worked Example 5.5

Show that if p is a prime number and p divides evenly into r^2, then p divides evenly into r.

Solution

Let $r = r_1^{\alpha_1} r_2^{\alpha_2} r_3^{\alpha_3} \ldots r_n^{\alpha_n}$, where each r_i is prime and each $\alpha_i \in N$.

Therefore, using the rules of indices: $r^2 = (r_1^{\alpha_1} r_2^{\alpha_2} r_3^{\alpha_3} \ldots r_n^{\alpha_n})^2$

$\qquad\qquad = r_1^{2\alpha_1} r_2^{2\alpha_2} r_3^{2\alpha_3} \ldots r_n^{2\alpha_n}$

If $p \mid r^2$ (p divides r^2), then $p \mid$ one of $r_i^{2\alpha_i}$.

Since each r_i is prime, $\Rightarrow p \mid$ one of r_i.

Hence, p divides $r_1^{\alpha_1} r_2^{\alpha_2} r_3^{\alpha_3} \ldots r_n^{\alpha_n} = r$.

For example, the prime 3 divides $6^2 = 36$, therefore 3 divides 6. Of course, the result need not hold for non-prime divisors. For example, 12 divides $6^2 = 36$, but 12 does not divide 6.

Exercise 5.1

1. Express each of the following numbers as a product of prime factors:

   (i) 160   (iv) 1,155   (vii) 102

   (ii) 273   (v) 1,870   (viii) 1,224

   (iii) 128   (vi) 10,500   (ix) 38,016

2. (a) Express each number within the following sets of numbers as a product of prime factors.

   (b) Hence, find the LCM and HCF for each set of numbers.

     (i) 102 and 170   (vi) 123 and 615

     (ii) 117 and 130   (vii) 69 and 123

     (iii) 368 and 621   (viii) 20, 30 and 60

     (iv) 58 and 174   (ix) 8, 10 and 20

     (v) 60 and 765   (x) 294, 252 and 210

3. Kate has two pieces of material. One piece is 72 cm wide and the other piece is 90 cm wide. She wants to cut both pieces into strips of equal width that are as wide as possible.

   How wide should she cut the strips?

4. Tom exercises every 14 days and Katie every nine days. Tom and Katie both exercised on March 12. On what date will they both exercise together again?

5. Ms Hoover has 160 crayons and 30 colouring books to give to her students. If each student gets an equal number of crayons and an equal number of colouring books, what is the largest number of students she can have in her class?

6. Bart is making a board game with dimensions of 16 cm by 25 cm. He wants to use square tiles. What are the dimensions of the largest tile he can use?

7. Beginning on Monday of each week and running until Friday, *The Breakfast Show* gives away €100 to every 100th caller who gets through to the show. During the week before a Saturday night concert, the show offers two free tickets to the concert for every 70th caller. How many callers must get through before one wins the tickets and the €100?

8. Let n be a natural number. What is the HCF of:

   (i) n and $2n$ (ii) n and n^2

9. If 3 divides $334{,}611^2$, explain why 3 must also divide 334,611.

10. Let n be a natural number. Define the function $F(n)$ as follows:

$$F(n) = \frac{n}{2} \quad \text{if } n \text{ is even.}$$

$$F(n) = \frac{3n + 1}{2} \text{ if } n \text{ is odd.}$$

   (i) Find F(1) and F(2).

   (ii) Explain why $F(n)$ is always a natural number.

   (iii) Consider the sequence:

     $n, F(n), F(F(n)), F(F(F(n)))$ ....

     Construct the first 15 terms of the sequence for each of the following values of n:

     6, 10, 15, 32 and 17.

     Note: If $F(n) = p$, then $F(F(n)) = F(p)$.

   (iv) Based on your results make a conjecture about the sequence.

   (v) Test your conjecture for $n = 39$.

> A conjecture is a statement that is likely to be true, but has not been formally proved.

11. Let u be any natural number with prime factorisation $u = u_1{}^{\phi_1} u_2{}^{\phi_2} u_3{}^{\phi_3} \dots u_n{}^{\phi_n}$.

   (The ϕs are natural numbers.)

   (i) Explain why none of the primes $u_1, u_2, u_3, \dots u_n$ divide $u + 1$.

   (ii) Hence, write down the HCF of u and $u + 1$.

   (iii) If u is even, then find the HCF of u and $u + 2$.

   (iv) If u is odd, then what is the HCF of u and $u + 2$?

12. Consider the finite sequence:

   $10! + 2, 10! + 3, 10! + 4, \dots, 10! + 9, 10! + 10$

   (i) How many terms are in the sequence?

   (ii) Explain why none of the terms are prime.

   (iii) Construct a sequence of 20 consecutive natural numbers, none of which are prime.

   (iv) Is it possible to have a set of consecutive natural numbers of any given size that does not contain any prime numbers? Explain.

13. When $2^n - 1$ is a prime number ($n \in N$), it is called a Mersenne prime. Furthermore, if $2^n - 1$ is prime, then so too is n. List the first four Mersenne primes.

14. Find the smallest positive natural number whose product with 2016 is a square number.

5.3 Integers and Rational Numbers

The integers are made up of zero and all the positive and negative whole numbers. Mathematicians use the letter Z to represent the set of integers.

$$Z = \{... -6, -5, -4, -3, -2, -1, 0, 1, 2, 3, 4, 5, 6, 7...\}$$

Note how the set of natural numbers is a proper subset of the set of integers.

Properties of Integers

Let a, b, c be arbitrary (any) integers.

- $a + b$ and $a \times b$ are integers whenever a and b are integers. (Closure property)
- $a + b = b + a$ and $a \times b = b \times a$ (Commutative properties)
- $(a + b) + c = a + (b + c)$ and $(a \times b) \times c = a \times (b \times c)$ (Associative properties)
- $a \times (b + c) = (a \times b) + (a \times c)$ (Distributive property)
- $a + 0 = a$ and $a \times 1 = a$. (Identity elements)
- For every integer a, there exists an integer $-a$, such that $a + (-a) = 0$. We say $-a$ is the additive inverse of a. (Additive inverse)

Rational Numbers

Any number that can be expressed as a ratio of integers is known as a rational number. More formally, a rational number is any number that can be written as $\frac{p}{q}$, where $p, q \in Z$, $q \neq 0$. We use the letter Q to represent the set of rational numbers.

What properties do rational numbers have?

$Q = \{x \mid x = \frac{p}{q}, p, q \in Z, q \neq 0\}$ is the set of rational numbers.

- When written as a decimal, a rational number will either terminate ($\frac{1}{2} = 0.5$, $\frac{126}{1000} = 0.126$, etc.) or recur ($\frac{1}{3} = 0.\dot{3}$, $\frac{2}{7} = 0.\dot{2}8571\dot{4}$).
- Rational numbers are often referred to as fractions.
- The properties outlined for the integers above also apply to the rationals.
- There is an infinite number of rational numbers.
- All integers are rational numbers.
- If $\frac{p}{q}$ is a rational number, and $p \neq 0$, then $\frac{q}{p}$ is its reciprocal. (Multiplicative inverse)

Worked Example 5.6

(i) Find the sum of the squares of the four consecutive integers, $-2, -1, 0$ and 1.

(ii) Show that the sum of the squares of any four consecutive integers is always an even number.

Solution

(i) $(-2)^2 + (-1)^2 + (0)^2 + (1)^2 = 4 + 1 + 0 + 1$

$$= 6$$

(ii) $n, n + 1, n + 2,$ and $n + 3, n \in Z$, are four consecutive integers.

$$\therefore (n)^2 + (n + 1)^2 + (n + 2)^2 + (n + 3)^2 = n^2 + n^2 + 2n + 1 + n^2 + 4n + 4 + n^2 + 6n + 9$$

$$= 4n^2 + 12n + 14$$

$$= 2(2n^2 + 6n + 7) \quad \text{(This must be an even number, as 2 is a factor.)}$$

$\therefore$ The sum of any four consecutive integers is an even number.

Exercise 5.2

1. Evaluate each of the following:

   (i) $-8 - 5 + 13$ (iii) $(-5)(-8)$

   (ii) $(2)(-3)$ (iv) $3(4)^2 + 2(4) - 56$

2. Evaluate each of the following, leaving your answers in their simplest form:

   (i) $\dfrac{14}{15} \times \dfrac{3}{8}$ (v) $\dfrac{2}{3} + \dfrac{5}{6}$

   (ii) $2\dfrac{1}{2} \times 5$ (vi) $\dfrac{1\frac{3}{4} \times 1\frac{2}{3} + \frac{2}{3} \times \frac{5}{6}}{7\frac{1}{2} - 4}$

   (iii) $1\dfrac{3}{4} \times 1\dfrac{2}{3}$ (vii) $\dfrac{8.4(19.6 - 12.2)^2}{(14.4 - 12.2)^3}$

   (iv) $\dfrac{1}{2} - \dfrac{1}{8}$ (viii) $3(2.5 - 1.2)^2$

3. A rectangle has a length of $\dfrac{3}{5}$ units and an area of $\dfrac{1}{3}$ units². What is the width of the rectangle?

4. A triangle has a base length of $\dfrac{3}{4}$ units and an area of $\dfrac{3}{20}$ units². What is the height of the triangle?

5. Three cans of juice fill $\dfrac{2}{3}$ of a 1 litre jug. How many cans of juice are needed to fill eight 1 litre jugs completely?

6. A box contains oranges and grapes. An equal number of the oranges and grapes are rotten. $\dfrac{2}{3}$ of all the oranges are rotten and $\dfrac{3}{4}$ of all the grapes are rotten. What fraction of the total number of pieces of fruit in the box are rotten?

7. Alice and Bob share an allotment. The ratio of the area of Alice's portion to the area of Bob's portion is 3:2. They each grow vegetables and fruit on the allotment. The entire allotment is covered by vegetables and fruit in the ratio 7:3. On Alice's portion of the allotment, the ratio of vegetables to fruit is 4:1. What is the ratio of vegetables to fruit in Bob's portion?

8. In the diagram, the number line is marked at consecutive integers, but the numbers themselves are not shown. The four red dots represent two numbers that are multiples of 3 and two numbers that are multiples of 5. Which of the black dots represents a number that is a multiple of 15? Give an explanation for your choice.

9. a, b, c, d are non-zero integers. Explain why $\dfrac{a}{b} + \dfrac{c}{d}$ is rational.

10. The rectangle shown has dimensions x and y, where x and y are both integers.
    Copy and complete the table shown below.

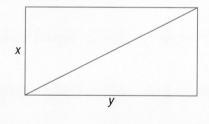

Statement	Always True	Always False	Sometimes True (Give an example)
The rectangle's area is an integer value.			
The rectangle's perimeter is rational.			
The rectangle's diagonal length is an integer value.			

REAL NUMBERS

11. Five square tiles are shown. Each tile has a side of integer length. The side lengths can be arranged as consecutive integers. The sum of the areas of the five squares is 1,815 units^2.

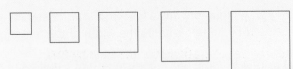

    (i) Show that the sum of the squares of five consecutive integers is divisible by 5.

    (ii) Find the dimensions of the largest square.

12. Seán has a pile of tiles, each measuring 1 cm by 1 cm. He tries to put these small tiles together to form a larger square of length n cm, but finds that he has 92 tiles left over. If he had increased the side length to $(n + 2)$ cm, then he would have been 100 tiles short. How many tiles does Seán have?

13. A palindromic number is a positive integer that is the same when read forwards or backwards. For example, 31213 and 1237321 are palindromic numbers.

    (i) Find the total number of three-figure palindromic numbers.

    (ii) Determine the total number of palindromic numbers between 10^6 and 10^7.

    (iii) If the palindromic numbers in part (ii) are written in order, find the 2,125th number on the list.

14. The integers from 1 to 9 are listed on a whiteboard. If an additional m 8s and n 9s are added to the list, then the mean of all the numbers is 7.3. Find $m + n$.

5.4 Irrational Numbers

In the right-angled triangle shown, the value for x can be found using the theorem of Pythagoras. Here is the solution:

$$x^2 = 1^2 + 1^2$$
$$x^2 = 1 + 1$$
$$x^2 = 2$$
$$x = \sqrt{2} \quad \text{(as } x > 0\text{)}$$

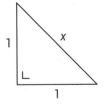

Can $\sqrt{2}$ be written as a ratio of integers? This problem preoccupied the ancient Greek mathematicians for many years. Around 500 BC, Hippasus, a follower of Pythagoras, proved that $\sqrt{2}$ could not be written as a fraction. Pythagoras, who believed that all numbers were rational, was so enraged by this proof that he supposedly had Hippasus thrown overboard from a ship and Hippasus subsequently drowned.

Numbers that cannot be written as fractions are called **irrational numbers**. $\sqrt{2}$ was the first known irrational number.

Hippasus, a follower of Pythagoras

An **irrational number** is a number that cannot be written in the form $\frac{a}{b}$, where a is an integer and b is a non-zero integer, i.e. an irrational number is a number that cannot be written as a ratio of integers.

While $\sqrt{2}$ cannot be written as a fraction, it is possible to find an approximation for $\sqrt{2}$. A calculator gives the approximation $\sqrt{2} = 1.414213562$, but this decimal in fact goes on forever with no pattern or repetition.

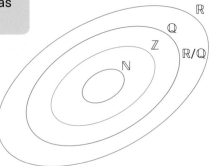

The same is true for any irrational number: when written as a decimal, the decimal is non-terminating and non-recurring.

> The rational numbers together with the irrational numbers make up the Real Number System.

Since every real number is either rational (Q) or irrational, the set of irrationals is denoted by $R\backslash Q$.

Proof by Contradiction

In mathematics, proof by contradiction is a form of proof that establishes the truth of a proposition by showing that the proposition being false would imply a contradiction.

Worked Example 5.7

Prove by contradiction that the set N of natural numbers is infinite.

Proof: By way of contradiction, assume that the set N of natural numbers is finite. So one of the elements of the set N, say l, must be the largest element, as N is non-empty.

Now sum all the elements in this finite set, to get another natural number x (closure property of the natural numbers ensures that x is a natural number).

So we now have a natural number x that has to be greater than l, the largest element of N.

This is a contradiction as, if N is finite, no natural number can be greater than l. Therefore, the set N is infinite.

Proof that $\sqrt{2}$ is Irrational (Examinable Proof)

To prove: $\sqrt{2}$ is irrational.

The proof of this result is another example of proof by contradiction.

Proof: Assume that $\sqrt{2}$ is rational and can therefore be written in the form $\frac{a}{b}$, $a, b \in Z$, $b \neq 0$.

Also, the fraction $\frac{a}{b}$ is written in simplest terms, i.e. HCF$(a, b) = 1$.

$$\sqrt{2} = \frac{a}{b}$$

$$\Rightarrow 2 = \frac{a^2}{b^2} \quad \text{(squaring both sides)}$$

$$\therefore a^2 = 2b^2 \qquad\qquad (*)$$

As b^2 is an integer, a^2 has to be even, which means that 2 divides a^2.

If 2 divides a^2, then 2 divides a. (See Worked Example 5.5.)

$\therefore a = 2k$, for some integer k. Substituting $2k$ for a in (*) gives:

$$(2k)^2 = 2b^2$$

$$4k^2 = 2b^2$$

$$\therefore b^2 = 2k^2$$

As k^2 is an integer, b^2 has to be even, which means that 2 divides b^2.

Therefore, 2 divides b. If 2 divides a and 2 divides b, then this contradicts the assumption that HCF$(a, b) = 1$. This completes the proof.

Constructing √2 and √3 (Examinable Constructions)

√2 and √3 cannot be written as fractions, but can be constructed.

Construct √2

1. Let the line segment [AB] be of length 1 unit.

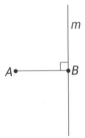

2. Construct a line *m* perpendicular to [AB] at B.

2. Construct a circle with centre A and radius length |AB|.

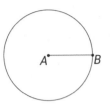

3. Construct a circle with centre B and radius length |AB| and mark the intersection, C, of the circle and *m*.

3. Construct a circle with centre B and radius length |AB|.

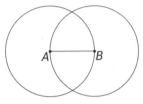

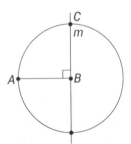

4. Mark the intersection of the two circles as C and D.

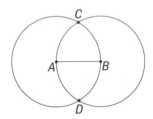

4. Draw the line segment [AC]. |AC| = √2 units

5. Draw the line segment [CD]. |CD| = √3 units

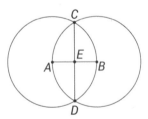

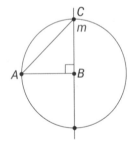

Proof: [CD] and [AB] are perpendicular bisectors of each other. (Method of construction)

$$\therefore |AE| = \frac{1}{2}|AB| = \frac{1}{2}$$

$|AC| = 1$ (Construction)

$|AE|^2 + |EC|^2 = |AC|^2$ (Theorem of Pythagoras)

$$\left(\frac{1}{2}\right)^2 + |EC|^2 = 1^2$$

$$|EC|^2 = 1 - \frac{1}{4} = \frac{3}{4}$$

$$\therefore |EC| = \sqrt{\frac{3}{4}} = \frac{\sqrt{3}}{2}$$

$$|CD| = 2|EC| = 2\left(\frac{\sqrt{3}}{2}\right)$$

$$\therefore |CD| = \sqrt{3}$$

Proof: |AB| = |BC| = 1   (radii of circle)

$|AB|^2 + |BC|^2 = |AC|^2$ (Theorem of Pythagoras)

$1^2 + 1^2 = |AC|^2$

$|AC|^2 = 2$

$\therefore |AC| = \sqrt{2}$

Construct √3

1. Let the line segment [AB] be of length 1 unit.

Exercise 5.3

1. Prove by contradiction that $\sqrt{2}$ is irrational.

2. p and q are two prime numbers and $p \neq q$.

   (i) If 3 divides p evenly, then what is p?

   (ii) If 5 divides p evenly, then what is p?

   (iii) If 3 divides pq evenly, then what can you say about p and q?

   (iv) If 3 divides a^2 evenly and $a^2 = (pq)^2$, then explain why 3 divides a evenly.

3. Prove by contradiction that $\sqrt{3}$ is irrational.

4. Prove by contradiction that $\sqrt{5}$ is irrational.

5. Prove by contradiction that $\sqrt{7}$ is irrational.

6. Prove by contradiction that $\sqrt{11}$ is irrational.

7. (a) Complete the following sentences.

   (i) The sum of two integers is an _____.

   (ii) The difference of two integers is an _____.

   (iii) The product of two integers is an _____.

   (iv) The ratio of two integers is a r_____   n_____.

   (b) $x = \dfrac{a}{b}$ and $y = \dfrac{c}{d}$, where $a, b, c, d \in Z$, $b, d \neq 0$.

   (i) Simplify $\dfrac{a}{b} - \dfrac{c}{d}$.

   (ii) Hence show that the difference of two rational numbers is a rational number.

   (c) Prove by contradiction that the sum of a rational number and an irrational number is an irrational number. (Hint: Begin by assuming that $\dfrac{a}{b} + x = \dfrac{c}{d}$, where $a, b, c, d \in Z$ and x is irrational, then derive a contradiction.)

8. Show that $x = \sqrt{3 + 2\sqrt{2}} - \sqrt{3 - 2\sqrt{2}}$ is a rational number. (Hint: Find x^2.)

9. Construct $\sqrt{2}$ and $\sqrt{3}$.

REAL NUMBERS

5.5 Rounding and Significant Figures

Rounding to Decimal Places

In geometry, the number of times the diameter of a circle divides into the circumference is called π. We normally substitute 3.14 for π in these calculations. However, 3.14 is just an approximation.

- There are infinitely many decimal places in π.
- π is 3.141592654 to nine decimal places.
- For simplicity, we often write π as 3.14, i.e. to two decimal places.
- Engineers use 3.1416 as an approximation for π.

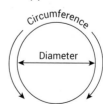

Worked Example 5.8

Write the following correct to one decimal place:

(i) 2.57   (ii) 39.32

Solution

(i) 2.57

When rounding to **one decimal place**, we look at the **second number after the decimal point**. If this number is 5 or greater, we will round up. With 2.57, as 7 is the second number after the decimal point, we round up to 2.6.

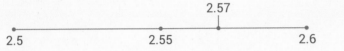

2.5   2.55   2.6   Answer = 2.6

(ii) 39.32

Here, the second number after the decimal point is 2, which is less than 5. Therefore, the number rounded to one decimal place is 39.3.

39.32

39.3   39.35   39.4   Answer = 39.3

Significant Figures

We do not always need detailed answers to problems. Sometimes an approximation is sufficient. One method of approximating answers is to round off using significant figures.

With the number 473,258, the 4 is the most significant figure, because it tells us that the number is 4 hundred thousand and something. It follows that the 7 is the next most significant and so on.

Worked Example 5.9

Correct the following numbers to two significant figures:

(i) 3.67765   (ii) 61,343   (iii) 0.00356

Solution

(i) 3.67765

The **first significant figure** in a number is the **first non-zero figure in the number**. In this number, 3 is the first significant figure in the number. It tells us the number is 3 units and something. We need to correct to two significant figures, so we look at the third significant figure. If this number is 5 or greater, we round up the second figure. The third figure is 7, so the corrected number is 3.7.

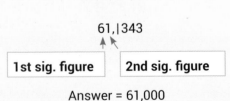

Answer = 3.7

(ii) 61,343

Here, the third figure is 3, which is less than 5. Therefore, the rounded number is 61,000.

Note that all other figures after the rounded figure change to zero.

Answer = 61,000

REAL NUMBERS

(iii) 0.00356

The first significant figure here is 3, telling us that the number is 3 thousandths and something.

The third significant figure is 6. Therefore, the rounded number is 0.0036.

0.0035|6

1st sig. figure   2nd sig. figure

Answer = 0.0036

- Leading zeros are not significant figures. For example, 0.0053 has two significant figures, 5 and 3.
- Zeros that appear between two non-zero figures **are** significant. For example, 503.25 has five significant figures.

5.6 Orders of Magnitude and Scientific Notation

When doing calculations, scientists often use very large numbers or very small numbers. For example, the speed of light is about 300,000,000 metres per second, whilst the radius of a hydrogen atom is 0.0000000000529 metres.

Very large or very small numbers can be awkward to write down. So, scientists use **scientific notation** to write down these numbers.

A positive number written in scientific notation is of the form $a \times 10^n$, where $1 \leqslant a < 10$ and $n \in Z$.

Another name for scientific notation is **standard form**.

Worked Example 5.10

Write the following numbers in scientific notation:

(i) 725,000,000,000   (ii) 980,000   (iii) 0.0000056   (iv) 0.000000034

Solution

(i) First, note that dividing a number by 10^n, where $n \in N$, moves the decimal point n places to the left.

For example, $\dfrac{144.25}{10^2} = 1.4425$ (Decimal point moves two places to the left)

$$725{,}000{,}000{,}000 = \frac{725{,}000{,}000{,}000}{10^{11}} \times 10^{11} = 7.25 \times 10^{11}$$

(ii) $980{,}000 = \dfrac{980{,}000}{10^5} \times 10^5 = 9.8 \times 10^5$

(iii) Note that dividing a number by 10^n, where n is a negative integer, moves the decimal point $-n$ places to the right.

For example, $\dfrac{0.00146}{10^{-3}} = 0.00146 \times \dfrac{1}{10^{-3}}$

$$= 0.00146 \times 10^3 \quad \text{(Rules of indices)}$$

$$= 1.46 \quad \text{(Decimal point moves three places to the right)}$$

$$0.0000056 = \frac{0.0000056}{10^{-6}} \times 10^{-6}$$

$$= 5.6 \times 10^{-6}$$

(iv) $0.000000034 = \dfrac{0.000000034}{10^{-8}} \times 10^{-8}$

$$= 3.4 \times 10^{-8}$$

REAL NUMBERS

When calculating the order of magnitude of a number, write the number in the form $a \times 10^n$, $1 \leqslant a < 10$. If $a < 10^{\frac{1}{2}}$ then the number has order of magnitude n, otherwise the number has order of magnitude $n + 1$.

Worked Example 5.11

Calculate the order of magnitude of (i) 345,632 and (ii) 567,123,923.

By how many orders of magnitude do these numbers differ?

Solution

(i) $345,632 = 3.45632 \times 10^5$

$3.45632 > 10^{\frac{1}{2}}$

∴ The order of magnitude is 6.

(ii) $567,123,923 = 5.67123923 \times 10^8$

$5.67123923 > 10^{\frac{1}{2}}$

∴ The order of magnitude is 9.

$\dfrac{567,123,923}{345,632} \approx 1.641 \times 10^3$

$1.641 < 10^{\frac{1}{2}}$

∴ The two numbers differ by 3 orders of magnitude.

Exercise 5.4

1. Write these numbers correct to three decimal places:

   (i) 5.1456
   (ii) 7.2983
   (iii) 17.8943
   (iv) 62.1235321
   (v) 23.7654
   (vi) 0.07893

2. (a) Write these numbers correct to two significant figures:

   (i) 0.00985
   (ii) 0.00234
   (iii) 0.0125
   (iv) 0.000849
   (v) 0.238
   (vi) 52.00285

   (b) Write these numbers correct to one significant figure:

   (i) 32.14
   (ii) 3.857
   (iii) 19,345
   (iv) 1,698
   (v) 5,965
   (vi) 999

3. Write these numbers in scientific notation:

   (i) 34,000,000
   (ii) 0.25
   (iii) 4,570
   (iv) 0.000032
   (v) 5,000,000
   (vi) 0.6464

4. Write these as decimal numbers:

   (i) 2.65×10^2
   (ii) 4.53×10^{-3}
   (iii) 7.2×10^6
   (iv) 4×10^{-2}
   (v) 2.64×10^7
   (vi) 7.612×10^3

5. Calculate each of the following, giving your answers as decimal numbers:

   (i) $3.4 \times 10^3 + 2.8 \times 10^3$
   (ii) $5.2 \times 10^9 + 3.5 \times 10^9$

6. The following numbers are written in scientific notation. Rewrite the numbers in ordinary form.

   (i) 2×10^6
   (ii) 1.69×10^4
   (iii) 2.48×10^3
   (iv) 6.47×10^5
   (v) 6.12×10^1
   (vi) 9.43×10^5

7. The following numbers are written in scientific notation. Rewrite the numbers in ordinary form.

   (i) 1.5×10^{-3}
   (ii) 2.54×10^{-4}
   (iii) 3.5×10^{-5}
   (iv) 6.67×10^{-6}

8. By how many orders of magnitude do the following numbers differ?

   (i) 868,932,145 and 284
   (ii) 453,987,312 and 3,548
   (iii) 767,894,567,000 and 23,000,000
   (iv) 0.1 and 0.00042
   (v) 1.8 and 234

Revision Exercises

1. The German mathematician Christian Goldbach conjectured that every odd positive integer greater than 5 is the sum of three primes. Verify this conjecture for each of the following odd integers:

   (i) 11   (ii) 33   (iii) 97   (iv) 17   (v) 199

2. Two bikers are riding on a circular path. The first rider completes a circuit in 12 minutes. The second rider completes a circuit in 18 minutes. They both started at the same place and at the same time and go in the same direction. After how many minutes will they meet again at the starting point?

3. Express each of the following numbers as the product of prime factors, and hence, find the LCM and HCF of each pair:

   (i) 68 and 102   (iii) 104 and 351

   (ii) 69 and 123   (iv) 123 and 615

4. (a) What fraction when added to $\frac{1}{4}$ gives $\frac{1}{3}$?

   (b) A mathematician states that her children's ages are all prime numbers that multiply together to give 7,429. She also says that two of her children are teenagers.

      (i) How many children does she have?

      (ii) What are their ages?

5. Given a line segment of length 1 unit, show clearly how to construct a line segment of length $\sqrt{2}$ units.

6. Prove by contradiction that $\sqrt{2}$ is not rational.

7. Write the following numbers correct to two significant figures:

   (i) 852,233   (iii) 2.00062   (v) 652,494

   (ii) 0.134   (iv) 0.000054   (vi) 0.000814

8. Prove that $\sqrt{13}$ is irrational.

9. A palindromic number is a number that reads the same forwards and backwards. For example, 52,325 is a palindromic number. All four-figure palindromic numbers have 11 as a prime factor.

   (i) Find the prime factorisations of the palindromic numbers 2,332 and 6,776.

   (ii) Hence, find the HCF and LCM of 2,332 and 6,776.

   (iii) Prove that all four-figure palindromic numbers have 11 as a prime factor.

10. A man died, leaving some money to be divided among his children in the following manner:

    - €x to the first child plus $\frac{1}{16}$ of what remains.
    - €$2x$ to the second child plus $\frac{1}{16}$ of what then remains.
    - €$3x$ to the third child plus $\frac{1}{16}$ of what then remains and so on.

    When all the money was distributed, each child received the same amount of money and no money was left over.

    How many children did the man have?

11. The figures 1, 2, 3, 4 and 5 are each used once to create a five-figure number $vwxyz$, which satisfies the following conditions:

    - The three-figure number vwx is odd.
    - The three-figure number wxy is divisible by 5.
    - The three-figure number xyz is divisible by 3.

    Determine the six five-figure numbers that satisfy all three conditions.

Exam Questions

1. Three natural numbers a, b and c, such that $a^2 + b^2 = c^2$ is called a Pythagorean triple.

   (i) Let $a = 2n + 1$, $b = 2n^2 + 2n$ and $c = 2n^2 + 2n + 1$.

      Pick one natural number n and verify that the corresponding values of a, b and c form a Pythagorean triple.

   (ii) Prove that $a = 2n + 1$, $b = 2n^2 + 2n$ and $c = 2n^2 + 2n + 1$, where $n \in N$, will always form a Pythagorean triple.

      SEC Leaving Certificate
      Higher Level, Paper 1, 2014

2. Explain, with the aid of an example, what is meant by proof by contradiction.

   SEC Leaving Certificate
   Higher Level, Sample Paper 2, 2014

 Solutions and chapter summary available online

REAL NUMBERS

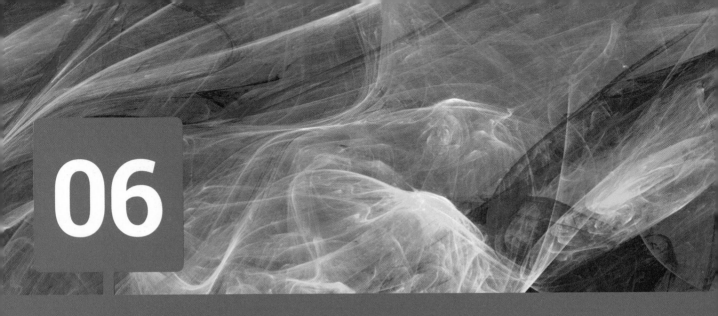

06

Functions

 In this chapter you will learn to:

- Recognise that a function assigns a unique output to a given input

- Form composite functions

- Graph functions of the form:
  - $ax + b$, where $a, b \in Q, x \in R$
  - $ax^2 + bx + c$, where $a, b, c \in Q, x \in R$
  - $ax^3 + bx^2 + cx + d$, where $a, b, c, d \in Z$, $x \in R$
  - ab^x, where $a, b \in R$

- Graph logarithmic functions

- Interpret equations of the form $f(x) = g(x)$ as a comparison of the above functions

- Use graphical methods to find approximate solutions to:
  - $f(x) = 0$
  - $f(x) = k$
  - $f(x) = g(x)$

  where $f(x)$ and $g(x)$ are of the stated form, or where graphs of $f(x)$ and $g(x)$ are provided

- Express quadratic functions in completed square form

- Use the completed square form to:
  - Find roots and turning points
  - Sketch the function

- Apply transformations to selected functions

- Recognise injective, surjective and bijective functions

- Find the inverse of a bijective function

- Sketch the inverse of a function given the function's graph

You should remember...

- Substitution in algebra
- Solving equations
- Number patterns
- Input–output tables
- Domain, codomain, range
- Linear, quadratic, cubic, exponential, logarithmic functions
- Turning points

Key words

- Relation
- Function
- Input
- Output
- Completing the square
- Turning points
- Transformation
- Mapping diagram
- Couples
- Ordered pairs
- Domain
- Codomain
- Range
- Composite function
- Injective ('one-to-one') function
- Surjective ('onto') function
- Bijective function
- Inverse function

6.1 Introduction

What is a Function?

A function is a rule that maps an input to a unique output.

Functions can be described as 'number machines' that transform one number into another. If we think of functions as machines, then something is put into the machine, something happens in the machine, and then something comes out of the machine.

Lowercase letters are used to name functions. f and g are often used, but remember any letter may be used to name/denote a function.

Functions in Everyday Life

You meet functions several times throughout your normal day.

Television remote controls are an example of functions at work. If you have programmed your television so that channel 103 is assigned to TV3 (for example), then when you key in 103 on your remote, TV3 appears on the television screen. Of course, you could also have TV3 pre-programmed for channel 104 (say), but you could not pre-programme two or more television stations for the same channel number. In other words, each input (channel number) is mapped to a unique output (television station).

Important Terms

- An input is an object that is put into the function.
- The domain is the set of all inputs for which a function is defined.
- An output is the object that comes out of the function.
- The range is the set of **actual** output values of a function.
- The codomain is the set of all **possible** output values of a function.

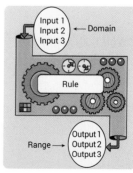

The following example illustrates the meanings of these terms.

Imagine a secondary school in which the Fifth Year classes are called 5.1, 5.2, 5.3 and 5.4. Each class is going on a class trip. They can choose from the following options:

cinema, ice-skating, go-karting, paint-balling or bowling

5.1 choose ice-skating, 5.2 choose go-karting, 5.3 choose ice-skating and 5.4 choose paint-balling. These choices can be represented by a function, as illustrated in the mapping diagram:

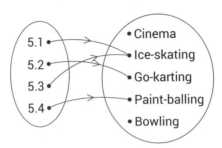

- 5.1 is an example of an input.
- Ice-skating is an example of an output.
- The domain is the set of all Fifth Year classes: {5.1, 5.2, 5.3, 5.4}.
- The range is the set of the three chosen activities: {ice-skating, go-karting, paint-balling}.
- The codomain is the set of all five trip options: {cinema, ice-skating, go-karting, paint-balling, bowling}.

Examples of Functions

Suppose you write $f(x) = x^2$. You have just defined a rule for a function f that transforms any number into its square.

Consider the following inputs to this function: {−1, 0, 1, 2}.

The resulting outputs can be computed using an input−output table:

Input (x)	Application of function (x²)	Output (y)
−1	$(-1)^2$	1
0	$(0)^2$	0
1	$(1)^2$	1
2	$(2)^2$	4

Here, y is the result of applying the rule (the function) to the input.

We can represent the rule for this function in a number of other ways.

Using function notation

$f(x) = x^2$

Pronounced 'f of x equals x-squared'.

OR

Using alternative function notation

$f: x \rightarrow x^2$

Pronounced 'f maps x to x^2'.

OR

As a set of couples/ordered pairs

$f = \{(-1,1), (0,0), (1,1), (2,4)\}$

For example, (2,4) tells us that if 2 is the input, then 4 is the output.

OR

Using a mapping diagram

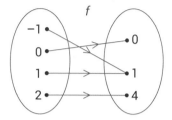

Points to Note: Inputs and Outputs

Look again at the function f defined as $f(x) = x^2$. You will note the following:

- An input can pass through the function and not change, i.e. the input 0 passes through the function and comes out as 0, giving the couple (0,0).
- Two inputs can result in the same output, i.e. the inputs −1 and 1 both result in the output 1.
- However, an input into a function will never result in two different outputs.

6.2 Functions as Mappings from One Set to Another

A function is a rule that maps an input from one set called the domain to a unique output in another set called the codomain. In dealing with functions, it is important to understand:

 (i) what set the inputs are coming from

(ii) what set the outputs are to be found in.

An understanding of the notation used in functions is needed.

Intervals for domain and codomain are very important when dealing with injective and surjective functions (see 6.9 Injective, Surjective and Bijective Functions).

Notation

N = Natural numbers

Z = Integers

Z^+ = Positive integers

R = Real numbers

R^+ = Positive real numbers

Q = Rational numbers

Q^+ = Positive rational numbers

Intervals

$[a, b] = \{x \in R \mid a \leqslant x \leqslant b\}$	This is a **closed interval**, which is denoted by square brackets.
	The a-value and b-value are included in this interval.
$(a, b) = \{x \in R \mid a < x < b\}$	This is an **open interval**, which is denoted by rounded brackets (also called parentheses).
	The a-value and b-value are not included in this interval.
$[a, b) = \{x \in R \mid a \leqslant x < b\}$	Here, the a-value is included but the b-value is not included in this interval.
$(a, b] = \{x \in R \mid a < x \leqslant b\}$	Here, the a-value is not included but the b-value is included in this interval.

Consider the functions below.

1. $f: N \to N: x \to 2x$	The domain is N. The codomain is N.
	For this particular function, the range consists of even natural numbers only. Odd natural numbers are not included in the range.
	Note that the codomain and the range can be different sets.
2. $f: R \to R: x \to x - x^2$	The domain is R. The codomain is R.
	For this particular function, the range is $(-\infty, 0.25]$.
3. $f: R \to R: x \to x^2$	The domain is R. The codomain is also R.
	For this particular function, the range is $[0, \infty)$.
	Zero is included, as $f(0) = 0$.
	Infinity is not included, as 'infinity' is not a finite number and so cannot be reached.
4. $f: R \to R^+: x \to e^x$	The domain is R. The codomain is R^+.
	For this particular function, the range is also R^+.
	For example: $f(-2) = e^{-2}$
	$= \dfrac{1}{e^2} > 0$
	For any x-value, $x \in R$, the output is a positive number.
	$\therefore$ The output is an element of R^+.

FUNCTIONS

Worked Example 6.1

$f: x \to 6x - n$ is a function.

(i) If $f(-2) = -23$, find the value of n.

(ii) Find the value of x for which $f(x + 3) = -29$.

Solution

(i) $f(-2) = 6(-2) - n$

$\quad\quad = -12 - n$

$\Rightarrow -12 - n = -23$

$\quad\quad - n = -23 + 12$

$\quad\quad - n = -11$

$\quad\quad \therefore n = 11$

(ii) From part (i): $n = 11$

$\quad\quad f(x) = 6x - 11$

$\Rightarrow f(x + 3) = 6(x + 3) - 11$

$\quad\quad\quad = 6x + 18 - 11$

$\quad\quad\quad = 6x + 7$

$\Rightarrow 6x + 7 = -29$

$\quad\quad 6x = -36$

$\quad\quad \therefore x = -6$

Worked Example 6.2

The diagram shows part of the graph of the function g given by $g(x) = ax^2 + bx - 2, x \in R$.

Find the value of a and the value of b.

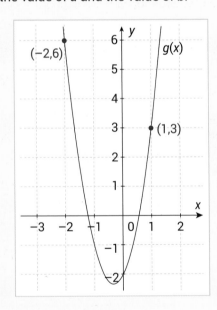

Solution

$(1,3) \in g$

$\Rightarrow a(1)^2 + b(1) - 2 = 3$

$a + b - 2 = 3$

$a + b = 5$ **Eq. 1**

$(-2,6) \in g$

$\Rightarrow a(-2)^2 + b(-2) - 2 = 6$

$4a - 2b - 2 = 6$

$4a - 2b = 8$

$2a - b = 4$ **Eq. 2**

Now solve the simultaneous equations 1 and 2:

$a + b = 5$ **Eq. 1**

$\underline{2a - b = 4}$ **Eq. 2**

$3a = 9$

$\therefore a = 3$

Substitute $a = 3$ into Equation 1:

$3 + b = 5$

$\therefore b = 2$

Answer: $a = 3$, $b = 2$

6.3 Composite Functions

Let us say we have a function f given by $f(x) = x^2 + 1$, $x \in R$.
You can replace x with any real number.

For example: $f(1) = (1)^2 + 1 = 2$ $f(-2) = (-2)^2 + 1 = 5$ $f(x + h) = (x + h)^2 + 1$

Now consider the function p given by $p(x) = 3x^2 + 5$.

If we take an input value of 4, let us describe what we do to find $p(4)$:

- Square the input, 4 in this case. $(4)^2 = 16$
- Multiply the square of the input by 3. $3(16) = 48$
- Then add 5. $48 + 5 = 53$

We could break the function p into two separate functions here:

- Function 1 tells us to square the input.
- Function 2 tells us to multiply the output of Function 1 by 3 and then add 5.

We can understand this type of function more easily if we break p into two separate functions, g and h.

- The function g is defined as $g(x) = x^2$, $x \in R$.
- The function h is defined as $h(x) = 3x + 5$, $x \in R$.

We want to find $g(x)$ first and then use $g(x)$ as the input for our function h.

It means that we perform the function g first and then perform the function h.

If we perform function g first and then function h, we express this as:

> This is read as 'the composition of h and g'. It is also read as 'h after g'.

$h \circ g(x)$ **OR** $(h \circ g)(x)$ **OR** $h(g(x))$ **OR** $hg(x)$

Note that the order in which we compose two functions is usually important.

For example, squaring 1 and adding 3 ($= 4$) is not the same as adding 3 to 1 and then squaring ($= 16$).

FUNCTIONS

Worked Example 6.3

$f(x) = 6x + 2$ and $g(x) = x^3$, where both f and g are functions that map from R to R.

(i) Find the value of $f \circ g(2)$.

(ii) Find the value of $g \circ f(2)$.

(iii) Comment appropriately on your answers to parts (i) and (ii).

Solution

(i) $f \circ g(2)$

First find $g(2)$.

$g(2) = (2)^3$

$\quad = 8$

Now find $f(8)$.

$f(8) = 6(8) + 2$

$\quad = 48 + 2$

$\quad = 50$

$\therefore f \circ g(2) = 50$

(ii) $g \circ f(2)$

First find $f(2)$.

$f(2) = 6(2) + 2$

$\quad = 12 + 2$

$\quad = 14$

Now find $g(14)$.

$g(14) = (14)^3$

$\quad = 2{,}744$

$\therefore g \circ f(2) = 2{,}744$

> In general, composition of functions is not commutative, i.e. $f \circ g(x) \neq g \circ f(x)$.

(iii) $\left.\begin{array}{l} f \circ g(2) = 50 \\ g \circ f(2) = 2{,}744 \end{array}\right\} \Rightarrow f \circ g(2) \neq g \circ f(2)$

Worked Example 6.4

Given the function h, where $h: R \mapsto R: t \mapsto (6t + 4)^3$:

(i) Decompose h into two separate functions.

(ii) Decompose h into three separate functions.

Solution

(i) Define the function a such that $a(t) = 6t + 4$.

Define the function b such that $b(t) = t^3$.

$\therefore h = b \circ a$

(ii) Define the function a such that $a(t) = 6t$.

Define the function b such that $b(t) = t + 4$.

Define the function c such that $c(t) = t^3$.

$\therefore h = c \circ b \circ a$

Worked Example 6.5

Write the following (a) as a single function and then (b) as a composition of functions.

(i) Square the input and add 6 to the answer (two functions).

(ii) Find the cubed root of the input, add 5 to this answer and then square it (three functions).

Solution

(i) (a) $f(x) = x^2 + 6$

(b) $g(x) = x^2$

$h(x) = x + 6$

$f(x) = h \circ g(x)$

(ii) (a) $f(x) = \left(\sqrt[3]{x} + 5\right)^2$

(b) $g(x) = \sqrt[3]{x}$

$h(x) = x + 5$

$j(x) = x^2$

$\therefore f(x) = j \circ h \circ g(x)$

Exercise 6.1

Note: $x \in R$ unless otherwise stated.

1. Which of the following mappings are functions? Give a reason for your answer.

   (a)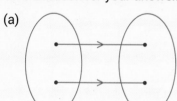

   (b)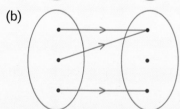

   (c)

   (d)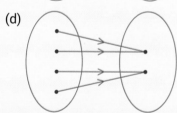

   (e)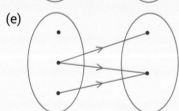

   (f)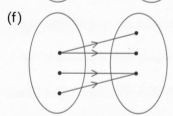

2. $f: x \mapsto 4x - 1$ defines a function.

   (a) Describe in words what the function f does.

   (b) (i) Find the value of $f(1)$.

   (ii) Find the value of $f\left(\frac{1}{2}\right)$.

   (iii) Find the value of k if $f(k) = 9$.

   (iv) Find the value of p if $f(p) = p$.

3. $f(x) = 2x + b$ defines a function.
   Find the value of b if $f(1) = 10$.

4. $g(x) = ax - 12$ defines a function.
   Find the value of a if $g(3) = 0$.

5. The following mapping is given:

   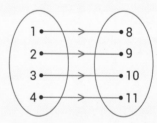

   (i) Is this mapping a function? Give a reason for your answer.

   (ii) Write out the domain and range of this mapping.

   (iii) Write an expression in terms of x for this mapping.

6. Write the following as functions, stating clearly what the letters you use stand for:

   (i) Square the input.

   (ii) The input is multiplied by 4 and 6 is then added.

   (iii) The temperature of the oil in a car engine on stopping is 98°C. Every five minutes that pass, the temperature decreases by 3°.

   (iv) The rate of change of the radius of a melting snowball is −2 cms⁻¹. The radius is initially 10 cm.

7. A function f is defined by the rule 'Divide the input by 2 and add 3.'

   (i) Write an expression in x to represent this function.

   (ii) Using this expression, find the value of $f(4)$, $f(18)$ and $f(-6)$.

   (iii) For what value of x is $f(x) = 9$?

   (iv) What is $f(f(x))$ equal to?

   (v) What is $f(x - 5)$ equal to?

   (vi) What is $f(x + k)$ equal to?

   (vii) Show that $\frac{1}{k}[f(x + k) - f(x)] = \frac{1}{2}$.

8. If $g(x) = 2x$, show that $g(x + 3) - g(x - 1) = 8$.

FUNCTIONS

9. The diagram shows part of the graph of a function given by $ax + by = 12$.

   Find the value of a and the value of b.

   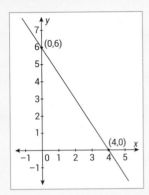

10. The diagram shows part of the graph of the function $f(x) = ax^2 + bx + 4$.

    Find the value of a and the value of b.

    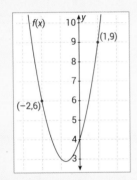

11. Water empties out of a leaking tank. The amount of water in the tank at any instant is given by the rule 'Two hundred minus the input squared', where the input is the number of minutes for which the tank has been leaking. (Volume is measured in litres.)

    (i) Define the function f such that $y = f(x)$, where y is the number of litres of water in the tank and x is the number of minutes passed.

    (ii) How long will it take the tank to empty?

    (iii) At what time will the tank be half empty?

12. A rectangular plot requires 200 metres of railings to enclose it. If one of the sides of the plot is x metres, express its area y as a function of x, and determine the domain of the function.

13. Express the length l of a chord of a circle of radius 5 as a function of its distance x from the centre of the circle, and determine the domain of the function.

14. A function is defined by $h(x) = 2x + 4$. A second function is defined by $g(x) = x^2 + 1$.

    The function f is defined as $f = h \circ g$.

(a) Find:

   (i) $f(0)$ (v) $f(-1)$

   (ii) $f(3)$ (vi) $f(-2)$

   (iii) $f(4)$ (vii) $f(-3)$

   (iv) $f(6)$ (viii) $f(-6)$

(b) A function f is called an even function if $f(-x) = f(x)$ for all x.

    Show that the function $f = h \circ g$ is even.

15. A function is defined by $h(x) = x + 1$. A second function is defined by $g(x) = x^2$ and a third function is defined by $f(x) = x - 2$.

    (a) Find:

       (i) $f \circ g(x)$ (v) $g \circ h \circ f(x)$

       (ii) $g \circ f(x)$ (vi) $g \circ f \circ g(x)$

       (iii) $g \circ h(x)$ (vii) $g \circ g \circ h(x)$

       (iv) $h \circ g \circ f(x)$ (viii) $h \circ f \circ f(x)$

    (b) If a fourth function is defined by $p(x) = x^2 - 2x + 1$, express p as a composition of functions f, g and h.

16. (i) Given that $f(x) = 3x + 1$ and $g(x) = 5x + c$, find c if $fg(x) = gf(x)$.

    (ii) Test your answer to part (i) by showing that $fg(3) = gf(3)$.

17. Given that $g(x) = 3x + 4$ and $h(x) = ax - 2$, find a if $hg(x) = gh(x)$.

18. (a) Decompose the following functions into two simpler functions:

       (i) $h(x) = x^2 + 1$ (ii) $f(x) = 2x^2$

    (b) Decompose the following functions into three simpler functions:

       (i) $g(x) = 3x^2 - 5$ (ii) $j(x) = (4x - 3)^2$

19. Write the following (a) as a single function and (b) as a composition of functions:

    (i) Square the input and then add 6 to the answer (two functions).

    (ii) Subtract 2 from the input, square the answer, and then multiply by 6 (three functions).

    (iii) Find the square root of the input, then add 4 to this answer, and then cube it (three functions).

    (iv) Find the sine of the input, square this answer, and then divide by 4 (three functions).

20. The functions f, g and h are defined by $f(x) = x^2 - 1$, $g(x) = 3x + 2$ and $h(x) = \frac{1}{x}$.

   Solve:

   (i) $fg(x) = 0$ (ii) $gh(x) = -12$

21. Suppose $f: x \rightarrow 2x - 4$, $g: x \rightarrow 3x^2 + 2$, and $h: x \rightarrow ax + b$, where $a, b \in R$.

   (i) Show that $fg: x \rightarrow 6x^2$.

   (ii) Find a and b if $fgh(x) = 24x^2 + 72x + 54$.

22. The function f is defined as $f = h \circ g \circ j$.

   $j(x) = x + 2$, and $g(x) = x^2$.

   Define a function h for each of the following situations:

   (i) $f(1) = 12$ (iii) $f(2) = 32$

   (ii) $f(1) = 3$ (iv) $f(-1) = -4$

23. Two functions are defined as $f(x) = 3x + 2$ and $g(x) = x^2 + 2$.

   Evaluate:

   (i) $f \circ g(x)$

   (ii) $g \circ f(x)$

   Is the composition of these two functions commutative? Explain.

24. Consider the functions $f(x) = 3x$ and $g(x) = x^2$, both defined for $x \in R \setminus \{0\}$.

   Which of the following composite functions would give you a higher output value for a given input value: $f \circ g$ or $g \circ f$? Explain.

Graphs of trigonometric functions are covered in detail in Book 2, Chapter 7.

6.4 Linear and Quadratic Functions

A **linear function** f in x is a function of the form $f(x) = ax + b$, where a and b are constants and x is a variable.

A constant is a value that does not vary.

A variable can change depending on the value we give it.

Variables are represented by letters.

Example: $f(x) = 2x + 1$. Here, x is the variable; 1 is the constant.

A graph is a pictorial representation of information showing how one quantity varies with another related quantity. The graph of a linear function is a straight line. The graph of $f(x) = 2x + 1$ is shown.

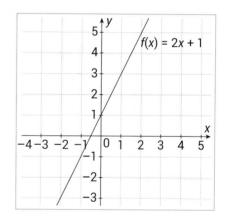

A **quadratic function** f in x involves an x^2 term and is of the form $f(x) = ax^2 + bx + c$, where a, b and c are constants ($a \neq 0$) and x is a variable.

The graph of a quadratic function takes the form of a curve, known as a parabola. The graph of a quadratic function can be drawn by making a table of values for x and finding the corresponding values for y. Then plot the resultant couples.

The graph can be ∩-shaped or ∪-shaped, depending on the coefficient of the squared variable.

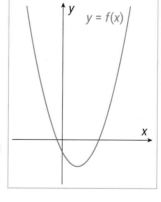

$f(x) = ax^2 + bx + c, x \in R$
Here, a is **positive**.

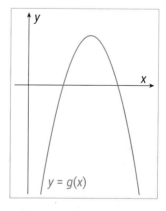

$g(x) = ax^2 + bx + c, x \in R$
Here, a is **negative**.

FUNCTIONS

Worked Example 6.6

Using the same scales and axes, graph the functions $g(x) = -x^2 + 6x$ and $h(x) = \frac{2}{3}x + 1$ in the domain $0 \leqslant x \leqslant 6$, $x \in R$.

Use your graph to estimate the values of x for which:

(i) $g(x) = 5.5$ (ii) $h(x) = 3.5$ (iii) $g(x) = h(x)$ (iv) $\frac{2}{3}x - 1 = 0$

Solution

Set up a table for each function to find the couples that need to be graphed.

$h(x) = \frac{2}{3}x + 1$ is a linear function, so three points will be sufficient to graph it.

Always pick the first and end value of the domain (if given). Pick a third value as a checking device.

g(x)			
x	$-x^2 + 6x$	y	(x,y)
0	$-0 + 0$	0	(0,0)
1	$-1 + 6$	5	(1,5)
2	$-4 + 12$	8	(2,8)
3	$-9 + 18$	9	(3,9)
4	$-16 + 24$	8	(4,8)
5	$-25 + 30$	5	(5,5)
6	$-36 + 36$	0	(6,0)

h(x)			
x	$\frac{2}{3}x + 1$	y	(x,y)
0	$0 + 1$	1	(0,1)
3	$2 + 1$	3	(3,3)
6	$4 + 1$	5	(6,5)

(i) Draw the line $y = 5.5$ (green line on graph). Where this line cuts the graph of $g(x)$, drop perpendiculars to the x-axis and read off the x-values: $x = 1.2$ and $x = 4.8$.

(ii) Draw the line $y = 3.5$ (red line on graph). Where this line cuts the graph of $h(x)$, drop a perpendicular to the x-axis and read off the x-value: $x = 3.7$.

(iii) Read off the two x-values where the graphs of the functions g and h intersect: $x = 0.2$ and $x = 5.2$.

(iv) $\frac{2}{3}x - 1 = 0$

$\Rightarrow \frac{2}{3}x + 1 - 2 = 0$

$\frac{2}{3}x + 1 = 2$

$\therefore h(x) = 2$

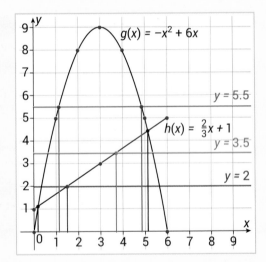

Draw the line $y = 2$ (blue line on graph). Where the line cuts the graph of $h(x)$, drop a perpendicular to the x-axis and read off the x-value: $x = 1.5$.

Transformations of Linear Functions

This section will cover what happens to a graph of a function when one or more parts of the function change. This is called a **transformation** of the graph of the function. When we graph a function under a transformation, the graph changes shape and/or location.

When we transform a linear function, the graph can shift up or down and/or change slope. If we add a number to the function, the function shifts up or down. If we change the slope, the steepness of the graph is changed.

Worked Example 6.7

The graph of the function $y = 3x - 4$ is shown.

Sketch the graphs of the following functions:

(i) $y = 3x + 2$

(ii) $y = \frac{3}{4}x - 4$

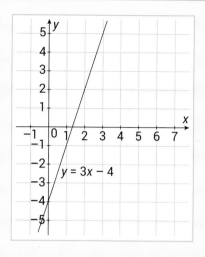

Solution

(i) $y = 3x + 2$

The slope has not changed but the y-intercept is now $(0,2)$.

The line will be parallel to the original line but it will shift up so that it goes through the point $(0,2)$.

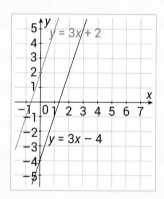

We added 6 to the original function, so it shifted up 6 on the y-axis.

(ii) $y = \frac{3}{4}x - 4$

The y-intercept has not changed, but the slope has changed.

Remember: Slope = $\dfrac{\text{Rise}}{\text{Run}}$

A slope of $\frac{3}{4}$ means that we move up three units for every four units we go to the right.

We draw a line that goes though the y-intercept $(0,-4)$ with a slope of $\frac{3}{4}$.

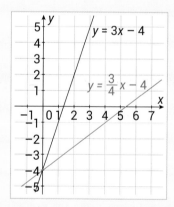

FUNCTIONS

Transformations of Quadratic Functions

When we transform a quadratic function, the graph can:

(1) Narrow

For a quadratic function $f(x) = ax^2$, $a > 0$, as the value of a increases, the graph of $y = f(x)$ becomes narrower.

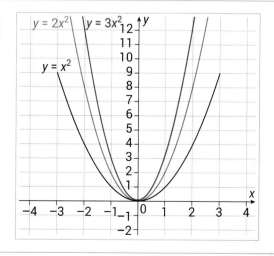

(2) Shift up or down

If b is positive, the graph of $f(x) = x^2 + b$ is the graph of $y = x^2$ shifted b units upwards.

If b is negative, the graph of $f(x) = x^2 + b$ is the graph of $y = x^2$ shifted $-b$ units downwards.

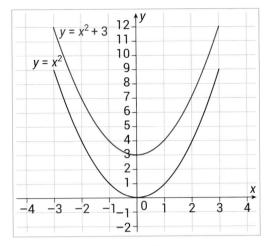

(3) Shift left or right

If b is positive, the graph of $f(x) = (x + b)^2$ is the graph of $y = x^2$ shifted b units to the left.

If b is negative, the graph of $f(x) = (x + b)^2$ is the graph of $y = x^2$ shifted $-b$ units to the right.

The y-intercept of the function $f(x) = (x + b)^2$ is $(0,(b)^2)$.

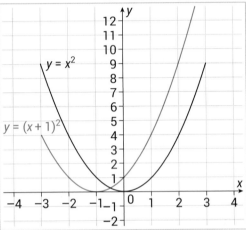

Worked Example 6.8

Graph the function $f(x) = (x + 2)^2$ in the domain $-5 \leqslant x \leqslant 1, x \in R$.

Use your graph to sketch the graphs of:

(i) $g(x) = (x - 1)^2$ (ii) $h(x) = (x + 2)^2 - 5$

Solution

We first draw the graph of the function $f(x) = (x + 2)^2$ in the domain $-5 \leqslant x \leqslant 1, x \in R$.

x	$(x + 2)^2$	y	(x,y)
−5	$(−3)^2$	9	(−5,9)
−4	$(−2)^2$	4	(−4,4)
−3	$(−1)^2$	1	(−3,1)
−2	$(0)^2$	0	(−2,0)
−1	$(1)^2$	1	(−1,1)
0	$(2)^2$	4	(0,4)
1	$(3)^2$	9	(1,9)

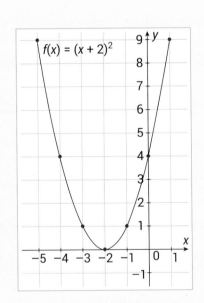

Couples: {(−5,9), (−4,4), (−3,1), (−2,0), (−1,1), (0,4), (1,9)}

(i) $g(x) = (x - 1)^2$

The graph touches the x-axis at (1,0).

The y-intercept is $(0,(-1)^2) = (0,1)$.

The graph of $g(x)$ is the graph of $f(x)$ shifted three units to the right.

Sketch the function through the point (1,0) and the point (0,1).

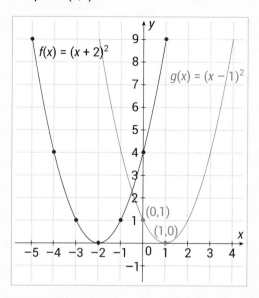

Here the graph shifted to the right by 3.

(ii) $h(x) = (x + 2)^2 - 5$

The graph of $h(x)$ is the graph of $f(x)$ shifted downwards by five units.

∴ The lowest point is (−2,−5) and the y-intercept is (0,−1).

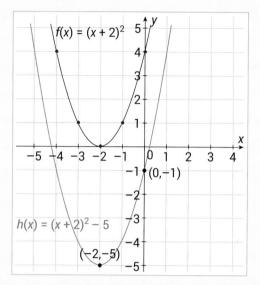

Here the graph shifted down by 5.

Exercise 6.2

1. Draw the graph of the linear function $f: x \rightarrow 4x - 3$ in the domain $-3 \leqslant x \leqslant 4, x \in R$.

   Use your graph to estimate:

   (i) The value of $f(x)$ for which $x = 2.5$

   (ii) The value of x for which $4x - 3 = 6$

   (iii) The value of x for which $4x - 3 = -7$

   (iv) The range of values of x for which $f(x) \geqslant 1$

2. The conversion formula for changing miles (M) into kilometres (K) is $K = 1.6M$.

   (i) Copy and complete the following table and, hence, graph the function, putting miles on the horizontal axis:

Miles	10	20	30	40	50	60	70	80	90	100
Kilometres					80					

   (ii) Estimate from your graph the distance in kilometres if 75 miles has been travelled.

   (iii) Estimate from your graph the distance in miles if 140 km has been travelled.

   (iv) What is the range of distances in kilometres if a trip is said to be between 65 and 75 miles long?

3. Graph the function $f: x \rightarrow x^2 - 2x - 5$ in the domain $-2 \leqslant x \leqslant 4, x \in R$.

   Estimate from your graph:

   (i) The value of $f(2.2)$

   (ii) The values of x for which $x^2 - 2x - 5 = 0$

   (iii) The values of x for which $x^2 - 2x - 5 \leqslant 0$

   (iv) The minimum value of $f(x)$

   Use an algebraic method to find the exact solutions to the equation given in part (ii).

FUNCTIONS

4. Graph the function $f: x \to \frac{1}{2}x^2$ in the domain $-2 \leqslant x \leqslant 2, x \in R$.

5. Graph the function $f: x \to \frac{1}{2}x^2 + \frac{3}{4}x + 2$ in the domain $-2 \leqslant x \leqslant 2, x \in R$.

6. Graph the function $h: [-3, 3] \to R: x \to 4 - \frac{1}{4}x^2$.

7. Graph the function $g: [-4, 0] \to R: x \to \frac{1}{4} - 6x - \frac{3}{2}x^2$.

8. The functions $f(x) = 8x - x^2$ and $g(x) = 0.5x + 4$ are graphed below on the domain $0 \leqslant x \leqslant 8, x \in R$.

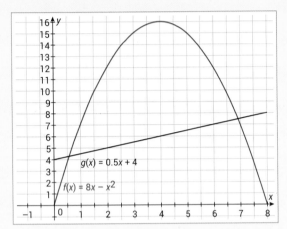

(i) What is the maximum value of $f(x)$?

(ii) Use the graph to estimate the values of x for which $f(x) = g(x)$.

(iii) Use the graph to estimate the values of x for which $f(x) \geqslant g(x)$.

(iv) Use the graph to estimate the values of x for which $f(x) < g(x)$.

9. Use the same scales and axes to draw the graphs of the two functions $f(x) = 2 + 2x + x^2$ and $g(x) = 5 - 2x - x^2$ in the domain $-3 \leqslant x \leqslant 2$, $x \in R$.

(i) Use your graph to estimate the values of x for which $f(x) = g(x)$.

(ii) Use your graph to estimate the values of x for which $f(x) \geqslant g(x)$.

10. A missile is launched into the air following the trajectory mapped out by the quadratic function $h(t) = 6t - t^2$, where h is the height in metres above the ground and t is the time in seconds.

(i) Graph the trajectory of the missile for 0–6 seconds.

(ii) At what times is the missile 8 metres above the ground?

A counter-attack missile is launched at the same time as the first missile from a height one metre above the ground. The trajectory of this missile is given by the function $j(t) = 1.2t + 1$, where j is the height in metres above the ground and t is the time in seconds.

(iii) Graph the trajectory of this counter-attack missile.

(iv) At what time will the two missiles collide?

(v) At what height will this collision take place?

11. The owner of a manufacturing company pays his workers on a piece-rate basis. The owner uses a quadratic function to determine the pay each employee will receive each month. He has determined that above a certain level of production by each employee, he encounters a problem with wastage. To eliminate wastage, he has told his employees that above a given level of production, their pay will decline.

The quadratic function he uses for calculating pay is defined as $P = 10Q - Q^2$, where P is monthly pay in €100s and Q is quantity produced in 100s.

(i) Graph the function for pay, with quantity produced on the horizontal axis and monthly pay on the vertical axis. Use the domain $0 \leqslant Q \leqslant 10$.

(ii) What is the optimal amount for an employee to produce?

(iii) If the optimal amount is produced, what pay will the employee receive that month?

(iv) If a worker receives monthly pay of €2,400, what are the two possible levels of production she has reached?

(v) Is it more lucrative for an employee to produce 250 units or 725 units? Explain how you came to your decision.

(vi) Pay of €2,100 can be achieved at two different levels of production. Explain how P can still be considered a function of Q if this is the case.

12. Based on data from previous years, the profit earned by a company selling barbeques is modelled by the function

$$p(x) = -\frac{x^2}{2} + 300x - 18,000$$

where x is the number of units sold.

(i) Plot the function $p(x)$ for sales from 0 to 600 units.

(ii) How many barbeques should be sold to maximise profit?

(iii) What is the profit per barbeque when making maximum profit?

(iv) Do you think it makes sense to pursue this business interest? Explain.

13. The graph of the linear function $f(x) = 2x + 5$ is shown. Use the graph to match the following functions with the functions shown below:

(a) $g(x) = 2x - 1$ (b) $h(x) = 2x + 2$

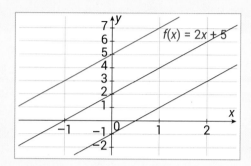

14. The graph of the function $y = 2x + 1$ is shown.

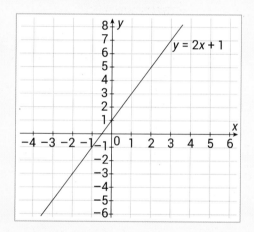

Copy this diagram into your copybook and sketch the graphs of the following functions:

(i) $y = 2x + 4$

(ii) $y = 2x - 3$

(iii) $y = 3x + 1$

15. Graph the function $y = -2x + 4$ in the domain $-3 \leqslant x \leqslant 3, x \in R$.

Hence, sketch the graphs of the following functions:

(i) $f(x) = -2x + 3$ (iii) $h(x) = x + 3$

(ii) $g(x) = 2x + 4$

16. The graph of $f(x) = x^2 + x + 2$ is shown. Use this graph to match the following functions with the functions shown below:

(i) $g(x) = 3x^2 + 3x + 6$

(ii) $h(x) = x^2 + x + 4$

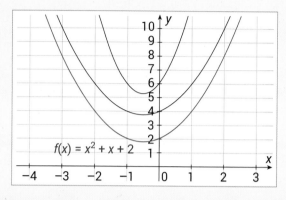

17. The graph of the function $y = x^2$ is shown. Use this graph to match the following functions with the functions shown below:

(i) $y = (x + 1)^2$ (ii) $y = (x - 5)^2$

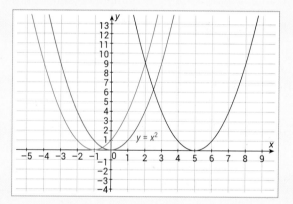

18. Graph the function $f(x) = 2x^2$ in the domain $-3 \leqslant x \leqslant 3, x \in R$.

Hence, sketch the following functions:

(i) $g(x) = 4x^2$ (ii) $h(x) = 3x^2$

19. Graph the function $f(x) = 2x^2 + 4$ in the domain $-4 \leqslant x \leqslant 3, x \in R$.

Hence, sketch the following functions:

(i) $g(x) = 2x^2 + 1$ (ii) $h(x) = 2x^2 - 2$

FUNCTIONS

6.5 Expressing Quadratic Functions in Completed Square Form (Vertex Form)

Consider the quadratic function $f(x) = x^2 - 4x + 7$. A graph of f is presented on the right. We can tell from the graph that the turning point of this function f is (2,3).

The turning point of a quadratic function is called the **vertex** of the function.

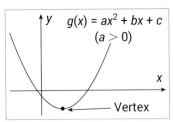

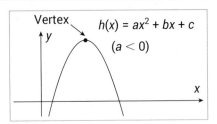

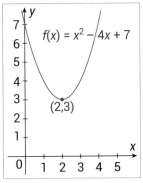

If we write the function f above in **completed square form** (**vertex form**), we can tell the co-ordinates of its vertex without having to graph the function.

Completing the square is the method of converting from standard form ($ax^2 + bx + c$) to completed square form ($a(x - h)^2 + k$). (h,k) are the co-ordinates of the vertex of the function. The axis of symmetry for the graph of f is $x = h$.

To write $f(x) = x^2 - 4x + 7$ in completed square form, we need to 'complete the square'.

Examine $f(x) = x^2 - 4x + 7$.

Half the x coefficient is -2. The square of -2 is 4.

So, $f(x) = x^2 - 4x + 7$

$\qquad = x^2 - 2x - 2x + \boxed{4} + 7 - \boxed{4}$

$\qquad = x^2 - 4x + 4 + 3$

$\qquad = (x - 2)^2 + 3 \quad \leftarrow$ Completed square form

The co-ordinates of this vertex can be read directly as (2,3).

To summarise:

To complete the square:

(1) Take the coefficient of x.

(2) Halve it.

(3) Square it.

(4) Add and subtract this square.

$$y = a(x - h)^2 + k$$

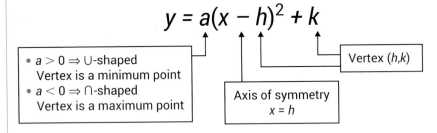

- $a > 0 \Rightarrow$ ∪-shaped
  Vertex is a minimum point
- $a < 0 \Rightarrow$ ∩-shaped
  Vertex is a maximum point

Axis of symmetry
$x = h$

Vertex (h,k)

Worked Example 6.9

Express the quadratic function $y = x^2 + 8x + 7$ in completed square form. What are the co-ordinates of the vertex?

To complete the square:

(1) Take the coefficient of x (here = 8).

Solution

Step 1 Start with $x^2 + 8x + 7$.

Step 2 Complete the square: $x^2 + 8x + \left(\frac{8}{2}\right)^2 + 7 - \left(\frac{8}{2}\right)^2$

(2) Halve it (here = 4).

(3) Square it (here = 16).

(4) Add and subtract this square.

Step 3 Tidy up the expression to the form $a(x - h)^2 + k$.

$$x^2 + 8x + (4)^2 + 7 - (4)^2$$

$$= x^2 + 8x + 16 + 7 - 16$$

$$= (x + 4)(x + 4) + 7 - 16$$

$$= (x + 4)^2 - 9$$

The co-ordinates of the vertex are $(h,k) = (4,-9)$.

Worked Example 6.10

Express the quadratic function $y = 7 - 6x - x^2$ in completed square form. State the turning point of this function.

Solution

$$7 - 6x - x^2$$

$$= 7 - (x^2 + 6x)$$

$$= 7 + 9 - (x^2 + 6x + 9)$$

> We get 9 by halving the coefficient of the x-term and squaring. $\left(\frac{6}{2}\right)^2 = 9$

> The +9 here is actually subtracting 9 in the expression due to the minus sign outside the bracket.

> Here, we are adding the 9.

Tidy up the expression to give the correct form.

$$= 7 + 9 - (x^2 + 6x + 9)$$

$$= 16 - (x + 3)(x + 3)$$

$$= 16 - (x + 3)^2$$

Given the general completed square form $a(x - h)^2 + k$, the turning point is (h,k).

$\therefore$ For $-(x + 3)^2 + 16$, the turning point is $(-3,16)$.

Worked Example 6.11

(i) Express the quadratic function $y = 3x^2 - 12x + 10$ in completed square form.

(ii) State the turning point of this function.

(iii) By considering the completed square form, solve the equation $3x^2 - 12x + 10 = 0$, correct to four decimal places.

(iv) Sketch the function.

(v) Write down the equation of the axis of symmetry of the function.

Solution

(i) $3x^2 - 12x + 10$

$$= 3\left(x^2 - 4x + \frac{10}{3}\right)$$

$$= 3\left[(x^2 - 4x) + \frac{10}{3}\right]$$

$$= 3\left[\left(x^2 - 4x + \left(\frac{4}{2}\right)^2\right) + \frac{10}{3} - \left(\frac{4}{2}\right)^2\right]$$

$$= 3\left[(x^2 - 4x + 4) + \frac{10}{3} - 4\right]$$

$$= 3\left[(x - 2)^2 - \frac{2}{3}\right]$$

$$\therefore y = 3(x - 2)^2 - 2$$

(ii) $y = 3(x - 2)^2 - 2$

$\therefore$ The turning point is $(2,-2)$.

(iii) $3x^2 - 12x + 10 = 0$

$$\Rightarrow 3(x - 2)^2 - 2 = 0$$

$$3(x - 2)^2 = 2$$

$$(x - 2)^2 = \frac{2}{3}$$

$$x - 2 = \pm\sqrt{\frac{2}{3}}$$

$$x = 2 \pm\sqrt{\frac{2}{3}}$$

$x = 2.8165$ **OR** $x = 1.1835$

FUNCTIONS

(iv)

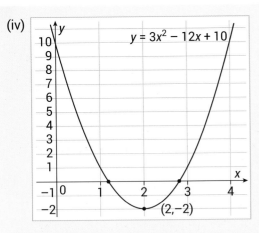

When sketching the graph, use the roots and the turning point to guide you as to where the function turns and where it cuts the x-axis. Also use the y-intercept of $(0,10)$ here.

(v) From the graph, the axis of symmetry is $x = 2$.

OR

From the completed square form
$$3(x - 2)^2 - 2$$

$x - 2 = 0$ is the equation of the axis of symmetry.

$\therefore x = 2$

Exercise 6.3

For Questions 1–11 below:

(i) Write the function in completed square form.

(ii) Hence, find the roots of each function.

(iii) State the turning point for each function and write down the equation of the axis of symmetry.

(iv) Sketch the function.

1. $y = x^2 - 12x + 36$

2. $f(x) = x^2 + 2x - 6$

3. $g(x) = x^2 - 6x - 16$

4. $f(x) = 2x^2 + 4x - 7$

5. $f(x) = 3x^2 + 12x + 4$

6. $g: x \rightarrow (x - 3)^2 + 8x - 12$

7. $y = 3 - 4x - x^2$

8. $y = 9 + 4x - x^2$

9. $h(x) = 13 - 4x - 2x^2$

10. $g(x) = -2(1 - 2x) - x^2$

11. $g: x \rightarrow (x - 4)(2 - 3x) + 6$

12. (i) Express the function $f(x) = 2x^2 - 8x + 4$ in completed square form.

    (ii) Write down the minimum value of the function.

    (iii) The function $g(x) = x^2 - 4x + k$ has the same minimum value as $f(x)$. Find the value of k.

13. (i) Express the function $h(x) = 9 - 6x - 3x^2$ in completed square form.

    (ii) Write down the maximum value of the function.

    (iii) The function $k(x) = m - 2x - x^2$ has the same maximum value as $h(x)$. Find the value of m.

14. (i) Express the function $f(x) = x^2 - 12x - 4$ in completed square form.

    (ii) Write down the minimum value of the function.

    (iii) The function $g(x) = 2x^2 - 24x + k$ has the same minimum value as $f(x)$. Find the value of k.

15. (i) Express the function $h(x) = 14 - 12x - x^2$ in completed square form.

    (ii) Write down the maximum value of the function.

    (iii) The function $k(x) = m - 24x - 2x^2$ has the same maximum value as $h(x)$. Find the value of m.

6.6 Cubic Functions

A **cubic function** f in x involves an x^3 term and is of the form $f(x) = ax^3 + bx^2 + cx + d$, where a, b, c and d are constants ($a \neq 0$) and x is a variable.

Examples of cubic functions:

$$f(x) = x^3 - 6x^2 + 11x - 6 \qquad g(x) = 4x^3 + 5 \qquad h: x \to -x^3 + 9x$$

The graph of any function of this form is called a **cubic graph**. The shape of the graph depends on whether a, the coefficient of x^3, is negative or positive (among other factors).

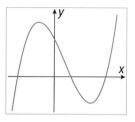 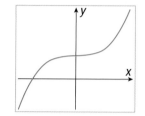

In these cases, a, the coefficient of x^3, is positive.

If the coefficient of x^3 is **positive**, the graph will **start low and end high**.

 Revision of Chapter 2, Section 2.6 will aid your understanding of this topic.

In these cases, a, the coefficient of x^3, is negative.

If the coefficient of x^3 is **negative**, the graph will **start high and end low**.

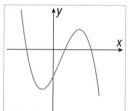 

- A quadratic function may cross the x-axis at a maximum of two points. A cubic function may cross the x-axis at a maximum of three points.

- It is possible for the graph of a quadratic function not to touch or cross the x-axis, i.e. if the function has no real roots. However, this is **not** the case for a cubic function. There will always be at least one point where the graph of the cubic function will cross the x-axis.

- Not all cubic functions have two turning points. This will be explored further in Chapter 14.

Worked Example 6.12

Graph the function g, where $g(x) = x^3 - 6x^2 + 11x - 6$, in the domain $0.5 \leqslant x \leqslant 3.5$, $x \in R$.

Solution

Set up the input–output table.

x	$x^3 - 6x^2 + 11x - 6$	y	(x,y)
0.5	$(0.5)^3 - 6(0.5)^2 + 11(0.5) - 6$	−1.875	(0.5,−1.875)
1	$(1)^3 - 6(1)^2 + 11(1) - 6$	0	(1,0)
1.5	$(1.5)^3 - 6(1.5)^2 + 11(1.5) - 6$	0.375	(1.5,0.375)
2	$(2)^3 - 6(2)^2 + 11(2) - 6$	0	(2,0)
2.5	$(2.5)^3 - 6(2.5)^2 + 11(2.5) - 6$	−0.375	(2.5,−0.375)
3	$(3)^3 - 6(3)^2 + 11(3) - 6$	0	(3,0)
3.5	$(3.5)^3 - 6(3.5)^2 + 11(3.5) - 6$	1.875	(3.5,1.875)

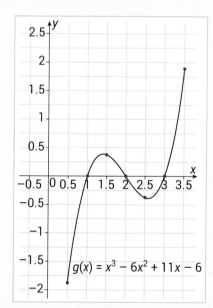

Graph the couples (x,y).

Points to note

- The graph starts low and finishes high.
  Reason: The coefficient of x^3 is positive (=1).

- The graph crosses the x-axis three times, at $x = 1$, $x = 2$ and $x = 3$. This indicates that the function has three real roots.

Worked Example 6.13

Graph the function $f: x \rightarrow x^3 - 5x^2 + 3x + 9$ in the domain $-1.5 \leq x \leq 4, x \in R$.

Use your graph to estimate:

(i) The values of x for which $f(x) = 0$

(ii) The value of $f(2.5)$

(iii) The minimum value of $f(x)$, where $x > 0$

(iv) The values of x for which $f(x)$ is decreasing

(v) The solutions of $x^3 - 5x^2 + 3x + 9 = 2$

(vi) The solutions of $x^3 - 5x^2 + 3x = -4$

Solution

x	$x^3 - 5x^2 + 3x + 9$	y	(x,y)
−1.5	$(-1.5)^3 - 5(-1.5)^2 + 3(-1.5) + 9$	−10.125	(−1.5,−10.125)
−1	$(-1)^3 - 5(-1)^2 + 3(-1) + 9$	0	(−1,0)
−0.5	$(-0.5)^3 - 5(-0.5)^2 + 3(-0.5) + 9$	6.125	(−0.5,6.125)
0	$(0)^3 - 5(0)^2 + 3(0) + 9$	9	(0,9)
0.5	$(0.5)^3 - 5(0.5)^2 + 3(0.5) + 9$	9.375	(0.5,9.375)
1	$(1)^3 - 5(1)^2 + 3(1) + 9$	8	(1,8)
1.5	$(1.5)^3 - 5(1.5)^2 + 3(1.5) + 9$	5.625	(1.5,5.625)
2	$(2)^3 - 5(2)^2 + 3(2) + 9$	3	(2,3)
2.5	$(2.5)^3 - 5(2.5)^2 + 3(2.5) + 9$	0.875	(2.5,0.875)
3	$(3)^3 - 5(3)^2 + 3(3) + 9$	0	(3,0)
3.5	$(3.5)^3 - 5(3.5)^2 + 3(3.5) + 9$	1.125	(3.5,1.125)
4	$(4)^3 - 5(4)^2 + 3(4) + 9$	5	(4,5)

(i) Using the graph, establish where the graph of the function crosses or touches the x-axis. This gives the values of x for which $f(x) = 0$.

$f(x) = 0$ at $x = -1$ or $x = 3$

(ii) Draw the vertical line $x = 2.5$ and read off the y-value where it crosses the graph of f, i.e. $y = 0.9$.

$\therefore f(2.5) = 0.9$

(iii) The minimum value of $f(x)$ where $x > 0$ is 0.

(iv) $f(x)$ is decreasing for $0.3 \leq x \leq 3, x \in R$.

(v) Draw the line $y = 2$ (green line). Where the line cuts the graph of f, drop perpendicular lines to the x-axis and read off the x-values. $x = -0.8, 2.2$ or 3.7

(vi) $x^3 - 5x^2 + 3x = -4$

$\Rightarrow x^3 - 5x^2 + 3x + 9 = -4 + 9$

$\therefore f(x) = 5$

Draw the line $y = 5$. This gives x-values of $x = -0.6, 1.6$ or 4.

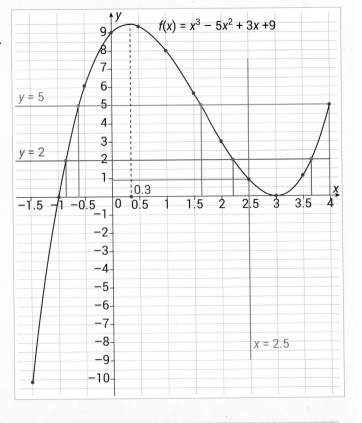

Answers to parts (ii), (iii), (iv), (v), and (vi) are estimates and depend on the accuracy of the graph drawn.

Worked Example 6.14

Graph the function $f(x) = x^3 - 2x^2 - 5x + 6$ in the domain $-2 \leqslant x \leqslant 3, x \in R$.

Hence, sketch the following functions:

(i) $g(x) = 0.5(x^3 - 2x^2 - 5x + 6)$ (ii) $h(x) = x^3 - 2x^2 - 5x + 9$

Solution

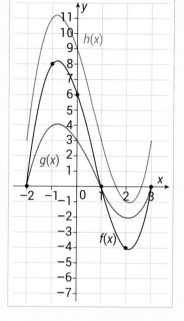

x	$x^3 - 2x^2 - 5x + 6$	y	(x,y)
−2	$(-2)^3 - 2(-2)^2 - 5(-2) + 6$	0	(−2,0)
−1	$(-1)^3 - 2(-1)^2 - 5(-1) + 6$	8	(−1,8)
0	$(0)^3 - 2(0)^2 - 5(0) + 6$	6	(0,6)
1	$(1)^3 - 2(1)^2 - 5(1) + 6$	0	(1,0)
2	$(2)^3 - 2(2)^2 - 5(2) + 6$	−4	(2,−4)
3	$(3)^3 - 2(3)^2 - 5(3) + 6$	0	(3,0)

(i) Multiplying the function by 0.5 causes the graph of $f(x)$ to be compressed by a factor of 0.5. Each y-value is halved. Note that the roots remain unchanged.

(ii) $h(x) = x^3 - 2x^2 - 5x + 9$

$= x^3 - 2x^2 - 5x + 6 + 3$

$\therefore h(x) = f(x) + 3$

Adding 3 to the function shifts the graph of $f(x)$ vertically upwards by three units.

Exercise 6.4

1. Graph the following functions in the given domains:

	Function	Domain
(i)	$b(x) = x^3 - x^2 - 2x + 2$	$-2 \leqslant x \leqslant 3, x \in R$
(ii)	$d(x) = 2x^3 - 3x^2 - 6x + 2$	$-2 \leqslant x \leqslant 3, x \in R$
(iii)	$f(x) = x^3 - 4x^2 + x + 6$	$-2 \leqslant x \leqslant 3, x \in R$
(iv)	$h(x) = -x^3 - 2x^2 + 4x + 2$	$-4 \leqslant x \leqslant 2, x \in R$
(v)	$j(x) = 8 - 12x + 6x^2 - x^3$	$0 \leqslant x \leqslant 4, x \in R$

2. The graphs of $f(x) = -5x^3 + 11x^2 - 3$ and $g(x) = 3x + 0.5$ for $-1 \leqslant x \leqslant 2, x \in R$, are shown.

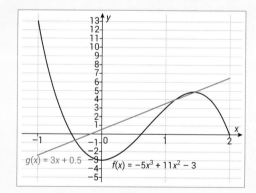

Use the graphs to find:

(i) The approximate value of $f(1.5)$

(ii) The approximate values of x for which $f(x) = 0$

(iii) The approximate values of x for which $f(x) = g(x)$

3. Using the same axes and scales, graph the functions $f: x \rightarrow x^3 - x^2 - 2x + 3$ and $g: x \rightarrow 4 + x - x^2$ in the domain $-2 \leqslant x \leqslant 3, x \in R$.

Use your graph to approximate the values of x for which $f(x) = g(x)$.

4. Shown below is the graph of the function $f(x) = x^3 - 5x + 1$. Use the graph to match the following functions with those graphed below.

   (i) $g(x) = 2(x^3 - 5x + 1)$

   (ii) $h(x) = 2(x^3 - 5x + 1) - 2$

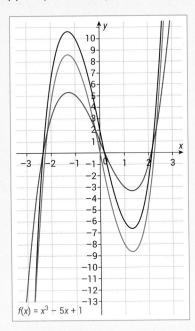

$f(x) = x^3 - 5x + 1$

5. Graph the function $f(x) = x^3$ over the domain $-2 \leqslant x \leqslant 2, x \in R$.

   Hence, sketch the following functions:

   (i) $g(x) = x^3 + 2$ (iii) $k(x) = 2x^3 - 2$

   (ii) $h(x) = 2x^3$

6. Graph the function $f(x) = -x^3$ over the domain $-2 \leqslant x \leqslant 2, x \in R$.

   Hence, sketch the function $g(x) = -x^3 + 4$.

7. The graph of $f(x) = 2x^3$ has been vertically compressed by a factor of 0.5.
   What is the new functional form?

8. The graph of $f(x) = x^3 - 3$ has been shifted right by two units and down by three units. What is the new functional form?

9. The graphs of $f(x)$ and $g(x)$ are given below.

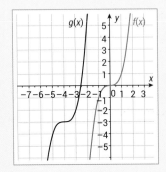

(i) Describe in your own words a transformation that would map the graph of $f(x)$ to the graph of $g(x)$.

(ii) Write the functional form of $g(x)$ in terms of x.

10. The growth model used for the weekly sales of a new product is given by the graph below.

(i) Estimate the maximum level of weekly sales reached in the first two years of the product's life cycle.

(ii) At approximately what time is this maximum level reached?

(iii) Two aggressive marketing campaigns are undertaken during the product's life cycle. Estimate from the graph when these two campaigns took place. Explain your answer.

(iv) If the product has an expected life of three years, what is the maximum level of weekly sales that the product can achieve?

11. The graph below models the temperature in degrees Celsius of a computer server over a four-minute period.

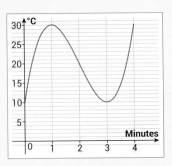

(i) What is the maximum temperature reached by the server?

(ii) After 2.5 minutes, what is the temperature of the server?

(iii) It is recommended that the temperature of the server should not exceed 28°C. Give the approximate time intervals for which the server is above the recommended temperature.

12. The annual profits of a company (in thousands of euro) can be modelled by the function $P(x) = -x^3 + x^2 + 5x + 4$, where x is the amount of money (in thousands of euro) spent on product promotion.

   (i) Draw a suitable graph to show the annual profit of the company.

   (ii) From your graph, estimate the maximum annual profit of the company.

   (iii) At approximately what level of spending on advertising is profit maximised?

   (iv) The CEO of this company suggested that the company could generate a certain level of profit without any product promotion. Would you agree with this statement? Explain the reason for your answer.

13. The height (in 5 cm units) of a mosquito is modelled by the function $f(x) = x^3 - 7x^2 - 5x + 75$, where x is the time passed in seconds.

   (i) Draw a suitable graph to show the height of the mosquito over the first 8 seconds.

   (ii) What is the height of the mosquito after 8 seconds?

   (iii) The mosquito is caught in the air at a height of 170 cm. At what two times can this happen? (Use your graph to answer.)

   (iv) Verify your answer to part (iii) using algebra methods.

6.7 Exponential Functions

Exponential functions are functions of the form $y = bx$, where b is constant and x is the variable exponent or power.

When dealing with **exponential functions**, we take a number called the **base** and raise it to a power called the **exponent**.

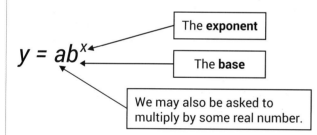

$$y = ab^x$$

The **exponent**

The **base**

We may also be asked to multiply by some real number.

The base and exponent make up the exponential function.

Before dealing with **exponential functions**, it is essential that you know the rules for working with indices. Some key laws of indices are shown below.

Law 1 $a^p \times a^q = a^{p+q}$ Law 3 $(a^p)^q = a^{pq}$

Law 2 $\dfrac{a^p}{a^q} = a^{p-q}$ Law 4 $a^0 = 1, a \neq 0$

These formulae appear on page 21 of *Formulae and Tables*.

Graphs of Exponential Functions

The graph of an exponential function has a very distinctive shape.

The graph of the function $f(x) = ab^x$ will pass through the point $(0,a)$.

Reason: At $x = 0$, $y = ab^0$
$\qquad\qquad = a(1)$
$\qquad\qquad = a$

The graph of an exponential function will never touch or cross the horizontal axis.

FUNCTIONS

Worked Example 6.15

Graph the function $f(x) = 10^x$ in the domain $-2 \leqslant x \leqslant 1$, $x \in R$.

Solution

x	10^x	y	(x,y)
-2	10^{-2}	0.01	(-2,0.01)
-1	10^{-1}	0.1	(-1,0.1)
0	10^0	1	(0,1)
1	10^1	10	(1,10)

If the exponent is x and the base is greater than 1, the curve slopes upwards.

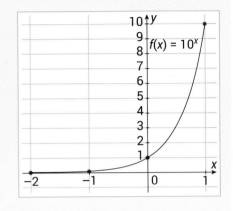

Worked Example 6.16

Graph the function $f(x) = 10^{-x}$ in the domain $-1 \leqslant x \leqslant 2$, $x \in R$.

Solution

x	10^{-x}	y	(x,y)
-1	$10^{-(-1)}$	10	(-1,10)
0	$10^{-(0)}$	1	(0,1)
1	10^{-1}	0.1	(1,0.1)
2	10^{-2}	0.01	(2,0.01)

10^{-x} can also be written as $\left(\dfrac{1}{10}\right)^x$ or 0.1^x.

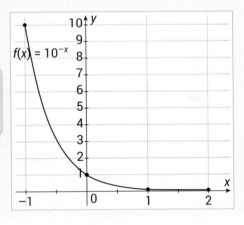

If the exponent is x and the base is positive and less than 1, the curve slopes downwards.

Worked Example 6.17

Graph the function $f(x) = 2(3^x)$ in the domain $-2 \leqslant x \leqslant 2$, $x \in R$.

Solution

x	$2(3^x)$	y	(x,y)
-2	$2(3^{-2})$	$\dfrac{2}{9}$	$\left(-2,\dfrac{2}{9}\right)$
-1	$2(3^{-1})$	$\dfrac{2}{3}$	$\left(-1,\dfrac{2}{3}\right)$
0	$2(3^0)$	2	(0,2)
1	$2(3^1)$	6	(1,6)
2	$2(3^2)$	18	(2,18)

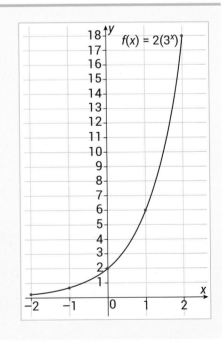

Worked Example 6.18

Find the value of a, given the graph of the function $f(x) = ab^x$, $b > 0$.

Solution

$f(0) = ab^0$

   $= a(1)$

   $= a$

From the graph, $f(0) = 3$.

$\therefore a = 3$

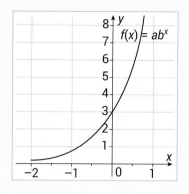

Worked Example 6.19

Bacterial growth can be modelled over finite time intervals using exponential functions.

The population of a particular bacteria is given by the function $p(x) = 150{,}000(2^x)$, where x is time in hours.

(i) Graph this population function for the first four hours of growth.

(ii) Estimate the population size after 2.5 hours of growth by taking a suitable reading from your graph.

(iii) Find the exact population size after 2.5 hours of growth using algebra. Answer correct to the nearest whole number.

(iv) Calculate the percentage error in your estimate in part (ii) by using your answer from part (iii). Answer correct to one decimal place.

(v) Do you think such exponential growth would continue indefinitely? Explain your answer.

Solution

(i)

x	$150{,}000(2^x)$	y
0	150,000(1)	150,000
1	150,000(2)	300,000
2	150,000(4)	600,000
3	150,000(8)	1,200,000
4	150,000(16)	2,400,000

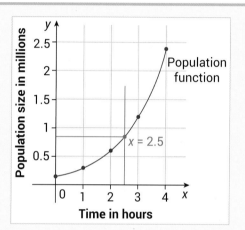

(ii) Draw the vertical line $x = 2.5$ and read off the y-value where it crosses the graph of the population function.

Answer: $\approx 850{,}000$

(iii) $p(2.5) = 150{,}000(2^{2.5}) = 848{,}528.1374 \approx 848{,}528$.

(iv) Percentage error $= \dfrac{850{,}000 - 848{,}528}{848{,}528} \times 100$

   $\approx 0.2\%$

(v) No. At some point (in time) the population will become so big that there will not be enough food and other resources for the bacteria population to grow further.

Summary:

For a function $f(x) = ab^x$, with $a > 0$, $b > 1$, $a, b, x \in R$:

- The graph of f passes through the point $(0, a)$.
- The graph of f is upward sloping.
- The graph of f lies above the x-axis.

For a function $f(x) = ab^{-x}$, with $a > 0$, $b > 1$, $a, b, x \in R$:

- The graph of f passes through the point $(0, a)$.
- The graph of f is downward sloping.
- The graph of f lies above the x-axis.

FUNCTIONS

Worked Example 6.20

Graph the function $y = 3(3^x)$ in the domain $-3 \leqslant x \leqslant 2$, $x \in R$.

Hence, sketch the functions:

(i) $f(x) = 3^x$ (ii) $g(x) = 3^{x-1}$

Solution

x	$3(3^x)$	y	(x,y)
-3	$3(3^{-3})$	0.11	(-3,0.11)
-2	$3(3^{-2})$	0.33	(-2,0.33)
-1	$3(3^{-1})$	1	(-1,1)
0	$3(3^0)$	3	(0,3)
1	$3(3^1)$	9	(1,9)
2	$3(3^2)$	27	(2,27)

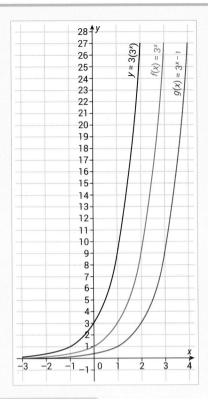

(i) $y = 3(3^x) \Rightarrow y = 3^{x+1}$
Therefore, the graph of $f(x) = 3^x$ is the graph of 3^{x+1} shifted one unit to the right.

(ii) $f(x) = 3^x$. Therefore, the graph of $g(x) = 3^{x-1}$ is the graph of 3^x shifted one unit to the right.

The graph of $f(x) = k^{x+h}$ is the graph of $y = k^x$ shifted h units to the left if $h > 0$, or $-h$ units to the right if $h < 0$.

Exercise 6.5

In Questions 1–5, graph each function in the domain $-2 \leqslant x \leqslant 3$, $x \in R$.

1. $y = 2^x$

2. $y = 4^x$

3. $y = 3^x$

4. $y = \left(\frac{1}{3}\right)^x$

5. $y = 5^{-x}$

In Questions 6–8, graph each function in the domain $-2 \leqslant x \leqslant 2$, $x \in R$.

6. $y = 3.5(3^x)$

7. $y = \frac{4}{3}(3^x)$

8. $y = 2^x(3^x)$

In Questions 9–10, identify the unknown values a and b.

9. $y = ab^x$

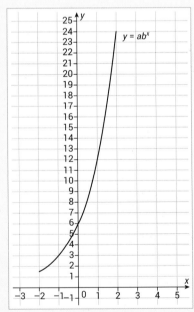

10. $y = ab^x$

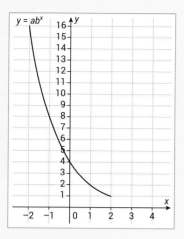

11. On 1 June, a type of algae was introduced to Lough Arrow. The algae grew and spread so that after t days the volume of water containing the algae was given by $A(t) = 2^t$, where A is the volume in m³.

   (i) Draw a graph to show the volume of algae in the lake for the first six days.

On the same date, a pollutant began to seep into the lake. The pollutant spread so that after t days the volume of water containing pollutant was given by $P(t) = 30 + 4t$, where P is the volume in m³.

   (ii) Using the same axes and scales as for part (i), draw the graph of P.

   (iii) After how much time will the volume of water containing the algae equal the volume of water containing the pollutant? Answer correct to the nearest six hours.

12. While making pizza dough in Home Economics class, the teacher points out that ideally the yeast mixture should be made about one hour before use. She points out that the mixture doubles in volume every hour.

Initially, Laura has 10 cm³ of the mixture.

   (i) Calculate the volume of the mixture each hour for the first four hours.
      (Use a table to display your results.)

   (ii) Draw a graph to display this data.

   (iii) Use your graph to estimate the volume of the mixture after 2.5 hours.

   (iv) Use your graph to estimate how long it takes for the volume of the mixture to reach 100 cm³ in size.

13. An economist estimates that the population of a country will increase by 25 per cent every 10 years. The population is 15 million in 2012.

   (i) If x represents the number of years since 2012, define a function P in x that represents the population of the country.

   (ii) Draw a graph to show the estimated population for the next 50 years.

   (iii) Use your graph to estimate when the population will reach 25 million.

14. Laser beams are very intense rays of light commonly used in medicine. The intensity of a laser beam decreases exponentially with the penetration of tissue. The intensity of a particular beam can be modelled as $I(x) = 800(0.6812^x)$, where x is depth of penetration in millimetres and I is intensity in watts per square metre (Wm⁻²).

   (i) Graph the intensity of a laser beam over the domain $0 \leqslant x \leqslant 5, x \in R$.

   (ii) Using your graph, estimate the intensity at a depth of 4 mm.

   (iii) Use algebra to find the exact intensity at a depth of 4 mm. Answer correct to two decimal places.

   (iv) At what depth is the intensity equal to 500 Wm⁻²?

      Estimate your answer using your graph and then use logs to find the exact answer correct to two decimal places.

15. Shown below is the graph of the function $f(x) = 4^x$. Use the graph to match the following functions with those graphed below:

   (i) $g(x) = (0.5)4^x$ (ii) $h(x) = 4^{x+1}$

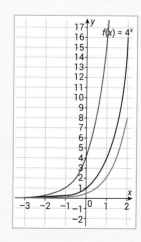

16. Shown below is the graph of the function $f(x) = 8^x$. Use the graph to match the following functions with those graphed below:

(i) $g(x) = 0.5(8^x)$ (ii) $h(x) = 8^x - 2$

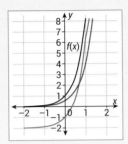

17. Graph the function $y = 2^x$ over the domain $-2 \leqslant x \leqslant 2, x \in R$.

Hence, sketch the following functions:

(i) $f(x) = 2^{x+1}$

(ii) $g(x) = 2^x + 2$

18. Graph the function $f(x) = \left(\frac{1}{2}\right)^x$ over the domain $-3 \leqslant x \leqslant 3, x \in R$.

Hence, sketch the following functions:

(i) $g(x) = 2\left(\frac{1}{2}\right)^x$

(ii) $h(x) = \left(\frac{1}{2}\right)^x + 1$

19. The graphs of the functions $f(x) = 2^x$ and $g(x)$ are given.

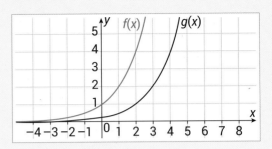

(i) Describe in your own words a transformation that would map the graph of $f(x)$ to the graph of $g(x)$.

(ii) What is the functional form of $g(x)$?

20. The graph of the function $y = 3^x$ is shifted three units to the right.

What is the new functional form?

21. The graph of the function $y = 4^x$ is stretched vertically by a factor of 3 and is shifted to the right by three units.

What is the new functional form?

22. The graph of the function $y = 2^x$ is shifted to the left by two units and is shifted upwards by three units.

What is the new functional form?

Note

Exponential and logarithmic functions are also covered in Chapter 7.

- For graphs of exponential functions, see 7.1 Indices (Exponents).
- For graphs of logarithmic functions, see 7.5 Logarithms.

6.8 Graphing Logarithmic Functions

Each exponential function has an inverse function. We call these inverses **logarithmic functions**.

Consider the graphs below (the red line is the graph of the function $y = x$).

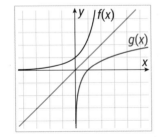
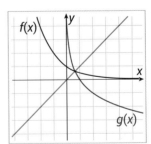

$f(x) = a^x$ (black curve); $g(x) = \log_a x$ (blue curve); $a > 1$. $f(x) = a^x$ (black curve); $g(x) = \log_a x$ (blue curve); $0 < a < 1$.

In these graphs, the exponential and logarithm functions are symmetric to each other across the line $y = x$.

Later in this chapter, we will show in greater detail how to graph inverse functions.

Worked Example 6.21

Graph the function $f(x) = \log_2 x$, $0 < x \leq 16$, $x \in R$.

Solution

As the base $= 2$, let x be equal to selected whole number powers of 2 within the given domain.

So, let $x = \frac{1}{2}$, 1, 2, 4, 8, 16.

x	y	(x,y)
$\frac{1}{2}$	-1	$\left(\frac{1}{2},-1\right)$
1	0	$(1,0)$
2	1	$(2,1)$
4	2	$(4,2)$
8	3	$(8,3)$
16	4	$(16,4)$

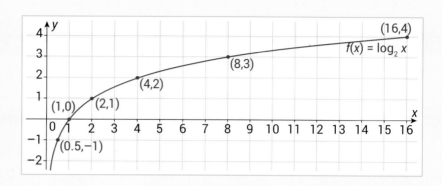

Exercise 6.6

1. Graph the following functions:

   (i) $f(x) = \log_4 x$, $x \in R$, $0 < x \leq 64$

   (ii) $f(x) = \log_5 x$, $x \in R$, $0 < x \leq 125$

   (iii) $f(x) = \log_3 x$, $x \in R$, $0 < x \leq 27$

   (iv) $f(x) = \log_e x$, $x \in R$, $0 < x < 8$

2. Use graphical methods to solve $\log_3 x = \log_2 x$, $x \in R$.

3. Use graphical methods to solve $\log_3 x \leq \log_4 x$, $x \in R$.

For practical problems involving logarithms, refer to Chapter 7, Exercise 7.5.

4. Shown below is the graph of the function $g(x) = \log_2 x$. Use the graph to match the following functions with those graphed below:

   (i) $h(x) = 4\log_2 x$ (ii) $f(x) = 3\log_2 x$

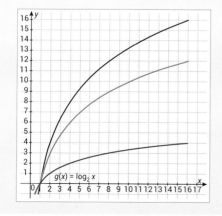

5. Shown below is the graph of the function $g(x) = \log_2 x$. Use the graph to match the following functions with those graphed below:

   (i) $h(x) = \log_2 (x + 1)$

   (ii) $f(x) = 0.5\log_2 x$

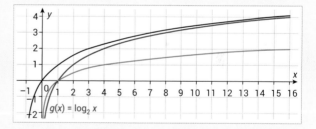

6. Graph the function $y = \log_3 x$ over the domain $0 < x \leq 27$, $x \in R$.

   Hence, sketch the following functions:

   (i) $f(x) = 2\log_3 x$

   (ii) $g(x) = \log_3 (x - 1)$

7. The graphs of $g(x) = \log_4 x$ and $f(x)$ are given.

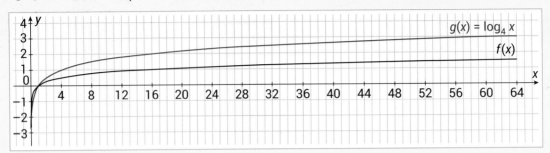

(i) Describe in your own words a transformation that would map the graph of $g(x)$ to the graph of $f(x)$.

(ii) What is the functional form of $f(x)$?

8. The graph of the function $y = \log_5 x$ is shifted five units to the right. What is the new functional form?

9. The graph of the function $y = 3\log_6 x$ is shifted three units downwards and three units to the right. What is its new functional form?

10. For each function below, identify the largest domain for which the function is defined and, hence, identify the corresponding range.

(i) $y = \log_3 (x - 1) - 5$ (ii) $y = \log_2 (x + 1) - 2$ (iii) $y = \log_3 (3x) - 5$ (iv) $y = \log_2 (3x - 1) + 2$

6.9 Injective, Surjective and Bijective Functions

Consider the following functions that map elements from set A to elements in set B.

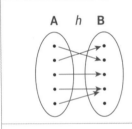	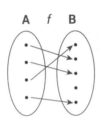	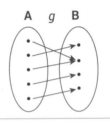	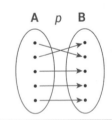
h is a function, as it maps every input to a unique output.	f is an injective ('1−1') function, as every output is the image of a unique input.	g is a surjective ('onto') function, as every element in B is an output.	p is a bijective function, as it is both injective and surjective ('1−1' and 'onto').

The Vertical Line Test

Usually when we draw a graph of a mapping, the horizontal axis is the input axis and the vertical axis is the output axis. If this is the case, then we can use the 'vertical line test' to determine if the mapping is a function or not.

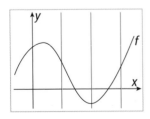

Within the domain of input values, any vertical line cuts the graph of f at one point only, so f is a function, as each input gets mapped to just one output.

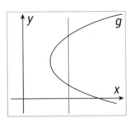

It is possible to draw a vertical line that cuts the curve at more than one point. So g cannot be a function, as some inputs get mapped to more than one output.

Vertical Line Test

The horizontal axis is the input axis. Then, within the domain of input values, if any vertical line cuts the graph of a mapping at more than one point, the mapping cannot be a function. Otherwise, it is a function.

Injective Functions ('One-to-One' or '1–1' Functions)

Let f be the function that maps the elements of a set A (domain) to the set B (codomain).

> The function f is injective if $\forall\, a, b \in A$, whenever $f(a) = f(b)$, then $a = b$.

> The symbol $\forall$ means 'for all' or 'for any'.

In other words, if a function is **injective** (also called a 'one-to-one' or '1–1' function), and an input value a gives the same output as an input value b, then $a = b$. Therefore, an injective function never assigns the same output value to two different input values.

A function f maps from a domain to a codomain as shown:

The function is injective, as no two domain values are assigned to the same output value. It does not matter that the element 3 in the codomain has no corresponding element in the domain; this is not necessary for the function to be injective.

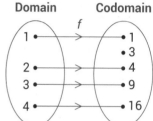

Horizontal Line Test for Injectivity

Consider the function $g: R \rightarrow R: x \rightarrow x + 3$.

A graph of g is shown.

Any horizontal line drawn will never cut the graph of g at more than one point. This shows that the function g is injective.

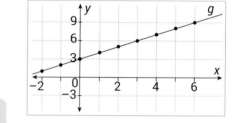

> **Horizontal Line Test for Injectivity**
>
> If the horizontal axis is the input axis, then, if any horizontal line cuts the graph of a function at no more than one point, the function is injective.

FUNCTIONS

Worked Example 6.22

Find the range of the function f where $f(x) = 1 - 3x$ on the domain $\{0, 1, 2, 3, 4\}$, and determine whether the function is injective or not.

Solution

x	$1 - 3x$	y
0	$1 - 3(0)$	1
1	$1 - 3(1)$	-2
2	$1 - 3(2)$	-5
3	$1 - 3(3)$	-8
4	$1 - 3(4)$	-11

Range = $\{1, -2, -5, -8, -11\}$

Each x-value maps to a different y-value.

$\therefore f$ is an injective function.

Find the range of the function g where $g(x) = 3x^2 - 1$ on the domain $x \in R$, and determine if the function is injective (one-to-one) or not.

Solution

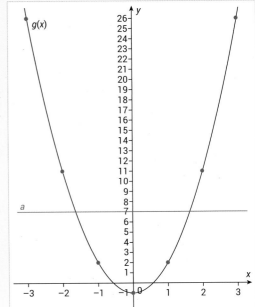

x	$3x^2 - 1$	y
−3	3(9) − 1	26
−2	3(4) − 1	11
−1	3(1) − 1	2
0	3(0) − 1	−1
1	3(1) − 1	2
2	3(4) − 1	11
3	3(9) − 1	26

From the sketch, we can see that the minimum value of $g(x)$ is −1.

∴ Range = $\{y \mid y \geqslant -1, y \in R\}$ (or Range = $[-1, \infty)$)

Horizontal line test

The horizontal line a intersects the graph of $g(x)$ at two points.

∴ g is not an injective function.

Alternatively, we can see from the input–output table that, for example, −2 is mapped to 11, as is 2.

∴ g is not an injective function.

Surjective Functions ('Onto' Functions)

Let f be the function that maps the elements of a set A (domain) to the set B (codomain).

> The function f is **surjective** if $\forall\, b \in B$, $\exists\, a \in A$ such that $f(a) = b$.

> The symbol $\exists$ means 'there exists'.

If a function is **surjective** or '**onto**', every element in the codomain is an output of the function. Every element in the codomain will have at least one matching element in the domain. Therefore, the codomain is also the range.

For example, if E is the set of all even natural numbers, then the function $h: N \to E$, where N is the set of naturals, defined by $h(x) = 2x$, is surjective.

Consider the set E. If the elements of the set N are substituted into the function h, every element in E will be the image of some element in N.

- $h(1) = 2$
- $h(2) = 4$
- $h(3) = 6$
- $h(n - 1) = 2(n - 1)$, which is an even number
- $h(n) = 2n$, which is an even number

> **Horizontal Line Test for Surjectivity**
>
> Consider the function $f: A \to B$.
>
> If f is surjective, then every horizontal line $y = b$, where $b \in B$, intersects the graph of f at **at least one** point.

Worked Example 6.24

What is the range of the function $f: [0, 2\pi] \to R: x \to \sin x$?

State, giving a reason in each case, if the function is:

(i) Injective   (ii) Surjective

Solution

From our knowledge of trigonometry, we know that the sine function is periodic, with a range of $[-1, 1]$.

(i) Consider the graph of the sine function in the domain $0 \leqslant x \leqslant 2\pi$.

The function is not injective.
Reason: Using the horizontal line test, it is clear that the line a cuts the graph at more than one point, so some inputs get mapped to the same output.

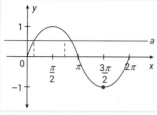

(ii) The function is not surjective.
Reason: The codomain is R, but the range is only $[-1, 1]$.

Using the horizontal line test:

If we draw a horizontal line through $y = 2$ (for example), it will not cut the graph of $y = f(x)$.

If the codomain had been defined as $[-1, 1]$, then the function would be surjective.

Worked Example 6.25

Consider the function $f: R \to [-1, 1]: x \to \sin x$.

Use the horizontal line test for surjectivity to determine whether the given function is surjective or not.

Solution

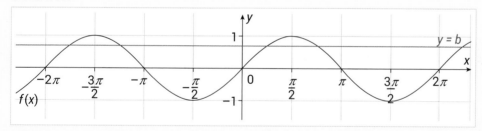

Draw a horizontal line $y = b$ on the graph where $b \in [-1, 1]$. As this line is moved up and down the y-axis, but within the codomain of $[-1, 1]$, b intersects the graph of f at least once. Therefore, the given function is surjective, as each element in the codomain has at least one matching element in the domain.

Bijective Functions

A function f is said to be **bijective** if it is both injective ('one-to-one') and surjective ('onto').

No two domain values are assigned to the same output value and every element in the codomain has at least one matching element in the domain.

FUNCTIONS

Worked Example 6.26

Is the function $f: R \to R: x \to 4x + 2$, a bijection?

Solution

Algebraic method

Show injective

Take any two elements of R, a and b.

$f(a) = 4(a) + 2$ $f(b) = 4(b) + 2$

Let $f(a) = f(b)$.

$$4a + 2 = 4b + 2$$
$$4a = 4b$$
$$\therefore a = b$$

So no two distinct domain values get mapped to the same output value.

$\therefore f(x)$ is injective.

Show surjective

Take any $c \in R$.

It can be written as $c = 4d + 2$, where d is some real number.

$\therefore f(x)$ is surjective.

As f is both injective and surjective, f is a bijection.

Graphical method

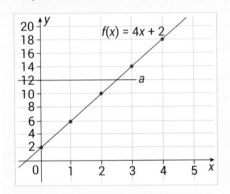

Any horizontal line intersects the graph at no more than one point.

$\therefore f$ is injective.

Any horizontal line intersects the graph of f once. Therefore, the function is surjective, as each element in the codomain has one matching element in the domain.

As f is both injective and surjective, f is a bijection.

Worked Example 6.27

Examine the following functions and state, giving reasons, whether each function is:

(a) Injective only   (b) Surjective only   (c) Bijective   (d) None of these

(i) $f: R \to R^+$, $f(x) = e^x$ (ii) $g: R \to R$, $g(x) = x^2$

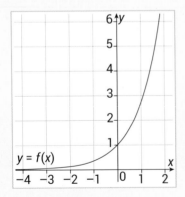

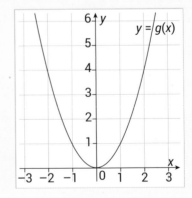

Solution

(i) The function is injective. The horizontal line test shows that the function is injective (there is no more than one point of intersection between any horizontal line and the curve).

The function is surjective. The codomain of this function is defined as R^+. Every element of the codomain has a corresponding domain value.

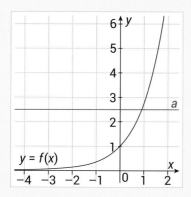

∴ As the function is injective and surjective, the function is (c) Bijective.

(ii) The function is not injective. The horizontal line test shows that the function is not injective (it is possible to draw a horizontal line with more than one point of intersection with the curve).

The function is not surjective. The codomain is R but the range is $[0, \infty)$.

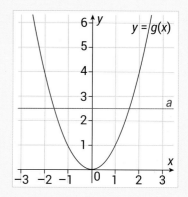

∴ The function is (d) None of these.

Exercise 6.7

1. State whether the following functions are surjective or not. Explain your answers.

(i)

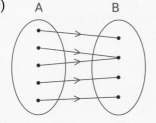

(ii)

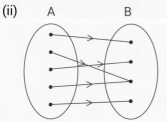

(iii)

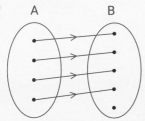

(iv)

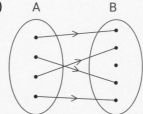

(v)

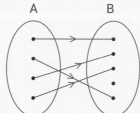

(vi)

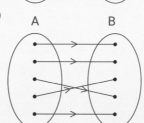

(vii)

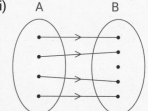

(viii)

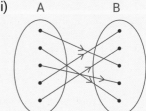

(ix)

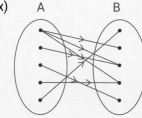

2. For each of the following functions from set A to B, state whether the function is:

(a) Injective only   (c) Bijective

(b) Surjective only   (d) None of the above

(i)

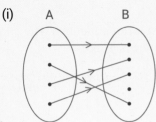

(ii)

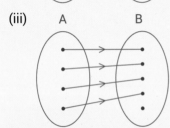

(iii)

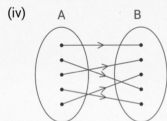

(iv)

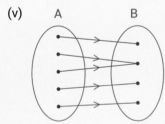

(v)

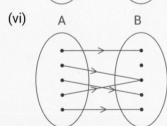

(vi)

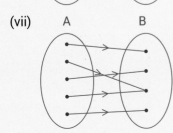

(vii)

3. Which of the following are **not** injective?

In the case of a function that is not injective, explain why not.

(i) $f: R \rightarrow R, f(x) = x^3 + 3$

(ii) $f: N \rightarrow N, f(x) = x^3 + 3$

(iii) $f: R \rightarrow R, f(x) = x^2 + 3$

(iv) $f: N \rightarrow N, f(x) = x^2 + 3$

4. By sketching their graphs, or otherwise, (a) find the range of each of the functions described below and (b) state whether each function is one-to-one or not.

(i) $f(x) = 2x$, for the domain $\{0, 2, 4, 8\}$

(ii) $f(x) = x^2 + 2, x \in R$

(iii) $f(x) = 3x - 1$ for the domain $-2 < x < 2, x \in R$

(iv) $f(x) = \dfrac{1}{x}, x \in R, x \neq 0$

(v) $f(x) = (x - 1)^2 + 2, x \in R$

(vi) $f(x) = x^3, x \in R$

(vii) $f(x) = \sin x$, for the domain $0 \leqslant x \leqslant 2\pi$

(viii) $f(x) = \sqrt{x}, x \in R, x \geqslant 0$

5. $f: N \rightarrow E, f(x) = 2x$. E is the set of even naturals. Is f onto? Explain.

6. $f: N \rightarrow E, f(x) = 4x$. E is the set of even naturals. Is f onto? Explain.

7. $f: R \rightarrow R, f(x) = 3x + 1$. Is f onto? Explain.

8. $f: R \rightarrow R, f(x) = |x|$. Is f onto? Explain.

9. $g: R \rightarrow R, g(x) = x^2$. Is g onto? Explain.

10. $h: R \rightarrow R, h(x) = \sin x$. Is h onto? Explain.

11. $p: R \rightarrow R, p(x) = e^x$. Is p onto? Explain.

12. $q: R \rightarrow R^+, q(x) = e^x$. Is q onto? Explain.

13. State whether each of the functions graphed below is:

(a) Injective only

(b) Surjective only

(c) Bijective

(d) None of the above

(i)

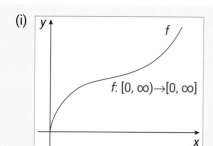

$f: [0, \infty) \rightarrow [0, \infty]$

(ii)

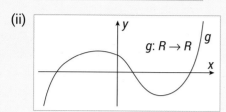

$g: R \rightarrow R$

(iii)

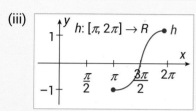

$h: [\pi, 2\pi] \rightarrow R$

14. State whether each mapping graphed below is a function or not.

(i)

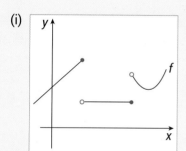

(ii)

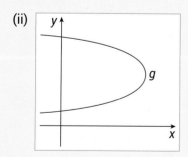

(iii)

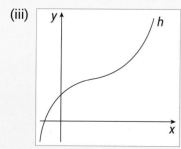

(iv)

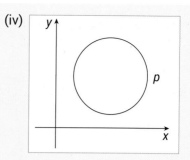

15. For each of the functions graphed below, state whether it is:

(a) Injective only

(b) Surjective only

(c) Bijective

(d) None of the above

(i)

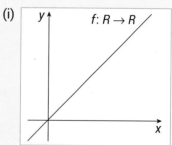

$f: R \rightarrow R$

(ii)

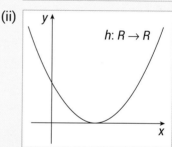

$h: R \rightarrow R$

(iii)

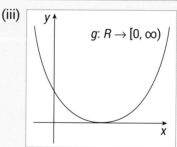

$g: R \rightarrow [0, \infty)$

(iv)

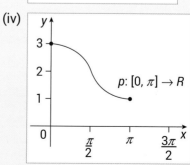

$p: [0, \pi] \rightarrow R$

16. Consider the function *f* graphed below.

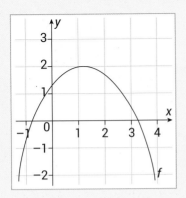

   (i) Is this function injective? Explain.

   (ii) Under what circumstances would this function be surjective?

> In Questions 17–19, investigate if the functions are injective using (a) algebraic methods and (b) graphical methods.

17. $f(x) = x^2 - 3x + 2$ in the domain $-1 \leqslant x \leqslant 4$, $x \in R$

18. $f(x) = x - 3x^2$, $x \in R$

19. $f(x) = 5x - 3$, $x \in R$

20. Define a 1–1 function from *N* to *E*, where *E* is the set of all positive even numbers.

21. Define a 1–1 function from *N* to *O*, where *O* is the set of all odd positive numbers.

22. Define a 1–1 function from *N* to *M*, where *M* is the set of all negative even numbers.

23. Given set $A = \{a, b, c\}$ and set $B = \{d, e, f, g\}$:

   (i) Is it possible to define a 1–1 function from *A* to *B*?

   (ii) Is it possible to define a 1–1 function from *B* to *A*?

   Explain your answers.

24. Show that the following functions are 'onto' functions using graphical methods:

   (i) $f: [-2, 2] \mapsto [-4, 0]: x \mapsto x^2 - 4$

   (ii) $g: [-6, 0] \mapsto [-5, 4]: x \mapsto x^2 + 6x + 4$

   (iii) $h: R \rightarrow [-1, 1]: x \rightarrow \sin x$

25. State whether the following functions are bijections or not:

   (i) $f: R \rightarrow R$, $f(x) = 3x + 1$

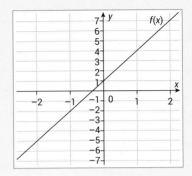

   (ii) $g: R \rightarrow R$, $g(x) = x^2 + 1$

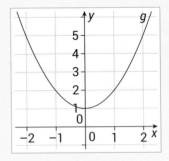

   (iii) $h: N \rightarrow Z \setminus N$, $h(x) = 1 - x$

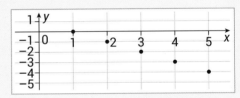

26. Consider the function $f: \left[-\dfrac{\pi}{2}, \dfrac{\pi}{2}\right] \rightarrow [-1, 1]$, $f(x) = \sin x$. Is *f* a bijection? Explain.

27. Is the function *f* where $f(x) = 2x$, which maps the natural numbers to the set of positive even numbers, a bijection? Explain.

28. $f: N \rightarrow Z$, $f(n) = \begin{cases} \dfrac{n-1}{2} & \text{if } n \text{ is odd} \\ -\dfrac{n}{2} & \text{if } n \text{ is even} \end{cases}$

   (i) Is this function 1–1?

   (ii) Is this function onto?

   (iii) Is this function bijective?

   Explain your answer in each case.

29. Consider the function $f: R \to R$.

   (i) If $f(x) = \sin x$, is the function a bijection? Explain your answer.

   (ii) If $f(x) = \cos x$, is the function a bijection? Explain your answer.

   (iii) If $f(x) = \tan x$, where $f: \left(-\dfrac{\pi}{2}, \dfrac{\pi}{2}\right) \to R$, is f a bijection? Explain your answer.

30. Show that $f: R \to R: x \to 4x^3 - 7$ is a bijection.

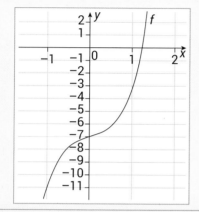

31. Consider the graph of $h(x) = 2^x$ below.

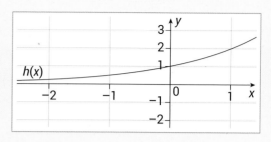

   (i) If $h: R \to R: x \to 2^x$, show that h is not a bijection.

   (ii) If $h: R \to R^+: x \to 2^x$, show that h is a bijection.

32. Show that the function f, where $f(x) = x^3 - 2x^2 - 5x + 6$, is not a bijection. (Assume a domain of R.)

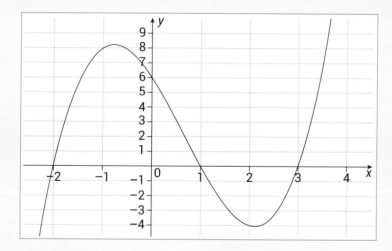

33. Give an example of a bijective function $f: Z \to N$.   (*Hint:* See Question 28.)

6.10 Inverse Functions

Consider the functions f and g defined below.

$$f: R \to R: x \to 3x + 1$$

$$g: R \to R: x \to \frac{x-1}{3}$$

Look at what happens if we input the value 2 into f.

$$f(2) = 3(2) + 1$$

$$= 6 + 1$$

$$= 7$$

FUNCTIONS

Now, if we input this value of 7 into g, we get:

$$g(7) = \frac{7-1}{3} = \frac{6}{3} = 2$$

Now, look at what happens if we input a value of, say, 5 into g.

$$g(5) = \frac{5-1}{3} = \frac{4}{3}$$

Now, if we input this value of $\frac{4}{3}$ into f, we get:

$$f\left(\frac{4}{3}\right) = 3\left(\frac{4}{3}\right) + 1 = 4 + 1 = 5$$

What appears to be happening here?

In the first example, g appears to undo the work of f. In the second example, f appears to undo the work of g.

The question is, was this coincidence due to the values that we picked, or do f and g undo each other's work, generally speaking?

To answer this question, let us take a closer look at both functions.

f is a bijection that maps from R to R, and g is a bijection that maps from R to R. So, the range of f (= R) is the domain of g (= R), and the range of g (= R) is the domain of f (= R).

Let us think about what each function does. f multiplies the input by 3 and then adds 1. How would you undo this work?

You would subtract 1 and then divide by 3. But this is exactly what g does.

Likewise, g subtracts 1 and then divides by 3. What does f do? It undoes this work by multiplying by 3 and then adding 1.

Two functions that have these characteristics are said to be **inverses** of each other.

> If two functions f and g are defined so that $f: A \to B$ and $g: B \to A$, then, if $(f \circ g)(x) = (g \circ f)(x) = x$, we say that f and g are *inverse functions* of each other.

Some functions do not have an inverse function. For example, consider the function $h: R \to R: x \to x^2$. h is not bijective. Therefore, h will not have an inverse.

To see this, consider input values of -2 and 2. $h(-2) = h(2) = 4$. So, undoing this work requires a mapping from 4 to two values, -2 and 2. However, such a mapping is not a function, since a function has to assign a unique output value to a given input value.

Also, consider $h(x) = -1$. $-1 \in R$, but there is no $x \in R$ that will give an output value of -1. The function h is not surjective.

> **Note**
>
> 1. A function f has an inverse function f^{-1} if and only if f is bijective (that is 'one-to-one' and 'onto').
> 2. A function f that is bijective will have a unique inverse function f^{-1}. A function cannot have more than one inverse.

Finally, note how important the domain and codomain are in determining if a function is invertible (has an inverse) or not.

For example, if we define a function h such that $h: R \to R: x \to e^x$, then h is not bijective (it is injective but not surjective) and so it has no inverse.

However, if we define h to be $h: R \to R^+: x \to e^x$, then h is bijective (invertible), with h^{-1} defined as $h^{-1}: R^+ \to R: x \to \ln x$.

Worked Example 6.28

Find the inverse of the function f where $f(x) = 2x + 3$, $x \in R$.

Solution

Consider what f does.

It multiplies the input by 2 and then adds 3.

f^{-1} must therefore subtract 3 from the input and then divide by 2.

So, f^{-1} is defined by $f^{-1}(x) = \dfrac{x-3}{2}$, $x \in R$.

(Note: f is bijective, so it is invertible, with domain R and range R.)

Worked Example 6.29

Given a function g, where $g(x) = \dfrac{12-4x}{3}$, $x \in R$:

(i) Find the inverse function g^{-1}.

(ii) Test the result in part (i) using $x = 2$.

(iii) Show that $gg^{-1}(x) = g^{-1}g(x) = x$, $\forall\, x \in R$.

Solution

(i) $g(x) = \dfrac{12-4x}{3}$

Write as $y = \dfrac{12-4x}{3}$.

Write x in terms of y.

$3y = 12 - 4x$

$4x = 12 - 3y$

$x = \dfrac{12-3y}{4}$

So, to undo the work of g you need to:

- Multiply by −3
- Add 12
- Divide by 4

$\therefore g^{-1}$ is defined by:

$g^{-1}(x) = \dfrac{12-3x}{4}$, $x \in R$

(ii) $g(2) = \dfrac{12-4(2)}{3}$

$= \dfrac{12-8}{3}$

$= \dfrac{4}{3}$

$g^{-1}\left(\dfrac{4}{3}\right) = \dfrac{12-3\left(\frac{4}{3}\right)}{4}$

$= \dfrac{12-4}{4}$

$= 2$

So we see how g^{-1} undoes the work of g.

(iii) $gg^{-1}(x) = g\left(\dfrac{12-3x}{4}\right)$

$= \dfrac{12-4\left(\frac{12-3x}{4}\right)}{3}$

$= \dfrac{12-12+3x}{3}$

$= \dfrac{3x}{3}$

$\therefore gg^{-1}(x) = x$

$g^{-1}g(x) = \dfrac{12-3\left(\frac{12-4x}{3}\right)}{4}$

$= \dfrac{12-12+4x}{4}$

$= \dfrac{4x}{4}$

$\therefore g^{-1}g(x) = x$

$\therefore gg^{-1}(x) = g^{-1}g(x) = x$, $\forall\, x \in R$

Alternative method for part (i)

(i) g is invertible, as g is bijective.

g has domain R and range R.

We could decompose g as $c \circ b \circ a$

where $a(x) = -4x$

$b(x) = x + 12$

$c(x) = \dfrac{x}{3}$.

So $a^{-1}(x) = -\dfrac{x}{4}$.

$b^{-1}(x) = x - 12$

$c^{-1}(x) = 3x$

So $g^{-1} = a^{-1} \circ b^{-1} \circ c^{-1}$.

$(b^{-1} \circ c^{-1})(x) = 3x - 12$

$a^{-1} \circ (b^{-1} \circ c^{-1})(x) = -\dfrac{3x-12}{4}$

$= \dfrac{12-3x}{4}$

$\therefore g^{-1}$ is defined by:

$g^{-1}(x) = \dfrac{12-3x}{4}$, $x \in R$

Since $g: R \to R$, $g^{-1}: R \to R$.

Worked Example 6.30

Investigate if the function $f: R \to R: x \to x^3 + 1$ has an inverse.

Solution

Consider the graph of the function.

The horizontal line test shows that the function is injective.

The function is also surjective, as every element in the codomain has a corresponding domain value.

∴ The function is a bijection and therefore has an inverse.

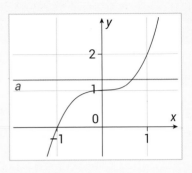

Exercise 6.8

In Questions 1–5, find the inverse of each function.

1. $f(x) = 2x, \, x \in R$

2. $g(x) = 3x + 1, \, x \in R$

3. $p(x) = 6x - 4, \, x \in R$

4. $f(x) = x^2 + 6, \, x \geq 0$

5. $g(x) = -x^2 - 1, \, x \leq 0$

6. For each of Questions 1–5, show that $F^{-1}F(x) = FF^{-1}(x) = x$, where F is the original function in each question.

In Questions 7–12, investigate if the functions have inverses.

7. $h(x) = x^2 + 2x - 3, \, x \leq -1$

8. $f: R \to R: x \to x^3$

9. $g: R \to R: x \to x^2$

10. $h: [0, \infty) \to [0, \infty): x \to x^2$

11. $f: \left[-\dfrac{\pi}{2}, \dfrac{\pi}{2}\right] \to [-1, 1]: x \to \sin x$

12. $g: \left[-\dfrac{\pi}{2}, \dfrac{\pi}{2}\right] \to [0, 1]: x \to \cos x$

13. Find the inverse of the function g defined as $g: [3, \infty) \to [-5, \infty): x \to 2(x - 3)^2 - 5$.

14. Find the inverse of the function $f: [0, \infty) \to [0, 1): x \to \dfrac{x^2}{x^2 + 1}$.

> Revise Chapter 7, Indices and Logarithms, to help you with Questions 15–18.

15. Find the inverse of the function $h(x) = e^x$, where $h: R \to R^+$.

16. $h: R \to R^+: x \to 2^x$

   (i) Find h^{-1}, the inverse of h.

   (ii) Verify that $h^{-1}h(x) = hh^{-1}(x) = x$.

17. Find the inverse of the function $f: x \to 2^{3x-1}$, where $f: [0, \infty) \to \left[\dfrac{1}{2}, \infty\right)$.

18. Find the inverse of the function f defined by $f(x) = \log_b(x + 1)$, where $f: (-1, \infty) \to R$, $b > 0$, $b \neq 1$.

6.11 Graphs of Functions and their Inverses

Consider the following functions and their graphs:

Function	Inverse function	Graph
f where $f(x) = 2x, \, x \in R$	f^{-1} where $f^{-1}(x) = \dfrac{x}{2}, \, x \in R$	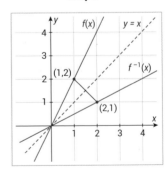

What do we notice about the graphs of f and f^{-1}?

The point (1,2) lies on the graph of f, since $f(1) = 2$.

So, since $f^{-1}(2) = \dfrac{2}{2} = 1$, the point (2,1) will lie on the graph of f^{-1}.

Consider a more general case:

The point $(a,2a)$ lies on the graph of f, since $f(a) = 2a$.

So, the point $(2a,a)$ lies on the graph of f^{-1}, since $f^{-1}(2a) = \dfrac{2a}{2} = a$.

Therefore, for any invertible function f and its inverse function f^{-1}, we get the following result:

If (c,d) is a point on the graph of f, then (d,c) is a point on the graph of f^{-1}.

Geometrically speaking, the graphs of f and f^{-1} are reflections of each other about the line $y = x$.

Worked Example 6.31

Below is the graph of the function f, where $f(x) = x + 2$, $x \in R$. Sketch the graph of the inverse of this function.

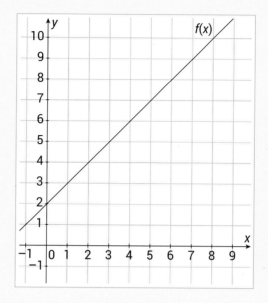

Solution

Method 1

Reverse the co-ordinates of the points that satisfy the given function, and plot the graph of the inverse.

From the graph, it can be seen that the points $(0,2)$, $(2,4)$ and $(4,6)$ satisfy the given function.

So $(2,0)$, $(4,2)$ and $(6,4)$ satisfy the inverse function.

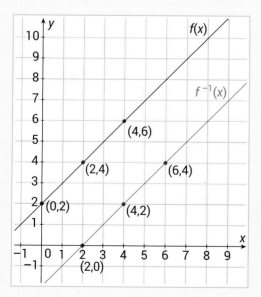

Method 2

Construct the line $y = x$ and find the image of the graph of f under axial symmetry in the line $y = x$.

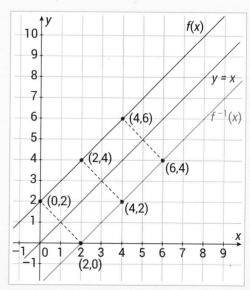

Transformation of graphs under axial symmetry is also shown in Book 2, Chapter 12.

Worked Example 6.32

Sketch the inverse of the function $f: [0, \infty) \to \left[\frac{1}{2}, \infty\right)$: $x \to x^2 + \frac{1}{2}$ on the graph below.

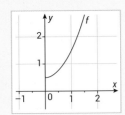

Solution

Step 1   Mark points A, B, C and D on the given curve.

Step 2   Draw the line $y = x$.

Step 3   Find the image of each point under axial symmetry in the line $y = x$.

Step 4   Sketch the resulting inverse function.

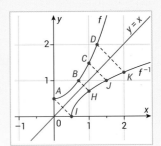

Exercise 6.9

Sketch the inverses of the following functions.

1. $f(x) = 2x$, $f: R \to R$

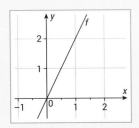

2. $g(x) = 3x + 1$, $g: R \to R$

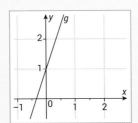

3. $h(x) = 6x - 4$, $h: R \to R$

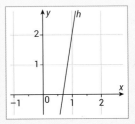

4. $f(x) = 2^x$, $f: [1, \infty) \to [2, \infty)$

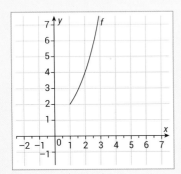

5. $f(x) = 2(x - 3)^2 - 5$, $f: [3, \infty) \to [-5, \infty)$

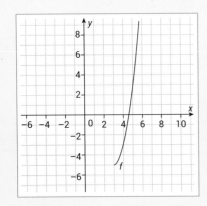

6. $f(x) = \dfrac{x^2}{x^2 + 1}$, $f: [0, \infty) \to [0, 1)$

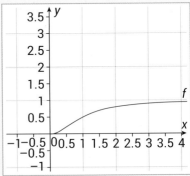

7. $g(x) = e^x$, $g: R \to R^+$

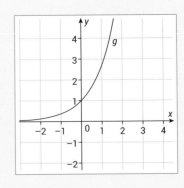

8. $h: [0, \infty) \to \left[\frac{1}{2}, \infty\right): x \to = 2^{3x-1}$

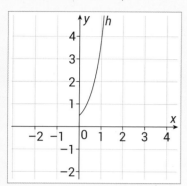

9. $p: R^+ \to R: x \to \ln x$

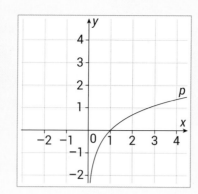

10. $f(x) = \ln(x + 1), f: (-1, \infty) \to R$

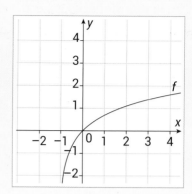

Revision Exercises

1. Given that the functions f and g are defined by $f(x) = 3x + 6$ and $g(x) = x^2 - 4x$, find:

   (i) $g(2)$ (ii) $fg(3)$ (iii) $gf(2)$ (iv) $fg(x)$

2. Given that the functions a, b and c are defined by

   $a: x \to x^2 - 3$, $b: x \to \frac{1}{x} - 4$ and $c: x \to x + 3$,

   define the following functions, writing your answer in the form FUNCTION NAME: $x \to$ ...:

   (i) bb (iii) cc (v) bac

   (ii) ba (iv) acb (vi) cab

3. The functions f, g and h are defined by $f(x) = x^2 - 1$, $g(x) = 3x + 4$ and $h(x) = \frac{1}{x}$.

   Solve the following equations, giving your answers correct to two decimal places:

   (i) $fg(x) = 16$ (ii) $fh(x) = 5$

4. (i) Graph the function $h: x \to x^3 + x^2 - x - 10$ in the domain $-2.5 \leqslant x \leqslant 2.5, x \in R$.

   (ii) From inspection of the graph, how many real roots does the function h have?

   (iii) Factorise the function. Then, solve $h(x) = 0$.

   How does your solution to part (iii) support your findings in part (ii)?

5. A function f is defined by the rule 'Divide the input by 4 and add 3.'

   (i) Write an expression in x to represent this function.

   (ii) Use this expression to find the value of $f(3)$, $f(-2)$ and $f(-8)$.

   (iii) For what value of x is $f(x) = 9$?

6. For each of the following functions, state whether the function is one-to-one only, onto only or one-to-one and onto.

(i)

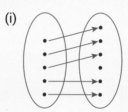

(ii)

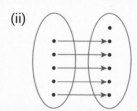

(iii)

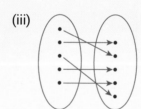

(iv)

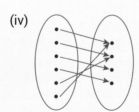

(v)

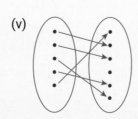

7. Consider the graphs below and identify the nature of the mapping in each case:

- Not a function
- 1–1 function
- Onto function
- 1–1 and onto function

(i)
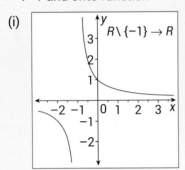

(ii)
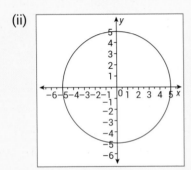

(iii)
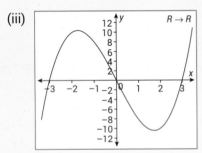

(iv)
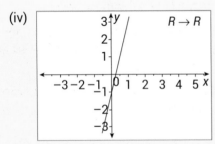

8. Identify which of the following functions are injective. In each case, the mapping is from R to R.

(i) $f(x) = 2x + 5$ (iii) $h(x) = x(x - 1)$

(ii) $g(x) = |x|$ (iv) $p(x) = x^3 + 5$

In the case of functions that are not injective, show by example why not.

9. The graph of $f(x) = x^2 + 2x + 3$ is shown. Use this graph to match the following functions with the functions shown below:

(i) $g(x) = 2x^2 + 4x + 6$

(ii) $h(x) = x^2 + 2x + 4$

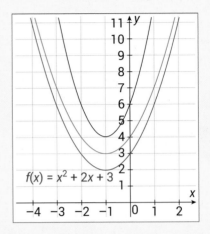

10. Identify the values of a and b in the function $y = ab^x$ graphed below.

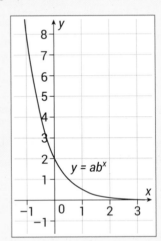

11. $f: R \rightarrow R$, $f(x) = 3x - 3$. Is $f(x)$ onto? Explain.

12. $f: R \rightarrow R$, $f(x) = |x + 1|$. Is $f(x)$ onto? Explain.

13. $g: R \rightarrow R$, $g(x) = (x + 2)^2$. Is $g(x)$ onto? Explain.

14. Are the following functions bijections?

(i) $f: R \rightarrow R$, $f(x) = 3x + 4$

(ii) $f: R \rightarrow R$, $f(x) = |x - 3|$

15. Show that $f: R \rightarrow R: x \rightarrow 4x^3$ is a bijection.

16. Show that $g: R \rightarrow R: x \rightarrow x^3 - 2$ is a bijection.

17. Show that $h: R \rightarrow R: x \rightarrow 3x^2$ is not a bijection.

18. Show that $f: R \rightarrow R$, $f(x) = x^3 + 3x^2 - x - 2$ is not a bijection.

19. A production manager is given the following blueprint for manufacturing a closed cylinder. The height of the cylinder is eight times the length of the radius, r.

   (i) Express the curved surface area of the cylinder as a function of r.

   (ii) Express the total surface area of the cylinder as a function of r.

   (iii) Express the volume of the cylinder as a function of r. Hence, find the volume of the cylinder when r is 4.5 cm.

20. A motor vehicle is depreciated at a rate of 12% per annum (reducing-balance method) from the date of purchase to the date of sale. The vehicle cost €40,000. Express the net book value of the vehicle as a function of t, where t is the number of years passed.

> In Questions 21–25, find the inverse of each function.

21. $f(x) = 3x - 3,\ f: R \to R$

22. $g(x) = \dfrac{1}{3 - x},\ g: R \setminus \{3\} \to R \setminus \{0\}$

23. $h(x) = \dfrac{12 - 3x}{8},\ h: R \to R$

24. $h(x) = -\dfrac{4}{x},\ h: R \setminus \{0\} \to R \setminus \{0\}$

25. $g(x) = \dfrac{4x}{7},\ g: R \to R$

26. $g(x) = 3x$ and $h(x) = \dfrac{1}{x},\ g: R \setminus \{0\} \to R \setminus \{0\}$ and $h: R \setminus \{0\} \to R \setminus \{0\}$

   (i) Find $g^{-1}(x)$, $h^{-1}(x)$ and $gh(x)$.

   (ii) Show that $(hg)^{-1}(x) = g^{-1}h^{-1}(x) = \dfrac{1}{3x}$.

27. The following functions are not invertible as is:

   (i) $f(x) = x^2,\ f: R \to R$

   (ii) $g(x) = (x + 3)^2,\ g: R \to R$

     (a) For each function, find the largest domain and codomain such that the function is invertible.

     (b) Then find the inverse of each function, using the restricted domain and codomain from part (a).

28. State which of the following functions are invertible, giving reasons in each case:

   (i) $f: x \to 4 - x^2,\qquad f: R \to R$

   (ii) $g: x \to \dfrac{1}{x - 3},\qquad g: R \setminus \{3\} \to R$

   (iii) $h: x \to 3 - x^2,\qquad h: [0, \infty) \to (-\infty, 3]$

29. A colony of bacteria grows according to the law of uninhibited growth at a rate of 18% per hour. The initial number of bacteria is 125.

   (i) Complete the following table:

x (number of hours passed)	$P(x)$ (population size)
0	
1	
2	
3	
4	
5	
6	

   (ii) Using suitable scales and axes, draw a graph for the population size for the first 6 hours of growth.

   (iii) Estimate the population size after 3.5 hours.

   (iv) By taking suitable readings, estimate the doubling time for the population.

   (v) If a quantity A grows by 18% per hour, then in one hour the quantity has grown to $A(1.18)$. In terms of x, what has the quantity grown to after x hours?

   (vi) Write down the population function for the colony of bacteria in terms of x. Answer in the form $P(x) = A.b^x$.

   (vii) Hence, check the accuracy of your answer to part (iii).

> Sketch the inverse function of each function graphed below in Questions 30–33.

30.

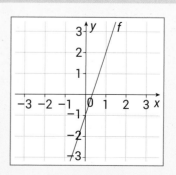

31.

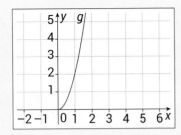

32.

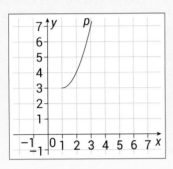

33.

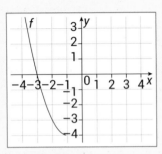

34. Sketch the inverse of $f(x) = e^x$, $f: R \to R^+$.

35. Use the same scales and axes to draw the graphs of the two functions $f(x) = 3 - 2x + x^2$ and $g(x) = 5 - 2x - x^2$ in the domain $-3 \leqslant x \leqslant 2$, $x \in R$.

   (i) Use your graphs to estimate the values of x for which $f(x) = g(x)$.

  (ii) Use your graphs to estimate the values of x for which $f(x) \geqslant g(x)$.

 (iii) Use your graphs to estimate the values of x for which $f(x) < g(x)$.

36. The function graphed below is $f(x) = ax^2 + bx + c$, $x \in R$.

Find the values of a, b and c.

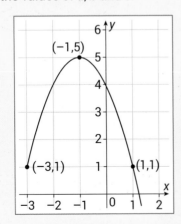

37. Draw the graph of the cubic function
$f: x \to x^3 + 3x^2 + 2x - 3$ in the domain $-3 \leqslant x \leqslant 1$, $x \in R$.

Estimate from your graph:

  (i) The value of x for which $f(x) = 0$

 (ii) The values of x for which $f(x) = -3$

How many real roots does the function f have?

38. Sketch the following graphs, showing relevant points:

  (i) $y = (x - 4)^2$ (iii) $y = 5 - (x + 2)^2$

 (ii) $y = x^3 - 8$ (iv) $y = 1 + 3(2^x)$

39. (a) Write the following quadratic functions in completed square form.

   (b) Hence, find the real roots of each function, where they exist.

   (c) State the turning point for each function, and write down the equation of the axis of symmetry of the curve.

   (d) Sketch each function.

      (i) $y = x^2 + 6x + 9$

     (ii) $y = x^2 + 2x - 8$

    (iii) $y = 2x^2 + 2x - 9$

    (iv) $y = (x - 3)^2 + 8x - 3$

     (v) $y = -(1 - 2x)^2 + x^2$

    (vi) $y = (x - 2)(2 + 3x) + 3$

40. Solve each of the following equations by first writing in completed square form:

  (i) $\dfrac{x + 3}{6} = \dfrac{2x}{x - 3}$ (ii) $\dfrac{x - 2}{5} = \dfrac{2x}{-x - 2}$

41. (a) Consider the quadratic $f(x) = x^2 + 2x - 3$. Write the function in completed square form.

   (b) Hence, find the real root of the function.

   (c) State the turning point of the function, and write down the equation of the axis of symmetry of the curve.

   (d) Sketch the function.

   (e) The function f is defined as follows:
$f: [1, \infty) \to [-4, \infty): x \to x^2 - 2x - 3$

     (i) State the codomain and range of f.

    (ii) Explain why f is invertible.

    (iii) State the domain and range of f^{-1}.

    (iv) Sketch the graph of f^{-1}, showing where the graph meets the co-ordinate axes.

42. The graph of the function $y = 3^x$ is stretched vertically by a factor of 2.

What is the new functional form?

43. An old satellite is falling back to Earth and will strike a city block if it is not shot down. Two different scientists recommend firing missiles using two different models to hit the satellite when it is still over water at a height of 2,000 m.

Model A is given by the function f, where $f(x) = 3x - x^2$.

Model B is given by the function g, where $g(x) = 0.25x$.

In each case, the function gives the height (in 1,000s of metres) of the missile, where x is the time passed in minutes.

   (i) Using suitable axes and scales, graph the height of each missile against time.

   (ii) Which missile takes longer to hit the satellite?

   (iii) How could you sequence the firing of the two missiles so that they both hit the satellite at exactly the same moment?

44. (i) Graph the function
   $f(x) = \log_2 x, x \in R, 0 < x \leqslant 64$.

   (ii) Describe what happens to the graph if $f(x)$ is changed to $\log_2 (x + 1), x \in R$, $0 < x \leqslant 64$.

45. An investment follows the following growth model: $F = P(1 + i)^t$, where P is the initial amount invested, i is the rate of interest as a decimal and t is the length of time in years.

Consider an initial investment of €400 invested at 12% per annum for five years.

   (i) Calculate the value of the investment at the end of each year for the first five years of the investment.

   (ii) Using the number of years as the x-variable and the final value as the y-variable, graph the growth of the investment over a five-year period.

   (iii) Clearly identify the base and the exponent in the formula $F = P(1 + i)^t$.

   (iv) Use your graph to estimate the value of the investment after three years and three months.

   (v) Use algebra to work out the percentage error made in answering part (iv).

46. The concentration of a drug, once injected into a patient's body, halves every 24 hours. A patient receives an injection of 120 mg of the drug.

   (i) Define a function in x that models the concentration of the drug, where x is the number of days from injection.

   (ii) Draw a graph to show the amount of the drug remaining in the patient's body over a period of seven days.

   (iii) After how long will 50 mg of the drug remain in the patient's body?

47. Statistics indicate that the world population has been growing at a rate of 1.9 per cent annually since the Second World War. The United States Census Bureau estimated the world population to be 7 billion in 2012.

   (i) Assuming exponential growth given by $P(t) = 7e^{0.019t}$, where t is years passed since 2012, use the graph shown to estimate what the world population will be in 2025.

   (ii) When will the world population be 8 billion? Use your graph to estimate a solution.

   (iii) Using the function $P(t) = 7e^{0.019t}$, investigate your answers to parts (i) and (ii) above.

   In each case, calculate, to one decimal place, the percentage error made in estimation using the graph.

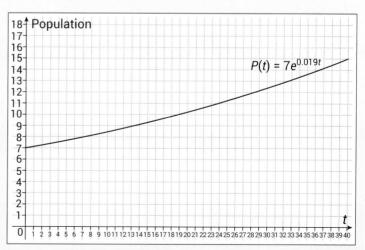

48. The rate at which a body cools is given by $\theta = 250e^{-0.05t}$, where the excess of temperature of a body above its surroundings at time t minutes is $\theta°C$.

Plot a graph showing the natural decay curve for the first hour of cooling.

Hence:

   (i) Determine the temperature after 25 minutes.

   (ii) Determine the time at which the temperature is 195°C.

   (iii) Use algebra to calculate how long it takes for the temperature to drop to 50°C. Answer correct to the nearest minute.

49. The amount of Product X (in $mol\,cm^{-3}$) found in a chemical reaction starting with $2.5\ mol\,cm^{-3}$ of reactant is given by $x = 2.5(1 - e^{-4t})$, where t is the time, in minutes, to form Product X.

Plot a graph at 30-second intervals up to 2.5 minutes and estimate the amount of Product X after 45 seconds.

Over which 30-second interval would you be most likely to make the greatest percentage error in using your graph to estimate the quantity of Product X? Explain your answer clearly.

50. The crushing strength of mortar varies with the percentage of water used in its preparation, as shown below.

Crushing strength, F (tonnes)	1.64	1.36	1.08	0.8	0.52	0.24
Percentage of water used, w (%)	6	9	12	15	18	21

   (i) Plot a graph of F (vertically) against w (horizontally).

   (ii) Estimate the crushing strength when 10 per cent of water is used.

   (iii) Assuming that the graph continues in the same manner, estimate the percentage of water used when the crushing strength is 0.15 tonnes.

   (iv) What is the equation of the graph?

Exam Questions

1. A is the closed interval $[0, 5]$. That is, $A = \{x \mid 0 \leqslant x \leqslant 5, x \in R\}$.
The function f is defined on A by:
$$f: A \rightarrow R: x \mapsto x^3 - 5x^2 + 3x + 5$$

   (a) Find the maximum and minimum values of f.

   (b) State whether f is injective. Give a reason for your answer.

SEC Leaving Certificate Higher Level, Sample Paper 1, 2014

Solutions and chapter summary available online

07

Indices and Logarithms

In this chapter you will learn:

- ◉ About exponents or indices
- ◉ About the exponential function
- ◉ About the natural exponential function
- ◉ About the laws of indices
- ◉ How to solve equations of the form $a^x = b$, where a and b are constants and $x \in R$

- ◉ About surds
- ◉ About logarithms
- ◉ About the laws of logarithms
- ◉ About using logs to solve real-life problems

You should remember...

- ◉ How to use your calculator to write numbers of the form a^b, $a, b \in Q$ in decimal form
- ◉ How to solve linear and quadratic equations

Key words

- ◉ Exponent
- ◉ Exponential function
- ◉ Natural exponential function
- ◉ Surd
- ◉ Logarithm

7.1 Indices (Exponents)

Indices (sometimes called exponents) and logarithms are routinely applied to a wide range of 'real-life' problems. They are used to compare earthquakes of different strengths. Biologists use them to predict future sizes of human and animal populations. Archaeologists use them to determine the ages of artefacts. Medical technicians use them to monitor the decay of radioactive material in various diagnostic tests, such as bone scans.

Archaeologists often estimate the age of an artefact as they excavate it, and use precise methods later to obtain a more accurate age.

A number in index form is of the form b^n. We call b the base and n the index, power or exponent.

For example, the decimal number 10,000,000,000,000,000 can be written as 10^{16}, or the decimal number 0.000000001 can be written as 10^{-9}.

Index notation is useful for writing very large or very small numbers in a manageable form.

Exponential Functions

A function of the form, $f(x) = a^x$, where a is a positive constant, is called an exponential function.

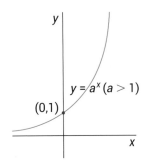

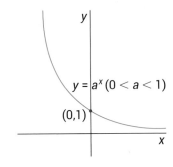

- For $a > 1$, the function *grows* as x increases.
- All such curves pass through (0,1) since $a^0 = 1$ (for $a > 1$).

- For $0 < a < 1$, the function *decays* as x increases.
- All such curves pass through (0,1) since $a^0 = 1$ (for $0 < a < 1$).

The Natural Exponential Function

Consider the infinite series:

$$1 + \frac{1}{1!} + \frac{1}{2!} + \frac{1}{3!} + \frac{1}{4!} + \ldots$$

$$e = 1 + \frac{1}{1!} + \frac{1}{2!} + \frac{1}{3!} + \frac{1}{4!} + \ldots$$

The limit of this series is an irrational number. Mathematicians have chosen the letter e to represent this irrational number, which is commonly called Euler's number.

To 20 decimal places, the value of e is 2.71828182845904523536.

The graph of the function $f(x) = e^x$ is shown on the right. This function is also called the **natural exponential function**, because it arises naturally in maths and physical sciences (that is, in real-life situations).

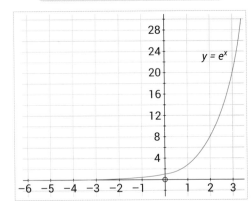

For example, the formula $A = A_0 e^{-\lambda t}$ can be used to measure the amount of radioactive material in a substance, where:

A_0 = the initial amount of radioactive material in the substance

λ = the decay constant

t = time in days since the initial amount of radioactive material was measured.

Worked Example 7.1

(i) Graph the function $f(x) = e^{\frac{1}{2}x}$, $-4 \le x \le 5$, $x \in R$.

(ii) Use your graph to find an approximation for $f(2.5)$.

(iii) Use your graph to solve the equation $f(x) = 4$.

Solution

(i) **Step 1** Draw a table of values. Use the calculator to evaluate the $f(x)$ row. (Write correct to one decimal place where necessary.)

x	-4	-3	-2	-1	0	1	2	3	4
$f(x)$	0.1	0.2	0.4	0.6	1	1.6	2.7	4.5	7.4

Step 2 Draw the graph.

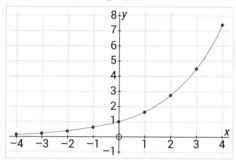

(ii)

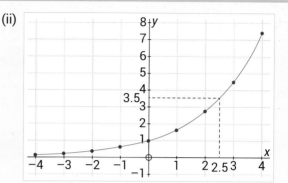

$f(2.5) \approx 3.5$

(iii)

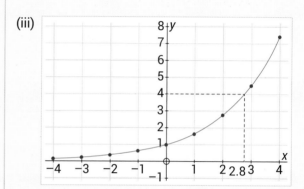

Solution set: {2.8}

7.2 Laws of Indices (Exponents)

Law 1 $a^p \times a^q = a^{p+q}$

Law 2 $\dfrac{a^p}{a^q} = a^{p-q}$

Law 3 $(a^p)^q = a^{pq}$

Law 4 $a^0 = 1$

Law 5 $a^{\frac{1}{q}} = \sqrt[q]{a}$

Law 6 $a^{\frac{p}{q}} = \left(\sqrt[q]{a}\right)^p$

Law 7 $a^{-p} = \dfrac{1}{a^p}$

Law 8 $(ab)^p = a^p b^p$

Law 9 $\left(\dfrac{a}{b}\right)^p = \dfrac{a^p}{b^p}$

These laws appear on page 21 of *Formulae and Tables*.

$\sqrt[n]{a}$ is called the nth root of a. If b is the nth root of a, then $b^n = a$.

$\sqrt{a} = a^{\frac{1}{2}}$

Worked Example 7.2

Evaluate each of the following as rational numbers:

(i) $64^{\frac{1}{6}}$ (ii) $125^{\frac{2}{3}}$ (iii) $64^{-\frac{4}{3}}$

Solution

(i) $64^{\frac{1}{6}} = \sqrt[6]{64}$

$= 2$

(ii) $125^{\frac{2}{3}} = \left(125^{\frac{1}{3}}\right)^2$

$= \left(\sqrt[3]{125}\right)^2$

$= 5^2$

$= 25$

(iii) $64^{-\frac{4}{3}} = \dfrac{1}{64^{\frac{4}{3}}}$

$= \dfrac{1}{\left(\sqrt[3]{64}\right)^4}$

$= \dfrac{1}{(4)^4}$

$\therefore 64^{-\frac{4}{3}} = \dfrac{1}{256}$

OR

$64^{-\frac{4}{3}} = \left(64^{\frac{1}{3}}\right)^{-4}$

$= \left(\sqrt[3]{64}\right)^{-4}$

$= 4^{-4}$

$= \dfrac{1}{4^4}$

$\therefore 64^{-\frac{4}{3}} = \dfrac{1}{256}$

Worked Example 7.3

(i) Simplify $\dfrac{e^5 + e^4}{e^3 + e^2}$

(ii) Simplify the following, giving your answer in index form:

    (a) $(-5)^{10}$ (b) $(-4)^3$

Solution

(i) $\dfrac{e^5 + e^4}{e^3 + e^2} = \dfrac{e^2(e^3 + e^2)^{\dagger}}{(e^3 + e^2)^{\dagger}}$

    $= e^2$

(ii) (a) $(-5)^{10} = 5^{10}$ (A negative number raised to an even power is always positive.)

    (b) $(-4)^3 = -4^3$ (A negative number raised to an odd power is always negative.)

Exercise 7.1

1. Graph the function
$f(x) = 2^x$ in the domain $-1 \leqslant x \leqslant 3$.

2. Graph the function
$f(x) = 2^x - 2$ in the domain $-1 \leqslant x \leqslant 3$.

3. Graph the function
$g(x) = 2.3^x - 1$ in the domain $-1 \leqslant x \leqslant 3$.

4. Graph the function
$h(x) = 2.5^x - 4$ in the domain $-1 \leqslant x \leqslant 3$.

5. Graph the function
$k(x) = \left(\dfrac{1}{2}\right)^x + 1$ in the domain $-1 \leqslant x \leqslant 3$.

6. Graph the function
$f(x) = 3^x, -1 \leqslant x \leqslant 3, x \in R$.

  (i) Use your graph to find an approximation for $f(1.6)$. Give your answer to the nearest whole number.

  (ii) Use your graph to solve the equation $f(x) = 18$. Give your answer correct to 1 decimal place.

7. Graph the function
$f(x) = \left(\dfrac{2}{3}\right)^x, -4 \leqslant x \leqslant 1, x \in R$.

  (i) Use your graph to find $f(0)$.

  (ii) $f(-2)$ lies in the range $[1, a]$. If $a \in N$, then what is the minimum value of a?

8. Graph the following functions:
  (i) $f(x) = e^{2x}, -2 \leqslant x \leqslant 1.5, x \in R$
  (ii) $f(x) = e^{\frac{x}{3}}, -2 \leqslant x \leqslant 5, x \in R$

9. Using the same axes and scales, graph the following functions:

$f(x) = \left(\dfrac{5}{2}\right)^x, -3 \leqslant x \leqslant 3, x \in R$

$g(x) = \left(\dfrac{2}{5}\right)^x, -3 \leqslant x \leqslant 3, x \in R$

  (i) Using your graph, solve the equation $f(x) = g(x)$.

  (ii) What transformation maps $g(x)$ to $f(x)$?

10. Without using a calculator, write the following in the form a^p:
  (i) $10^7 \times 10^2$ (vi) $\dfrac{1}{e^3}$
  (ii) $20^4 \times 20^2$
  (iii) $7^4 \times 7^4$ (vii) $\dfrac{(-5)^{10}}{(-5)^3}$
  (iv) $(e)^2 \times (e)^3$
  (v) $\dfrac{4^6}{4}$ (viii) $(10^4)^9$
    (ix) $(e^2)^2$
    (x) $(e^5)^5$

11. Simplify the following, giving your answer in index notation:
  (i) $(-3)^3$ (v) $(-4)^{12}$
  (ii) $(-2)^{20}$ (vi) $-(-1)^{100}$
  (iii) $(-5)^{19}$ (vii) $-(6)^3$
  (iv) $(3)^3$ (viii) $-(-6)^3$

12. Without using your calculator, write each of the following as fractions in their simplest form:
  (i) 2^{-3} (iii) 4^{-2} (v) $4(3^{-4})$
  (ii) 7^{-2} (iv) 3^{-4} (vi) $2(4^{-2})$

(vii) $2(8^{-2})$ (x) $36^{-\frac{1}{2}}$ (xiii) $8^{-\frac{2}{3}}$

(viii) $5(10^{-3})$ (xi) $16^{-\frac{1}{4}}$ (xiv) $9^{-\frac{5}{2}}$

(ix) $100^{-\frac{1}{2}}$ (xii) $81^{-\frac{3}{4}}$

13. Evaluate the following, without using a calculator:

(i) $\sqrt{49}$ (iv) $\sqrt[5]{32}$ (vii) $\sqrt[4]{81}$

(ii) $\sqrt[3]{27}$ (v) $\sqrt[10]{1}$ (viii) $\sqrt[6]{64}$

(iii) $\sqrt[4]{16}$ (vi) $\sqrt{36}$ (ix) $\sqrt{121}$

14. Evaluate the following, without using a calculator:

(i) $8^{\frac{1}{3}}$ (iii) $1{,}000^{\frac{1}{3}}$ (v) $36^{\frac{1}{2}}$

(ii) $9^{\frac{1}{2}}$ (iv) $64^{\frac{1}{3}}$ (vi) $256^{\frac{1}{4}}$

15. Evaluate the following, without using a calculator:

(i) $(-8)^{\frac{1}{3}}$ (iii) $(-1{,}000)^{\frac{1}{3}}$ (v) $(128)^{\frac{1}{7}}$

(ii) $(-64)^{\frac{1}{3}}$ (iv) $(32)^{\frac{1}{5}}$ (vi) $(64)^{\frac{1}{6}}$

16. Write each of the following in the form a^p, where $p \in Q$:

(i) $a^7 \div a^2$ (v) $\sqrt{a^7}$

(ii) $a^7 \times a^2$

(iii) $(a^7)^2$ (vi) $\dfrac{1}{a^3}$

(iv) $\sqrt{a}$ (vii) $\dfrac{1}{\sqrt{a}}$

17. Using the law $a^{\frac{m}{n}} = (\sqrt[n]{a})^m$, evaluate each of the following:

(i) $100^{\frac{3}{2}}$ (vii) $\left(\dfrac{1}{25}\right)^{\frac{3}{2}}$

(ii) $125^{\frac{2}{3}}$

(iii) $16^{\frac{5}{4}}$ (viii) $\left(\dfrac{4}{9}\right)^{\frac{5}{2}}$

(iv) $81^{\frac{3}{4}}$ (ix) $\left(\dfrac{81}{25}\right)^{\frac{1}{2}}$

(v) $9^{\frac{3}{2}}$ (x) $\left(\dfrac{8}{27}\right)^{\frac{2}{3}}$

(vi) $64^{\frac{4}{3}}$

18. The law $(ab)^p = a^p b^p$ can be used to find the prime factorisation of numbers of the form $q^n, q, n \in N$.

   (i) Write 15 as a product of prime numbers.

   (ii) Hence, find the prime factorisation of 15^9.

19. Write 36 as a product of prime factors and, hence, find the prime factorisation of $36^{2{,}011}$.

20. Write 100 as a product of prime factors and, hence, find the prime factorisation of $100^{1{,}601}$.

21. Find k, if:

$$\sqrt{\frac{(e^8 + e^4)(e^3 - 1)}{(e^8 - 1)(e^2 + e + 1)}} = \frac{e^k}{\sqrt{(e^k + 1)(e + 1)}}$$

INDICES AND LOGARITHMS

7.3 Equations with *x* as an Index

$2^x = 64$ is an example of an equation in which the unknown quantity x is an index or power. The laws of indices will help us to solve many equations where the unknown quantity is an index.

> If $a^x = a^y$, and $a \neq -1, 0, 1$, then $x = y$.
>
> For example, if $2^x = 2^5$, then $x = 5$.

Worked Example 7.4

Solve $4^x = \dfrac{8}{\sqrt{2}}$, $x \in Q$.

Solution

All numbers in the equation can be written as powers of 2.

$2 = 2^1 \quad 4 = 2^2 \quad 8 = 2^3$

The equation can now be written as:

$(2^2)^x = \dfrac{2^3}{\sqrt{2}}$

$2^{2x} = \dfrac{2^3}{2^{\frac{1}{2}}}$

$2^{2x} = 2^{\frac{5}{2}}$

> Remember that $\sqrt{2} = 2^{\frac{1}{2}}$.

$2x = \dfrac{5}{2}$ (Drop the common base of 2.)

$\therefore x = \dfrac{5}{4}$ $\left(\text{or } 1\dfrac{1}{4}\right)$

Worked Example 7.5

Solve the equation:
$$3^{2x+1} - 28(3^x) + 9 = 0$$

Solution

Step 1 Transform the equation into a quadratic equation.

Let $y = 3^x$.

Then:

$3^{2x+1} = 3(3^{2x})$ (Law 1 of Indices)

$= 3(3^x)^2$ (Law 3 of Indices)

$= 3y^2$

Thus, the equation can be written as:

$3y^2 - 28y + 9 = 0$

Step 2 Solve the associated quadratic equation:

$$3y^2 - 28y + 9 = 0$$
$$(3y - 1)(y - 9) = 0$$
$$\Rightarrow 3y - 1 = 0 \quad \text{or} \quad y - 9 = 0$$
$$y = \frac{1}{3} \quad \text{or} \quad y = 9$$

Step 3 Solve for x:

$y = 3^x$

$\Rightarrow 3^x = \frac{1}{3}$ or $3^x = 9$

$3^x = 3^{-1}$ or $3^x = 3^2$ (Write as powers of 3.)

$\therefore x = -1$ or $x = 2$

Exercise 7.2

1. (a) Write the following numbers in the form 2^k, $k \in Q$:

   (i) 4   (vi) $\frac{1}{16}$

   (ii) 8   (vii) $\frac{1}{32}$

   (iii) 16

   (iv) 1   (viii) $\sqrt{2}$

   (v) $\frac{1}{2}$ (ix) $\sqrt[3]{2}$

        (x) $\sqrt[3]{8}$

   (b) Write the following numbers in the form 3^k, $k \in Q$:

   (i) 1   (vi) 729

   (ii) 9   (vii) $\frac{27}{\sqrt{3}}$

   (iii) $\frac{1}{3}$

   (iv) $\frac{1}{27}$ (viii) $\frac{729}{\sqrt{27}}$

   (v) $\sqrt[3]{81}$ (ix) $(81)^{\frac{3}{4}}$

2. Solve the following equations:

   (i) $3^x = 81$ (v) $3^x = 729$

   (ii) $10^x = 10{,}000$ (vi) $2^x = \frac{1}{32}$

   (iii) $6^x = 216$ (vii) $(0.2)^x = 125$

   (iv) $7^x = 49$ (viii) $7^{-x} = 1$

3. Solve the following equations:

   (i) $2^{x+4} = 128$ (iv) $6^x = \frac{1}{216}$

   (ii) $3^{x-5} = 27$

   (iii) $5^{x+2} = \sqrt{5}$ (v) $2^{4-x} = \frac{1}{64}$

        (vi) $7^{2x} = \frac{1}{49}$

4. Using the laws of indices, solve the following equations:

   (i) $2^x = 2^7\sqrt{2}$ (iv) $7^x = \frac{49}{\sqrt[3]{7}}$

   (ii) $5^x = \frac{125}{\sqrt{5}}$ (v) $49^x = \frac{49}{\sqrt{7}}$

   (iii) $10^{x-3} = \frac{\sqrt{10}}{100}$ (vi) $8^{\frac{4}{3}} = \frac{2^{5x-2}}{\sqrt{2}}$

5. Write in the form 2^k, $k \in Q$:

   (i) 16   (iii) $\sqrt{8}$

   (ii) 8   (iv) $\frac{16}{\sqrt{8}}$

   (v) Hence, solve the equation $2^{2x-1} = \left(\frac{16}{\sqrt{8}}\right)^3$.

6. Solve the following equations:

   (i) $3^{3x-1} = \left(\frac{27}{\sqrt{3}}\right)^5$ (ii) $25^x = \left(\frac{\sqrt{125}}{\sqrt[3]{5}}\right)^{12}$

7. (a) Copy and complete the table below. Answers in the second row must be in index form.

$2^2 - 2$	$2^3 - 2^2$	$2^4 - 2^3$	$2^5 - 2^4$	$2^6 - 2^5$	$2^7 - 2^6$
2	2^2				

(b) Hence, write $2^{p+1} - 2^p$ as a power of 2.

(c) Solve for x:

   (i) $\left(\dfrac{2^{12}}{16}\right) = 2^{x+1} - 2^x$ (ii) $\left(\dfrac{2^{16}}{8}\right) = 2^x - 2^{x-1}$

8. Solve for x:

   (i) $3^{2x} + 3^x = 90$ (iii) $2^{2x+1} - 15(2^x) - 8 = 0$ (v) $2^{2x} + 2^x - 6 = 0$

   (ii) $5^{2x} + 2(5^x) = 35$ (iv) $3^{2x+1} + 26(3^x) - 9 = 0$ (vi) $2^{2x} - 6(2^x) + 8 = 0$

9. Solve for x:

   (i) $2^x + 2^{2-x} = 5$ (iii) $2^x + 2^{-x} = \dfrac{17}{4}$ (v) $3^{2x+1} - 4(3^x) + 1 = 0$

   (ii) $3^x + 3^{1-x} = 4$ (iv) $3^x - 3^{1-x} + 2 = 0$ (vi) $5^{2x+1} - 5^x - 4 = 0$

10. Solve for x:

   (i) $5^{2x+1} - 124(5^x) - 25 = 0$

   (ii) $4^{2x+1} + 63(4^x) - 16 = 0$

11. (i) Show that $9^x = (3^x)^2$.

   (ii) Hence, solve $9^x - 4(3^{x+1}) + 27 = 0$.

7.4 Surds

Suppose we wish to simplify $\sqrt{\dfrac{1}{25}}$. We can write it as $\dfrac{1}{5}$.

However, some numbers involving roots, such as
$\sqrt{5}, \sqrt[3]{19}, \sqrt{\pi}$, cannot be written as fractions. We call such numbers **surds**.

> Any number of the form $\sqrt[n]{a}$, $n > 1$, $n \in N$, which cannot be
> written as a fraction, is called a **surd**.

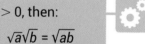

If $a, b > 0$, then:

Law 1 $\sqrt{a}\sqrt{b} = \sqrt{ab}$

Law 2 $\dfrac{\sqrt{a}}{\sqrt{b}} = \sqrt{\dfrac{a}{b}}$

Worked Example 7.6

What is $\sqrt{a^2}$?

Solution

$\sqrt{a^2} = |a| = \begin{cases} a & \text{if } a \geqslant 0 \\ -a & \text{if } a < 0 \end{cases}$

Worked Example 7.7

If $a > 0$, what is $\sqrt{a}\sqrt{a}$?

Solution

$\sqrt{a}\sqrt{a} = \sqrt{(a)(a)}$ (Law 1 of Surds)

        $= \sqrt{a^2}$

        $= a$

Reducing Surds

Surds can be reduced or simplified if the number under the radical sign (square root sign) has a square number greater than 1 as a factor.

You should know the first few square numbers: 1, 4, 9, 16, 25, 36, 49, 64, 81, 100, 121, 144, 169, ...

Worked Example 7.8

Simplify $\sqrt{32}$.

Solution

Step 1 Find the largest square number that is a factor of 32. 16 is the largest square number that is a factor of 32.

Step 2 $\sqrt{32} = \sqrt{16}\sqrt{2}$ (Law 1 of Surds)

$= 4\sqrt{2}$

Worked Example 7.9

Simplify $\sqrt{50} + \sqrt{8} + \sqrt{32}$.

Solution

$\sqrt{50} + \sqrt{8} + \sqrt{32} = \sqrt{25}\sqrt{2} + \sqrt{4}\sqrt{2} + \sqrt{16}\sqrt{2}$

$= 5\sqrt{2} + 2\sqrt{2} + 4\sqrt{2}$

$= 11\sqrt{2}$

Worked Example 7.10

Simplify $(\sqrt{5} + 2\sqrt{2})(\sqrt{5} - \sqrt{2})$.

Solution

$(\sqrt{5} + 2\sqrt{2})(\sqrt{5} - \sqrt{2}) = \sqrt{5}(\sqrt{5} - \sqrt{2}) + 2\sqrt{2}(\sqrt{5} - \sqrt{2})$

$= \sqrt{5}\sqrt{5} - \sqrt{5}\sqrt{2} + 2\sqrt{2}\sqrt{5} - 2\sqrt{2}\sqrt{2}$

$= 5 - \sqrt{10} + 2\sqrt{10} - 2(2)$

$= 1 + \sqrt{10}$

OR

	$\sqrt{5}$	$+ 2\sqrt{2}$
$\sqrt{5}$	5	$2\sqrt{10}$
$-\sqrt{2}$	$-\sqrt{10}$	-4

$(\sqrt{5} + 2\sqrt{2})(\sqrt{5} - \sqrt{2}) = 1 + \sqrt{10}$

Rationalising the Denominator

If we have a fraction that contains an irrational denominator, then we are often required to rationalise the denominator. If the denominator is a single surd, $\sqrt{a}$, then multiplying the numerator and denominator by $\sqrt{a}$ will rationalise the denominator. If the denominator is of the form $\sqrt{a} + \sqrt{b}$ or $\sqrt{a} - \sqrt{b}$, then multiplying the numerator and denominator by the **conjugate** of the denominator will rationalise the denominator.

The **conjugate** of $x + y$ is $x - y$ where $x, y \in R$.

Note how $(x + y)(x - y) = x^2 - y^2$.

Worked Example 7.11

Rationalise the denominator of: (i) $\dfrac{5}{\sqrt{5}}$ (ii) $\dfrac{4\sqrt{15}}{\sqrt{20}}$ (iii) $\dfrac{\sqrt{2} - \sqrt{3}}{\sqrt{2} + \sqrt{3}}$

Solution

(i) $\dfrac{5}{\sqrt{5}} = \dfrac{5\sqrt{5}}{\sqrt{5}\sqrt{5}}$

$= \dfrac{5\sqrt{5}}{5}$

$= \sqrt{5}$

(Multiply numerator and denominator by $\sqrt{5}$. This is equivalent to multiplying the original number by 1, which does *not* change its value.)

(ii) $\dfrac{4\sqrt{15}}{\sqrt{20}} = \dfrac{4\sqrt{15}}{\sqrt{4}\sqrt{5}}$

$= \dfrac{4\sqrt{15}}{2\sqrt{5}}$

$= 2\sqrt{3}$ (Laws of Surds)

(iii) $\dfrac{\sqrt{2} - \sqrt{3}}{\sqrt{2} + \sqrt{3}} = \dfrac{(\sqrt{2} - \sqrt{3})(\sqrt{2} - \sqrt{3})}{(\sqrt{2} + \sqrt{3})(\sqrt{2} - \sqrt{3})}$

$= \dfrac{\sqrt{2}(\sqrt{2} - \sqrt{3}) - \sqrt{3}(\sqrt{2} - \sqrt{3})}{(\sqrt{2})^2 - (\sqrt{3})^2}$

$= \dfrac{2 - \sqrt{6} - \sqrt{6} + 3}{2 - 3}$

$= \dfrac{5 - 2\sqrt{6}}{-1}$

$= -5 + 2\sqrt{6}$

(Multiply numerator and denominator by $(\sqrt{2} - \sqrt{3})$, which is the conjugate of the denominator.)

Exercise 7.3

1. Evaluate each of the following, without the use of a calculator:

   (i) $(2\sqrt{7})^2$ (iv) $(10\sqrt{2})^2$

   (ii) $(5\sqrt{10})^2$ (v) $(3\sqrt{15})^2$

   (iii) $(2\sqrt{5})^2$ (vi) $(2\sqrt{5})^4$

2. Evaluate each of the following, without the use of a calculator:

   (i) $\sqrt{2}\sqrt{8}$ (iv) $\dfrac{\sqrt{27}}{\sqrt{3}}$ (vi) $\dfrac{\sqrt{200}}{\sqrt{8}}$

   (ii) $\sqrt{2}\sqrt{32}$

   (iii) $\sqrt{50}\sqrt{2}$ (v) $\dfrac{\sqrt{50}}{\sqrt{2}}$

3. Simplify these surds:

   (i) $\sqrt{8}$ (vi) $\sqrt{500}$

   (ii) $\sqrt{45}$ (vii) $\sqrt{27}$

   (iii) $\sqrt{300}$ (viii) $\sqrt{54}$

   (iv) $\sqrt{12}$ (ix) $\sqrt{75}$

   (v) $\sqrt{32}$ (x) $\sqrt{98}$

4. Write $\sqrt{50} + \sqrt{8}$ in the form $k\sqrt{2}$, $k \in Q$.

5. Write $\sqrt{27} + \sqrt{12}$ in the form $k\sqrt{3}$, $k \in Q$.

6. Write $\sqrt{125} + \sqrt{20}$ in the form $k\sqrt{5}$, $k \in Q$.

7. If $\sqrt{44} + \sqrt{11} = n\sqrt{11}$, then find n where $n \in N$.

8. For each of the following, rationalise the denominator:

   (i) $\dfrac{6}{\sqrt{2}}$ (iv) $\dfrac{3}{\sqrt{5}}$ (vii) $\dfrac{2\sqrt{3}}{\sqrt{6}}$

   (ii) $\dfrac{7}{\sqrt{7}}$ (v) $\dfrac{2}{\sqrt{11}}$ (viii) $\dfrac{-4\sqrt{5}}{\sqrt{12}}$

   (iii) $\dfrac{1}{\sqrt{2}}$ (vi) $\dfrac{3\sqrt{3}}{\sqrt{5}}$ (ix) $\dfrac{3}{\sqrt{45}}$

9. For each of the following, rationalise the denominator:

   (i) $\dfrac{1}{\sqrt{5} - 2}$ (iv) $\dfrac{2 - \sqrt{3}}{5 - \sqrt{3}}$ (vii) $\dfrac{1 + \sqrt{2}}{5\sqrt{2}}$

   (ii) $\dfrac{1}{3 + \sqrt{3}}$ (v) $\dfrac{\sqrt{3} - 7}{\sqrt{3} + 7}$ (viii) $\dfrac{\sqrt{3} - \sqrt{5}}{\sqrt{3} + \sqrt{5}}$

   (iii) $\dfrac{5\sqrt{2}}{\sqrt{2} - 1}$ (vi) $\dfrac{2 - \sqrt{11}}{3\sqrt{11} + 5}$ (ix) $\dfrac{2\sqrt{7} - 3\sqrt{3}}{5\sqrt{3} + 4\sqrt{7}}$

7.5 Logarithms

John Napier (1550–1617) is credited with inventing logarithms. Napier was a Scottish landowner who devoted much of his spare time to the study of mathematics. He invented logarithms to allow for the easier calculation of products and quotients involving large quantities.

John Napier (1550–1617)

Consider the following information in index form:	**Index form** $2^3 = 8$ ('2 to the power of 3 is 8')
We can express the same information in logarithmic form:	**Log form** $\log_2 8 = 3$ ('log of 8 to base 2 is 3')

So, logarithms reverse the process of exponentiation.

As $a^m = n > 0$, for all $a > 0$, $m \in R$, we can write: $\log_a n = m$.

However, if $a \le 0$, $m \in R$, $a^m = n$ is not always real. For example, $(-1)^{\frac{1}{2}} = i$ is not real. Also, $(0)^0$ is not defined. Therefore, we always use a **positive base** when working with logarithms.

> $a^m = n \Leftrightarrow \log_a n = m$, where a (the base) > 0, $m \in R$, $n > 0$.

For example, $4^2 = 16 \Leftrightarrow \log_4 16 = 2$.

Graphing a Logarithmic Function

A logarithmic function is a function of the form

$$f(x) = \log_a x$$

where $x \in R$, $x > 0$, and a is a positive constant.

We can study the behaviour of logarithms by looking at the graphs of logarithmic functions.

The graph of the logarithmic function

$$f(x) = \log_2 x, x \in R, x > 0$$

is shown on the right.

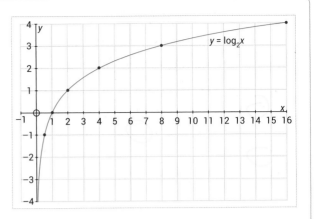

x	$\frac{1}{2}$	1	2	4	8	16
$f(x)$	−1	0	1	2	3	4

The graph of $y = \log_2 x$ is a reflection of the graph of $y = 2^x$ in the line $y = x$.

We noted earlier that $a^x = a^y \Leftrightarrow x = y$.
Therefore, if $\log_a x = \log_a y$, then $x = y$.

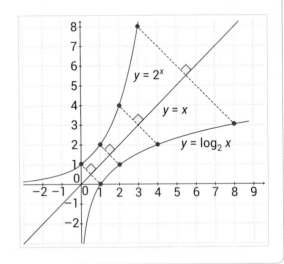

Worked Example 7.12

(i) Graph the function $f(x) = \log_3 x$, $x \in R$, $0 < x \leqslant 27$.

(ii) 'Logarithms expand small variations and compress large ones.'
Explain this statement in the context of the graph of $y = f(x)$.

Solution

(i) Let $x = 1$ and all whole number powers of 3 within the given domain.

So, let $x = 1, 3, 9, 27$ in the input–output table.

Then, let $x = 3^{-1}$ and 3^{-2} in the input–output table.

This will give a sufficient number of points with which to construct a graph.

x	$\log_3 x$
$\frac{1}{9} = 3^{-2}$	−2
$\frac{1}{3} = 3^{-1}$	−1
$1 = 3^0$	0
$3 = 3^1$	1
$9 = 3^2$	2
$27 = 3^3$	3

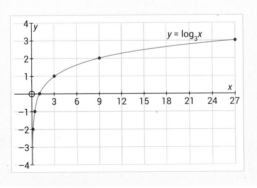

(ii) If we look at small variations in x, for $x < 1$ we see a comparitively large variation in $\log_3 x$.

For example, if $\frac{1}{9} \leqslant x \leqslant \frac{1}{3}$, we have $-2 \leqslant \log_3 x \leqslant -1$.

If we look at large variations in x, for $x > 1$ there is a comparitively small variation in $\log_3 x$.

For example, if $3 \leqslant x \leqslant 27$, we have $1 \leqslant \log_3 x \leqslant 3$.

The Laws of Logarithms

Law 1 $\log_a(xy) = \log_a x + \log_a y$ Law 5 $\log_a\left(\frac{1}{x}\right) = -\log_a x$

Law 2 $\log_a\left(\frac{x}{y}\right) = \log_a x - \log_a y$ Law 6 $\log_a(a^x) = x$

Law 3 $\log_a(x^q) = q\log_a x$ Law 7 $a^{\log_a x} = x$

Law 4 $\log_a 1 = 0$ Law 8 $\log_b x = \dfrac{\log_a x}{\log_a b}$

Note: $\log_a a = 1$.

These laws appear on page 21 of *Formulae and Tables*.

The **natural logarithm function**, $\log_e x$, has the irrational number e as its base. It is also written as $\ln x$.

Worked Example 7.13

Justify the laws of logarithms using suitable examples.

Solution

Law 1:
$$\log_2(4)(8) = \log_2 32$$
$$= 5$$
$$\log_2 4 + \log_2 8 = 2 + 3$$
$$= 5$$
$$\therefore \log_2(4)(8) = \log_2 4 + \log_2 8$$

Law 2:
$$\log_4\left(\frac{16}{4}\right) = \log_4 4$$
$$= 1$$
$$\log_4 16 - \log_4 4 = 2 - 1$$
$$= 1$$
$$\therefore \log_2\left(\frac{16}{4}\right) = \log_4 16 - \log_4 4$$

Law 3:
$$\log_5 5^3 = \log_5 125$$
$$= 3$$
$$3\log_5 5 = 3(1)$$
$$= 3$$
$$\therefore \log_5 5^3 = 3\log_5 5$$

Law 4: $2^0 = 1 \Rightarrow \log_2 1 = 0$

Law 5:
$$\log_3 \frac{1}{27} = \log_3\left(\frac{1}{3}\right)^3$$
$$= 3\log_3\left(\frac{1}{3}\right)$$
$$= 3[\log_3 1 - \log_3 3]$$
$$= 3[0 - \log_3 3]$$
$$= -3\log_3 3$$
$$= -\log_3 3^3 = -\log_3 27$$

Law 6:
$$\log_2 2^4 = \log_2 16$$
$$= 4$$

Law 7:
$$10^{\log_{10} 100} = 10^2$$
$$= 100$$

Law 8:
$$\frac{\log_2 16}{\log_2 4} = \frac{4}{2}$$
$$= 2$$
$$\log_4 16 = 2$$
$$\therefore \log_4 16 = \frac{\log_2 16}{\log_2 4}$$

Worked Example 7.14

Evaluate $\log_{16} 64$.

Solution

Let $\log_{16} 64 = x$.
$$\Rightarrow 16^x = 64$$
$$(4^2)^x = 4^3 \quad \text{(Write each number as a power of a common base, 4.)}$$
$$4^{2x} = 4^3 \quad \text{(Apply Law 3 of Indices.)}$$

$2x = 3$ (Equate powers.)
$$\therefore x = \frac{3}{2}$$

INDICES AND LOGARITHMS

Alternative Method

$$\log_{16} 64 = \frac{\log_4 64}{\log_4 16} \quad \text{(Apply Law 8 of Logs using a suitable common base.)}$$

$$= \frac{\log_4 4^3}{\log_4 4^2}$$

$$= \frac{3}{2} \quad \text{(Law 6 of Logs)}$$

The function $f(x) = \log_a x$ is defined only for $x > 0$. Therefore, when solving equations using logarithms, it is important to check that all solutions satisfy the original equation. Solutions that do not satisfy the original equation have to be discarded. These discarded solutions are known as extraneous solutions.

Worked Example 7.15

(i) If $\log_{10}(3x + 1) = 2$, find x.

(ii) If $\log_2(x + 3) = \log_2(x - 9)^2$, find x.

Solution

(i) $\log_{10}(3x + 1) = 2$

$\Rightarrow 3x + 1 = 10^2$ (Write in index form.)

$3x + 1 = 100$

$3x = 99$

$\therefore x = 33$

(ii) $\log_2(x + 3) = \log_2(x - 9)^2$

$\Rightarrow x + 3 = (x - 9)^2$ (Drop log notation.)

$x + 3 = x^2 - 18x + 81$

$x^2 - 19x + 78 = 0$

$(x - 6)(x - 13) = 0$

$x = 6 \quad \textbf{OR} \quad x = 13$

Both $x = 6$ and $x = 13$ satisfy the original equation.

Worked Example 7.16

Solve for x: $\log_2(x + 1) - \log_2(x - 1) = 1, x > 1, x \in R$

Solution

$\log_2(x + 1) - \log_2(x - 1) = 1$

$\log_2\left[\frac{x + 1}{x - 1}\right] = 1$ (Law 2 of Logarithms)

$\frac{x + 1}{x - 1} = 2^1$ (Write in index form.)

$x + 1 = 2x - 2$

$\therefore x = 3$

As $3 > 1$, $x = 3$ is the solution.

Worked Example 7.17

Solve for x:

$4\log_x 2 = \log_2 x + 3$, $x > 1$, $x \in R$

Solution

Step 1 Ensure that all logs have the same base.

$$\log_x 2 = \frac{\log_2 2}{\log_2 x} \quad \text{(Law 8 of Logarithms)}$$

$$= \frac{1}{\log_2 x}$$

Step 2 $\quad 4\left[\dfrac{1}{\log_2 x}\right] = \log_2 x + 3$

Let $y = \log_2 x$.

$$4\left[\frac{1}{y}\right] = y + 3$$

$$4 = y^2 + 3y$$

$$y^2 + 3y - 4 = 0$$

$$(y + 4)(y - 1) = 0$$

$$\Rightarrow y = -4 \quad \textbf{OR} \quad y = 1$$

Step 3 $\log_2 x = -4 \quad \textbf{OR} \quad \log_2 x = 1$

$$x = 2^{-4} \qquad \qquad \therefore x = 2$$

$$\therefore x = \frac{1}{16}$$

As $\dfrac{1}{16} < 1$, $x = 2$ is the solution (given that $x > 1$).

Worked Example 7.18

Solve the equation $2^{2x} - 8(2^x) + 15 = 0$.

Give your answers correct to two decimal places.

Solution

Step 1 Transform the equation into a quadratic equation.

Let $y = 2^x$.

Then:

$2^{2x} = (2^x)^2 \quad$ (Law 3 of Indices)

$\quad = y^2$

Thus, the equation can be written as:

$y^2 - 8y + 15 = 0$

Step 2 Solve the associated quadratic equation.

$$y^2 - 8y + 15 = 0$$

$$(y - 3)(y - 5) = 0$$

$$\Rightarrow y - 3 = 0 \quad \textbf{OR} \quad y - 5 = 0$$

$$y = 3 \quad \textbf{OR} \quad y = 5$$

Step 3 Solve for x.

$$y = 2^x$$

$$2^x = 3$$

$$\log 2^x = \log 3$$

$$x\log 2 = \log 3$$

$$\Rightarrow x = \frac{\log 3}{\log 2} \quad \begin{array}{l}\text{(Any common} \\ \text{base can be used.)}\end{array}$$

$$\Rightarrow x = 1.58 \quad \text{(to two decimal places)}$$

OR

$$2^x = 5$$

$$\log 2^x = \log 5$$

$$x\log 2 = \log 5$$

$$\Rightarrow x = \frac{\log 5}{\log 2}$$

$$\Rightarrow x = 2.32 \quad \text{(to two decimal places)}$$

Exercise 7.4

1. Write the following in exponential form:

   (i) $\log_3 x = 9$ (iv) $\log_4 x = 3$

   (ii) $\log_2 8 = x$ (v) $\log_2 y = 5$

   (iii) $\log_3 27 = x$ (vi) $\log_5 y = 2$

2. Write the following in logarithmic form:

   (i) $y = 3^4$ (iv) $y = 3^5$

   (ii) $27 = 3^x$ (v) $32 = x^5$

   (iii) $m = 4^2$ (vi) $64 = 4^x$

3. Evaluate, without using a calculator:

   (i) $\log_9 3$ (v) $\log_{27} 3$

   (ii) $\log_{\frac{1}{2}} 4$ (vi) $\ln e$

   (iii) $\log_{121} 11$ (vii) $\ln e^2$

   (iv) $\log_5 1$ (viii) $\log_a a^3$ $(a > 0)$

4. Evaluate each of the following, without using a calculator:

   (i) $\log_2 16$ (v) $\log_{10} 1{,}000$

   (ii) $\log_3 81$ (vi) $\log_8 32$

   (iii) $\log_5 125$ (vii) $\log_2 \frac{1}{128}$

   (iv) $\log_4 64$ (viii) $\log_3 \frac{1}{81}$

5. Use a calculator to evaluate to three significant figures:

   (i) e^2 (v) $\ln 0.201$

   (ii) $e^{1.5}$ (vi) $\ln 15.3$

   (iii) $e^{0.1}$ (vii) $\log_{10} 6.4$

   (iv) $\ln 3$ (viii) $\log_{10} 250$

6. Graph the function:

   $f(x) = \log_4 x, x \in R, 0 < x \leqslant 64$.

7. Graph the function:

   $f(x) = \log_e x, x \in R, 0 < x \leqslant 30$.

8. Use the laws of logs to express as single logarithms:

   (i) $\log 2 + \log 5$

   (ii) $\log 20 - \log 4$

   (iii) $\log 4 + 2\log 3 - \log 6$

   (iv) $3\log 2 + 2\log 3 - 2\log 6$

   (v) $\log p - \frac{1}{3} \log q$ $(p, q > 0)$

   (vi) $3\log a - \frac{1}{3} \log b + 1$ $(a, b > 0)$

9. Solve for x:

   (i) $\log_2 (3x + 1) = 2$ (iii) $\log_3 (5x + 2) = 3$

   (ii) $\log_2 (x - 1) = 3$ (iv) $\log_5 (8x + 1) = 2$

10. Solve for x:

    (i) $\log_3 (2x + 5) - \log_3 (x - 8) = 1$

    (ii) $\log_3 (10x + 7) - \log_3 (x + 1) = 2$

    (iii) $\log_2 3 + \log_2 (x + 1) = \log_2 (x + 11)$

    (iv) $\log_5 (x + 1) = \log_5 (7x + 1) - 1$

11. Change the following logarithms to base 10. Give your answer in the form $\dfrac{\log_{10} a}{\log_{10} b}$.

    (i) $\log_4 27$ (ii) $\log_2 100$ (iii) $\log_4 500$

12. Change the following logarithms to base e. Give your answer in the form $\dfrac{\log_e a}{\log_e b}$.

    (i) $\log_4 20$ (ii) $\log_5 30$ (iii) $\log_6 40$

13. Change the following logarithms to base 2:

    (i) $\log_{16} x$

    (ii) $\log_4 (x + 4)$

    (iii) $\log_8 (3x - 2)$

14. Solve for x:

    (i) $\log_4 (3x - 2) = \dfrac{\log_2 (x - 1)}{2}, x > 1, x \in R$

    (ii) $\log_5 (2x+1) + \log_{125} (2x+1) = 16$, $x > -\frac{1}{2}, x \in R$

    (iii) $\log_{16} x - \log_4 (x + 3) = 0, x > -3, x \in R$

    (iv) $\log_{27} (x + 2) + \log_3 (x + 2) = 4, x > -2, x \in R$

    (v) $\log_{27} (2x+4) + \log_{81} (6x+12) = \frac{5}{6}, x > -2, x \in R$

15. Solve for x:

    (i) $\log_4 (3x + 1) = \log_2 (x - 1)$

    (ii) $\log_5 (x + 1) + \log_4 (x + 1) = 3$

    (iii) $\log_8 x - \log_9 x = 1$

    (iv) $\log_2 x + \log_3 x = 1$

16. Solve each of the following equations. Give your answers correct to two decimal places.

    (i) $2^{2x} - 8(2^x) + 15 = 0$

    (ii) $3^{2x} = 24 - 5(3^x)$

    (iii) $10^{2x} - 5(10^x) = 0$

    (iv) $(7^{x+1})^2 = 100$

    (v) $3^{2x+1} + 5(3^x) - 2 = 0$

17. Solve $9^x - 3^{x-1} - 8 = 0$.

18. Solve each of the following equations. Give your answers correct to two significant figures.

    (i) $3^{2x+1} - 13(3^x) + 14 = 0$

    (ii) $9(5^{2x}) = 4(3(5^x) - 1)$

    (iii) $2^{2x+1} = 12 - 5(2^x)$

    (iv) $6^{2x} - 7(6^x) + 10 = 0$

    (v) $2^{x+1} 5^{x+1} - 9(2^x 5^x) - 2 = 0$

19. Solve for x:

   (i) $x = \log_e e$ (iii) $\log_e \dfrac{1}{e} = x$

   (ii) $\log_e x = 2$ (iv) $\log_e \sqrt[3]{e} = x$

20. Solve for x:

   (i) $e^{\log_e x} = 5$ (iii) $e^{\log_e 2} = x$

   (ii) $\log_e e^4 = x$ (iv) $2\log_e x = 1 - \log_e 7$

21. Solve the following equations:

   (i) $3 = e^{2x}$ (iii) $\ln x^{-\frac{1}{5}} = 1$

   (ii) $2 = \ln 3x$ (iv) $7e^{7x} = 1$

22. Solve the following equations:

   (i) $e^{\ln 5x} = 10$

   (ii) $\ln e^{3x} + 4\ln e^{2x} = 7$

   (iii) $e^x + e^{-x} = 2$

   (iv) $5^{2x} = \dfrac{1}{3}$ (answer correct to two decimal places)

7.6 Using Logarithms to Solve Practical Problems

Many mathematical models that represent real-life situations contain unknown powers or indices. Here are two examples:

- $F = P(1 + i)^t$ (**Compound interest formula**)
- $p = ae^{bt}$ (**Exponential model:** describes population growth, radioactive decay, etc. For $a > 0$, if $b > 0$, then p is growing. If $b < 0$, then p is decaying.)

When looking for the unknown exponent (power), logarithms are used to convert the exponential equation into a linear equation. The linear equation is then solved to find the unknown exponent.

There are other real-life models that use logarithmic scales. Here are two examples:

- $M = \log_{10}\left[\dfrac{I}{S}\right]$ (**Richter scale:** to measure the magnitude of locally occurring earthquakes)

- $D = 10\log_{10}\left[\dfrac{I}{I_0}\right]$ (**Decibel scale:** approximates loudness of sound as perceived by the human brain)

The laws of logarithms are used to solve problems involving these models.

Worked Example 7.19

Scientists have shown that a particular population of insects grows exponentially according to the model $p = ae^{bt}$, where a and b are constants and t is time measured in weeks. A remote area of forest has a population of 500 of these insects. In one week the population increases to 560.

(i) Find the value of the constants a and b.

(ii) Find, to the nearest week, the time for the population to increase to 181,262, assuming the population remains unchecked (i.e. its increase is not interrupted by disease, etc.).

Solution

(i) $p = ae^{bt}$

   We know that at time $t = 0$, $p = 500$.

   $\Rightarrow 500 = ae^0$

     $\therefore a = 500$

   Substitute the value for a in the model.

     $p = 500e^{bt}$

We also know that at time $t = 1$, $p = 560$.

   $\Rightarrow 560 = 500e^b$

     $e^b = \dfrac{28}{25}$

     $b = \log_e \dfrac{28}{25}$

   $\therefore b = 0.11332869$

Therefore the model is:

     $p = 500e^{0.11332869t}$

(ii) $\quad 500e^{0.11332869t} = 181{,}262$

$$e^{0.11332869t} = \frac{181{,}262}{500}$$

$$\log_e\left(e^{0.11332869t}\right) = \log_e\left(\frac{181{,}262}{500}\right)$$

$$0.11332869t = \log_e\frac{181{,}262}{500}$$

$$0.11332869t = 5.893090679$$

$$t = 51.999\ldots$$

$$\therefore t \approx 52 \text{ weeks}$$

Exercise 7.5

1. A population of bacteria grows exponentially according to the model

$$P = 600\,e^{0.1144t}$$

   where t is measured in minutes.

   (i) What is the size of the population at time $t = 0$?

   (ii) What will be the size of the population at time $t = 10$?

   (iii) Find, to the nearest minute, the time at which the population will have grown to 6,000.

2. The population growth of a certain city is modelled by the equation

$$P = 136{,}000\,e^{0.006t}$$

   where P is the population of the city after t years.

   (i) What is the current population of the city?

   (ii) What will the population of the city be in 5 years time?

   (iii) After how many years will the city's population be 153,000?

3. The radioactive substance Iodine-131 is used in medicine to measure liver and heart activity and in the treatment of certain cancers. It has a half-life of eight days, i.e. the quantity of Iodine-131 decays by a factor of 2 in eight days. A hospital purchases 30 g of the substance. In eight days 15 g remain. The decay can be modelled using the exponential model:

$$Q = ae^{bt}$$

   where a and b are constants, t is time measured in days and Q is the quantity of the substance.

   (i) Find the value of each of the constants a and b.

   (ii) What quantity of the substance will remain after 20 days?

   (iii) Find the time taken for the substance to decay to 1.49 g.

4. Scientists can estimate the age of fossils by measuring the amount of carbon-14 in the fossil. When an animate object dies, the amount of carbon-14 (measured in grams) in the object is given by

$$A = me^{-0.00012t}$$

   where t is the number of years since the death of the object and m is a constant.

   (i) Show that m is the mass of carbon-14 in the object at death.

   (ii) An object is 3,000 years old. Find in terms of m the mass of carbon-14 in the object.

   (iii) If an object now contains half the carbon-14 that it contained at death, how old is the object?

5. John deposits €8,000 in an account that pays 4% p.a. The model $A = P(1 + i)^t$ describes the growth of the investment over time, where P is the present value of the investment, i is the rate of interest expressed as a decimal and t is the period of time, in years, for which the deposit is invested.

   (i) Explain why $A = 8000(1.04)^t$ describes the growth of John's investment over time.

   (ii) What will the value of John's investment be in 3 years time?

   (iii) How long will it take for John's money to double?

6. pH is a measure of the acidity or basicity of a solution. Solutions with a pH less than 7 are said to be acidic. Solutions with a pH greater than 7 are said to be basic or alkaline. A solution with a pH equal to 7 is said to be neutral. Chemists define pH by the formula pH = $-\log10[H^+]$, where $[H^+]$ is the hydrogen ion concentration of the solution measured in moles per litre.

   (i) A substance has a hydrogen ion concentration of 1.5×10^{-5} moles per litre. Determine the pH and classify the substance as an acid or a base.

(ii) A substance has a hydrogen ion concentration of 1.4×10^{-9} moles per litre. Determine the pH and classify the substance as an acid or a base.

(iii) If a solution has a pH of 8.2, find the hydrogen ion concentration of the solution. Give your answer in the form $a \times 10^n$, where $a \in N$ and $n \in Z$.

7. Normally, human blood has a hydrogen ion concentration of 1.3×10^{-8} moles per litre. pH is given by the formula pH $= -\log_{10}[H^+]$, where $[H^+]$ is the hydrogen ion concentration of the solution measured in moles per litre.

(i) Determine the normal pH of human blood.

(ii) A condition known as acidosis sets in when the pH of a person's blood drops below 7.45. Acidosis can result in death if the pH reaches 7. What would the hydrogen ion concentration of a person's blood be at a pH value of 7?

8. The soil in a vegetable garden is tested and is found to have a hydrogen ion concentration of 7.2×10^{-7} moles per litre. If potatoes prefer soil that has a pH in the range 7.5 to 6, should potatoes be planted in the garden? pH is given by the formula pH $= -\log_{10}[H^+]$, where $[H^+]$ is the hydrogen ion concentration of the solution measured in moles per litre.

9. The future value, F, of an investment is given by the formula $F = P(1 + i)^t$, where P is the present value of the investment, i is the annual rate of interest and t is the time in years. A sum of money, P, is invested in a post office account. Use logarithms to find the time taken for the investment to double in value if the annual rate of interest is:

(i) 5%   (ii) 7%   (iii) 10%

(Give your answers correct to the nearest month.)

10. Use logarithms to find the time taken for an investment of €15,000 to amount to €26,937 at a rate of 5% p.a. The interest is compounded annually.

Revision Exercises

1. Write the following in index notation:

(i) $5^3 \times 5^8$

(ii) $(3^2)^3$

(iii) $\dfrac{16^9}{16^5}$

(iv) $\dfrac{1}{7^5}$

(v) $\sqrt[5]{17^3}$

(vi) $\dfrac{5^3}{\sqrt{5^5}}$

2. Write these in the form a^n:

(i) $a^4 \times a^6$

(ii) $(a^4)^6$

(iii) $\sqrt[4]{a^6}$

(iv) $\sqrt[5]{a^3 \times a^7}$

3. Use the laws of surds to simplify each of the following:

(i) $\sqrt{125} + \sqrt{98} + \sqrt{128}$

(ii) $\sqrt{80} + \sqrt{245} + \sqrt{405}$

4. (i) Evaluate $64^{-\frac{1}{2}}$.

(ii) Write (a) 128 and (b) $\sqrt{2}$ as a power of 2.

(iii) Hence, solve the equation $2^{2x+1} = \dfrac{128}{\sqrt{2}}$.

5. (i) Simplify $a^4 + a^4 + a^4 + a^4$.
Hence, write $2^4 + 2^4 + 2^4 + 2^4$ as a power of 2.

(ii) Write $2^{\frac{1}{4}} + 2^{\frac{1}{4}} + 2^{\frac{1}{4}} + 2^{\frac{1}{4}}$ as a power of 2.

(iii) Simplify $3a^5 + 6a^5$.
Hence, write $3(3^5) + 6(3^5)$ as a power of 3.

(iv) Write $20(3^8) + 7(3^8)$ as a power of 3.

6. Simplify the following by rationalising the denominator:

(i) $\dfrac{5}{\sqrt{2}}$

(ii) $\dfrac{6}{\sqrt{3}}$

(iii) $\dfrac{12\sqrt{2}}{4\sqrt{3}}$

(iv) $\dfrac{2\sqrt{2} + \sqrt{3}}{\sqrt{2} - \sqrt{3}}$

(v) $\dfrac{\sqrt{5} - \sqrt{2}}{4\sqrt{5}}$

(vi) $\dfrac{\sqrt{7} - \sqrt{2}}{2\sqrt{7} + 3\sqrt{2}}$

(vii) $\dfrac{\sqrt{5}}{\sqrt{3} - 2}$

(viii) $\dfrac{\sqrt{7}}{\sqrt{7} - \sqrt{5}}$

7. Solve for x, each of the following:

(i) $\log 5 + \log x = \log 30$, $x > 0$, $x \in R$

(ii) $\log 4 + 2 \log x = \log 16$, $x > 0$, $x \in R$

(iii) $2\log 2 + \log (x - 1) = \log 15$, $x > 1$, $x \in R$

(iv) $\log_2 (1 + x) - \log_2 (1 - x) = 2$, $-1 < x < 1$, $x \in R$

(v) $\log_7 (x + 1) + \log_7 (x - 5) = 1$, $x > 5$, $x \in R$

8. Solve for x:

   (i) $\log_x x - \log_9 x + 1 = 0$

   (ii) $\log_5 (x + 100) - \log_5 x = 1$

   (iii) $\log_{25} (6x + 25)^8 + \log_5 (x + 25) = 5, x \in N$

   (iv) $\log_5 x = 1 + \log_5 \left[\dfrac{3}{2x - 1}\right]$

9. (a) Use logarithms to find the least value of $n \in N$ for which $3^n > 1{,}000{,}000$.

   (b) Use logarithms to find the largest value of $n \in N$ for which $2^n < 500{,}000$.

10. Solve the following equations:

   (i) $2^{2x} - 3(2^x) - 40 = 0$ (iv) $3e^x - 7 + 2e^{-x} = 0$

   (ii) $5^{2x} - 2(5^x) - 575 = 0$ (v) $2^{x^2} = 8^{2x + 9}$

   (iii) $3^x - 3^{1 - x} + 2 = 0$

11. Solve the following simultaneous equations:

   (i) $\log_x (y + 1) = 2$

   $\log_2 (y - 2x) = 1$

   (ii) $\log_3 (3x - y) - \log_3 (y + 1) = 0$

   $\log_3 2 + \log_3 (x + y) = 2$

   (iii) $\log_2 x - \log_3 3 = \log_2 (1 - y)$

   $\log_2 x + \log_2 (x + 2y) = 3$

12. (a) Show that $\log_b a = \dfrac{1}{\log_a b}$.

   (b) Hence, show that:

   $$\frac{1}{\log_2 x} + \frac{1}{\log_3 x} + \frac{1}{\log_5 x} = \frac{1}{\log_{30} x}$$

13. Two functions, $f(x) = \log_a x$ and $g(x)$, where a is a positive constant, are graphed below. $f(x)$ is defined for all $x > 0, x \in R$, while $g(x)$ is defined for all $x \in R$. The image of the graph of $y = f(x)$ by a reflection in the line $y = x$ is the graph of $y = g(x)$.

   (i) Using the graphs, find the value of a.

   (ii) Hence, write the function $g(x)$ in the form $g(x) = b^x$, where b is a constant.

   (iii) Show that the image of $(m, \log_a m)$ by a reflection in the line $y = x$ lies on the curve of $g(x)$.

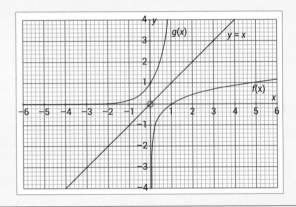

14. Radioactive substances decay exponentially. The half-life of a radioactive substance is the amount of time that it takes for 50% of the quantity of the substance to decay (to become more stable).

   Some radioactive substances decay very quickly, e.g. Lithium-8 has a half-life of only 0.84 seconds. Other substances decay very slowly, e.g. Uranium-238 has a half-life of 4.47 billion years!

   Below is a diagram showing how a radioactive substance, Cobalt-60, decays over time.

   (a) The equation for the curve is $Q = Ae^{-kt}$. The intial quantity of Cobalt-60 is 10 kg. Using this information, show algebraically that $A = 10$.

   (b) Using the graph, estimate, to the nearest decimal place, the half-life (in years) of Cobalt-60.

   (c) Using the fact that $A = 10$ and the value for the half-life that you calculated in part (b), find the value of the decay constant k in the equation of the curve $Q = 10e^{-kt}$.

   (d) Using your answer from part (c), calculate, to the nearest decimal place, how long (in years) it would take for 90% of a quantity of Cobalt-60 to decay.

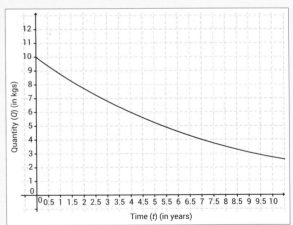

15. $y = Ae^{-kt}$ represents the rate of decay of radium, where y is the amount present at a time t.

   A is the initial quantity of radium present. If it takes 1,600 years for half the original amount to decay, find the percentage of the original amount that remains after 200 years.

Exam Questions

1. In a science experiment, a quantity $Q(t)$ was observed at various points in time t. Time is measured in seconds from the instant of the first observation. The table below gives the results.

t	0	1	2	3	4
$Q(t)$	2.920	2.642	2.391	2.163	1.957

Q follows a rule of the form $Q(t) = Ae^{-bt}$, where A and b are constants.

(i) Use any two of the observations from the table to find the value of A and the value of b, correct to three decimal places.

(ii) Use a different observation from the table to verify your values for A and b.

(iii) Show that $Q(t)$ is a constant multiple of $Q(t-1)$, for $t \geqslant 1$.

(iv) Find the value of the constant k for which $Q(t+k) = \frac{1}{2}Q(t)$, for all $t \geqslant 0$. Give your answer correct to two decimal places.

SEC Leaving Certificate Higher Level, Paper 1, 2011

2. Scientists can estimate the age of certain ancient items by measuring the proportion of carbon-14, relative to the total carbon content in the item. The formula used is $Q = e^{-\frac{0.693t}{5730}}$, where Q is the proportion of carbon-14 remaining and t is the age, in years, of the item.

(i) An item is 2,000 years old. Use the formula to find the proportion of carbon-14 in the item.

(ii) The proportion of carbon-14 in an item found at Lough Boora, County Offaly, was 0.3402. Estimate, correct to two significant figures, the age of the item.

SEC Leaving Certificate Higher Level, Paper 1, 2013

3. Ciarán is preparing food for his baby and must use cooled boiled water. The equation $y = Ae^{kt}$ describes how the boiled water cools. In this equation:

- t is the time, in minutes, from when the water boiled.
- y is the *difference* between the water temperature and room temperature at time t, measured in degrees Celsius.
- A and k are constants.

The temperature of the water when it boils is 100°C and the room temperature is a constant 23°C.

(i) Write down the value of the temperature difference, y, when the water boils, and find the value of A.

(ii) After five minutes, the temperature of the water is 88°C.
Find the value of k, correct to three significant figures.

(iii) Ciarán prepares the food for his baby when the water has cooled to 50°C. How long does it take, correct to the nearest minute, for the water to cool to this temperature?

(iv) Using your values for A and k, sketch the curve $f(t) = Ae^{kt}$ for $0 \leqslant t \leqslant 100$, $t \in R$.

(v) (a) On the same diagram, sketch a curve $g(t) = Ae^{mt}$, showing the water cooling at a *faster* rate, where A is the value from part (a), and m is a constant. Label each graph clearly.

(b) Suggest one possible value for m for the sketch you have drawn and give a reason for your choice.

SEC Leaving Certificate Higher Level, Paper 1, 2014

Solutions and chapter summary available online

INDICES AND LOGARITHMS

08

Number Patterns, Sequences and Series

In this chapter you will learn to:

- Investigate patterns and generalise and explain patterns in algebraic form

- Recognise whether a sequence is arithmetic, geometric or neither

- Find the sum to n terms of an arithmetic series

- Investigate geometric sequences and series

- Find by inspection the limits of sequences such as $\lim\limits_{n\to\infty} \dfrac{n}{n+1}$ and $\lim\limits_{n\to\infty} r^n, |r| < 1$

- Derive the formula for the sum to infinity of a geometric series by considering the limit of a sequence of partial sums

- Solve problems involving finite and infinite geometric series (including applications such as recurring decimals)

You should remember...

- How to solve linear and quadratic equations
- How to graph functions

Key words

- Pattern
- Linear pattern
- Arithmetic sequence
- Arithmetic series

- First difference (common difference)
- Second difference
- Third difference

- Quadratic sequence
- Cubic sequence
- Geometric sequence

- Geometric series
- Limits
- Infinite series

'Perhaps I could best describe my experience of doing mathematics in terms of entering a dark mansion. One goes into the first room, and it's dark, completely dark. One stumbles around bumping into the furniture, and gradually, you learn where each piece of furniture is, and finally, after six months or so, you find the light switch. You turn it on, and suddenly, it's all illuminated. You can see exactly where you were.'

Andrew Wiles, Professor of Mathematics, Oxford University, and famous for discovering a proof of Fermat's Last Theorem

Modern mathematics is considered by many to be the study of **patterns**. By studying patterns in the real world around us, mathematicians derive mathematical representations that help explain and even predict a host of real-world phenomena.

8.1 Patterns

Patterns appear all around us: a **recurring** theme or motif in a piece of music, a **repeating** decimal such as 0.232323..., or the passage of the seasons over time.

The word 'pattern' comes from the French word *patron*. In the 14th century, when the word 'pattern' first appeared, a patron was somebody who paid for work (like the construction of a sword or a piece of pottery) to be done, often by giving an example to the workman to **copy**.

This leads us to the following definition:

A **pattern** is a set of numbers, objects or diagrams that repeat in a particular manner.

Here are some examples of patterns:

(a)

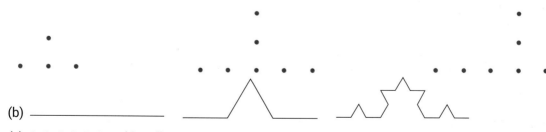

(b)

(c) 1, 1, 2, 3, 5, 8, ... (the **Fibonnacci pattern**; the first two terms are 1 and each successive term is the sum of the two previous terms)

(d) 101, 1,001, 10,001, 100,001, 1,000,001, ...

We call each distinct object, number or diagram in a pattern a **term** of the pattern.

The first term of a pattern is called T_1, the second term T_2, and so on. To predict what will come next in a pattern, we must find a rule that links one number, object or diagram in the pattern with the next.

Worked Example 8.1

A four-tile repeating pattern is made up of the shapes shown:

(i) Draw the next two shapes in the pattern.

(ii) What is the shape of T_{100}, the 100th tile?

(iii) What is the shape of T_{253}?

(iv) What is the shape of T_{4n}, $n \in N$?

Solution

(i)

As the pattern repeats every four tiles, the 5th and 6th tiles will be the same as the 1st and 2nd tiles.

(ii) We can draw a table to help us:

Tile	Shape
1	Triangle
2	Square
3	Pentagon
4	Hexagon
5	Triangle
6	Square
7	Pentagon
8	Hexagon
9	Triangle

$\frac{100}{4} = 25$, with a remainder of 0.

(25 repeating blocks of four tiles)

∴ 100 is a multiple of 4.

If we consider our table we see that every multiple of 4 will be a hexagon.

∴ The 100th tile is a hexagon.

(iii) $\frac{253}{4} = 63$, with a remainder of 1.

This is one more than a multiple of 4. Therefore the 253rd tile is a triangle.

(iv) If $n \in N$, then T_{4n} is the set of tiles, $\{T_4, T_8, T_{12}, T_{16}, ...\}$. This set consists of every 4th tile. From part (ii), we know that every 4th tile is a hexagon. Therefore, the shape of T_{4n} is a hexagon.

Worked Example 8.2

The Tower of Hanoi puzzle: there are three pegs. On the first peg is a stack of discs of different sizes arranged in order of descending size. The goal is to move all of the discs to another peg. Only one disc can be moved at a time and a disc cannot be placed on top of a smaller disc.

(a) What is the least number of moves needed to complete the Tower of Hanoi puzzle with

(i) one disc   (iii) three discs

(ii) two discs   (iv) four discs

Note: You can complete the puzzle manually, or by using an online Tower of Hanoi simulator.

(b) Let T_n stand for the least number of moves needed to complete the puzzle with n discs.

(i) Write out the sequence T_1, T_2, T_3, T_4.

(ii) Use your answer to (i) to derive a formula for T_n.

(iii) What is the least number of moves needed to complete the Tower of Hanoi puzzle with 8 discs.

Solution

(a) (i) 1   (ii) 3   (iii) 7   (iv) 15

(b) (i) 1, 3, 7, 15

(ii) Note how 1, 3, 7, 15 is the sequence 2, 4, 8, 16 with 1 taken away from each term.

$T_1 = 2^1 - 1$, $T_2 = 2^2 - 1$, $T_3 = 2^3 - 1$, $T_4 = 2^4 - 1$

∴ $T_n = 2^n - 1$

(iii) $T_8 = 2^8 - 1$

$= 255$

Exercise 8.1

1. A three-tile repeating pattern is shown below.

  (i) What is the shape of the 40th tile?

 (ii) What is the shape of the 30th tile?

(iii) If T_1 is the shape of the first tile, T_2 the shape of the second and so on, then what shape will T_{3n}, $n \in N$, always be? Explain your answer.

2. A four-tile repeating pattern is shown below.

  (i) What is the shape of the 15th tile?

 (ii) What is the shape of the 94th tile?

(iii) What colour is the 100th tile?

(iv) Copy and complete the following sentence:

If n is even, then T_n will always be a _____-shaped tile, while if n is odd, T_n will always be a _____-shaped tile.

 (v) Solve the equation $3(x + 2) = 5x + 2$.

(vi) Taking your solution for x from part (v), what colour will T_{xn}, $n \in \{1, 3, 5, 7, ...\}$ always be? Explain your answer.

3. In the following pattern, draw the correct next term.

4. To predict what will come next in a pattern, we must find a rule that will link one number or diagram with the next.

  (i) Identify two different rules for the above pattern.

 (ii) For each of the rules, draw the next two diagrams in the pattern.

5. A ring of stepping stones has 14 stones in it, as shown in the diagram.

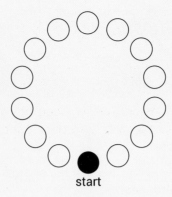

start

A girl hops around the ring, stopping to change feet every time she has made three hops. She notices that when she has been around the ring three times, she has stopped to change feet on each one of the 14 stones.

(i) The girl now hops around the ring, stopping to change feet every time she has made four hops. Explain why in this case she will not stop on each one of the 14 stones no matter has long she continues hopping around the ring.

(ii) The girl stops to change feet every time she has made n hops. For which values of n will she stop on each one of the 14 stones to change feet?

(iii) Find a general rule for stopping on every stone when the ring contains more (or fewer) than 14 stones.

6. Consider the sequence formed by adding successive multiples of 10 to 7 and then squaring:

$$7^2, 17^2, 27^2, 37^2, \ldots$$

(i) Find a formula for T_n, the nth term of the sequence.

(ii) By considering the following pattern, find another formula for T_n:

$$7^2 = 100 - 6 \times 10 + 9$$
$$17^2 = 400 - 6 \times 20 + 9$$
$$27^2 = 900 - 6 \times 30 + 9$$

(iii) Prove that the formula in part (i) is identical to the formula in part (ii).

8.2 Arithmetic Sequences

Arithmetic sequences can be used to predict real-life situations. Here is an example of a real-life problem that can be solved using arithmetic sequences. A theatre has an auditorium with 22 rows of seats. There are 18 seats in Row 1 and each row after Row 1 has two more seats than the previous row. How many seats are in Row 22?

A **sequence** is a set of terms, in a definite order, where the terms are obtained by some rule.
A **number sequence** is an ordered set of numbers, with a rule to find every number in the sequence.

2, 6, 10, 14, 18, ... is an example of a **number sequence**. The first term is 2 ($T_1 = 2$). The rule for finding a particular term is to add 4 to the previous term.

In an **arithmetic (linear) sequence** the difference or change between one term and the next is always the same number. This means that the change in an arithmetic sequence is always constant. An arithmetic sequence is sometimes called an **arithmetic progression**.

In the **arithmetic sequence** 2, 6, 10, 14, 18, ... the difference between consecutive terms is 4.

> The difference, $T_n - T_{n-1}$, between consecutive terms in any sequence is referred to as the **first difference**. (It is also known as the first change.)
>
> The difference between consecutive terms in an arithmetic sequence can also be referred to as the **common difference**. The letter d is used to represent the common difference.

The two sequences shown below are arithmetic. The first sequence has first term, or start term, 11 and first difference 7. The second sequence has first term, or start term, 2 and first difference −3.

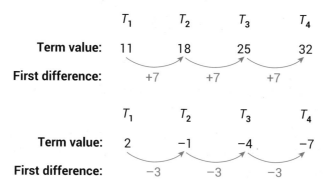

When we graph the terms of an arithmetic sequence against the term number, the plotted points lie on a straight line, hence the name 'linear sequence'. The first six terms of the arithmetic sequence 2, 5, 8, 11, 14, 17, ... are graphed below.

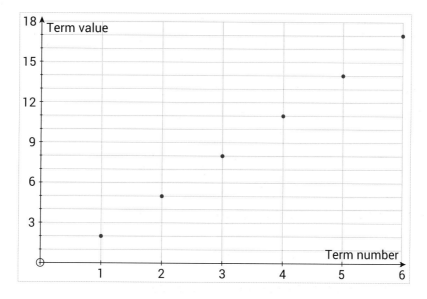

The General Term of an Arithmetic Sequence

Let a be the first term of an arithmetic sequence and d be the common difference. The table shows the first five terms of this sequence.

T_1	T_2	T_3	T_4	T_5
a	$a + d$	$a + 2d$	$a + 3d$	$a + 4d$

What is T_n, the nth term of the sequence?

We can see that T_n must equal a with $(n - 1)d$ added on.

This formula appears on page 22 of *Formulae and Tables*.

> The **general term** for any arithmetic sequence is $T_n = a + (n - 1)d$, where a is the first term and d is the common difference.

To come back to the earlier problem regarding the seats in a theatre auditorium, $a = 18$, $d = 2$, $n = 22 \Rightarrow T_{22} = 18 + 21(2) = 60$ seats.

Worked Example 8.3

A number sequence has general term $T_n = 5 - 3n$.

Prove that the sequence has a common difference.

Solution

$$T_n = 5 - 3n$$

$$T_{n-1} = 5 - 3(n - 1)$$

$$= 5 - 3n + 3$$

$$= 8 - 3n$$

$$T_n - T_{n-1} = (5 - 3n) - (8 - 3n)$$

$$= 5 - 3n - 8 + 3n$$

$$= -3 \text{ (a constant)}$$

To prove a sequence is arithmetic show that $T_n - T_{n-1} =$ a constant.

$\therefore$ The sequence has a common difference. (In other words the sequence is arithmetic.)

Worked Example 8.4

The first three terms of a pattern are shown.

$$T_1 = \qquad T_2 = \qquad T_3 =$$

(i) Draw the next two terms of the pattern.

(ii) Count the number of dots in each of the first five terms and display the results in a table.

(iii) Describe the sequence of numbers generated by the pattern.

(iv) How many dots are there in T_7, the seventh term?

(v) How many dots are there in T_n, the nth term?

Solution

(i)

$$T_4 = \qquad T_5 =$$

(ii)

T_1	T_2	T_3	T_4	T_5
6	8	10	12	14

(iii) The sequence is arithmetic, with first term 6 and common difference 2.

(iv)

T_1	T_2	T_3	T_4	T_5	T_6	T_7
6	8	10	12	14	16	18

$+2 \quad +2 \quad +2 \quad +2 \quad +2 \quad +2$

From the diagram it is clear that $T_7 = 6 + (6)2 = 18$.

(v) Using the same reasoning as in part (iv),

$$T_n = 6 + (n - 1)2$$

$$= 6 + 2n - 2$$

$$\therefore T_n = 4 + 2n$$

Worked Example 8.5

x, $2x + 1$ and $5x - 4$ are the first three terms of an arithmetic sequence. Find:

(i) The value of x

(ii) The fourth term of the sequence

Solution

(i) Since the sequence is arithmetic, the difference between any two consecutive terms is a constant.

$$T_2 - T_1 = T_3 - T_2$$
$$\Rightarrow (2x + 1) - x = (5x - 4) - (2x + 1)$$
$$2x + 1 - x = 5x - 4 - 2x - 1$$
$$x + 1 = 3x - 5$$
$$-2x = -6$$
$$\therefore x = 3$$

(ii) If $x = 3$, then the sequence is $3, 2(3) + 1, 5(3) - 4, \ldots$
This gives the sequence $3, 7, 11, \ldots$
The common difference is 4.

$$\therefore T_4 = 11 + 4 = 15$$

Worked Example 8.6

How many terms of the arithmetic sequence $45, 43, 41, \ldots$ are positive?

Solution

$a = 45$ and $d = -2$

We need to find the largest value of n, for which $T_n > 0$.

$$T_n = a + (n - 1)d$$
$$= 45 + (n - 1)(-2)$$
$$= 45 - 2n + 2$$
$$\therefore T_n = 47 - 2n$$

Let $T_n > 0$

$$\Rightarrow 47 - 2n > 0$$
$$-2n > -47$$
$$2n < 47 \quad \text{(Multiplying both sides by a negative number changes the direction of the inequality sign.)}$$
$$n < 23.5$$
$$\therefore n = 23 \quad (n \text{ must be a whole number.})$$

$\therefore$ 23 terms of the sequence are positive.

Exercise 8.2

1. The first three terms of a pattern are shown below.

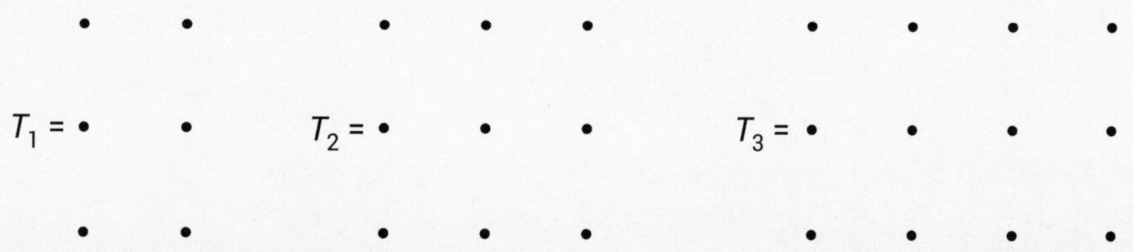

$T_1 = \bullet$ $T_2 = \bullet$ $T_3 = \bullet$

(i) Draw the next two terms of the pattern.

(ii) Count the number of dots in each of the first five terms and display the results in a table.

(iii) Describe the sequence of numbers generated by the pattern.

(iv) How many dots are there in T_9, the ninth term?

(v) How many dots are there in T_n, the nth term?

2. The first three terms of a pattern are shown below.

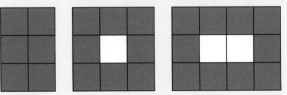

   (i) Draw the next two terms of the pattern.

   (ii) Count the number of dots in each of the first five terms and display the results in a table.

   (iii) Describe the sequence of numbers generated by the pattern.

   (iv) How many dots are there in T_9, the ninth term?

   (v) How many dots are there in T_n, the nth term?

3. The first three terms of a pattern are shown.

   (i) Draw the next two terms of the pattern.

   (ii) Count the number of red squares in each of the first five terms and display the results in a table.

   (iii) Describe the sequence of numbers generated by the pattern.

   (iv) How many red squares are there in T_7, the seventh term?

   (v) How many red squares are there in T_n, the nth term?

   (vi) How many white squares are there in T_n, the nth term?

4. $-11, -15, -19, \ldots$ is an arithmetic sequence.

   (i) Find the nth term of the sequence.

   (ii) Hence, write down the 55th term.

5. $0, 7, 14, 21, 28, \ldots$ is an arithmetic sequence.

   (i) Find the nth term of the sequence.

   (ii) Hence, write down the 85th term.

6. $3, 11, 19, \ldots$ is an arithmetic sequence.

   (i) Find the nth term of the sequence.

   (ii) Hence, write down the 96th term.

7. $31, 25, 19, \ldots$ is an arithmetic sequence.

   (i) Find the nth term of the sequence.

   (ii) Hence, write down the 21st term.

8. 116 is a term in the arithmetic sequence $14, 17, 20, \ldots$

  Which term is 116?

9. The 51st term of an arithmetic sequence is 248. If d, the common difference, is 15, then find a, the first term.

10. A pattern consisting of isosceles triangles is drawn. The first triangle has a base length of 2 cm and a height of 1 cm. The base of the second triangle is 2 cm longer than the base of the first triangle and the height of the second triangle is 1 cm longer than the height of the first triangle. The same pattern of enlargement will continue with each triangle that follows.

   (i) What is the base length and height of the 100th triangle?

   (ii) Derive a formula for finding the area of the nth triangle.

   (iii) Which triangle has an area of 4.41 m²?

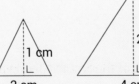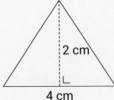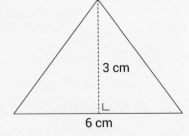

   (iv) If the perimeter of the nth triangle is $an(1 + \sqrt{2})$ cm, $a \in R$, find the value of a.

   (v) Which triangle has a perimeter of $4(1 + \sqrt{2})$ m?

11. State which of the following sequences are arithmetic:

   (i) 3, 5, 7, 9, ...

   (ii) 2, 4, 6, 8, 10, ...

   (iii) 1, 2, 4, 8, 16, ...

   (iv) 1, 1, 2, 3, 5, 8, ...

   (v) 5, 10, 15, 20, 25, ...

   (vi) $\dfrac{1}{2}, \dfrac{1}{3}, \dfrac{1}{4}, \dfrac{1}{5}, \dfrac{1}{6}, ...$

   (vii) −5, −1, 3, 7, 11, ...

   (viii) 17, 14, 11, ...

   (ix) 3, −2, −8, −15, ...

   (x) 1.1, 1.35, 1.6, 1.85, ...

   (xi) 0.21, −0.43, −1.07, −1.71, ...

12. The nth terms of some sequences are given below. By considering the difference $T_n - T_{n-1}$, state which of the following sequences are arithmetic:

   (i) $T_n = 2n + 1$

   (ii) $T_n = 3n - 1$

   (iii) $T_n = n^2 + 3$

   (iv) $T_n = 12 - 2n$

   (v) $T_n = \dfrac{1}{n}$

13. If the nth term of a sequence is of the form $xn + y$, where x and y are constants, prove that the sequence is arithmetic.

14. The graphs of three sequences are shown. Lines and curves are included for clarity.

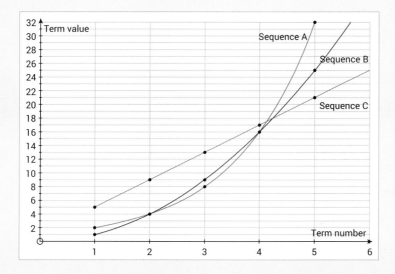

   (i) Identify the arithmetic sequence.

   (ii) Write down the first four terms of each sequence.

   (iii) Calculate the value of d, the common difference, in the arithmetic sequence.

15. The graphs of three sequences are shown. Lines are included for clarity.

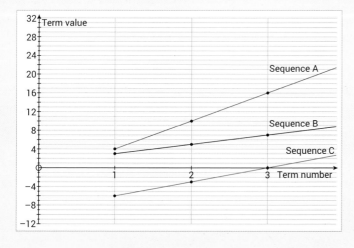

   (i) Find the common differences, d_A, d_B and d_C for each of the three sequences.

   (ii) Find m_A, m_B and m_C, the slopes of each of the lines associated with each sequence.

   (iii) What is the connection between each common difference and slope?

16. $3x - 2$, $2x + 1$ and $18 - x$ are the first three terms of an arithmetic sequence. Find:

   (i) The value of x

   (ii) The value of d, the common difference

   (iii) The fourth and fifth terms (T_4 and T_5)

17. A sequence has the following three consecutive terms:

$7(x + 1) - 2$, $3(x + 2) + 2(3 + 2x)$, $7(x + 3) - 2$.

Prove that the sequence is arithmetic.

18. A sequence has the following three consecutive terms:

$5(x - 4) + 3$, $3(x + 2) - 23$, $5x - 17$.

Prove that the sequence is not arithmetic ($x \neq 0$).

19. How many terms of the arithmetic sequence 91, 89, 87, ... are positive?

20. How many terms of the arithmetic sequence 17, 21, 25, ... are less than 100?

21. How many terms of the arithmetic sequence 100, 97, 94, ... are positive?

22. The natural numbers greater than 1 are arranged as shown in the following chart:

	A	B	C	D	E
Row 1			2	3	4
Row 2	7	6	5		
Row 3			8	9	10
Row 4	13	12	11		
Row 5			14	15	16
Row 6					
Row 7					
Row 8					
Row 9					

(i) Copy and complete the pattern for rows 6 to 9.

(ii) What number will appear in row 100 of column A?

(iii) What number will appear in row 99 of column E?

(iv) Determine the position of the integer 2,011.

23. Show that the sequence $T_n = \log ar^{n-1}$, where $a, r \in R$, $a > 0$ and $r > 0$, is arithmetic.

24. As part of a new tree-planting initiative, Seán has to plant 30 trees on his farm in 2016, 35 in 2017, 40 in 2018 and so on until the year 2035.

(i) How many trees will Seán plant in 2029?

(ii) In what year will Seán plant 75 trees?

(iii) Draw a graph showing the number of trees that will be planted in each of the years from 2030 to 2035.

25. A person just fitted for contact lenses is told to wear the lenses for two hours the first day and to increase the amount of time they wear the lenses by 15 minutes per day.

(i) Complete the table.

(ii) On which day will the person be able to wear the contact lenses for 14 hours?

Day	Number of hours wearing lenses
1	2
2	2.25
3	
4	
5	

26. An architect is designing a skyscraper. He has been told that each floor must contain exactly 90 rooms. He has constructed a table showing the total number of rooms for each floor and all floors below it. Part of the table is shown below.

Floor number	Number of rooms on the floor and all floors below
1	90
2	180
3	270
4	360
5	450

(i) Construct the next five rows of the table.

(ii) All rooms on the first 20 floors will be equipped with a special security door. How many of these doors will be required?

(iii) The building must contain 9,090 rooms. How many floors will the skyscraper have?

8.3 Arithmetic Series

An arithmetic series is the sum of all the terms in an arithmetic sequence.

Carl Friedrich Gauss (1777–1855) was a German mathematician who made significant contributions to many fields, including number theory, statistics, calculus, geometry and physics. He is often referred to as 'the greatest mathematician since antiquity'.

Gauss was a child prodigy. When he was in primary school, he was punished by his teacher for misbehaviour. His punishment was to add all the whole numbers from 1 to 100. To the amazement of his teacher, he calculated the sum in a matter of seconds. How did he do it?

Carl Friedrich Gauss
(1777–1855)

Gauss's Method

It is most likely that the young Gauss used the following method to sum the first 100 natural numbers:

Step 1 Write the series in ascending order from 1 to 100.

$1 + 2 + 3 + 4 + \ldots + 97 + 98 + 99 + 100$

Step 2 Write the series in descending order from 100 to 1.

$100 + 99 + 98 + 97 + \ldots + 4 + 3 + 2 + 1$

Step 3 Add together both representations of the series.

$$\begin{array}{cccccccccc}
1+ & 2+ & 3+ & 4+ & \ldots & + 97+ & 98+ & 99+ & 100 \\
100+ & 99+ & 8+97+ & \ldots & + & 4+ & 3+ & 2+ & 1 \\
\hline
101+ & 101+ & 101+ & \ldots+ & & & 101+ & 101+ & 101
\end{array}$$

This gives $100(101) = 10{,}100$.

This is the sum of two series; therefore, the sum of one series is $\frac{1}{2}(10{,}100) = 5{,}050$.

$\therefore\ 1 + 2 + 3 + 4 + \ldots + 97 + 98 + 99 + 100 = 5{,}050$

The sum of the first n terms of an arithmetic series is given by the formula:

$$S_n = \frac{n}{2}[2a + (n-1)d]$$

This formula appears on page 22 of *Formulae and Tables*.

- a is the first term.
- d is the common difference.

Worked Example 8.7

Find the sum of the first 100 terms of the arithmetic series $7 + 10 + 13 + \ldots$

Solution

$$S_n = \frac{n}{2}[2a + (n - 1)d]$$

$$a = 7, \quad d = 3, \quad n = 100$$

$$S_{100} = \frac{100}{2}[2(7) + (100 - 1)3]$$

$$= 50[14 + 99(3)]$$

$$= 50[311]$$

$$\therefore S_{100} = 15{,}550$$

Worked Example 8.8

Find the sum of all the terms of the arithmetic series $11 + 13 + 15 + \ldots + 51$.

Solution

Step 1 We need to know how many terms there are in the series.

Let n = the number of terms.
Therefore, $T_n = 51$.

$$a = 11, \quad d = 2$$

$$T_n = a + (n - 1)d$$

$$\Rightarrow T_n = 11 + (n - 1)2$$

$$= 11 + 2n - 2$$

$$\therefore T_n = 2n + 9$$

Let $2n + 9 = 51$

$$2n = 51 - 9$$

$$2n = 42$$

$$\therefore n = 21$$

There are 21 terms.

Step 2 Next we must find the sum of these 21 terms.

$$S_n = \frac{n}{2}[2a + (n - 1)d]$$

$$a = 11, \quad d = 2, \quad n = 21$$

$$S_{21} = \frac{21}{2}[2(11) + (21 - 1)2]$$

$$= 10.5[22 + 20(2)]$$

$$= 10.5[62]$$

$$\therefore S_{21} = 651$$

Worked Example 8.9

Show that, for any series, $T_n = S_n - S_{n-1}$.

Solution

$$S_n = T_1 + T_2 + T_3 + T_4 + \ldots + T_{n-1} + T_n$$

$$S_{n-1} = T_1 + T_2 + T_3 + T_4 + \ldots + T_{n-1}$$

$$\therefore S_n - S_{n-1} = T_n$$

Worked Example 8.10

An arithmetic sequence is defined by:

$$S_n = 4n^2 - 3n$$

where S_n is the sum of the first n terms of the sequence.

(i) Find T_n.

(ii) Hence, find T_{100}.

Solution

(i) $T_n = S_n - S_{n-1}$

$= [4n^2 - 3n] - [4(n-1)^2 - 3(n-1)]$

$= [4n^2 - 3n] - [4(n^2 - 2n + 1) - 3n + 3]$

$= 4n^2 - 3n - [4n^2 - 8n + 4 - 3n + 3]$

$= 4n^2 - 3n - 4n^2 + 8n - 4 + 3n - 3$

$\therefore T_n = 8n - 7$

(ii) $T_{100} = 8(100) - 7$

$\therefore T_{100} = 793$

Worked Example 8.11

In an arithmetic sequence, the sixth term is half the first term. The sum of the third and tenth terms is 27.

(i) Find the first term and the common difference of the sequence.

(ii) How many terms of the sequence are positive?

Solution

(i) In an arithmetic sequence, $T_n = a + (n-1)d$.

$T_1 = a$

$T_6 = a + (6-1)d$

$\quad = a + 5d$

$T_6 = \frac{1}{2}T_1$

$\Rightarrow a + 5d = \frac{1}{2}a$

$2a + 10d = a$

$a + 10d = 0 \qquad (*)$

$T_3 = a + (3-1)d$

$\quad = a + 2d$

$T_{10} = a + (10-1)d$

$\quad = a + 9d$

$T_3 + T_{10} = 27$

$a + 2d + a + 9d = 27$

$2a + 11d = 27 \qquad (**)$

$(*) \quad a + 10d = 0 \qquad (\times -2) \Rightarrow -2a - 20d = 0$

$(**) \quad 2a + 11d = 27 \qquad \underline{+2a + 11d = 27}$

$-9d = 27$

$\therefore d = -3$

$a + 10(-3) = 0$

$\therefore a = 30$

(ii) We need to find the greatest value of n, for which $T_n > 0$.

$T_n = a + (n-1)d$

$\quad = 30 + (n-1)(-3)$

$\quad = 30 - 3n + 3$

$\therefore T_n = 33 - 3n$

$33 - 3n > 0$

$3n < 33$

$n < 11 \ (n \in N)$

$\therefore n = 10$

Exercise 8.3

1. Find the sum of the first 30 terms of each of the following arithmetic series:

   (i) $4 + 7 + 10 + \ldots$

   (ii) $3 + 8 + 13 + \ldots$

   (iii) $-5 + 2 + 9 + \ldots$

   (iv) $35 + 33 + 31 + \ldots$

   (v) $20 + 19 + 18 + \ldots$

   (vi) $-2 + 3 + 8 + \ldots$

   (vii) $-5 + 6 + 17 + \ldots$

   (viii) $5 + 2 - 1 - \ldots$

   (xi) $-5 - 8 - 11 - \ldots$

   (x) $-10 - 20 - 30 - \ldots$

2. $S_{80} = 1 + 2 + 3 + 4 + \ldots + 79 + 80$ is the sum of the first 80 natural numbers. Find S_{80}.

3. Find the sum of the first 30 odd natural numbers:
   $1 + 3 + 5 + \ldots + 59$

4. How many terms are there in the arithmetic series $2 + 4 + 6 + \ldots + 80$? Find their sum.

5. Given the arithmetic series $2 + 10 + 18 + \ldots$

   (i) Find the sum of the first 20 terms.

   (ii) Find the sum of the first 40 terms.

   (iii) Hence, find the sum of the second 20 terms.

6. On 1 January 2015, John opened a bank account and deposited €100 in the account. On 1 February 2015, he deposited €105 in the account. He plans to make deposits on the first of every month, increasing the amount deposited by €5 each month.

   (i) How much will John deposit on 1 December 2019?

   (ii) In total, how much will John have deposited by the end of December 2019?

7. An athlete begins a training programme for a 10 km road race 50 weeks before the event. He plans to train each day for 49 weeks and rest on the week before the race. In the first week he runs 2 km each day, in the second week he runs 2.25 km, in the third 2.5 km, and so on, increasing his distance by 0.25 km each successive week.

   (i) How many kilometres will he run each day in the 30th week?

   (ii) During which week will he run the race distance each day?

   (iii) How many kilometres in total will he run on the training programme, assuming he trains seven days a week?

8. A snail is crawling up a wall. The first hour it climbs 20 cm, the second hour it climbs 18 cm, the third hour 16 cm and so on.

   (i) After how many hours will it have stopped climbing?

   (ii) Assuming that the snail reaches the top of the wall just as it stops climbing, how high is the wall?

9. In an arithmetic sequence, the sixth term is half the fourth term and the third term is 15.

   (i) Find the first term and the common difference.

   (ii) How many terms are needed to give a sum that is less than 65?

10. A shop assistant is arranging a triangular display of tins so as to have one tin in the top row, two in the second, three in the third and so on.

    If there are 100 tins altogether, how many rows can be completed and how many tins will be left over?

11. A lecture theatre has a trapezium-shaped floor plan, so that the number of chairs in successive rows are in arithmetic sequence. The back row of chairs contains eight chairs and the front row contains 30. There are 12 rows altogether.

    (i) Find the number of seats in the theatre.

    (ii) Find the percentage of seats that are in the back six rows of the theatre.

12. The sum to n terms of an arithmetic sequence is given by $S_n = 4n^2 - 5n$.

    (i) Show that $T_n = 8n - 9$.

    (ii) Show that the first difference $T_n - T_{n-1}$ is a constant.

13. The sum to n terms of an arithmetic sequence is given by $S_n = 3n^2 - 6n$.

    (i) Show that $T_n = 6n - 9$.

    (ii) Show that the first difference $T_n - T_{n-1}$ is a constant.

14. The sum to n terms of an arithmetic sequence is given by $S_n = 2n - 5n^2$.

    (i) Show that $T_n = 7 - 10n$.

    (ii) Show that the first difference $T_n - T_{n-1}$ is a constant.

15.   (i) Show that:

$$\log a + \log ar + \log ar^2 + \ldots + \log ar^{n-1}$$

forms an arithmetic series.

    (ii) Hence, prove that:

$$\log a + \log ar + \log ar^2 + \ldots + \log ar^{n-1} = \frac{1}{2}n \log(a^2 r^{n-1}).$$

16. The sum of the first n terms of an arithmetic sequence is $S_n = n^2 - 3n$. Write down the fourth term and the nth term.

17. Given that, in an arithmetic sequence, T_n, the general term, is of the form $xn + y$, where x and y are constants, prove that S_n, the sum of the first n terms in the corresponding arithmetic series, is of the form $pn^2 + qn$, where p and q are constants.

18. Prove that S_n, the sum of the first n terms in an arithmetic series, is given by the formula $S_n = \frac{n}{2}[2a + (n-1)d]$, where a is the first term and d is the common difference.

8.4 Some Non-Linear Sequences

In arithmetic (linear) sequences, the difference between consecutive terms, also called the first difference, is always constant. If the difference between consecutive terms is **not constant**, then we say that the sequence is **non-linear**.

> In **non-linear sequences**, the first difference changes between each pair of consecutive terms.

The sequence 1, 8, 27, 64, ... is non-linear.

Quadratic Sequences

Consider the non-linear sequence 2, 5, 10, 17, ...

We can see that the first difference between each term is **not** the same.

> A **quadratic sequence** is a sequence where the nth term is of the form $T_n = an^2 + bn + c$, $a, b, c \in R$, $a \neq 0$.
>
> The **second difference** is a non-zero constant. It is also known as the second change.

When we look at the **second difference**, i.e. the difference between the first differences, we see that the second difference is the same non-zero constant each time.

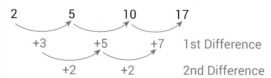

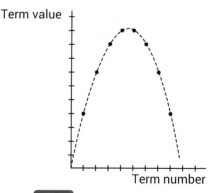

In this case, the pattern is referred to as a **quadratic pattern**.

The graph of a quadratic pattern will be in the shape of a parabolic **curve** and **not** a straight line.

Quadratic sequences have many real-life applications. Consider a ball kicked from a point, p, on level ground, which hits the ground again after 10 seconds at a point q. The vertical heights of the ball above the ground at discrete time intervals ($t = 1$, $t = 2$, ...) form a quadratic sequence.

Worked Example 8.12

Show that the sequence 1, 6, 15, 28, 45, ... is quadratic.

Solution

Term	Sequence	First difference	Second difference
T_1	1		
T_2	6	5	
T_3	15	9	4
T_4	28	13	4
T_5	45	17	4

From the table we see that the second difference is a non-zero constant. Therefore, the sequence is quadratic.

The General Term of a Quadratic Sequence

The general term for any quadratic sequence is $T_n = an^2 + bn + c$ where $a, b, c \in R$ and $a \neq 0$.

The terms either side of T_n are:

$$T_{n-1} = a(n-1)^2 + b(n-1) + c = an^2 + (b-2a)n + a - b + c$$

and

$$T_{n+1} = a(n+1)^2 + b(n+1) + c = an^2 + (b+2a)n + a + b + c$$

Let us calculate the first differences and second difference associated with these three consecutive terms:

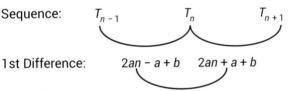

Sequence: T_{n-1} T_n T_{n+1}

1st Difference: $2an - a + b$ $2an + a + b$

2nd Difference: $2a$

Therefore, in any quadratic sequence defined by $T_n = an^2 + bn + c$, the second difference is the non-zero constant $2a$.

Worked Example 8.13

Find the value of a, the coefficient of n^2, in the quadratic sequence $T_n = an^2$. Also find the value of the tenth term. The first five terms of the sequence are 3, 12, 27, 48, 75, ...

Solution

Draw a table:

Term	Sequence	First difference	Second difference
T_1	3		
T_2	12	9	
T_3	27	15	6
T_4	48	21	6
T_5	75	27	6

$2a$ = second difference

$\Rightarrow 2a = 6$

$\therefore a = 3$

$T_n = 3n^2$

$T_{10} = 3(10)^2$

$\quad\ = 3(100)$

$\therefore T_{10} = 300$

NUMBER PATTERNS, SEQUENCES AND SERIES

Worked Example 8.14

$T_n = an^2 + bn + c$ is a quadratic sequence. The first five terms of the sequence are 12, 16, 23, 33, 46, ...

(i) Find the values of a, b and c.

(ii) Hence find T_{30}, the 30th term of the sequence.

Solution

(i) **Step 1** Find the value of a.

Draw a table:

Term	Sequence	First difference	Second difference
T_1	12		
T_2	16	4	
T_3	23	7	3
T_4	33	10	3
T_5	46	13	3

$2a$ = second difference

$\Rightarrow 2a = 3$

$\therefore a = 1.5$

$\therefore T_n = 1.5n^2 + bn + c$ (substituting for a into T_n)

Step 2 Set up equations in b and c.

$T_1 \Rightarrow 1.5(1)^2 + b(1) + c = 12$

$\therefore b + c = 10.5$

$T_2 \Rightarrow 1.5(2)^2 + b(2) + c = 16$

$\therefore 2b + c = 10$

Step 3 Solve the simultaneous equations.

$b + c = 10.5$

$2b + c = 10$

$\therefore b = -0.5$ (subtracting the equations)

$\Rightarrow -0.5 + c = 10.5$

$\therefore c = 11$

(ii) $T_n = 1.5n^2 - 0.5n + 11$

$\Rightarrow T_{30} = 1.5(30)^2 - 0.5(30) + 11$

$\therefore T_{30} = 1,346$

Worked Example 8.15

The first three terms of a pattern are shown.

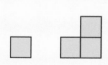 

(i) Draw the next term of the pattern.

(ii) Count the number of squares in each of the first four terms and display the results in a table.

(iii) What type of sequence is the sequence of numbers generated by the pattern?

(iv) How many squares are there in T_7, the seventh term?

Solution

(i)

(ii)

Term	Number of squares
1	1
2	3
3	6
4	10

NUMBER PATTERNS, SEQUENCES AND SERIES

(iii)

Term	Number of squares	First difference	Second difference
1	1		
2	3	2	
3	6	3	1
4	10	4	1

T_1	=	1			
T_2	=	1	+ 2	=	3
T_3	=	3	+ 3	=	6
T_4	=	6	+ 4	=	10
T_5	=	10	+ 5	=	15
T_6	=	15	+ 6	=	21
T_7	=	21	+ 7	=	28

The sequence is quadratic, as the second differences are all 1, a non-zero constant.

(iv) The second difference is a constant of 1.

Therefore, the first difference will increase by 1 each term.

Use a table to help find T_7.

$\therefore T_7$ has 28 squares.

Cubic Sequences

A **cubic sequence** is a sequence of the form $T_n = an^3 + bn^2 + cn + d$, $a, b, c, d \in R$, $a \neq 0$.

For a **cubic sequence** the **third difference** is always a non-zero constant.

Worked Example 8.16

Show that the sequence 2, 10, 30, 68, 130, 222, ... is cubic.

Solution

Sequence	First difference	Second difference	Third difference
2			
10	8		
30	20	12	
68	38	18	6
130	62	24	6
222	92	30	6

The third difference is a non-zero constant. Therefore, the sequence is cubic.

Exercise 8.4

Remember: Linear sequence $\Rightarrow$ 1st difference is a constant.

Quadratic sequence $\Rightarrow$ 2nd difference is a non-zero constant.

Cubic sequence $\Rightarrow$ 3rd difference is a non-zero constant.

1. The first four terms of a pattern are shown below.

(i) Draw the next two terms of the pattern.

(ii) Count the number of dots in each of the first six terms and display the results in a table.

(iii) Describe the sequence of numbers generated by the pattern.

(iv) How many dots are there in T_7, the seventh term?

(v) Find a formula for T_n, the nth term.

(vi) The numbers generated by the pattern are called triangular numbers. By considering T_{n-1}, T_n and T_{n+1}, prove that the sum of any three consecutive triangular numbers is always 1 more than three times the middle of these triangular numbers.

2. The first three terms of a pattern are shown.

  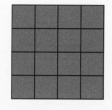

(i) Draw the next two terms of the pattern.

(ii) Count the number of red squares in each of the first five terms and display the results in a table.

(iii) Describe the sequence of numbers generated by the pattern.

(iv) How many red squares are there in T_7, the seventh term?

(v) Derive the formula for T_n, the nth term.

3. Determine whether the following sequences are arithmetic or quadratic.

In each case give a reason for your answer.

(i) –1, 2, 9, 20, ...   (iv) 5, 10, 15, 20, ...

(ii) 1, 5, 11, 19, ...   (v) 3, 6, 13, 24, ...

(iii) 5, 20, 45, 80, ...   (vi) 6, 8, 10, 12, ...

4. For each of the following quadratic sequences, find:

(a) a, the first term

(b) The first and second differences

(c) The next three terms

   (i) 8, 14, 24, 38, ...

   (ii) 1, 3, 6, 10, ...

   (iii) 15, 23, 39, 63, ...

   (iv) 5, 7, 5, –1, –11, ...

   (v) 10, 4, 1, 1, 4, ...

5. Find T_n, the nth term for each of the following quadratic sequences:

   (i) 3, 7, 13, 21, ...   (iii) 6, 11, 18, 27, ...

   (ii) 1, 3, 7, 13, ...   (iv) 13, 15, 23, 37, ...

6. Find T_n, the nth term for each of the following quadratic sequences:

   (i) 20, 28, 44, 68, ...   (iii) 8, 10, 8, 2, –8, ...

   (ii) 11, 15, 17, 17, 15, ...   (iv) 6, 6, 4, 0, ...

7. The patterns of dots shown below represent the first three star numbers.

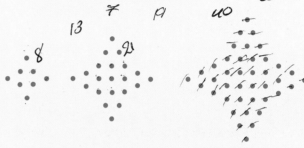

(i) What are the first three star numbers?

(ii) Find a formula for T_n, the nth star number.

(iii) Using your formula from part (ii), find the 50th star number.

(iv) Are there any star numbers that are prime numbers? Explain.

8. $T_n = an^2 + bn + c$ is a quadratic sequence. The first five terms of the sequence are 12, 16, 23, 33, 46.

(i) The second differences are constant. Find the value of this constant.

(ii) Find the first three terms, T_1, T_2 and T_3, in terms of a, b, and c.

(iii) Form three simultaneous equations in a, b, and c.

(iv) Solve the equations to find a, b, and c and, hence, find a formula for T_n.

(v) Find T_{30}, the 30th term of the sequence.

9. The first four terms of a pattern are shown.

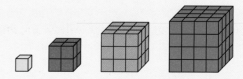

(i) How many cubes are there in each of the next three terms of the pattern?

NUMBER PATTERNS, SEQUENCES AND SERIES

(ii) Construct a table showing the first six terms of the sequence, the first difference, the second difference and the third difference.

(iii) Hence, explain why the sequence is cubic.

10. The first six terms of a pattern are shown.

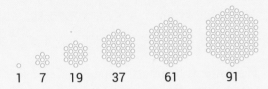

1   7   19   37   61   91

(i) Construct a table showing the first six terms of the corresponding number sequence, the first difference, the second difference and the third difference.

(ii) Hence, explain why the sequence is quadratic.

(iii) How many circles are there in the seventh term?

11. The first three terms of a pattern are shown.

(i) Draw the next shape in the pattern.

(ii) How many dots are there in terms 5 and 6?

(iii) Construct a table showing the first six terms of the corresponding number sequence, the first difference, the second difference and the third difference.

(iv) What type of sequence is this? Explain your answer.

8.5 Geometric Sequences and Series

A geometric sequence, also known as a geometric progression, is a set of numbers where each term after the first is found by multiplying the previous term by a fixed non-zero real number called the common ratio.

For example, the sequence 2, 8, 32, 128, ... is a geometric sequence with first term 2 and common ratio 4. Similarly 10, 5, 2.5, 1.25, ... is a geometric sequence with first term 10 and common ratio $\frac{1}{2}$.

The sum of the terms of a geometric sequence is known as a geometric series.

General Term of a Geometric Sequence

Let a be the first term of a **geometric sequence** and let r be the **common ratio**. The table below shows the first five terms of the sequence.

T_1	T_2	T_3	T_4	T_5
a	ar	ar^2	ar^3	ar^4

What is T_n, the nth term of the sequence?

Note how in T_n the power of r will be $(n-1)$.

The general term for any geometric sequence is $T_n = ar^{n-1}$, where a is the first term and r is the common ratio.

This formula appears on page 22 of *Formulae and Tables*.

Geometric sequences and series have many real-world applications. For example, geometric sequences are used to calculate bacterial growth or the amount of radioactive material in a substance at regular time intervals. Geometric sequences can be used to show that recurring decimals are rational.

Geometric Series

A geometric series is a series where each term after the first is found by multiplying the previous term by a fixed non-zero real number called the common ratio. In other words, a geometric series is the sum of the terms of a geometric sequence. We will now derive a formula to find the sum of a finite geometric series.

Step 1 Write out the series.

$$S_n = a + ar + ar^2 + ar^3 + ... + ar^{n-2} + ar^{n-1} \qquad (*)$$

Step 2 Multiply both sides by the common ratio, r.

$$rS_n = \quad ar + ar^2 + ar^3 + ar^4 + ... + ar^{n-1} + ar^n \qquad (**)$$

Step 3 Subtract (**) from (*).

$$S_n = a + ar + ar^2 + ar^3 + ... + ar^{n-2} + ar^{n-1}$$

$$- \quad (rS_n = \quad ar + ar^2 + ar^3 + ar^4 + ... + ar^{n-1} + ar^n)$$

$$\overline{S_n - rS_n = a \qquad\qquad\qquad\qquad\qquad - ar^n}$$

$$S_n(1 - r) = a(1 - r^n)$$

$$\therefore S_n = \frac{a(1 - r^n)}{1 - r}$$

> The sum of the first n terms of a geometric series is given by:
> $$S_n = \frac{a(1 - r^n)}{1 - r}$$

> If we multiply both numerator and denominator by -1,
> then $S_n = a\left(\dfrac{r^n - 1}{r - 1}\right)$.
> This is useful when $r > 1$.

This formula appears on page 22 of *Formulae and Tables*.

- a is the first term.
- r is the common ratio.

Worked Example 8.17

The first three terms of a geometric series are 5, 10 and 20.

(i) Find T_n, the nth term of the series.

(ii) Find S_n, the sum to n terms of the series.

(iii) Hence, evaluate $5 + 10 + 20 + 40 + ... + 2,560$.

Solution

(i) $a = 5$ and $r = \dfrac{10}{5} = 2$

$$T_n = ar^{n-1}$$

$$\therefore T_n = 5(2)^{n-1}$$

$$r = \frac{T_2}{T_1}$$

(ii) $S_n = \dfrac{a(r^n - 1)}{r - 1}$

$$= \frac{5((2)^n - 1)}{2 - 1}$$

$$= \frac{5(2)^n - 5}{1}$$

$$= 5(2^n) - 5$$

$$\therefore S_n = 5(2^n - 1)$$

(iii) Firstly, we need to find which term is 2,560.

Let $T_n = 2,560$.

$$\Rightarrow 5(2)^{n-1} = 2,560$$

$$2^{n-1} = 512$$

$$2^{n-1} = 2^9$$

$$n - 1 = 9 \quad \text{(Equate the powers.)}$$

$$\therefore n = 10$$

Next we need to find S_{10}.

$$S_{10} = 5(2^{10} - 1)$$

$$\therefore S_{10} = 5,115$$

Worked Example 8.18

An initial population of 600 turtles triples in size each year for five years.

Find:

(i) The growth factor for the population

(ii) The size of the population at the beginning of year 6

Solution

(i) The sequence is geometric and the growth factor (common ratio) is 3.

(ii) $T_n = ar^{n-1}$

  $a = 600$

  $r = 3$

  $T_6 = (600)3^{6-1}$

   $= (600)3^5$

   $= 145,800$

  ∴ Size of population is 145,800

Worked Example 8.19

Show that the sequence $T_n = \left(\dfrac{1}{4}\right)^n$ is geometric.

Solution

$T_n = \left(\dfrac{1}{4}\right)^n$

$T_{n-1} = \left(\dfrac{1}{4}\right)^{n-1}.$

$\dfrac{T_n}{T_{n-1}} = \dfrac{\left(\dfrac{1}{4}\right)^n}{\left(\dfrac{1}{4}\right)^{n-1}}$

$= \left(\dfrac{1}{4}\right)^{n-(n-1)}$

$= \left(\dfrac{1}{4}\right)^{n-n+1}$

$= \dfrac{1}{4}$ (a constant)

∴ $T_n = \left(\dfrac{1}{4}\right)^n$ is geometric

> To prove a sequence is geometric, show that $\dfrac{T_n}{T_{n-1}}$ = a constant.

Exercise 8.5

1. In each of these geometric sequences, write down the value of r, the common ratio, and T_n, the nth term:

   (i) 1, 2, 4, 8, ..

   (ii) 5, 10, 20, 40, ...

   (iii) 7, 21, 63, 189, ...

   (iv) $\dfrac{1}{2}, \dfrac{1}{4}, \dfrac{1}{8}, \dfrac{1}{16}, \cdots$

   (v) 32, 16, 8, 4, ...

   (vi) 3, −6, 12, ...

2. Write down the first four terms of these geometric sequences, given the following nth terms:

   (i) $T_n = 3^n$

   (ii) $T_n = 3(2)^n$

   (iii) $T_n = 2(10)^n$

   (iv) $T_n = 5^{n-1}$

   (v) $T_n = 2(3)^{n-1}$

3. The nth term of a geometric sequence is given by $T_n = 2^n$.

  (i) Write down the first five terms.

  (ii) Write down r, the common ratio.

  (iii) What is the difference between the 10th term and 1,000?

4. Which of the following sequences are geometric? Explain your reasoning.

  In cases where a sequence is not geometric, state what type of sequence it is.

  (i) $T_n = 5^n$ (iv) $T_n = 3(4)^n$

  (ii) $T_n = 2n$ (v) $T_n = n^2$

  (iii) $T_n = \left(\dfrac{1}{3}\right)^n$

5. Find the sum of the first eight terms of the following geometric series:

  (i) $3 + 6 + 12 + \dots$

  (ii) $1 + 5 + 25 + \dots$

  (iii) $5 + 10 + 20 + \dots$

  (iv) $2 + 6 + 18 + \dots$

  (v) $\dfrac{1}{2} + \dfrac{1}{4} + \dfrac{1}{8} + \dots$

6. The nth term of a geometric sequence is given by $T_n = 12(4)^{n-8}$.

  (i) Find T_1, the first term, and r, the common ratio.

  (ii) Find the sum of the first 13 terms.

7. The first two terms of a geometric series are 216 and 54.

  (i) Find the common ratio.

  (ii) Find the sum of the first six terms correct to two decimal places.

  (iii) Find the sum of the second six terms correct to two decimal places.

8. Three terms, x, y and $x + y$, are in arithmetic sequence, $x \neq 0$.

  Three terms, x, y and xy, are in geometric sequence.

  (i) Find the value of x and the value of y.

  (ii) Find the difference between the sum of the first eight terms of the arithmetic sequence and the sum of the first eight terms of the geometric sequence.

9. Find the sum of the finite geometric series:

  $$3 - 6 + 12 - \dots + 49{,}152$$

10. The sixth term of a geometric sequence is 16 and the third term is 2. Find the first term and the common ratio.

11. Find the common ratio, given that it is negative, of a geometric progression whose first term is 8 and whose fifth term is $\dfrac{1}{2}$.

12. Evaluate $\displaystyle\sum_{r=1}^{15} (1.06)^r$. Answer correct to two decimal places.

13. Find the sum of the first n terms of the geometric series $2 + \dfrac{1}{2} + \dfrac{1}{8} + \dots$ and find the least value of n for which this sum exceeds 2.65.

14. Evaluate $\displaystyle\sum_{r=1}^{10} 3\left(\dfrac{3}{4}\right)^r$. Answer correct to two decimal places.

15. The population of a town is presently 38,300. The town grows at an annual rate of 1.2%. Find the number of years it takes for the population to grow to 43,158. Answer to the nearest year.

16. A mortgage is taken out for €150,000 and is repaid by annual instalments of €20,000.

  Interest is charged on the outstanding debt at 10%, calculated annually.

  If the first repayment is made one year after the mortgage is taken out, find the number of years it takes for the mortgage to be repaid.

17. The third term of a geometric series is 10 and the fifth term is 18. Find two possible values of the common ratio and the second term in each case.

18. Estimates are produced for the number of babies born worldwide each year. The estimates for 2009 and for 2013, given in thousands of births to the nearest thousand, were 130,350 and 137,804 respectively. Assume that successive yearly estimates are in geometric progression.

  (i) Find the annual percentage increase in the number of births. Answer correct to one decimal place.

  (ii) Find the estimates for 2011 and 2016 (to the nearest thousand).

  (iii) Find the estimated total number of births between 2009 and 2017 inclusive (to the nearest thousand).

19. The value of a stock when purchased on 1 June was €10 a share. The stock grew daily at a rate of 3% during the month of June. On 1 July the stock fell by 2% and continued this pattern daily, until a recovery on 28 July.

   (i) Find the share value of the stock on 21 June.

   (ii) Find the share value of the stock on 15 July.

20. If a patient takes A milligrams of a drug at time $t = 0$, then $y = A(0.7)^t$ gives the concentration left in the blood after t hours.

   (i) If the initial dose is 125 mg, what is the concentration of the drug in the bloodstream after three hours?

   (ii) A patient has a concentration of 1.938 mg of the drug in their bloodstream. The patient was given 140 mg of the drug. How many hours ago was the drug administered? Answer correct to the nearest hour.

   (iii) Another patient has a concentration of 0.0798 mg in their bloodstream. The drug was given 20 hours ago. How many milligrams of the drug were administered to the patient? Answer correct to the nearest mg.

Limits of Sequences

> The **limit of a sequence** is the unique number, L, such that T_n, the nth term of the sequence, gets closer and closer to L for larger and larger values of n.

- If $T_n \to L$ as $n \to \infty$, then $\lim\limits_{n \to \infty} T_n = L$ $(L \in R)$.
- $\lim\limits_{n \to \infty} \dfrac{1}{n^p} = 0$, for $p > 0$.

If a limit exists, then we say that the sequence is **convergent** and that the nth term converges to L. If a limit does not exist, then we say that the sequence is **divergent**.

The geometric sequence $1, \frac{1}{2}, \frac{1}{4}, \ldots$ converges to 0. As the number of terms increases, the term value approaches 0. The reason is as follows:

The terms $1, \frac{1}{2}, \frac{1}{4}, \ldots$ can be written as powers of $\frac{1}{2}$ $\left(\left(\frac{1}{2}\right)^0, \left(\frac{1}{2}\right)^1, \left(\frac{1}{2}\right)^2, \ldots\right)$. Consider the number $\left(\frac{1}{2}\right)^q = \frac{1}{2^q}$, where $q \in N$. As q gets bigger and bigger, $\frac{1}{2^q}$ gets closer and closer to 0.

Similarly, if $p > 0$, then as $n \in N$ gets bigger and bigger, $\frac{1}{n^p}$ gets closer and closer to 0.

Properties of Limits

The following are some important properties of limits:

> Suppose that $\lim\limits_{x \to a} f(x) = L$ and $\lim\limits_{x \to a} g(x) = M$, where $L, M \in R$. Then the following properties apply:
>
> (1) $\lim\limits_{x \to a} [f(x) + g(x)] = \lim\limits_{x \to a} f(x) + \lim\limits_{x \to a} g(x)$ (Sum property)
>
> (2) $\lim\limits_{x \to a} [f(x) \times g(x)] = \lim\limits_{x \to a} f(x) \times \lim\limits_{x \to a} g(x)$ (Product property)
>
> (3) $\lim\limits_{x \to a} \left[\dfrac{f(x)}{g(x)}\right] = \dfrac{\lim\limits_{x \to a} f(x)}{\lim\limits_{x \to a} g(x)}$ (Quotient property)
>
> (4) $\lim\limits_{x \to a} \sqrt{f(x)} = \sqrt{\lim\limits_{x \to a} f(x)}$ (Root property)

A more in-depth treatment of limits will be given in Chapter 13.

Worked Example 8.20

Evaluate $\lim\limits_{n\to\infty} \dfrac{n}{n+1}$.

Solution

Step 1 Divide above and below by the highest power of n.

$$\lim_{n\to\infty} \frac{n}{n+1} = \lim_{n\to\infty} \frac{\dfrac{n}{n}}{\dfrac{n}{n}+\dfrac{1}{n}}$$

$$= \lim_{n\to\infty} \frac{1}{1+\dfrac{1}{n}}$$

Step 2 Apply the property that $\lim\limits_{n\to\infty} \dfrac{1}{n^p} = 0 \quad (p>0)$

$$\therefore \lim_{n\to\infty} \frac{1}{1+\dfrac{1}{n}} = \frac{1}{1+0}$$

$$= 1$$

Worked Example 8.21

Evaluate $\lim\limits_{n\to\infty} \dfrac{2n^2+15n-1}{3n^2-3n+2}$.

Solution

Step 1 Divide above and below by the highest power of n.

$$\lim_{n\to\infty} \frac{2n^2+15n-1}{3n^2-3n+2} = \lim_{n\to\infty} \frac{\dfrac{2n^2}{n^2}+\dfrac{15n}{n^2}-\dfrac{1}{n^2}}{\dfrac{3n^2}{n^2}-\dfrac{3n}{n^2}+\dfrac{2}{n^2}}$$

$$= \lim_{n\to\infty} \frac{2+\dfrac{15}{n}-\dfrac{1}{n^2}}{3-\dfrac{3}{n}+\dfrac{2}{n^2}}$$

Step 2 Apply the property that $\lim\limits_{n\to\infty} \dfrac{1}{n^p} = 0 \quad (p>0)$

$$\therefore \lim_{n\to\infty} \frac{2n^2+15n-1}{3n^2-3n+2} = \frac{2+0-0}{3-0+0}$$

$$= \frac{2}{3}$$

Worked Example 8.22

Evaluate $\lim\limits_{n\to\infty} \dfrac{\sqrt{3n^4-5}}{n^2+2}$.

Solution

Here we use the root property of limits.

$$\lim_{n\to\infty} \frac{\sqrt{3n^4-5}}{n^2+2} = \lim_{n\to\infty} \frac{\sqrt{3n^4-5}}{\sqrt{(n^2+2)^2}}$$

$$= \lim_{n\to\infty} \sqrt{\frac{3n^4-5}{n^4+4n^2+4}}$$

$$= \sqrt{\lim_{n\to\infty} \frac{3n^4-5}{n^4+4n^2+4}}$$

$$= \sqrt{\lim_{n\to\infty} \frac{3-\dfrac{5}{n^4}}{1+\dfrac{4}{n^2}+\dfrac{4}{n^4}}}$$

$$= \sqrt{\frac{3-0}{1+0+0}}$$

$$= \sqrt{3}$$

Exercise 8.6

1. Evaluate each of the following limits:

   (a) (i) $\lim\limits_{n\to\infty} \dfrac{3n-1}{n+2}$

   (ii) $\lim\limits_{n\to\infty} \dfrac{4n-3}{3n+2}$

   (iii) $\lim\limits_{n\to\infty} \dfrac{5n+1}{6n+2}$

   (iv) $\lim\limits_{n\to\infty} \dfrac{1-3n}{9n-5}$

   (v) $\lim\limits_{n\to\infty} \dfrac{13n+12}{15n-8}$

   (b) (i) $\lim\limits_{n\to\infty} \dfrac{3n^2-1}{n^2+2}$

   (ii) $\lim\limits_{n\to\infty} \dfrac{4n^2-1}{2n^2+2}$

   (iii) $\lim\limits_{n\to\infty} \dfrac{5n^3-1}{2n^3+2}$

   (iv) $\lim\limits_{n\to\infty} \dfrac{3n^4-1}{n^4+2}$

   (v) $\lim\limits_{n\to\infty} \dfrac{3n^8-1}{n^8+2}$

2. Evaluate each of the following limits:

   (i) $\lim\limits_{n\to\infty} \left(\dfrac{2n+4}{5n-3} + \dfrac{2}{2n+4}\right)$

   (ii) $\lim\limits_{n\to\infty} \left(\dfrac{3n+2}{2n+1} + \dfrac{5n-3}{2n-1}\right)$

   (iii) $\lim\limits_{n\to\infty} \left(\dfrac{2n-3}{6n+2} - \dfrac{6n^2+3n}{5n^2-7n}\right)$

   (iv) $\lim\limits_{n\to\infty} \left[\left(\dfrac{n^2-2}{n^3-4}\right)\left(\dfrac{n+2}{5}\right)\right]$

   (v) $\lim\limits_{n\to\infty} \left[\left(\dfrac{2n+3}{5n-3}\right)\left(\dfrac{3n^2+5}{7n^2-3}\right) + \left(\dfrac{2n-3}{5n+1}\right)\right]$

3. Evaluate each of the following limits:

   (i) $\lim\limits_{n\to\infty} \dfrac{6n-1}{3n^2+2}$

   (ii) $\lim\limits_{n\to\infty} \dfrac{5n^2-2n+1}{n^3+2}$

   (iii) $\lim\limits_{n\to\infty} \dfrac{6n^2-2n+3}{2n^2+3n-5}$

   (iv) $\lim\limits_{n\to\infty} \dfrac{3n-n^2}{n^2+2n}$

   (v) $\lim\limits_{n\to\infty} \dfrac{8n^3-2n^2+4}{5n^3+n+2}$

4. Evaluate each of the following limits:

   (i) $\lim\limits_{n\to\infty} \left[\dfrac{5}{3} - \dfrac{n-1}{2n+2}\right]$

   (ii) $\lim\limits_{n\to\infty} \left[\dfrac{17}{25} + \dfrac{7n^2-3n+1}{5n^3+2}\right]$

   (iii) $\lim\limits_{n\to\infty} \left[\dfrac{3}{4} - \dfrac{2n-1}{3n+2}\right]$

   (iv) $\lim\limits_{n\to\infty} \left[16 - \dfrac{12n^2+15n-1}{3n^2-3n+2}\right]$

   (v) $\lim\limits_{n\to\infty} \left[10 - \dfrac{5n^2-2n+1}{n^2+2}\right]$

5. Evaluate each of the following limits:

   (i) $\lim\limits_{n\to\infty} \sqrt{\dfrac{36n+2}{n+4}}$

   (ii) $\lim\limits_{n\to\infty} \sqrt{\dfrac{18n^2-3n}{2n^2+4}}$

   (iii) $\lim\limits_{n\to\infty} \dfrac{\sqrt{2n-3}}{\sqrt{72n+4}}$

   (iv) $\lim\limits_{n\to\infty} \dfrac{\sqrt{4n^2+5}}{n+1}$

6. S_n is the sum to n terms of the arithmetic series $1 + 2 + 3 + \ldots + n$.

   (i) Find S_n.

   (ii) Evaluate $\lim\limits_{n\to\infty} \sqrt{\dfrac{S_n}{3n^2}}$.

8.6 Infinite Series

Consider the infinite sequence $a_1, a_2, a_3, \ldots$ of real numbers. The addition of all the terms of this sequence

$$\sum_{n=1}^{\infty} a_n = a_1 + a_2 + a_3 + \ldots$$

is called an **infinite series**.

For an infinite series there are infinitely many terms to add. If we add a_1 to a_2 and the result to a_3, then add this new result to a_4, etc., by hand or even by computer, then the operation will go on forever. Rather than adding in this way, we use limits to find the sum to infinity of such a series.

We consider the sequence $S_1, S_2, S_3, ..., S_n, ...$ of **partial sums** of the infinite series, where

$$S_1 = a_1$$
$$S_2 = a_1 + a_2$$
$$S_3 = a_1 + a_2 + a_3$$

.
.
.

$$S_n = a_1 + a_2 + a_3 + ... + a_n$$

.
.
.

Thus, the sum of the series is now defined as the limit of the sequence $S_1, S_2, S_3, ..., S_n$, as n approaches infinity.

Infinite Geometric Series

Consider the infinite geometric series $a + ar + ar^2 + ...$

The sequence of partial sums for this series is $S_1, S_2, S_3, ..., S_n, ...$, where

$$S_1 = a$$
$$S_2 = a + ar$$
$$S_3 = a + ar + ar^2$$

.
.
.

$$S_n = a + ar + ar^2 + ... + ar^{n-1}$$

The limit of S_n as n approaches infinity is:

$$\lim_{n\to\infty} \frac{a(1 - r^n)}{1 - r} = \frac{a}{1 - r} \lim_{n\to\infty}(1 - r^n)$$

Does $(1 - r^n)$ get closer and closer to some finite value as n gets bigger and bigger? The answer depends on whether or not the absolute value of r is less than 1.

A proper fraction is a rational number bigger than -1 but less than 1.

Examples include $-\frac{9}{10}, \frac{1}{3}, \frac{6}{7}$.

Since any proper fraction is less than 1 unit away from zero, the modulus of any proper fraction is always less than 1.

$$\left| -\frac{9}{10} \right| = \frac{9}{10} < 1$$

$$\left| \frac{1}{3} \right| = \frac{1}{3} < 1$$

$$\left| \frac{6}{7} \right| = \frac{6}{7} < 1$$

This property means that as a proper fraction is raised to a larger and larger power, the result gets closer and closer to zero.

We can summarise as follows:

Let r be a proper fraction.

Then, $-1 < r < 1$, so $|r| < 1$.

Therefore, $\lim_{n\to\infty} r^n = 0$.

Note that the above result holds even if r is not rational. As long as $|r| < 1$, $\lim_{n\to\infty} r^n = 0$.

Therefore, if $-1 < r < 1$, the limit of S_n as n approaches infinity $= \dfrac{a}{1-r}(1-0) = \dfrac{a}{1-r}$.

Hence, the limit of the sequence $S_1, S_2, S_3, \ldots, S_n$ is $\dfrac{a}{1-r}$.

Therefore, the sum of the infinite geometric series

$a + ar + ar^2 + \ldots$ is $\dfrac{a}{1-r}$, $-1 < r < 1$.

$S_\infty = \dfrac{a}{1-r}$, $|r| < 1$

> If the sequence of partial sums of an infinite series tends to a limit, we say that the series **converges**.

This formula appears on page 22 of *Formulae and Tables* and its derivation is a stated syllabus outcome. You must be able to derive the formula, as shown above.

Worked Example 8.23

Find the sum to infinity of the geometric series $1 + \left[\dfrac{2}{5}\right] + \left[\dfrac{2}{5}\right]^2 + \ldots$

Solution

$a = 1 \qquad r = \dfrac{2}{5}$

As $|r| < 1$, the series converges.

$S_\infty = \dfrac{a}{1-r}$

$ = \dfrac{1}{1 - \dfrac{2}{5}}$

$\therefore S_\infty = \dfrac{5}{3}$

Worked Example 8.24

Show that the infinite series $\displaystyle\sum_{n=0}^{\infty}\left[\dfrac{2x}{2x+1}\right]^n$, $x > 0$, converges and find its sum. Hence, evaluate $\displaystyle\sum_{n=0}^{\infty}\left(\dfrac{4}{5}\right)^n$.

Solution

$\displaystyle\sum_{n=0}^{\infty}\left[\dfrac{2x}{2x+1}\right]^n = 1 + \left[\dfrac{2x}{2x+1}\right] + \left[\dfrac{2x}{2x+1}\right]^2 + \ldots$

> It is a good idea to write out the first few terms to visualise the series and get an idea about a and r.

This is an infinite geometric series with $a = 1$ and $r = \dfrac{2x}{2x+1}$.

Because $x > 0$, $0 < r < 1$. The series therefore converges and we can calculate the sum to infinity, S_∞.

$S_\infty = \dfrac{a}{1-r}$

$ = \dfrac{1}{1 - \dfrac{2x}{2x+1}}$

$ = \dfrac{2x+1}{2x+1-2x}$

$\therefore S_\infty = 2x + 1$

Let $2x = 4$

$ x = 2$

So $\dfrac{2x}{2x+1} = \dfrac{4}{5}$

$\therefore S_\infty = 2(2) + 1$

$ = 5$

Worked Example 8.25

Express 1.2222... in the form $\frac{p}{q}$, $p, q \in z$, $q \neq 0$.

Solution

$1.2222... = 1 + 0.2 + 0.02 + 0.002 + 0.0002 + ...$

$= 1 + (0.2 + 0.02 + 0.002 + 0.0002 + ...)$

The expression in brackets is an infinite geometric series.

$a = 0.2 \qquad r = \frac{1}{10}$

$S_\infty = \frac{a}{1 - r} \quad \Rightarrow S_\infty = \frac{0.2}{1 - \frac{1}{10}}$

$= \frac{2}{9}$

$\Rightarrow 1.2222... = 1 + \frac{2}{9}$

$= \frac{11}{9}$

This example illustrates the property that recurring decimals are rational numbers.

Worked Example 8.26

Express $1.5\dot{2}0\dot{7}$ in the form $\frac{p}{q}$, $p, q \in z$, $q \neq 0$.

Solution

$1.5\dot{2}0\dot{7} = 1.5 + \frac{207}{10,000} + \frac{207}{10,000,000} + ...$

$= 1\cdot5 + \left(\frac{207}{10,000} + \frac{207}{10,000,000} + ... \right)$

The expression in brackets is an infinite geometric series.

$a = \frac{207}{10,000} \qquad r = \frac{1}{1000}$

$S_\infty = \frac{a}{1 - r} \Rightarrow S_\infty = \frac{\frac{207}{10,000}}{1 - \frac{1}{1000}}$

$= \frac{207}{10,000 - 10}$

$= \frac{207}{9990}$

$\Rightarrow 1.5\dot{2}0\dot{7} = 1.5 + \frac{207}{9990}$

$= \frac{15,192}{9990} = \frac{844}{555}$

Exercise 8.7

1. Find the sum to infinity of each of the following geometric series:

(i) $\frac{1}{2} + \frac{1}{4} + \frac{1}{8} + ...$

(ii) $\frac{3}{7} + \frac{1}{7} + \frac{1}{21} + ...$

(iii) $5 + 1 + \frac{1}{5} + ...$

(iv) $4 + \frac{4}{3} + \frac{4}{9} + ...$

(v) $\frac{2}{3} + \frac{1}{12} + \frac{1}{96} + ...$

2. Find the sum to infinity of each of the following geometric series:

(i) $3 - \frac{3}{2} + \frac{3}{4} - ...$

(ii) $\frac{8}{5} - \frac{4}{5} + \frac{2}{5} - ...$

(iii) $7 - \frac{7}{3} + \frac{7}{9} - ...$

(iv) $\frac{1}{2} - \frac{1}{4} + \frac{1}{8} - ...$

(v) $\frac{1}{2} - \frac{1}{8} + \frac{1}{32} - ...$

3. Evaluate each of the following:

(i) $\displaystyle\sum_{n=0}^{\infty} (0.4)^n$

(ii) $\displaystyle\sum_{n=1}^{\infty} \left(\frac{1}{2}\right)^{n-1}$

(iii) $\displaystyle\sum_{n=1}^{\infty} \left(-\frac{1}{2}\right)^{n-1}$

4. The sum to infinity of a geometric series is twice the first term. Find the common ratio.

5. The sum to infinity of a geometric progression is 16 and the sum of the first four terms is 15. Find the first four terms.

   There are two possible series.

6. The second term of a geometric series is $\frac{1}{2}$ and the sum to infinity of the series is 4. Find the first term and the common ratio of the series.

7. Write the following recurring decimals in the form $\frac{p}{q}$, $p, q \in Z$, $q \neq 0$:

(i) 0.999...   (iii) 1.777...   (v) 77.44...

(ii) 0.333...   (iv) 3.111...   (vi) 1.00$\dot{4}$

8. Write the following recurring decimals in the form $\frac{p}{q}$, $p, q \in Z$, $q \neq 0$:

(i) 1.2333...   (iii) 8.1777...   (v) 3.4555...

(ii) 4.6111...   (iv) 9.1888...   (vi) 0.$\dot{7}\dot{2}$

9. Write the following recurring decimals in the form $\frac{p}{q}$, $p, q \in Z$, $q \neq 0$:

(i) 8.343434...   (vi) 2.9$\dot{6}\dot{0}$

(ii) 0.121212...   (vii) 1.$\dot{2}3\dot{4}$

(iii) 6.181818...   (viii) 5.2$\dot{5}\dot{6}$

(iv) 3.454545...   (ix) 4.3$\dot{5}0\dot{6}$

(v) 0.656565...   (x) 6.7$\dot{2}1\dot{8}$

10. Find the range of values of x for which the following series converge:

(i) $x + 1 + \dfrac{1}{x} + \dfrac{1}{x^2} + \ldots$

(ii) $1 + 2x + 4x^2 + 8x^3 + \ldots$

(iii) $(a + x) + 1 + \dfrac{1}{a+x} + \dfrac{1}{(a+x)^2} + \ldots$

11. Show that the series

$$\sum_{n=1}^{\infty} \left[\frac{4x}{x^2 + 9}\right]^n$$

is convergent for all values of $x \in R$ and find the sum to infinity of the series.

12. $\displaystyle\lim_{n \to \infty} r^n = 0$ if $-1 < r < 1$

Solve for x ($x \in R$):

(i) $\displaystyle\lim_{n \to \infty} (2x - 1)^n = 0$

(ii) $\displaystyle\lim_{n \to \infty} (x^2 - 5)^n = 0$

Revision Exercises

1. Consider the pattern consisting of equilateral triangles shown below. The first pattern is constructed by joining together the midpoints of the sides of an equilateral triangle and shading the resulting triangle enclosed as shown. This creates a total of four equilateral triangles within the larger triangle. The second pattern is constructed by carrying out the same process on the remaining non-shaded triangles. The process is continued to create further patterns.

(i) How many triangles will be shaded in the fourth pattern?

(ii) What fraction of the area of the original triangle is shaded in the first pattern?

(iii) What fraction of the area of the original triangle is shaded in the third pattern?

2. Consider the pattern shown.

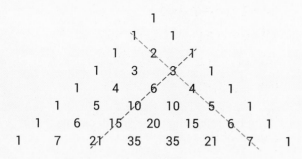

(i) Write down the next two rows of the pattern.

(ii) Identify the type of sequence along the diagonal marked with a broken red line and find its nth term.

(iii) Identify the type of sequence along the diagonal marked with a broken blue line and find its nth term.

(iv) Identify one further sequence along some diagonal.

3. $T_n = 3n - 7$ is the nth term of an arithmetic sequence.

(i) Write down the first four terms of the sequence.

(ii) Find S_n, the sum to n terms of the sequence.

(iii) Show that $T_n = S_n - S_{n-1}$.

4. The sum to n terms of an arithmetic sequence is given by $S_n = \frac{1}{2}[3n^2 + 11]$.

(i) Show that $T_n = \frac{1}{2}(6n - 3)$.

(ii) Show that $T_n - T_{n-1}$ is a constant.

5. For each of the following quadratic sequences, find:

(a) The first term

(b) The first and second differences

(c) T_n, the nth term of the sequence

(d) T_{100}, the 100th term of the sequence

(i) 16, 17, 19, 22, ...

(ii) 1, 3, 6, 10, ...

(iii) 12, 14, 17, 21, ...

(iv) 1, 6, 15, 28, 45, ...

(v) 8, 9, 8, 5, ...

6. The nth term of a geometric sequence is given by $T_n = 5^{n-1}$.

(i) Write down the first five terms of the sequence.

(ii) Find r, the common ratio.

(iii) Find S_n, the sum of the first n terms.

(iv) Find in the form $4(5^P)$, the difference between the 1,000th term and the 999th term.

7. The sum of the first n terms of a series is given by $S_n = n^2 \log_e 3$.

(i) Find the nth term and prove that the series is arithmetic.

(ii) How many terms of the series are less than $12 \log_e 27$?

8. Three numbers are in arithmetic sequence. Their sum is 27 and their product is 704. Find the three numbers, if the sequence is increasing.

9. $T_n = an^2 + bn + c$ is a quadratic sequence. The first five terms of the sequence are 1, 13, 30, 52, 79.

(i) Graph the first five terms of the sequence.

(ii) Find the values of a, b and c.

10. $P(n) = (U_1)(U_2)(U_3)(U_4) \ldots (U_n)$ where $U_k = ar^{k-1}$ for $k = 1, 2, 3, \ldots n$ and $a, r, \in R$.
Write $P(n)$ in the form $a^n r^{f(n)}$, where $f(n)$ is a quadratic expression in n.

11. 3, 12, 29, 54, ... is a sequence of numbers.

(i) Determine what type of sequence this is.

(ii) Find T_n, the nth term of the sequence.

(iii) Hence, find T_{30}, the 30th term of the sequence.

12. $T_n = an^2 + bn + c$ is a quadratic sequence. The first five terms of the sequence are:

$$3, 7, 13, 21, 31$$

(i) The second differences are constant. Find the value of this constant.

(ii) Find the first three terms, T_1, T_2, T_3, in terms of a, b and c.

(iii) Solve the equations to find a, b and c and hence find a formula for T_n.

(iv) Using the fact that the second difference is $2a$, find a formula for T_n.

(v) Find T_{30}, the 30th term of the sequence.

NUMBER PATTERNS, SEQUENCES AND SERIES

13. Evaluate each of the following limits:

(i) $\lim\limits_{n\to\infty} \dfrac{3n-1}{n+2}$ (iii) $\lim\limits_{n\to\infty} \dfrac{\sqrt{3n^2+6}}{n+1}$

(ii) $\lim\limits_{n\to\infty} \dfrac{4n^2-3n+3}{7n^2+8n-5}$

14. S_n is the sum to n terms of the arithmetic series $4 + 8 + 12 + \ldots + 4n$.

(i) Find S_n.

(ii) Evaluate $\lim\limits_{n\to\infty} \sqrt{\dfrac{S_n}{3n^2}}$.

15. Consider the geometric series:

$$1 + \frac{5}{6} + \left[\frac{5}{6}\right]^2 + \ldots$$

(i) Find S_n, the sum to n terms of the series.

(ii) Hence, find S_∞, the sum to infinity of the series.

16. Write the following recurring decimals in the form $\dfrac{p}{q}$, $p, q \in Z$, $q \neq 0$.

(i) $5.262626\ldots$ (iii) $2.545454\ldots$

(ii) $0.8888\ldots$ (iv) $3.1\dot{2}$

Exam Questions

1. A rectangular jigsaw puzzle has pieces arranged in rows. Each row has the same number of pieces. For example, the picture on the right shows a 4 × 6 jigsaw puzzle – there are four rows with 6 pieces in each row.

Every piece of the puzzle is either an *edge piece* or an *interior piece*. The puzzle shown has 16 edge pieces and 8 interior pieces.

Investigate the number of edge pieces and the number of interior pieces in an $m \times n$ jigsaw puzzle, for different values of m and n. Start by exploring some particular cases, and then attempt to answer the questions that follow, with justification.

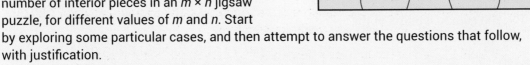

(a) How do the number of edge pieces and the number of interior pieces compare in cases where either $m \leqslant 4$ or $n \leqslant 4$?

(b) Show that if the number of edge pieces is equal to the number of interior pieces, then
$$m = 4 + \frac{8}{n-4}.$$

(c) Find all cases in which the number of edge pieces is equal to the number of interior pieces.

(d) Determine the circumstances in which there are *fewer* interior pieces than edge pieces. Describe fully all such cases.

SEC Leaving Certificate Higher Level, Sample Paper 1, 2013

2. Shapes in the form of small equilateral triangles can be made using matchsticks of equal length. These shapes can be put together into patterns. The beginning of a sequence of these patterns is shown below.

(a) (i) Draw the fourth pattern in the sequence.

(ii) The table below shows the number of small triangles in each pattern and the number of matchsticks needed to create each pattern. Complete the table.

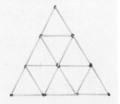

Pattern	1st	2nd	3rd	4th
Number of small triangles	1		9	
Number of matchsticks	3	9		

(b) Write an expression in n for the number of triangles in the nth pattern in the sequence.

(c) Find an expression, in n, for the number of matchsticks needed to turn the $(n-1)$th pattern into the nth pattern.

(d) The number of matchsticks in the nth pattern in the sequence can be represented by the function $u_n = an^2 + bn$ where $a, b \in Q$ and $n \in N$. Find the value of a and the value of b.

(e) One of the patterns in the sequence has 4,134 matchsticks. How many small triangles are in that pattern?

SEC Leaving Certificate Higher Level, Paper 1, 2013

3. Mary threw a ball onto level ground from a height of 2 m. Each time the ball hit the ground it bounced back up to $\frac{3}{4}$ of the height of the previous bounce, as shown.

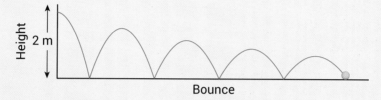

(a) Complete the table below to show the maximum height, in fraction form, reached by the ball on each of the first four bounces.

Bounce	0	1	2	3	4
Height (m)	$\frac{2}{1}$				

(b) Find, in metres, the total vertical distance (up and down) the ball had travelled when it hit the ground for the 5th time. Give your answer in fraction form.

(c) If the ball were to continue to bounce indefinitely, find, in metres, the total vertical distance it would travel.

SEC Leaving Certificate Higher Level, Paper 1, 2015

4. By writing the recurring part as an infinite geometric series, express the following number as a fraction of integers:

$$5.2\dot{1} = 5.2121212121\ldots$$

SEC Leaving Certificate Higher Level, Paper 1, 2012

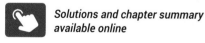

Solutions and chapter summary available online

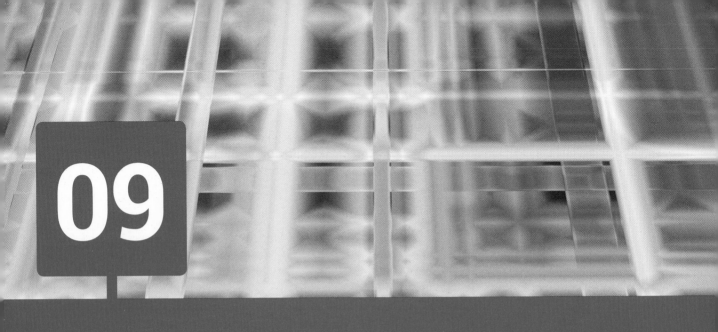

09

Arithmetic

★ In this chapter you will learn to:

- ⊙ Calculate percentage error and tolerance
- ⊙ Accumulate error

- ⊙ Solve problems involving:
  - ⊙ Costing (materials, labour and wastage)
  - ⊙ Rates, income tax and PRSI
  - ⊙ Value added tax (VAT)

 ! You should remember...

- ⊙ Fractions
- ⊙ Decimals
- ⊙ Percentages

 Key words

- ⊙ Percentage error
- ⊙ Accumulated error
- ⊙ Tolerance
- ⊙ Gross income
- ⊙ Net/take-home pay

- ⊙ Statutory deductions
- ⊙ Non-statutory deductions
- ⊙ Income tax (PAYE)
- ⊙ PRSI
- ⊙ USC

- ⊙ Standard rate cut-off point
- ⊙ Tax credit
- ⊙ Gross tax
- ⊙ Tax payable
- ⊙ VAT

9.1 Approximation, Percentage Error and Tolerance

Estimates and Approximations of Calculations

Sometimes it is necessary for us to make **estimates** and **approximations** of calculations. This can be to save time or money or simply for convenience. In performing rough calculations or estimates we sometimes round off numbers to make our calculations easier and quicker.

If a hardware store was doing a stocktake (i.e. a count of all stock in the shop), it would be far too time consuming and costly for staff to count every single screw. Equally if a shop owner had a pick-and-mix stand for sweets, they would rarely count every sweet. They would simply make estimates.

Rounding is often used when we are estimating or approximating calculations.

Error

Humans are bound to make errors from time to time. These errors are sometimes unavoidable. Using estimates and approximations also leads to errors. To improve our precision, it is good practice to have an idea of how much we have possibly erred. Also, small errors left unchecked can grow over time. That is why we calculate **percentage error**.

Calculating Percentage Error

Step 1   Get the **observed value** and the **accurate value**.

Step 2   Subtract the observed value from the accurate value and take the 'absolute value' of this:

Error = |Accurate − Observed|

Step 3   Divide the error by the accurate value:

$$\text{Relative error} = \frac{\text{Error}}{\text{Accurate value}}$$

$$\text{Relative error} = \frac{\text{Error}}{\text{Accurate value}}$$

Percentage error = Relative error × 100

Step 4   Multiply by 100 to calculate the percentage error.

ARITHMETIC

Worked Example 9.1

Find the percentage error in taking 1 cm for 0.8 cm.

Solution

Step 1   Observed value = 1 cm

Accurate value = 0.8 cm

Step 2   Error = |0.8 − 1|

= |−0.2|

= 0.2

Step 3   Relative error $= \frac{0.2}{0.8} = \frac{1}{4}$

Step 4   Percentage error

$= \frac{1}{4} \times 100$

= 25%

Tolerance

Any measurement made with a measuring device is approximate.

If two students were asked to measure an object, they may very well come back with two different measurements. The difference between the two measurements is called a **variation**.

> Note that variations and errors due to approximations are not the same as 'mistakes'.

> Tolerance is the greatest range of variation that can be allowed.

> Precision is the indication of how close you are to the true measurement. It is determined by the smallest division of the scale on the measuring device. The smaller the scale, the more precise the measurements.

> To determine the tolerance in a measurement, add and subtract one-half of the precision of the measuring instrument that is being used.

For example, a metric ruler is used to measure the length of an object. The length of the object is 10.5 cm and the ruler has a **precision** of 0.1 cm (i.e. the ruler gives measurement to the nearest millimetre). The **tolerance interval** is 10.5 ± 0.05 cm. Any measurements within the tolerance interval are regarded as correct or acceptable.

Worked Example 9.2

Colin works as a quality control officer in a factory that manufactures 14-cm-long pencils. He uses a metric ruler to check the length of pencils he randomly samples. The ruler has a precision of 0.5 cm.

(i) What is the tolerance interval for a pencil in this factory?

(ii) If Colin picks a pencil at random and it is 14.06 cm, will it be accepted or rejected?

Solution

(i) Tolerance interval = $14 \pm \frac{1}{2}(0.5)$

$$= 14 \pm 0.25 \text{ cm}$$

(ii) The pencil will be accepted, as its length (14.06 cm) is inside the tolerance interval, i.e. $13.75 \leqslant 14.06 \leqslant 14.25$.

Accumulated Error

> Accumulated error is the collected inaccuracy that can occur when multiple errors are combined.

If the solution of a problem requires many arithmetic operations, each of which is performed using rounded numbers, the **accumulated error** may significantly affect the result.

Worked Example 9.3

ABC Ltd has a policy of rounding its invoices to the nearest euro when billing clients. If ABC had the following invoices in the last month, calculate the accumulated error.

Invoice 1   Amount before rounding = €1,560.46

Invoice 2   Amount before rounding = €950.32

Invoice 3   Amount before rounding = €144.52

> Give all answers correct to the nearest cent when dealing with money.

Solution

Step 1 Calculate the actual amount billed.

Invoice 1   Rounded amount = €1,560

Invoice 2   Rounded amount = €950

Invoice 3   Rounded amount = €145

Amount billed = €2,655

Step 2 Calculate the amount that would be billed if rounding was not applied.

Total bill = 1,560.46 + 950.32 + 144.52

= €2,655.30

Step 3 Calculate the accumulated error.

Error = 2,655.30 − 2,655

= €0.30

Exercise 9.1

1. Copy and complete the following table:

	Accurate value	Observed value	Error	Relative error	% Error correct to 2 decimal places
(i)	150	149			
(ii)	36	36.9			
(iii)	180	183			
(iv)	4.8	5			
(v)	6.7	7			
(vi)	54.15	55			
(vii)	1.36	1.5			
(viii)	502	500			
(ix)	360	359			
(x)	58.6	60			

2. If 56 is taken as an approximation for 55.4, calculate to two decimal places the percentage error.

3. If 2.3 is taken as an approximation for 2.33, calculate to three significant figures the percentage error.

4. The mass of a bag of flour should be 1 kg. A quality control inspector misreads the weight of one bag and finds it to be 1,010 grams. What is the percentage error?

5. The depth of water in a reservoir is estimated to be 1.6 m. The true depth is 1.56 m. What is the percentage error, correct to one decimal place?

6. The value of $\dfrac{49.27 + 11.15}{15.24 - 3.06}$ was estimated to be 5. Calculate:

(i) The error

(ii) The percentage error, correct to one decimal place

ARITHMETIC

7. What is the precision of 3.250 litres?

8. What is the precision of 16.400 kg?

9. The value of $\frac{40.354}{\sqrt{16.45}}$ was estimated to be 10.
   Calculate:

   (i) The error

   (ii) The percentage error, correct to one decimal place

10. A statement arrives at an office showing four invoices that need to be paid:

Invoice 1	€245.45
Invoice 2	€364.78
Invoice 3	€1,445.12
Invoice 4	€4,500.25

    The office manager checks the statement quickly to make sure the final figure is accurate. She ignores the cent amount on each invoice.

    (i) What is the total that she arrives at?

    (ii) What is the correct amount owed?

    (iii) What is the accumulated error?

11. A door is measured with a measuring tape with a precision of 0.1 cm. The observed measurement is 54 cm.

    What is the tolerance interval on this measurement?

12. A coffee producer sells coffee in 450 g bags. Packets of coffee are randomly picked and weighed with a precision of 5 g.

    (i) What is the tolerance interval for the weight of a bag of coffee?

    (ii) If a bag of coffee is picked at random and is found to be 453 g, should the packet be rejected?

9.2 Costing: Materials, Labour and Wastage

Managers need to know the costs involved in getting their products to the market, for a number of reasons:

- **Planning** – Having an accurate cost of a product allows managers to set an accurate price.
- **Control** – By comparing the budgeted cost of a product with the actual cost of the product, managers can identify areas of the business that are underperforming or doing very well.
- **Stock valuation** – At the end of the financial year, all stocks need to be valued for accounting purposes. It is also important that businesses that manufacture their own products have a value for their goods for insurance purposes.

To get an accurate value, all the costs involved in getting the product to its finished state must be included in the valuation. The table below shows examples of both direct and indirect costs for a company manufacturing school desks.

Direct costs (costs directly linked to production)	Materials	Raw materials used in the manufacture of the product	Wood, metal frames
	Labour	Wages of those who work directly in the manufacture of the product	Saw operators who cut table tops, workers who assemble the desks, workers who spray the desk frames and varnish the table tops
	Direct expenses	Any expenses that may be attributed directly to the product	Hire of special equipment
Indirect costs (costs not directly linked to production)			Factory rent, rates, light and heat

Direct costs are costs linked directly to production.

Indirect costs are costs not linked directly to production, e.g. factory rent, rates, light and heat bills.

Variable costs are costs that vary directly with the level of output or activity, e.g. sales commission based on unit sales.

Fixed costs are costs that are not affected by the level of activity (within a given range of activity). For example, the rent for the factory is fixed regardless of the amount of product produced. If production exceeds the level the factory can cope with, additional space may need to be rented, causing the cost to rise.

Wastage

A manager will try to minimise wastage where possible in a business, as it reduces any profit that the company might make. However, there will inevitably be some wastage in almost all businesses because of human error, machine faults, inaccurate sales predictions and so on.

Worked Example 9.4

A company budgets to manufacture 5,000 units of its product.

The materials required are 50 kg per unit @ €0.50 per kg.

Each unit produced requires six hours of direct labour @ €7 per hour.

Indirect costs are €15,000.

Calculate:

(i) The cost of manufacture of the 5,000 units

(ii) The unit cost of manufacture

$$\text{Unit cost} = \frac{\text{Total cost}}{\text{No. of units produced}}$$

The unit cost is the cost of making one of the products.

Solution

(i)

Cost of manufacture (5,000 units)		
Direct materials	5,000 units @ 50 kg	250,000 kg
Cost per kg		€0.50
Cost of materials	250,000 × 0.50	€125,000
Direct labour	5,000 units × 6 hours	30,000 hrs
Cost per labour hour		€7
Total labour cost	30,000 × 7	€210,000
Indirect costs		€15,000
Total cost of manufacture	125,000 + 210,000 + 15,000	€350,000

(ii) The unit cost of manufacture $= \dfrac{350,000}{5,000}$

$= €70$

A confectionary company receives an order for 250 custom-made products for Christmas hampers. The production team has given the following breakdown for the product:

Material requirements	
Material A	25 g per unit
Material B	100 g per unit
Labour hours	0.05 per unit
Variable costs	€0.75 per unit
Fixed costs allocated to the product	€500
Cost material A	€0.01 per g
Cost material B	€0.05 per g
Labour rate	€7 per hour

(i) Find the total cost of the order and the cost per unit.

(ii) Find the price the company should charge per unit to make a profit on cost of 25% on each unit produced (assuming no wastage).

(iii) If on average 5% of the finished goods are damaged in the warehouse, how many units should the company produce to ensure the order is covered?

Solution

(i)

Costs		Cost (€)
Material A	25 g × 250 × €0.01	62.50
Material B	100 g × 250 × €0.05	1,250.00
Labour	0.05 × 250 × €7	87.50
Variable costs	250 × €0.75	187.50
Fixed costs		500.00
Total cost		**2,087.50**

The total cost of the order is €2,087.50.

$$\therefore \text{Unit cost} = \frac{€2,087.50}{250} = €8.35$$

(ii) A profit on cost of 25%:

Profit: €8.35 × 0.25 = €2.0875

Selling price: €8.35 + €2.0875 = €10.4375

$$\approx €10.44$$

∴ The company should charge approximately €10.44 per unit to make a profit on cost of 25% on each unit produced.

(iii) On average 5% of goods are damaged.

So the 250 units represent 95% of the required production.

95% = 250 units

$$1\% = \frac{250}{95}$$

$$100\% = \frac{250}{95} \times 100$$

$$= 263.1579 \text{ units}$$

∴ The company should produce 264 units to ensure that there will be enough stock to meet the order.

Exercise 9.2

1. Distinguish between:

   (i) Direct and indirect costs   (ii) Fixed and variable costs

2. Jimmy Jeans received an order from a retail outlet for a batch of 10,000 pairs of jeans.
   The following information relates to the production costs of the jeans:

	€
Direct materials	25,000
Factory rent	11,000
Wages of material cutters	4,000
Wages of machinists	€0.75 per unit produced
Factory overheads	20,000

   (i) Calculate the total manufacturing costs of the batch.

   (ii) Calculate the unit cost of a pair of jeans.

3. A deli recently received an order for 135 mini quiches.

   (i) If wastage of the finished product is assumed to be 10%,
   how many quiches should the deli prepare?

   The production costs of the quiches are as follows:

Direct materials	€250
Labour	€11 per hour
Labour hours required	4
Deli overheads allocated to this job	€100

   (ii) Calculate the cost of the batch (based on the number of units calculated in part (i)).

   (iii) Calculate the cost per unit.

   (iv) If the deli wishes to make a profit on cost of 20%, what price should it charge per quiche?

4. Townsend Ltd manufactures two products, X and Y. Both products use the same raw materials.
   The production costs are as follows:

	Product X	Product Y
Units produced	6,000	5,000
Materials in each product	8 kg	9 kg
Production time per unit	6 hours	5 hours
Wages	€5 per hour	
Cost of materials per kg	€3	

   (i) Calculate the quantity of materials required for the production of product X.

   (ii) Calculate the quantity of materials required for the production of product Y.

   (iii) Calculate the cost of materials for each of product X and product Y.

   (iv) Calculate the total cost of labour for products X and Y.

5. Nolan Plc is a boat manufacturing company. Two materials are used in the manufacture of the boat. An order is placed for 60 units.

The following table gives the production costs for one unit:

Material A	36 metres
Material B	108 metres
Expected price per metre	€7
Labour hours required	60
Labour rate	€7 per hour

There is approximate wastage of 10% on all materials used.

(i) How many metres of material A should be purchased to meet the requirements of the order?

(ii) How many metres of material B should be purchased to meet the requirements of the order?

(iii) Calculate the cost price of this order.

(iv) Calculate the selling price per unit this company should charge if they wish to make a profit on cost of 15%.

6. SIOAL Ltd manufactures two products, Primary and Superb.

It expects to sell Primary at €190 per unit and Superb at €230 per unit.

Sales demand is expected to be 6,000 units of Primary and 4,500 units of Superb.

Both products use the same raw materials and skilled labour but in different quantities per unit as follows:

	Primary	Superb
Material W	6 kg	5 kg
Material X	4 kg	7 kg
Skilled labour	7 hours	8 hours

The expected prices for raw materials during 2016 are:

● Material W: €3 per kg
● Material X: €5 per kg

The skilled labour rate is expected to be €11.00 per hour.

The company's production overhead costs are expected to be:

● Variable: €4.50 per skilled labour hour
● Fixed: €116,000 per annum

If SIOAL produces all units required for sales, find:

(i) The amount of material W needed

(ii) The total labour hours used in production

(iii) The total labour cost of production

(iv) The total cost of production (including variable and fixed costs)

(v) The total profit made if the company sells at the expected prices

(vi) The profit made if actual prices turn out to be 10% less than those expected

9.3 Income Tax

Income and Deductions

Employees expect to earn money for the work they carry out.

- If you are paid according to the number of hours worked or goods produced, this is called a **wage**.
- If you are paid the same amount regardless of the number of hours worked or goods produced, this is called a **salary**.

Most people cannot keep all the money they earn. Employees have several **deductions** made to their earnings before they receive their money.

> **Gross pay** or **gross income** is money earned before deductions are made.

> **Net pay** or **net income** is money received after all deductions have been made.

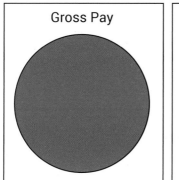
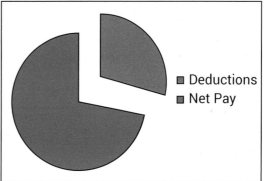

Statutory and Non-Statutory Deductions

Deductions can be **statutory** or **non-statutory**.

Statutory deduction	What is it used for?
Income tax (PAYE – Pay As You Earn)	Payment of public services, e.g. Gardaí, health care, education, etc.
Pay-Related Social Insurance (PRSI)	Old-age pensions, jobseeker's benefit, jobseeker's allowance, child benefit, etc.
Universal Social Charge (USC)	Income for the state

Statutory deductions are payments that **must** be made to the state. They are taken from gross pay by the employer.

The rates for the universal social charge (USC) are as follows (figures accurate for 2016):

- Zero, if total income is €13,000 or less

For people with an income of above €13,000, the rates will be:

Rate of USC	Charged on income from
1%	€0 to €12,012
3%	€12,012.01 to €18,668
5.5%	€18,668.01 to €70,044
8%	Income above €70,044
11%	Self-employed income in excess of €100,000.01

Non-statutory deductions are voluntary deductions. They are taken from gross pay by the employer at the request of the employee.

Income Tax (PAYE)

There are two rates of income tax in Ireland.

Note that these rates can vary from year to year.

- The lower rate is called the **standard rate** of tax.
- The higher rate is called the **higher rate** of tax.

For example, the first €33,800 that a single person earns is taxed at 20%, and any income above this amount is taxed at 40% (figures accurate for 2016).

The amount up to which an employee is taxed at the standard rate is called the standard rate cut-off point.

Every employee receives a **tax credit** certificate. This shows the employee's tax credit. This amount can change for individual employees.

Gross tax is the amount of tax owed to the state before tax credits are deducted.

The tax credit is a sum deducted from the total amount (gross tax) a taxpayer owes to the state.

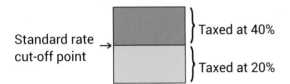

Standard rate cut-off point →

} Taxed at 40%

} Taxed at 20%

Tax payable is gross tax less the tax credit.

Worked Example 9.6

Sanabel earns €50,000 per annum.
Calculate the amount that will be deducted from her pay for the universal social charge.

Rate of USC	Charged on income from
1%	€0 to €12,012
3%	€12,012.01 to €18,668
5.5%	€18,668.01 to €70,044
8%	Income above €70,044

Solution

Step 1

Break the salary down into the various threshold amounts.

€12,012 @ 1%

€18,668 − €12,012 = €6,656 @ 3%

€50,000 − €18,668 = €31,332 @ 5.5%

Step 2

Calculate the USC from each part.

First	Next	Remainder
€12,012	€6,656	€31,332
1%	3%	5.5%
€120.12	€199.68	€1,723.26

∴ The total USC = €120.12 + €199.68 + €1,723.26

= €2,043.06

Pay-Related Social Insurance (PRSI)

The amount of PRSI you pay depends on your earnings and the class under which you are insured.

For people in employment in Ireland, social insurance contributions are divided into different categories, known as classes or rates of contribution. The type of class and rate of contribution you pay is determined by the nature of your work.

ARITHMETIC

There are 11 different classes of social insurance in Ireland. The majority of people fall into Class A. The other classes are B, C, D, E, H, J, K, M, P and S. If you are insured under one of these classes, you are paying insurance at a lower rate than Class A contributors, which means that you are not entitled to the full range of social insurance payments.

PRSI is calculated on the employee's weekly or reckonable pay.

PRSI Contribution Rates from 1 January 2016:

A class PRSI	Employee	Employer
Non-cumulative weekly earning bands €	%	%
38 – 352	0	8.5
352.01 – 376	4	8.5
376 – 500	4	10.75
Over 500	4	10.75

A new weekly tapered PRSI credit of €12 is being introduced for employees insured at Class A whose earnings are between €352.01 and €424 in a week.

For the purposes of the questions in this text we will ignore this tax credit.

Worked Example 9.7

Chloe earns €650 per week. She is in Class A1 for PRSI, which has the following rates:

Employee %	4
Employer %	10.75

Calculate:

(i) Her PRSI payment this week

(ii) Her employer's PRSI payment this week

(iii) The total amount of PRSI that will be paid this week

Solution

(i) Calculate the amount she must pay PRSI on.

Calculate the PRSI.

€650 × 4% = €26

∴ Chloe's PRSI payment is €26.

(ii) Calculate the amount of PRSI paid.

€650 × 0.1075 = €69.875

≈ €69.88

∴ The PRSI payment by Chloe's employer is approximately €69.88.

(iii) Total PRSI payment = €26 + €69.88

= €95.88

∴ Total PRSI payment is €95.88.

Calculating Income Tax and Net Income

Worked Example 9.8

Derek has a gross annual income of €50,000. His standard rate cut-off point is €32,000. The standard rate of tax is 20%. The higher rate is 40%. His tax credit is €3,500. Derek is in Class A1 for PRSI. Assuming a 52-week year, calculate Derek's:

(i) Gross tax

(ii) Tax payable

(iii) Net income (ignoring PRSI)

(iv) PRSI payment

(v) Net income after PRSI has been paid

ARITHMETIC

Solution

(i) Gross tax = standard tax + higher tax

Standard tax = standard rate cut-off point × standard rate

$$= €32,000 × 0.20$$

$$= €6,400$$

Higher tax = income above standard cut-off point × higher rate

Income above standard rate cut-off point = €50,000 − €32,000

$$= €18,000$$

Higher tax = €18,000 × 0.40

$$= €7,200$$

Gross tax = standard tax + higher tax

$$= €6,400 + €7,200$$

$$= €13,600$$

∴ The gross tax is €13,600.

(ii) Tax payable = gross tax − tax credit

$$= €13,600 − €3,500$$

$$= €10,100$$

∴ The tax payable is €10,100.

(iii) Net income = gross income − tax payable

$$= €50,000 − €10,100$$

$$= €39,900$$

∴ Derek's net income is €39,900.

(iv) PRSI payment

€50,000 × 0.04 = €2,000

∴ The PRSI payment is €2,000.

(v) Net income − PRSI

€39,900 − €2,000 = €37,900

∴ The net income after **all** deductions is €37,900.

Exercise 9.3

Ignore USC and PRSI unless asked to calculate.

If asked to calculate USC and/or PRSI, use the tables given earlier in this section to assist you.

1. Ian earns €37,000 a year. His standard rate cut-off point is €37,400. The standard rate of tax is 20%. His tax credit is €2,100. His union fees are €450 and his annual health insurance is €350. What is Ian's annual take-home pay?

2. Abdul earns €33,000 a year. His tax bill for the year is €6,930. What percentage of his income is paid in tax?

3. Neasa's tax bill for last year was €6,300. Her tax credit was €1,300. Her gross income was €38,000. She paid tax at the standard rate only.

   (i) How much was her gross tax?

   (ii) What rate did she pay tax at?

4. Lorraine and Ger had a net income of €60,400 last year. They paid tax at the standard rate, which amounted to €14,700. They had a combined tax credit of €3,600. Their non-statutory deductions were €2,000. How much was their combined gross pay?

5. Sally earns €94,500 per annum. She has a standard rate cut-off point of €34,000. She pays tax at a standard rate of 20% and a higher rate of 40%. Her tax credit is €2,450. Calculate:

   (i) Her tax payable   (ii) Her net pay

6. Carol has a standard rate cut-off point of €36,400. The standard rate of tax is 20% and the higher rate is 40%. If Carol's gross tax is €10,396, what is her gross income?

ARITHMETIC

7. Nicky earns €35,000 a year. What is her USC charge?

8. Conor has a gross income of €72,000. His standard rate cut-off point is €33,800. The standard rate of tax is 20% and the higher rate is 40%. He has a tax credit of €3,000. He is in the class A1 for PRSI. (Assume a 52-week year.)

    (i) What is his PRSI contribution per week? (Answer to two decimal places.)

    (ii) What is his employer's PRSI contribution per week?

    (iii) Calculate his USC payment for the year.

    (iv) What is his weekly net income after all deductions?

9. (i) Sorcha has tax credits of €2,800 for the year and her standard rate cut-off point is €32,000. Her gross income is €45,000. The standard rate of income tax is 20% and the higher rate is 40%. Calculate her total tax payable.

    (ii) Eoin pays tax at the same rate as Sorcha. Eoin's tax credits are €2,900, and he has the same standard cut-off point as Sorcha. His total tax payable amounts to €13,680. Calculate Eoin's gross income.

    (iii) What is Eoin's and Sorcha's universal social charge, respectively?

9.4 VAT: Value-Added Tax

VAT is a tax charged by the state on spending.

For example, if you buy a computer game, you pay **VAT** on the game.

VAT is collected by the Revenue Commissioner. It is collected in stages, starting with the manufacturing stage and ending with the sale of the finished product to the consumer. VAT is collected at the following stages from the following people:

- Manufacturer
- Wholesaler
- Distributor
- Retailer
- Consumer

A tax is placed on the value added to the product or service at each stage, and this is where the name 'value-added tax' comes from.

VAT Rates

There are several different rates of VAT (standard for 2016):

Standard rate	Applies to most goods and services	23%
Reduced rate	Applies to labour-intensive services, e.g. hairdressing	13.5%
Second reduced rate	Applies to restaurants	9%
Zero rate	Applies to many foods and medicines and to children's clothes	0%
Special rate	Applies to the sale of livestock	4.8%

Remember that these rates can change from year to year and country to country.

Rates of VAT vary depending on the product or service being purchased. For example, chocolate spread has a zero rate but chocolate biscuits have a 23% rate.

You can find which rate of VAT applies to different goods and services by checking the list available on the Revenue website at www.revenue.ie.

Worked Example 9.9

Craig buys his boyfriend a birthday present that costs €215.65 including VAT @ 13.5%.

What was the original bill before VAT was added?

Solution

Original bill = 100%

Original bill + VAT = 113.5%

$$113.5\% = €215.65$$

$$\Rightarrow 1\% = \frac{€215.65}{113.5}$$

$$1\% = €1.90$$

$$100\% = €1.90 \times 100$$

$$= €190$$

$$\therefore \text{Original bill} = €190$$

Worked Example 9.10

Una bought a new TV for €484. When she looked at the receipt, she noticed the amount of VAT charged was €84. What rate of VAT was charged?

Solution

Step 1 Find the price before VAT.

$$\text{Price before VAT} = \text{Final price} - \text{VAT}$$

$$= €484 - €84$$

$$\therefore \text{Price before VAT} = €400$$

Step 2 Express the VAT as a percentage of the original price.

$$\text{Rate of VAT} = \frac{\text{VAT}}{\text{Price before VAT}} \times \frac{100}{1}$$

> Note that VAT is charged on the **original** cost figure.

$$= \frac{84}{400} \times \frac{100}{1}$$

$$\therefore \text{Rate of VAT} = 21\%$$

Exercise 9.4

Remember to give all answers correct to the nearest cent where necessary.

1. If VAT charged on hairdressing is 13.5%, find the VAT to be charged on a haircut if the price before VAT is €16.

2. The VAT charged on TVs is 21%. Find the total price of a TV if the price before VAT is €899.

3. The school canteen bought 600 bottles of fruit juice from a wholesaler at €0.50 each + VAT @ 21%. Find the total cost of the fruit juice.

4. Mohamed was shopping in a cash and carry. He didn't realise that all the prices stated were before VAT. When he got to the cash desk his bill came to €283.75.

   If VAT was charged at 13.5%, what was the cost of his bill before VAT?

5. The government of a particular country have decided to charge one standard rate of VAT @ 25%. If the price of a car (including VAT) is €9,000, how much of this price is VAT?

6. In a particular year's budget, the VAT rate falls from 13% to 12.5%. The price of a phone drops by €3.50.

   (i) What was the price of the phone before the change in VAT rate?

   (ii) What is the new VAT amount on the phone?

   (iii) What is the total price of the phone now?

   (iv) If the VAT rate had increased to 17%, how much would the phone have cost?

Revision Exercises

Where necessary, use the tables for USC and PRSI given earlier in this chapter.

1. SVC Ltd has recently completed its sales forecasts for the year to 31 December 2016. It expects to sell two products:

   Product 1 @ €125 and Product 2 @ €145.

   Its budgeted sales for Product 1 are 12,000 units and 5,000 units for Product 2.

   Both products use the same materials but in different quantities per unit as follows:

	Product 1	Product 2
Material X	10 kg	5 kg
Material Y	5 kg	7 kg
Skilled labour	5 hours	4 hours

   - Material X: €1.50 per kg
   - Material Y: €3.50 per kg
   - Skilled labour: paid at €7.50 per hour
   - Variable costs: €7 per unit
   - Fixed costs: €180,000

   Calculate:

   (i) The amount of material X needed

   (ii) The amount of material Y needed

   (iii) The total labour hours used in production

   (iv) The total labour cost of production

   (v) The total cost of production (including variable and fixed costs)

   (vi) The profit made if the company sells at the expected prices

   (vii) The profit made if the prices realised are 10% higher than expected

    Solutions and chapter summary available online

2. Shane has an annual gross income of €60,000. He pays tax at 20% on the first €32,000 he earns and 40% on the remainder. His tax credit is €3,100. What is his tax payable?

3. Laura has a gross income of €45,000 a year. Her standard rate cut-off point is €33,000. The standard rate of tax is 20% and the higher rate is 40%. She has a tax credit of €2,400. She is in Class A1 for PRSI. (Assume a 52-week year.)

   (i) What is her PRSI contribution per week?

   (ii) What is her employer's PRSI contribution per week?

   (iii) Calculate her USC payment.

   (iv) What is her weekly net income after all deductions?

4. The standard rate of income tax is 20% and the higher rate is 42%. Eoin has tax credits of €1,493 for the year and a standard rate cut-off point of €30,000. He has a gross income of €31,650 for the year.

   (i) After tax is paid, what is Eoin's income for the year?

   (ii) What would Eoin's gross income for the year need to be in order for him to have an after-tax income of €29,379?

5. In a particular year's budget, the VAT rate falls from 13.5% to 12.5%. The price of a phone drops by €4.50.

   (i) What was the price of the phone before the change in VAT rate?

   (ii) What is the new VAT amount?

   (iii) What is the price of the phone now?

   (iv) If the VAT rate had increased to 15%, how much would the phone have cost?

10

Financial Mathematics

In this chapter you will learn to:

- Solve problems and perform calculations on compound interest and depreciation (reducing-balance method)
- Use present value when solving problems involving loan repayments and investments
- Solve problems involving finite and infinite geometric series
- Use financial applications such as deriving the formula for a mortgage repayment

You should remember...

- How to calculate percentages
- How to find a given root of a number
- Laws of logs

- Compound interest formula $F = P(1 + i)^t$
- Geometric series

Key words

- Present value
- Future value
- Net present value (NPV)

- Annual percentage rate (APR)
- Annual equivalent rate (AER)

- Equivalent annual rate (EAR)
- Compound annual rate (CAR)

10.1 Present Value

The **time value of money** is the value of money when factoring in a given amount of interest earned over a given time period.

For example, if you are given €100 today and invest it for one year at a rate of 5% per annum, it will be worth €105 one year from now. That is to say, €100 today has the same value as €105 one year from now, given an interest rate (also referred to as a growth rate) of 5%.

Present value, also known as **present discounted value**, is the value on a given date of a future payment or series of future payments, discounted to reflect the time value of money and other factors such as investment risk, etc.

Present value calculations are widely used in business and economics to provide a means to compare cash flows at different times on a meaningful like-to-like basis.

$$P = \frac{F}{(1 + i)^t}$$

F = Final value (amount borrowed/invested + interest)

P = Present value (amount borrowed/invested)

i = Rate of interest per time period (always use decimal form)

t = Time (number of time periods you had the loan or investment)

This formula can be found on page 30 of *Formulae and Tables*.

When future values are brought back to present values at a given rate of interest, the interest rate is often referred to as the discount rate.

Worked Example 10.1

Compute the present value of a future payment of €58,564 in four years' time, given a discount rate of 10% per annum.

Solution

$$P = \frac{F}{(1 + i)^t}$$ $F = 58{,}564$ $t = 4$ $i = 0.10$ (i.e. 10% = 0.10 as a decimal)

$$P = \frac{58{,}564}{(1 + 0.10)^4}$$

i must be written in decimal form.

$\Rightarrow P = €40{,}000$

The present value is €40,000.

This means that, given an interest rate of 10%, €58,564 in four years' time is worth €40,000 today.

FINANCIAL MATHEMATICS

Worked Example 10.2

An investment opportunity arises for Andy. He will receive a payment of €10,000 at the end of each of the next three years if he invests €25,000 now. Growth over this time period is estimated to be 5%.

Use present values to assess whether or not this is a good investment opportunity for Andy.

Solution

To assess the investment, we need to compare like with like; therefore, it is necessary to calculate the present values of the future cash inflows.

Present values $\quad P = \dfrac{F}{(1 + i)^t}$

Payment 1 $\quad P1 = \dfrac{10,000}{(1.05)^1}$

$\qquad\qquad = €9,523.81 \quad$ (€9,523.81 would yield €10,000 in one year's time if invested at 5%.)

Payment 2 $\quad P2 = \dfrac{10,000}{(1.05)^2}$

$\qquad\qquad = €9,070.29 \quad$ (€9,070.29 would yield €10,000 in two year's time if invested at 5%.)

Payment 3 $\quad P3 = \dfrac{10,000}{(1.05)^3}$

$\qquad\qquad = €8,638.38 \quad$ (€8,638.38 would yield €10,000 in three year's time if invested at 5%.)

The present value of all future cash inflows from this investment is:

$$€9,523.81 + €9,070.29 + €8,638.38 = €27,232.48$$

The **net present value** (NPV) = present value of all cash inflows − present value of all cash outflows.

- If the NPV > 0 ⇒ Invest in the project.
- If the NPV ⩽ 0 ⇒ Do not invest in the project.

Net present value = €27,232.48 − €25,000 = €2,232.48

As the NPV is positive, Andy should invest in the project.

Note: This is just the first step in evaluating the opportunity. Andy would carry out other research about the investment.

We are just checking if the numbers look good!

Worked Example 10.3

Conor is a young entrepreneur hoping to set up a new business. He approaches L. Jordan, a venture capitalist, with the following proposal, detailing cash outflows and inflows for the first four years of the investment. (Note: Year 0 = at this present time, i.e. right now.)

Year	0	1	2	3	4
Cash flow €	−50,000	−10,000	15,000	20,000	35,000

If L. Jordan were to apply a discount rate of 5% to this project, would it be worthwhile for him to support Conor?

Solution

To assess the investment we need to compare like with like; it is necessary, therefore, to calculate the present values of the future cash outflows and inflows.

Year 0	$-50{,}000 = -€50{,}000$
Year 1	$\dfrac{-10{,}000}{(1.05)^1} = -€9{,}523.81$
Year 2	$\dfrac{15{,}000}{(1.05)^2} = €13{,}605.44$
Year 3	$\dfrac{20{,}000}{(1.05)^3} = €17{,}276.75$
Year 4	$\dfrac{35{,}000}{(1.05)^4} = €28{,}794.59$
NPV	€152.97

Initial outflow is not discounted.

Outflows are discounted in the same way as inflows.

As the NPV > 0, it would be worthwhile for L. Jordan to support Conor.

Exercise 10.1

1. Calculate the present value of each of the following cash flows:

	Cash flow (€)	Years from now	Discount rate (%)	Present value (€)
(i)	2,160.00	1	8.0	
(ii)	1,458.00	2	8.0	
(iii)	27,562.50	2	5.0	
(iv)	47,590.40	2	4.0	
(v)	635,548.16	3	4.0	
(vi)	13,676.31	3	11.0	
(vii)	375,340,318.70	7	14.0	
(viii)	341,907.75	3	11.0	
(ix)	488,410.00	2	10.5	
(x)	58,985,820.45	4	7.0	

2. Compute the present value of receiving €6,298.50 in three years' time when the discount rate is 8% (to the nearest cent).

3. Compute the present value of receiving €15,000 in three years' time when the discount rate is 7% (correct to the nearest cent).

4. Calculate the present value of €6,000 that is expected to be received in three years' time when the rate of interest for the period is 7.5% per annum compounded annually.

5. A project manager is presented with the following project as detailed in the table below.

Year	Cash flow
1	€20,000
2	€20,000
3	€20,000
Initial cash outflow (Year 0) €55,000	Discount rate = 6%

   (i) Calculate the present value for each cash flow.

  (ii) Calculate the net present value for the project.

 (iii) Should the manager take on this project?

6. An advertising executive brings a marketing proposal to his managing director. He proposes an initial spend on the campaign of €50,000. He projects that this advertising campaign will generate cash inflows of €15,000 each year for the next four years. Given a predicted growth rate of 5%, is this a good proposal? (Use present values in arriving at your conclusion.)

7. Sorcha is presented with the following investment projects. All amounts are in euro.

Year	0	1	2	3	4
Project A	−10,000	−3,000	4,000	6,000	8,000
Project B	−5,000	−2,000	1,000	3,000	7,000

Advise Sorcha as to which project is the more profitable, if a discount rate of 6% is used.
(Hint: Compare the NPVs.)

8. A new shopping centre is opening in a beach resort. The management company have to decide between building an area for restaurants or an area for amusements.

The following are the projections for both projects for the first five years. All amounts are in euro.

Year	0	1	2	3	4	5
Restaurant area	−420,000	−5,000	120,000	130,000	145,000	150,000
Amusements area	−95,000	−10,000	−120,000	200,000	110,000	−52,000

Use present values to advise the management company as to which project is more profitable if the discount rate used is:

  (i) 6%   (ii) 9%

9. Shields and Larkin Enterprises is a start-up business developing a new Spanish verb book. The company directors decide to approach a venture capitalist to look for funding. They present the following cash flows for consideration:

Initial cash outflow	Year 0	−€12,000
Cash inflow	Year 1	€5,000
Cash inflow	Year 2	€7,000
Cash inflow	Year 3	€5,000
Cash outflow	Year 4	−€5,000
Cash inflow	Year 5	€8,000

What advice would you give the venture capitalist, given a projected growth rate of 2% (per year)?

10. You are offered an annuity that will pay €24,000 per year for 11 years (the first payment will be paid to you one year from today). The discount rate you use is 13%. What is the annuity worth to you today?

11. You are offered an annuity that will pay €1,700 per year for 7 years (the first payment will be made today). The discount rate you use is 11%. What is the annuity worth to you today?

10.2 Compound Interest: Loans and Investments

Individuals and businesses do not always have enough cash to buy what they want or to pay their bills. It is sometimes necessary for them to borrow money. Equally, there are individuals and businesses that have large amounts of cash and so they decide to invest some of it.

If you borrow money from a bank or any financial institution, they will expect you to pay back the money you borrowed, but they will also charge you for the use of the money they loaned you. This is called **interest payable**.

In the case of loans and other forms of credit, there is a legal obligation to display the **annual percentage rate (APR)** prominently. APR is the rate at which the loan interest is calculated.

Annual Percentage Rate (APR) and Annual Equivalent Rate (AER)

The annual percentage rate (APR) is the annual interest rate (expressed as a percentage to at least one decimal place) that makes the present value of all future payments equal to the present value of the loan.

There are clear rules stated in legislation regarding how APR is to be calculated:

● All monies the customer will have to pay must be included in the calculation, i.e. loan repayments, set-up charges, etc.

● In calculating the present values, time is measured in years from the date the loan is drawn down (received).

When you invest money in an investment account or a financial institution, you are giving the people who run the account or institution the use of your money. So they must pay you for the use of this money. This is called **investment interest**.

In the case of investments, the rate of interest that is used to calculate the amount that is to be paid to the investor is called the annual equivalent rate (AER).

In Ireland there are a number of different names for **annual equivalent rate (AER),** all of which mean the same thing: equivalent annual rate (EAR), compound annual return/compound annual rate (CAR).

- Rules governing AER are not as specific as those governing APR.
- Investments do not have a guaranteed return.
- Calculation of AER involves estimates of future interest/growth rates.

When a loan or an investment is paid back in full, the total amount is the sum borrowed or invested plus the interest that was paid.

Despite the difference in name (APR and AER), the method of calculation of both is exactly the same.

When dealing with interest, we use the following symbols:

F = Final value (amount borrowed/invested + interest)

P = Present value (amount borrowed/invested)

i = Rate of interest per time period (always use decimal form)

t = Time (number of time periods you had the loan or investment)

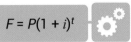

$$F = P(1 + i)^t$$

This formula can be found on page 30 of *Formulae and Tables*.

The rate of interest that is used here, i, is the annual equivalent rate (AER) in the case of investments or annual percentage rate (APR) in the case of loans, as this formula assumes that compounding takes place once every year.

However, if compounding takes place more frequently, the respective AER/APR must be adjusted for this change in the compounding period.

Worked Example 10.4

Noreen borrows €10,000 for three years at an APR of 5% compounded annually.

How much will she owe at the end of the third year?

Solution

$F = P(1 + i)^t$ $P = 10,000$ $t = 3$ $i = 0.05$

$F = 10,000(1 + 0.05)^3$

$\therefore F = €11,576.25$

Worked Example 10.5

€15,000 is invested in a savings account at an AER of 3%. At the beginning of the second year, €1,000 is withdrawn from this amount. The AER rises to 3.5% in the second year and remains at this rate for three years.

Calculate:

(i) The value of the investment at the end of Year 1

(ii) The value of the investment at the end of Year 4

Solution

(i) $F = P(1 + i)^t$

   $P_0 = €15,000$

     $i = 3\% = 0.03$ $t = 1$

     $F = 15,000(1 + 0.03)^1$

       $= 15,000(1.03)$

   $\therefore F = €15,450$

(ii) Value at the end of Year 1 = €15,450

     At the beginning of Year 2, €1,000 is withdrawn.

     $P_1 = €15,450 - €1,000 = €14,450$

      $i = 3.5\% = 0.035$ $t = 3$

     $F = €14,450(1 + 0.035)^3$

       $= €14,450(1.035)^3$

   $\therefore F = €16,020.97$

     The value at the end of Year 4 is €16,020.97.

FINANCIAL MATHEMATICS

A **bond** is a cash payment made to the government or to a private company for an agreed number of years. In return, the investor is paid a fixed sum at the end of each year; in addition, the government or company repays the original value of the bond to the investor with the final payment. The final payment may or may not be part of the bond.

Worked Example 10.6

Mark invested money in a 5.5 year bond when he started First Year. In the middle of Sixth Year the bond matures and he has earned 21% interest in total. Calculate the AER for this bond.

Solution

Step 1 Write down the formula.

$$F = P(1 + i)^t$$

Step 2 Identify the parts that we are given in the question.

F	Final value	= Original amount + interest
		= 100% + 21%
		= 121%
		= 1.21
P	Principal	= Original amount
		= 100%
		= 1.00
t	Time in years = 5.5	
i	Annual equivalent rate = (This is what we are looking for.)	

Step 3 Solve for the unknown value i.

$$1.21 = 1.00(1 + i)^{5.5}$$
$$1.21 = (1 + i)^{5.5}$$
$$\sqrt[5.5]{1.21} = 1 + i$$
$$1.0353 = 1 + i$$
$$1.0353 - 1 = i$$
$$i = 0.0353$$
$$\Rightarrow i = 3.53\%$$

∴ The annual equivalent rate is 3.53%.

 It is good practice to quote such a rate of interest as a percentage to two decimal places where appropriate.

Compounding Made Easy

Suppose you invest €10,000. The first year the investment rises 20%. Your investment is now worth €12,000. Based on good performance, you keep the investment. In Year 2, the investment gains another 20%. Therefore, your €12,000 grows to €14,400. Rather than your investment gaining an additional €2,000 (20%) like it did in the first year, it gains an additional €2,400, because the €2,000 you gained in the first year grew by 20% too.

So at the end of two years, €10,000 has grown to €14,400 without adding any additional money to the investment.

Compounding

Compounding is the ability of an asset to generate earnings, which are then reinvested in order to generate their own earnings. In other words, compounding refers to generating earnings from previous earnings. It is also known as **compound interest**.

FINANCIAL MATHEMATICS

Worked Example 10.7

A loan advertisement quotes an APR of 14.9%. Find, correct to four significant figures, the equivalent rate of interest, if compounded monthly.

Solution

Take a simple case of borrowing €1.

If you were to borrow €1 today, a year from now you would expect to pay back €1.149.

Future value = €1.149

Present value = €1.00

Compounding periods = $t \times 12$ (t in years)

$$= 1 \times 12$$

The formula in *Formulae and Tables* gives t as time in years. If we compound more frequently than annually, simply multiply t by the number of compounding periods, in this case 12 (12 months in a year).

So:
$$F = P(1 + i)^t \quad \text{(t now stands for number of time periods.)}$$
$$1.149 = 1(1 + i)^{12} \quad \text{(i now stands for monthly interest rate.)}$$
$$1.149 = (1 + i)^{12}$$
$$\sqrt[12]{1.149} = 1 + i$$
$$1.01164 - 1 = i$$
$$i = 0.01164 \Rightarrow i = 1.164\%$$

If compounding is to take place monthly, the rate of interest used is 1.164%.

Worked Example 10.8

Calculate the number of years it will take for a sum of €20,000 to grow to €23,152.50 when invested at 5% interest compounded annually.

Solution

Step 1 Using the formula $F = P(1 + i)^t$ fill in the information given.

$$23{,}152.50 = 20{,}000(1.05)^t$$

Step 2 Isolate the term that has t.

$$\frac{23{,}152.50}{20{,}000} = 1.05^t$$

Step 3 Solve for t.

$$\log\left(\frac{23{,}152.50}{20{,}000}\right) = \log 1.05^t$$

$$\log\left(\frac{23{,}152.50}{20{,}000}\right) = t \log 1.05$$

If the variable you are solving for is in the power, take the log of each side.
This allows you to bring the power down.
We have seen this rule in Chapter 7.

$$t = \frac{\log\left(\dfrac{23{,}152.50}{20{,}000}\right)}{\log 1.05}$$

$$t = 3$$

The time needed is 3 years.

Exercise 10.2

In Questions 1–10, no repayments or withdrawals are made until the end of the loan/investment.

1. €23,500 was invested at 5% per annum for three years. Calculate the final value.

2. €16,000 was invested at 3% per annum for six years. Calculate the interest.

3. €100,200 was invested at 4% per annum for eight years. Calculate the final value.

4. €12,000 was borrowed at 8% per annum for four years. Calculate the final value.

5. €105,000 was borrowed at 6% per annum for five years. Calculate the interest.

6. €25,400 was borrowed at 3.5% per annum for 10 years. Calculate the interest.

7. €200,500 was invested at 4.25% per annum for 15 years. Calculate the interest.

8. €100,500 was borrowed at 4.5% per annum for six years. Calculate the final value.

9. €1,000,000 was invested at 10.5% per annum for 3.5 years. Calculate the final value.

10. €90,600 was borrowed at 2.35% per annum for four years. Calculate the interest.

11. Find the amount, to the nearest cent, that needs to be invested at a rate of 5% per annum to give €2,500 in five years' time?

12. Find the amount, to the nearest cent, that needs to be invested at a rate of 3.2% per annum to give €120,500 in six years' time?

13. How much would Sharon need to invest now at a rate of 3.5% per annum to have €15,000 two years from now?

14. Mustafa borrowed €365,000 at 3.6% per annum. At the end of Year 1 he repaid €20,000. The rate of interest was then lowered to 3.2%.

    How much does he owe at the end of the second year?

15. A not-for-profit organisation is trying to secure funding for an overseas aid project. They need €150,000 in total for the project and are advised that a grant is available for half of the funds if they can secure the other half before the date of application (five years from today).

    How much needs to be invested now if the rate of interest being offered is:

    (i) 6% per annum compounded annually

    (ii) 5% per annum compounded annually

16. Howard receives a tax bill from the Revenue Commissioners for €14,000. He has the option to repay the lump sum in three years' time.

    He shops around for investment accounts and finds one that offers a return of 6% compounded annually for the three years; however, all investments must be in multiples of €1,000.

    How much will Howard need to invest to have the €14,000 in three years' time?

17. A football club borrowed €15,000,000 to revamp its stadium. The rate for the first year was 3.5% and the rate for the second year was 4.2%. Calculate the amount owing at the end of the second year.

18. A business secures a three-year loan for €45,000 with the following conditions attached:

    ● The loan must be repaid in full by the end of the third year.

    ● The rate of interest is 3% for the first two years. Then it decreases by 0.5%.

    Calculate the total interest that will be paid on this loan (to the nearest euro).

FINANCIAL MATHEMATICS

19. A 10-year loan is drawn down for €350,000. The rate of interest is 5.2% per annum compound interest.

 (i) How much interest is charged in the first year?

 (ii) How much interest will have been charged after 10 years if no repayment is made in the 10 years? (Answer to the nearest cent.)

 (iii) If €60,000 euro is paid off at the end of Year 1, what will the interest charge be for Year 2?

20. Fagan & Hanlon Ltd secures a loan from a private bank at €50,000 for five years at a rate of 6% per annum. If the loan is repaid with interest in one lump sum at the end of five years, the lender will give a 15% discount. Alternatively, the business can repay €10,000 at the end of each of Years 1–4 and the balance at the end of Year 5.

 Which option will cost the business less?

21. A sum of €6,000 is invested in an eight-year government bond with an annual equivalent rate (AER) of 6%. Find the value of the investment when it matures in eight years' time.

22. A sum of €5,000 is invested in an eight-year government bond with an annual equivalent rate (AER) of 3%. Find the value of the investment when it matures in eight years' time.

23. A bond offers a return of 20% after six years. Calculate the AER for this bond.

24. The National Treasury Management Agency offers a three-year savings bond with a return of 10%. Calculate the AER for this bond.

25. There are two types of National Solidarity Bond on offer.

 (A) A 4-year bond offering a gross return of 13.5%.

 (B) A 10-year bond offering a gross return of 45%.

 Using the AER, compare the two bonds and state which bond offers the better return.

26. Calculate the AER offered on this bond.

27. Calculate the number of years that it will take for a sum of €5,000 to grow to €20,000 when invested at 5.5% interest compounded annually (answer to two decimal places).
 (Hint: Use logs.)

28. Calculate the number of years that it will take for a sum of €400,000 to grow to €539,693.05 when invested at an AER of 10.5%

29. After a number of years, a €45,000,000 loan had risen in value to €58,985,820.45. If the fixed rate of interest on this loan was 7%, how many years had passed?

30. Calculate the number of years it will take for an investment fund to mature to €15,000, if €10,000 is invested at a growth rate of 5.5% per annum (answer to two decimal places).

31. An investment bond quotes an annual equivalent rate of 12.5%. If interest on the investment fund is compounded bi-annually (twice a year), what is the rate of interest for each compounding period?

32. A loan advertisement quotes an APR of 14.5%. If the loan interest is compounded monthly, what is the rate of interest per month?

33. Joe recently retired and received a lump sum of €100,000. He wants to invest his money in an An Post savings scheme. He gets information on two different products that are on offer.

Investments	Description
National Solidarity Bond (10-year)	50% gross return over 10 years
National Solidarity Bond (4-year)	15% gross return over 4 years

Which bond offers the better AER?

34. A bank is offering a Thrifty Savers account to all recent graduates. The account offers an AER of 6%. If the interest is to be compounded on a quarterly basis, what will the rate per quarter be?

35. (i) Danny borrowed €15,000 at an APR of 6%. Several years later, he discovered that the amount he repaid was €17,865.24.

How many years did Danny have this loan for?

(ii) At the time of the initial loan, Danny was offered a loan for €16,000 at a rate of 4.5% for the same period of time. Which loan would have been a better choice? Use your calculations to justify your answer.

(iii) Danny is currently borrowing money to purchase a new car. He saw an advertisement that quotes an APR of 7.8%. If this loan is compounded monthly, what is the rate of interest per month?

(iv) Will there be a difference in the amount to be repaid if the loan is compounded monthly or annually? Explain your answer.

36. If you deposit €15,000 per year for 9 years (each deposit is made at the beginning of the year) in an account that pays an annual interest rate of 8%, what will your account be worth at the end of 9 years?

10.3 Depreciation (Reducing-Balance Method)

Depreciation is calculated in order to write off the value of an asset over its useful economic life.

Causes of Depreciation

Wear and tear	Assets that are used over a period of time eventually wear out.	Example: Vehicles
Obsolescence	An asset becomes out of date because of the development of a more efficient or less expensive alternative.	Example: Computers
Passage of time	Assets lose value as they near the end of their licence.	Example: Patents
Extraction	The value of an asset reduces as the asset is extracted.	Example: Mining

Types of Depreciation

There are two methods of calculating depreciation in practice:

- **Straight-line method:** The amount written off the asset is the same each year until the total value of the asset is written off or it is reduced to its residual value (the value of the asset after we are finished with it).

- **Reducing-balance method:** Rather than writing off a fixed amount every year, a (fixed) percentage of the remaining value of the asset is charged every year. Compared to straight-line depreciation, this method is more heavily weighted towards the early years.

For our syllabus, we will study the reducing-balance method only.

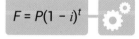

$$F = P(1 - i)^t$$

This formula appears on page 30 of *Formulae and Tables*.

F is called the **later value** in *Formulae and Tables* (page 30). In accounting, this is known as the **net book value (NBV)** of the asset.

Worked Example 10.9

A van was purchased for €45,000. It is company policy to depreciate all vans at a rate of 20% per annum using the reducing-balance method.

(i) What is the net book value (NBV) of the asset after three years?

(ii) How much depreciation is written off this van in the first three years?

Solution

(i) $F = P(1 - i)^t$

$F = 45{,}000(1 - 0.20)^3$

$\quad = 45{,}000(0.8)^3$

$F = \text{€}23{,}040$

After three years, NBV = €23,040.

(ii) Depreciation written off:

= Cost − Net book value

= €45,000 − €23,040

= €21,960

∴ Depreciation = €21,960

Worked Example 10.10

ABC Ltd purchased equipment costing €60,000. It is the policy of the company to depreciate all such equipment at a rate of 20% using the reducing-balance method.

(i) Complete the schedule of depreciation below for the first five years of the asset's useful economic life.

Year	Cost (€)/NBV	Rate of depreciation	Depreciation (€)	NBV (€)
1	60,000.00	0.2	12,000.00	48,000.00
2				
3				
4				
5				

(ii) Verify the NBV at the end of Year 5 by using the formula for depreciation.

Solution

(i) **Step 1** Calculate the depreciation for the first year.

Step 2 Calculate the NBV of the asset at the end of Year 1.

NBV = Cost − Depreciation

Step 3 Repeat for Years 2 to 5.

Year	Cost (€)/NBV	Rate of depreciation	Depreciation (€)	NBV (€)
1	60,000.00	0.2	12,000.00	48,000.00
2	48,000.00	0.2	9,600.00	38,400.00
3	38,400.00	0.2	7,680.00	30,720.00
4	30,720.00	0.2	6,144.00	24,576.00
5	24,576.00	0.2	4,915.20	19,660.80

The value of the asset at the end of five years will be €19,660.80.

(ii) $F = P(1 - i)^t$

$F = 60{,}000(1 - 0.20)^5$

$\quad = 60{,}000(0.8)^5$

$\quad = 19{,}660.80$

∴ NBV after five years = €19,660.80

FINANCIAL MATHEMATICS

Worked Example 10.11

An accountant is auditing a set of books and sees that the net book value of an asset eight years after the date of purchase is €154,624. The policy of the company is to depreciate this asset at a rate of 12.5% using the reducing-balance method.

What was the original cost of the asset to the nearest euro?

Solution

$F = P(1 - i)^t$

$154{,}624 = P(1 - 0.125)^8$

$154{,}624 = P(0.875)^8$

$\Rightarrow \dfrac{154{,}624}{(0.875)^8} = P$

$\therefore P = €449{,}999.9647$

The original cost was approximately €450,000.

Worked Example 10.12

An asset that cost €150,000 now has a net book value of €88,573.50. The asset has been depreciated at a rate of 10% per annum. How many years' depreciation have been written off on the asset?

Solution

$F = P(1 - i)^t$

$88{,}573.50 = 150{,}000(1 - 0.10)^t$

$\dfrac{88{,}573.50}{150{,}000} = (0.9)^t$

$0.59049 = (0.9)^t$

$\ln(0.59049) = \ln(0.9)^t$

$\ln(0.59049) = t \ln(0.9)$

$\dfrac{\ln(0.59049)}{\ln(0.9)} = t$

$\therefore t = 5$ years

Exercise 10.3

1. Using the reducing-balance method for depreciation, calculate the missing values in the table below correct to the nearest euro where necessary.

	Asset cost (€)	Rate of depreciation (%)	Number of years	Net book value
(i)	200,000	10	1	
(ii)	1,500,000	15	4	
(iii)	60,600	3	8	
(iv)	21,000	3.5	2	
(v)	34,000	18	4	
(vi)	16,000	10.5	6	
(vii)	12,000	7.5	4	

2. Using the reducing-balance method, calculate the missing values in the table below correct to two decimal places where necessary.

	Asset cost (€)	Rate of depreciation (%)	Number of years	Net book value
(i)	400,000		4	208,802.50
(ii)	100,000		2	93,122.50
(iii)	120,000		4	37,968.75

3. How much will a €30,000 car be worth at the end of five years, given a depreciation rate of 20% per annum (reducing-balance method)?

4. A coal mine is depleted at a rate of 15% per annum. If the initial volume of coal in the mine is 400,000 m³, what volume of coal would there be in the mine after six years?

5. A car has a net book value of €19,660.80 at the end of five years, having been depreciated at a rate of 20% per annum (reducing-balance method).

What was the initial cost of the car?

6. A building has an NBV of €800,000 at the end of 10 years, having been depreciated at a rate of 2% (reducing-balance method). What was the original cost of the building? Give your answer correct to the nearest €100.

7. An asset that costs €95,000 now has a net book value of €56,096.55, having been depreciated for a number of years at a rate of 10%. For how many years was the asset depreciated?

8. The NBV of an asset is €162,901.25 and the depreciation rate for this particular asset is 5%. If the original cost was €200,000, how many years' depreciation have been written off this asset?

9. An accountant recently secured a new client who had not been keeping complete accounting records. The only information in relation to motor vehicles the client could present was as follows:

She changed her fleet of vehicles a number of years ago. The cost of the new fleet was €350,000. Her accountant at the time advised that she depreciate the fleet at a rate of 10% per annum. She provided one account that stated the net book value of the fleet was €206,671.50 and the date on this account was 31/12/2012.

(i) What was the net book value of the assets on 31/12/2015?

(ii) How many years' depreciation had been written off the asset by 31/12/2012?

(iii) In what year were the assets purchased (assuming a full year's depreciation is charged in the year of acquisition)?

10. A company's policy is to change all of its vehicles after three years, as it helps to reduce maintenance costs. If a vehicle that originally cost €45,400 now has a net book value of €29,056, having been depreciated for a number of years, is it due for a change? The company uses a 20% rate of depreciation per annum.

11. A data analysis system, with a total cost of €346,000, was installed in a university. The policy of the university is to depreciate all

analysis equipment and systems at a reducing-balance rate of 12.5% per annum. Due to the rapid development of technology, it is felt that such a system will be due for renewal every two and a half years. If the net book value of the system is now €264,906.25, how much longer will it be before the system should be updated?

12. A computer was purchased at the start of 2015 for €2,500. It is expected that the computer will only be worth €1,378.42 at the end of 2017.

   What is the rate of depreciation (reducing-balance method)?

13. A lorry was purchased for €150,000 at the end of 2011. At the start of 2016 the lorry was sold at its NBV of €49,152. What was the annual rate of depreciation charged (reducing-balance method) on the lorry? (Answer correct to four significant figures.)

14. A pharmaceutical company has a patent on its newest headache tablet. The patent office has granted the patent for a 10-year period. In line with company policy, the accountants for the firm decide to write off the patent using a reducing-balance method. The patent is estimated to be worth €15,000,000 now. What annual rate of depreciation should the firm's accountants use in order to write the patent off over a 10-year period? (Hint: Let the residual value be €0.01.)

15. A company has a policy to depreciate all computers at a reducing-balance rate of 20%. Computers owned by the firm are valued (net book value) at €150,000. An auditor recently pointed out that due to increases in technology, computers were losing value at a much quicker rate than in previous years. The auditor estimated that the value of the computers in two years' time would only be €95,000. Does the firm have an adequate depreciation policy? Explain your answer.

10.4 Applications and Problems Involving Geometric Series

Savings schemes and **loans** often involve making regular payments at fixed intervals of time.

- A **Smart Save account** is an example of a product where banks encourage customers to save a set amount each week or each month.
- A **mortgage** holder must make a monthly repayment against their loan.

Calculations involving regular payments discounted back to present values or adjusted to future values will involve the **summation** of a geometric series.

An **annuity** is a regular stream of fixed payments over a specified period of time, taking into account the time value of money. It is sometimes used in relation to a regular pension payment that lasts as long as the person is alive.

Amortisation is the process of accounting for a sum of money by making it equivalent to a series of payments over time.

An **amortised loan** is a loan that involves paying back a fixed amount at regular intervals over a fixed period of time, e.g. term loans and mortgages.

A **bond** is a cash payment made to the government or to a private company for an agreed number of years. In return, the investor is paid a fixed sum at the end of each year; in addition, in some cases, the government or company repays the original value of the bond to the investor with the final payment.

An annuity is a form of investment involving a series of fixed regular payments (sometimes called contributions) made by a person to an account for a specified time period.

Interest may be compounded at the beginning **or** end of each period.

Pension funds involve making contributions to an annuity before retirement and receiving payments from the annuity after retirement.

- When receiving payments from an annuity, the present value of the annuity is the lump sum that would have to be invested **now** in order to provide those regular future payments.
- The future value of an annuity is the total value of the investment at the end of the specified period of time – it includes all payments as well as the interest earned.

Amortisation: Mortgages and Loans

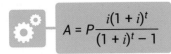 $A = P\dfrac{i(1+i)^t}{(1+i)^t - 1}$ This formula appears on page 31 of *Formulae and Tables*.

A = Repayment amount   *i* = Interest rate (as decimal)

P = Principal   *t* = Time (compounding periods)

> This formula is usually used for calculating loan repayments.
>
> The formula assumes that payments are made at the end of each accounting period.
>
> To use it for calculating the payment that must be made into an annuity or pension fund, the total value of the fund must be discounted back to present value.

Worked Example 10.13

A building society offers a savings account with an AER of 4%. If a customer saves €1,000 per annum starting now, how much will the customer have in five years' time?

Solution

Method 1

Present value		Future value
€1,000 invested for 5 years	$1{,}000(1.04)^5$	€1,216.65
€1,000 invested for 4 years	$1{,}000(1.04)^4$	€1,169.86
€1,000 invested for 3 years	$1{,}000(1.04)^3$	€1,124.86
€1,000 invested for 2 years	$1{,}000(1.04)^2$	€1,081.60
€1,000 invested for 1 year	$1{,}000(1.04)^1$	€1,040.00
	Total future value =	€5,632.97

Method 2

Write as a series.

Final value $(F) = 1{,}000(1.04)^5 + 1{,}000(1.04)^4 + 1{,}000(1.04)^3 + 1{,}000(1.04)^2 + 1{,}000(1.04)^1$

$\qquad = 1{,}000[(1.04)^5 + (1.04)^4 + (1.04)^3 + (1.04)^2 + (1.04)^1]$

$\qquad = 1{,}000[(1.04)^1 + (1.04)^2 + (1.04)^3 + (1.04)^4 + (1.04)^5]$

Consider $(1.04)^1 + (1.04)^2 + (1.04)^3 + (1.04)^4 + (1.04)^5$.

> Calculations may be easier if the order of the geometric series is reversed, i.e. write as $(1.04)^1 + (1.04)^2 + (1.04)^3 + (1.04)^4 + (1.04)^5$.

This is a geometric series (see Chapter 8) with:

$\qquad a = 1.04 \qquad r = 1.04 \qquad n = 5$

This formula appears on page 22 of *Formulae and Tables*.

$S_n = \dfrac{a(1 - r^n)}{1 - r}$

$\therefore F = 1{,}000\left[\dfrac{1.04\,(1 - (1.04)^5)}{1 - 1.04}\right]$ (multiplying above and below by 1.04)

$\qquad = 1{,}000(5.632975462)$

$\therefore F = €5{,}632.98$

> • Using a geometric series is particularly useful if *n* is large.
> • Using the fraction button on the calculator allows you to calculate this in one go.

Derivation of the Amortisation Formula

When money is borrowed it is normally repaid by regular payments for a fixed amount of time. To calculate what this regular payment should be there is an amortisation formula.

This formula is given in *Formulae and Tables* but we also need to be able to derive it.

The amount borrowed is given by P.

The regular amount that is repaid is given by A.

Students must be able to derive this formula.

The payment period is given by t.

The rate of interest that is paid each period is given by i.

The amount borrowed is equal to the sum of the present values (PV) of each repayment.

So $P = PV$ of first repayment + PV of second repayment + ……. + PV of last repayment.

$$P = \frac{A}{(1 + i)^1} + \frac{A}{(1 + i)^2} + \frac{A}{(1 + i)^3} + \ldots + \frac{A}{(1 + i)^t}$$

So P is the sum, S_n, of a geometric series, where $n = t =$ number of compounding periods, $a = \frac{A}{1 + i}$ and $r = \frac{1}{1 + i}$.

$$P = \frac{a(1 - r^n)}{1 - r} = \frac{\left(\frac{A}{1 + i}\right)\left(1 - \left(\frac{1}{1 + i}\right)^t\right)}{\left(1 - \left(\frac{1}{1 + i}\right)\right)}$$

Remember the formula for the sum of a geometric series:

$$S_n = \frac{a(1 - r^n)}{1 - r}$$

This is covered in detail in Chapter 8.

$$P = \frac{\frac{A}{1 + i}\left(1 - \frac{1^t}{(1 + i)^t}\right)}{\frac{1(1 + i) - 1}{(1 + i)}} \qquad \text{(Bring in the power, and find a common denominator.)}$$

$$P = \frac{\frac{A}{1 + i}\left(\frac{(1 + i)^t - 1}{(1 + i)^t}\right)}{\frac{i}{1 + i}}$$

$$P = \frac{A}{\cancel{1 + i}}\left(\frac{(1 + i)^t - 1}{(1 + i)^t}\right)\frac{\cancel{1 + i}}{i} \qquad \text{(To divide by a fraction, invert the fraction and multiply.)}$$

$$P = A\left(\frac{(1 + i)^t - 1}{(1 + i)^t}\right)\frac{1}{i} \qquad \text{(Isolate } A.\text{)}$$

$$A = \frac{P}{\dfrac{(1 + i)^t - 1}{i(1 + i)^t}} \qquad\qquad \text{So } A = \frac{P(i(1 + i)^t)}{(1 + i)^t - 1}.$$

Worked Example 10.14

If a loan for €60,000 is taken out at an APR of 3%, how much should the annual repayments be if the loan is to be repaid in 10 equal instalments over a 10-year period? Assume the first instalment is paid one year after the loan is drawn down. Give your answer correct to the nearest euro.

$P = €60,000 \qquad i = 0.03 \qquad t = 10$

$$A = 60,000\left[\frac{0.03(1 + 0.03)^{10}}{(1 + 0.03)^{10} - 1}\right]$$

$A = 7,033.830396$

$\therefore A \approx €7,034$, i.e. the annual repayments should be €7,034.

Solution

Method 1 Using the amortisation formula:

$$A = P\frac{i(1 + i)^t}{(1 + i)^t - 1}$$

Method 2   Using present values and geometric series:

Let the annual repayments = A.

The sum of all the discounted payments equals the loan amount.

As the initial repayment is made at the end of the first year, all repayments will be discounted.

$$\text{€}60{,}000 = \frac{A}{1.03} + \frac{A}{1.03^2} + \frac{A}{1.03^3} + \dots + \frac{A}{1.03^{10}}$$

$$= A\left[\frac{1}{1.03} + \frac{1}{1.03^2} + \frac{1}{1.03^3} + \dots + \frac{1}{1.03^{10}}\right]$$

Consider $\dfrac{1}{1.03} + \dfrac{1}{1.03^2} + \dfrac{1}{1.03^3} + \dots + \dfrac{1}{1.03^{10}}$.

This is a geometric series with:

$$a = \frac{1}{1.03} \qquad r = \frac{1}{1.03} \qquad n = 10$$

$$\therefore\ 60{,}000 = A\left[\frac{\frac{1}{1.03}\left[1 - \left(\frac{1}{1.03}\right)^{10}\right]}{1 - \frac{1}{1.03}}\right]$$

The calculator can be used to perform the calculations in one go. Just be careful to key in accurately.

$$\Rightarrow 60{,}000 = A(8.530202837)$$

$$\therefore\ \frac{60{,}000}{8.530202837} = A$$

Note: Both methods must be known, as a particular method may be specified in a question.

$$A = \text{€}7{,}033.83 \approx \text{€}7{,}034$$

Regular Payments at Intervals Other than Annually

Calculations are the same as for annual payments, but the AER or APR must be treated properly.

Option 1

- Leave time in years.
- Do not change the APR/AER.
- Use fractional units of time.

Option 2

- Switch to a different unit of measurement for time.
- We must adjust the APR/AER.
- Use integer units of time.

Worked Example 10.15

Alan borrows €10,000 at an APR of 6%. The terms of the loan state that the loan must be repaid in equal monthly instalments over 10 years. The first repayment will be one month from the date the loan is taken out. How much should the monthly repayment be? Give your answer to the nearest cent.

Solution

Using Option 1: Leave time in years

$$10{,}000 = \frac{A}{1.06^{\frac{1}{12}}} + \frac{A}{1.06^{\frac{2}{12}}} + \frac{A}{1.06^{\frac{3}{12}}} + \dots + \frac{A}{1.06^{\frac{120}{12}}}$$

$$a = \frac{A}{1.06^{\frac{1}{12}}} \qquad r = \frac{1}{1.06^{\frac{1}{12}}} \qquad n = 120$$

Do not round off answers throughout the question. Leave it until the end as it can lead to answers that are inaccurate.

Geometric series

The formula can also be written as:

$$S_n = \frac{a(r^n - 1)}{r - 1}$$

$$S_{120} = \frac{\dfrac{A}{1.06^{\frac{1}{12}}}\left(\left(\dfrac{1}{1.06^{\frac{1}{12}}}\right)^{120} - 1\right)}{\dfrac{1}{1.06^{\frac{1}{12}}} - 1}$$

$\Rightarrow 10{,}000 = A(90.72432164)$

$$A = \frac{10{,}000}{90.72432164}$$

$A = 110.2240261$

$A \approx \text{€}110.22$

Using Option 2: Change time to months

Adjust APR.

$F = P(1 + i)^t$

$1.06 = 1(1 + i)^{12}$ (*i* is now the monthly rate.)

$\sqrt[12]{1.06} = 1 + i$

$i = 0.00486755$ (Don't round for increased accuracy.)

$$A = P\frac{i(1 + i)^t}{(1 + i)^t - 1}$$ This formula should only be used for a LOAN.

$P = \text{€}10{,}000$

$t = 120$, i.e. compounded every month for 10 years

$i = 0.00486755$

$$A = 10{,}000\left[\frac{0.00486755(1 + 0.00486755)^{120}}{(1 + 0.00486755)^{120} - 1}\right]$$

$A \approx \text{€}110.22$

Worked Example 10.16

Denise wants to have €10,000 in her savings account in five year's time. If the expected interest rate is 2%, how much would Denise need to invest at the end of each year to reach her target?

Solution

Method 1: Using a geometric series

> It is important to note that Denise is investing at the **end** of each year.

$A(1.02)^4 + A(1.02)^3 + A(1.02)^2 + A(1.02) + A = 10{,}000$

$10.000 = A[1 + (1.02) + (1.02)^2 + (1.02)^3 + (1.02)^4]$

Consider $1 + (1.02) + (1.02)^2 + (1.02)^3 + (1.02)^4$.

This is a geometric series with:

$a = 1$ $r = 1.02$ $n = 5$

$$S_5 = \frac{1(1 - (1.02)^5)}{1 - 1.02} = 5.20404016$$

$\Rightarrow 10{,}000 = A(5.20404016)$

$$\Rightarrow A = \frac{10{,}000}{5.20404016}$$

$\Rightarrow A \approx \text{€}1{,}921.58$

Method 2: Using the formula for amortisation of a loan

The only way to use this formula for an investment is to find the present value of the sum required and establish how many payments would be required to generate this amount.

Payments must also be made **at the end** of each accounting period (year in this case) for this formula to work.

Step 1   Find the present value of €10,000.

$$P = \frac{F}{(1 + i)^t}$$

$$P = \frac{10{,}000}{(1.02)^5}$$

$\therefore P = \text{€}9{,}057.31$

Step 2   Using the amortisation formula:

$$A = P\frac{i(1 + i)^t}{(1 + i)^t - 1}$$

$$A = 9{,}057.31\frac{0.02(1 + 0.02)^5}{(1 + 0.02)^5 - 1}$$

$\Rightarrow A \approx \text{€}1{,}921.58$

Exercise 10.4

1. A building society offers a savings account with an AER of 4%. If a customer saves €2,000 per annum starting now, how much will the customer have in five years' time?

2. A building society offers a savings account with an AER of 4.5%. If a customer saves €2,000 per annum starting now, how much will the customer have in four years' time?

FINANCIAL MATHEMATICS

3. A building society offers a savings account with an AER of 4% compounded monthly. If a customer saves €150 each month starting now, how much will the customer have in five years' time?

4. A bank offers a savings account with an AER of 10% compounded monthly. If a customer saves €110 per month starting now, how much will the customer have in five years' time?

5. (a) A loan for €450,000 is taken out at an APR of 5.2%. How much should annual repayments be if the loan is to be repaid in 15 equal instalments over a 15-year period? Assume the first instalment is paid one year after the loan is drawn down.

   (b) A loan for €450,000 is taken out at an APR of 5.2%. If the customer wishes to make monthly repayments, how much should the repayments be if the loan is to be repaid in equal instalments over a 15-year period? Assume the first instalment is paid one month after the loan is drawn down.

6. A student wishes to set up his own business. He borrows €5,000 to finance the initial set-up costs and charges. The terms of the loan are as follows: interest is compounded monthly at a rate of 1% and the duration of the loan is six months.

   (a) Calculate the monthly repayment amount.

   (b) Make a schedule showing the monthly payment, the monthly interest and the balance outstanding at the end of each month.

7. A company wishes to raise capital to expand. It offers a 10-year €2,000 bond that will pay €100 every year for 10 years. The €2,000 sum will be paid back on maturity (i.e. after 10 years). Given that the expected annual market interest rate over the lifetime of the bond is 5%, is €2,000 a fair price to pay for this bond? Be careful to state clearly any assumptions that have been made.

8. ABC Finance issues a bond offer as detailed below.

   - 10-year bond
   - Pays €30 at the end of every six months for 10 years

- AER = 6% interest compounded bi-annually

What is a fair price for this bond?

> Hint: Calculate the PV of future payments to the bond holder.

9. Nicki deposits €200 at the end of each quarter in her savings account. The money earns 5.5% (AER). How much will the investment be worth at the end of four years? State clearly any assumptions that you make.

10. Eoin wants to have €5,000 in three years' time to travel to the USA on a J1 visa. How much will he need to deposit at the end of each month into an account that pays 8% (EAR)? (Remember: EAR and AER are used interchangeably.)

11. Mercedes took part in a TV game show and won the top prize. She is given two options:

    (a) Receive €1,000 at the end of every month for the next 20 years.

    (b) Take a lump sum now.

    If the AER is 8%, what is the minimum amount Mercedes should accept as a lump sum?

12. Suppose you expect to receive a payment of €200 at the end of each year for an indefinite period of time. What is the present value of this annuity?

13. Jack and David borrow €200,000 over 25 years at 3% APR.

    (i) How much will they repay annually on this mortgage?

    (ii) If they decide to make monthly repayments, how much will these repayments be?

    (iii) How much will their monthly repayments increase by if the APR increases to 4%?

14. Carol and James bought a house in 1992. They obtained a 35-year mortgage at a fixed annual interest rate of 5.2%. They had monthly payments of €1,800. In 2012, they decided to repay the mortgage in full. How much did they need to pay? (Assume they had been paying their mortgage for exactly 20 years.)

15. Chelsea's parents wish to set up a regular savings account from the day she is born so that on her 21st birthday she will have €21,000. How much should they plan to deposit each month if they choose a regular savings plan with an AER of 3.5%? (No payment is made on her 21st birthday.)

16. Julie contributed €200 at the end of each week for 20 years to a pension fund earning 4.5% AER. The pension paid a lump sum on the date she retired.

(a) Find the rate of interest per week that, if compounded weekly, would be equivalent to an AER of 4.5% (assume a 52-week year).

(b) What was her lump sum payment when she retired?

(c) Julie used her lump sum to purchase an annuity at 3.8% AER, giving her a regular payment at the start of each month for the next 20 years. What was her monthly payment?

Revision Exercises

1. Calculate the present value of each of the following correct to the nearest cent:

	Cash flow (€)	Years from now	Discount rate (%)	Present value (€)
(i)	210,000.00	1	8.0	
(ii)	148,000.50	2	8.0	
(iii)	27,800.00	2	5.0	
(iv)	450,000.00	10	4.0	
(v)	635,548.00	15	4.0	

2. Calculate the present value of €16,000 that is expected to be received in three years' time when the rate of interest for the period is 7.5% per annum compounded annually.

3. A project manager is presented with the following project as detailed in the table below:

Year	Cash flow (€)
1	120,000
2	120,000
3	120,000
Initial cash outflow (year 0) €40,000	Discount rate = 6%

(a) Calculate the present value for each cash flow.

(b) Calculate the net present value for the project.

(c) Should the manager take on this project? Justify your answer.

4. Greg is presented with the following investment projects (all amounts are in euro).

Year	0	1	2	3	4
Project A	−50,000	−13,000	14,000	26,000	28,000
Project B	−5,000	−2,000	1,000	4,000	7,000

Using present values, advise Greg as to which project is the more profitable, if a discount rate of 6% is used.

5. (a) €1,000,000 was invested at 11.5% for 4.5 years. Calculate the final value. (No withdrawal is made over the 4.5 years.)

   (b) €90,000 was borrowed at 2.35% for 15 years. Calculate the interest earned. (No repayments are made until the end of the term.)

6. Find the amount, to the nearest cent, that needs to be invested at a rate of 3.2% per annum to give €245,000 in eight years' time.

7. How much would Sarah need to invest now at a rate of 3.25% to have €105,000 two years from now?

8. An investment bond quotes an annual equivalent rate of 13.5%. If interest on the investment fund is compounded bi-annually, what is the rate of interest for each compounding period? Answer correct to four significant figures.

9. A loan advertisement quotes an APR of 17.5%. If the loan interest is compounded monthly, what is the rate of interest per month? Answer correct to four significant figures.

10. Verify that the figures given in this advertisement are accurate.

Investments	Description
Savings certificates	Interest 21% after 5.5 years, AER 3.53% tax free
Savings bonds	Interest 10% after 3 years, AER 3.23% tax free

11. Calculate the missing values in the table below.

	Principal	Discount/interest rate (annual)	Time (years)	Final value (€)
(i)	€120,000	10%	1	
(ii)	€4,000,000		6	8,327,807.01
(iii)	€100,000		2	106,090

12. A car has a net book value of €22,185.27 at the end of five years, having been depreciated at a rate of 20% per annum (reducing-balance method).
What was the initial cost of the car?

13. A building has an NBV of €700,000 at the end of eight years, having been depreciated at a rate of 2% (reducing-balance method). What was the original cost of the building? (Give your answer correct to the nearest €100.)

14. An asset that cost €95,000 now has a net book value of €50,486.90, having been depreciated for a number of years at a rate of 10%. How many years was the asset depreciated for?

15. The NBV of an asset is €694,511.89. The depreciation rate for this particular asset is 2%. Having originally cost €850,000, how many years depreciation have been written off this asset?

16. A building society offers a savings account with an AER of 4%. If a customer saves €5,000 per annum starting now, how much will the customer have in five years' time?

17. A bank offers a savings account with an effective annual rate of 3%. If a customer saves €1,500 per annum starting now, how much will the customer have in 12 years' time?

18. If a loan for €150,000 is taken out at an APR of 3%, how much should the annual repayments be if the loan is to be repaid in 10 equal instalments over a 10-year period? Assume the first instalment is paid one year after the loan is drawn down.

19. The management company for a sports centre estimates that it will need €30,000 to replace the floors in the squash courts in five years' time. If regular payments are made to an investment fund earning 2.75% AER, calculate:

    (a) The rate of interest per month that would be equivalent to an AER of 2.75% (answer correct to four significant figures)

    (b) The amount that must be deposited at the end of each month to meet this target

    (c) How much interest will be earned in the five-year period

20. O'Reilly-Elwood Finance Company issues a bond offer as detailed below.

    - 10-year bond
    - Pays €100 at the end of every six months for 10 years
    - AER = 5% interest compounded bi-annually

    What is a fair price for this bond?

21. (i) Derive the amortisation formula
    $$A = \frac{P(i(1 + i)^t)}{(1 + i)^t - 1}.$$

    (ii) If Larry and Michelle get a mortgage for €350,000 over 35 years at a fixed rate of interest of 5.2% per annum, what should their monthly repayments be? The first payment is to be made one month after the mortgage is drawn down.

Exam Questions

1. Pádraig is 25 years old and is planning for his pension. He intends to retire in forty years' time, when he is 65. First, he calculates how much he wants to have in his pension fund when he retires. Then he calculates how much he needs to invest in order to achieve this. He assumes that in the long run, money can be invested at an inflation-adjusted annual rate of 3%. Your answers throughout this question should therefore be based on a 3% annual growth rate.

   (a) Write down the present value of a future payment of €20,000 in one year's time.

   (b) Write down, in terms of t, the present value of a future payment of €20,000 in t years' time.

   (c) Pádraig wants to have a fund that could, from the date of his retirement, give him a payment of €20,000 at the start of each year for 25 years. Show how to use the sum of a geometric series to calculate the value on the date of retirement of the fund required.

   (d) Pádraig plans to invest a fixed amount of money every month in order to generate the fund calculated in part (c). His retirement is 40 × 12 = 480 months away.

      (i) Find, correct to four significant figures, the rate of interest per month that would, if paid and compounded monthly, be equivalent to an effective annual rate of 3%.

      (ii) Write down, in terms of n and P, the value on the retirement date of a payment of €P made n months before the retirement date.

      (iii) If Pádraig makes 480 equal monthly payments of €P from now until his retirement, what value of P will provide him with the fund he wants?

      (iv) If Pádraig waits for 10 years before starting his pension investments, how much will he then have to pay each month in order to generate the same pension fund?

   SEC Leaving Certificate Higher Level, Sample Paper 1, 2011

FINANCIAL MATHEMATICS

2. Most lottery games in the USA allow winners of the jackpot prize to choose between two forms of the prize: an *annual-payments* option or a *cash-value* option. In the case of the New York Lotto, there are 26 annual payments in the annual-payments option, with the first payment immediately, and the last payment in 25 years' time. The payments increase by 4% each year. The amount advertised as the jackpot prize is the total amount of these 26 payments. The cash-value option pays a smaller amount than this.

(a) If the amount of the first annual payment is A, write down, in terms of A, the amount of the second, third, fourth and 26th payments.

(b) The 26 payments form a geometric series. Use this fact to express the advertised jackpot prize in terms of A.

(c) Find, correct to the nearest dollar, the value of A that corresponds to an advertised jackpot prize of $21.5 million.

(d) A winner who chooses the cash-value option receives, immediately, the total of the present values of the 26 annual payments. The interest rate used for the present-value calculations is 4.78%. We want to find the cash value of the prize referred to in part (c).

   (i) Complete the table below to show the actual amount and the present value of each of the first three annual payments.

Payment number	Time to payment (years)	Actual amount ($)	Present value($)
1	0		
2	1		
3	2		

   (ii) Write down, in terms of n, an expression for the present value of the nth annual payment.

   (iii) Find the amount of prize money payable under the cash-value option. That is, find the total of the present values of the 26 annual payments. Give your answer in millions, correct to one decimal place.

(e) The jackpot described in parts (c) and (d) above was won by an Irish woman earlier this year. She chose the cash-value option. After tax, she received $7.9 million. What percentage of tax was charged on her winnings?

SEC Leaving Certificate Higher Level, Paper 1, 2011

3. (a) Niamh has saved to buy a car. She saved an equal amount at the beginning of each month in an account that earned an annual equivalent rate (AER) of 4%.

   (i) Show that the rate of interest, compounded monthly, which is equivalent to an AER of 4%, is 0.327%, correct to 3 decimal places.

   (ii) Niamh has €15,000 in the account at the end of 36 months. How much has she saved each month, correct to the nearest euro?

(b) Conall borrowed to buy a car. He borrowed €15,000 at a monthly interest rate of 0.866%. He made 36 equal monthly payments to repay the entire loan. How much, to the nearest euro, was each of his monthly payments?

SEC Leaving Certificate Higher Level, Paper 1, 2013

4. (a) Donagh is arranging a loan and is examining two different repayment options.

   (i) Bank A will charge him a monthly interest rate of 0.35%. Find, correct to three significant figures, the annual percentage rate (APR) that is equivalent to a monthly interest rate of 0.35%.

   (ii) Bank B will charge him a rate that is equivalent to an APR of 4.5%. Find, correct to three significant figures, the monthly interest rate that is equivalent to an APR of 4.5%.

(b) Donagh borrowed €80,000 at a monthly interest rate of 0.35%, fixed for the term of the loan, from Bank A. The loan is to be repaid in equal monthly repayments over ten years. The first repayment is due one month after the loan is issued. Calculate, correct to the nearest euro, the amount of each monthly repayment.

SEC Leaving Certificate Higher Level, Paper 1, 2015

Solutions and chapter summary available online

11

Proof by Induction

 In this chapter you will learn:

- ⊙ About the notation for summations

- ⊙ How to use induction to prove statements about series

- ⊙ How to use induction to prove statements about divisibility

- ⊙ How to use induction to prove statements about inequalities

 You should remember...

- ⊙ $n! = n(n - 1)(n - 2) \ldots (3)(2)(1), n \in N$

 Key words

- ⊙ Proposition
- ⊙ Induction
- ⊙ Series
- ⊙ Divisibility
- ⊙ Factor
- ⊙ Inequality

11.1 Introduction

Proof is central to mathematics and is one of the reasons why the subject is regarded as having many 'truths'. In mathematics, theories must be proved to be accepted as being true. Proof is the process of reaching the conclusion that is then accepted as being true. A proof may begin with an **axiom** or the conclusion of a previously proven theorem.

> **Axioms** are mathematical statements that we accept as true from the start. They do not need to be proved (perhaps because they are self-evidently true).

Francesco Maurolico

Andrew Wiles

The earliest example of mathematical induction can be found in Euclid's proof that there are an infinite number of prime numbers. The Greek mathematician Francesco Maurolico, in his *Arithmeticorum libri duo* (1575), used the technique to prove that the sum of the first n odd natural numbers is n^2.

In more recent times, the British-born mathematician Andrew Wiles used mathematical induction to prove Fermat's Last Theorem. He spent 10 years working on the proof, which was published in 1994.

11.2 Summations

In this section we introduce notation for summations. The following notation represents the sum of the terms in the linear or arithmetic sequence 3, 6, 9, 12, ... 3n.

$$\sum_{r=1}^{n} 3r = 3(1) + 3(2) + 3(3) + ... + 3(n) = 3 + 6 + 9 + 12 + ... + 3n$$

The symbol on the left-hand side of the equation above is the Greek capital letter **sigma**. r runs through all the natural numbers from 1 to n, to give each term in the series.

Worked Example 11.1

(i) Evaluate $\sum_{r=1}^{8} r^4$.

(ii) Evaluate $\sum_{r=1}^{5} 3$.

Solution

(i) $\sum_{r=1}^{8} r^4 = 1^4 + 2^4 + 3^4 + 4^4 + 5^4 + 6^4 + 7^4 + 8^4$

$= 8,772$

(ii) $\sum_{r=1}^{5} 3 = \sum_{r=1}^{5} 3r^0$

$= 3(1^0) + 3(2^0) + 3(3^0) + 3(4^0) + 3(5^0)$

$= 3 + 3 + 3 + 3 + 3 = 15$

Exercise 11.1

1. Find the value of each of the following sums:

(i) $\displaystyle\sum_{r=1}^{10} r$

(iii) $\displaystyle\sum_{r=1}^{10} 2^r$

(ii) $\displaystyle\sum_{r=1}^{10} r^2$

(iv) $\displaystyle\sum_{r=1}^{10} 2$

2. Find the value of each of the following sums:

(i) $\displaystyle\sum_{r=4}^{8} (r-2)$

(iii) $\displaystyle\sum_{r=1}^{6} r!$

(ii) $\displaystyle\sum_{r=2}^{7} (r-2)^2$

(iv) $\displaystyle\sum_{r=3}^{9} r(r+1)$

3. Express each of the following using $\sum$ notation:

(i) $1^3 + 2^3 + 3^3 + 4^3 + 5^3 + 6^3$

(ii) $5 + 5 + 5 + 5 + 5 + 5$

(iii) $3 + 3^2 + 3^3 + 3^4 + 3^5$

(iv) $5 + 25 + 125 + 625 + 3{,}125$

4. Express each of the following using $\sum$ notation:

(i) $1 + 2 + 3 + 4 + 5 + \ldots + (n-1) + n$

(ii) $5^2 + 6^2 + 7^2 + \ldots + n^2$

(iii) $3! + 4! + 5! + \ldots + n!$

(iv) $16 + 20 + 24 + \ldots + 4n$

5. Prove each of the following:

(i) $\displaystyle\sum_{r=5}^{12} 6r^2 = 6\sum_{r=5}^{12} r^2$

(ii) $\displaystyle\sum_{r=6}^{10} (r^2 - 1) = \sum_{r=6}^{10} r^2 - \sum_{r=6}^{10} 1$

(iii) $\displaystyle\sum_{r=3}^{8} r^3 + \sum_{r=3}^{8} 1 = \sum_{r=3}^{8} (r+1)(r^2 - r + 1)$

6. Express each of the following in terms of x and y, where $x = \displaystyle\sum_{r=m}^{n} r$ and $y = \displaystyle\sum_{r=m}^{n} r^2$:

(i) $\displaystyle\sum_{r=m}^{n} 7r$

(iii) $\displaystyle\sum_{r=m}^{n} r(r-1)$

(ii) $\displaystyle\sum_{r=m}^{n} (r^2 + r)$

(iv) $\displaystyle\sum_{r=m}^{n} (3r^2 + 2r)$

11.3 Proof by Induction

The Greek mathematician Francesco Maurolico proved that the sum of the first n odd natural numbers is n^2. Before he embarked on this proof, he would have first **conjectured** that the sum was n^2.

> To **conjecture** is to make a guess based on the available evidence.

How would Maurolico have come up with the idea that the sum of the first n odd natural numbers is n^2? More than likely he would have studied patterns of numbers, as shown in the table below.

The table suggests that the sum of the first n odd natural numbers is n^2. To be more confident that the conjecture could be true, we should include more rows. However, no matter how many rows we include, we could not include every case as there is an infinite amount of natural numbers. What is needed is a proof for every natural number that exists and the correct method of proof in this case is mathematical induction.

1	1	1^2
$1 + 3$	4	2^2
$1 + 3 + 5$	9	3^2
$1 + 3 + 5 + 7$	16	4^2
$1 + 3 + 5 + 7 + 9$	25	5^2

Mathematical Induction

Mathematical induction is a method of mathematical proof used to establish that a given statement is true for natural numbers.

The first step in the proof is proving that the first statement in the infinite sequence of statements is true (i.e. verifying that $1 = 1^2$ in the example above).

The next step is proving that if any one statement in the infinite sequence of statements is true, then so is the next one.

11.4 Proofs Involving Series

In this section we will use induction to prove statements involving series.

Worked Example 11.2

Prove by induction, for all $n \in N$: $4 + 8 + 12 + \ldots + 4n = 2n(n + 1)$

Solution

To prove:

$P(n): 4 + 8 + 12 + \ldots + 4n = 2n(n + 1)$, for all $n \in N$ | $P(n)$ means 'Proposition, case n'.

Proof:

Step 1   Show that $P(1)$ is true, i.e. that the proposition is true for $n = 1$.

LHS: 4

RHS: $2(1)(1 + 1) = 4$

LHS = RHS, so $P(1)$ is true.

Step 2   Assume that $P(k)$ is true, i.e. that the proposition is true for $n = k$.

$P(k): 4 + 8 + 12 + \ldots + 4k = 2k(k + 1)$ is assumed true.

Step 3   Prove that $P(k + 1)$ is true, i.e. that the proposition is true for $n = k + 1$, given that it is true for $n = k$.

To prove:

$P(k + 1): 4 + 8 + 12 + \ldots + 4k + 4(k + 1) = 2(k + 1)(k + 2)$

Proof:

LHS $= 4 + 8 + 12 + \ldots + 4k + 4(k + 1) = 2k(k + 1) + 4(k + 1)$ [$P(k)$ assumed true]

$$= 2k^2 + 2k + 4k + 4$$
$$= 2k^2 + 6k + 4$$
$$= 2(k^2 + 3k + 2)$$
$$= 2(k + 1)(k + 2)$$
$$= \text{RHS}$$

$P(k + 1)$ is true, having assumed $P(k)$ is true.

Step 4 $P(1)$ is true.

If $P(k)$ is true then $P(k + 1)$ is true.

∴ By induction, $P(n)$ is true for all $n \in N$.

Worked Example 11.3

Prove by induction, for all $n \in N$: $7 + 7^2 + 7^3 + \ldots + 7^n = \dfrac{7}{6}(7^n - 1)$.

Solution

To prove:

$P(n): 7 + 7^2 + 7^3 + \ldots + 7^n = \dfrac{7}{6}(7^n - 1)$

PROOF BY INDUCTION

Proof:

Step 1 Show that $P(1)$ is true, i.e. that the proposition is true for $n = 1$.

LHS: 7

RHS: $\dfrac{7}{6}(7^1 - 1) = \dfrac{7}{6}(6)$

$= 7$

LHS = RHS

$\therefore P(1)$ is true.

Step 2 Assume that $P(k)$ is true, i.e. that the proposition is true for $n = k$.

$P(k)$: $7 + 7^2 + 7^3 + \dots + 7^k = \dfrac{7}{6}(7^k - 1)$ is assumed true.

Step 3 Prove that $P(k + 1)$ is true, i.e. that the proposition is true for $n = k + 1$, given that it is true for $n = k$.

To prove:

$P(k + 1)$: $7 + 7^2 + 7^3 + \dots + 7^k + 7^{k+1} = \dfrac{7}{6}(7^{k+1} - 1)$

Proof:

$P(k + 1)$: $7 + 7^2 + 7^3 + \dots + 7^k + 7^{k+1} = \dfrac{7}{6}(7^k - 1) + 7^{k+1}$ $[P(k)$ assumed true]

$= \dfrac{7^{k+1}}{6} - \dfrac{7}{6} + 7^{k+1}$

$= 7^{k+1}\left(\dfrac{1}{6} + 1\right) - \dfrac{7}{6}$

$= \dfrac{7}{6}(7^{k+1}) - \dfrac{7}{6}$

$= \dfrac{7}{6}(7^{k+1} - 1)$

$=$ RHS

$\therefore P(k + 1)$ is true, having assumed $P(k)$ is true.

Step 4 $P(1)$ is true.

If $P(k)$ is true then $P(k + 1)$ is true.

$\therefore$ By induction, $P(n)$ is true for all $n \in N$.

Exercise 11.2

1. Prove by induction for all $n \in N$:

   $1 + 2 + 3 + \dots + n = \dfrac{n}{2}(n + 1)$

2. Prove by induction for all $n \in N$:
   $1 + 3 + 5 + \dots + (2n - 1) = n^2$

3. Prove by induction that the sum of the first n even natural numbers is $n^2 + n$.

4. Prove by induction for all positive integers n:

   $1 + 5 + 9 + 13 + \dots + (4n - 3) = \dfrac{n}{2}(4n - 2)$

5. Prove by induction for all $n \in N$:

   $1 + 6 + 11 + \dots + (5n - 4) = \dfrac{n}{2}(5n - 3)$

6. Prove by induction for all $n \in N$:
   $3 + 7 + 11 + \dots + (4n - 1) = 2n^2 + n$

7. Prove by induction for all $n \in N$:
   $10 + 20 + 30 + \dots + 10n = 5n(n + 1)$

8. Prove by induction for all $n \in N$:
   $7 + 9 + 11 + \dots + (2n + 5) = n^2 + 6n$

9. Prove by induction for all $n \in N$:

   $\displaystyle\sum_{r=1}^{n} 2r = n(n + 1)$

10. Prove by induction for all $n \in N$:

$$\sum_{r=1}^{n} 5r = \frac{5n}{2}(n+1)$$

11. Prove by induction for all positive integers n:

$$\sum_{r=1}^{n} 3r = \frac{3n}{2}(n+1)$$

12. Prove by induction that:

$$10 + 10^2 + 10^3 + \ldots + 10^n = \frac{10}{9}(10^n - 1)$$
for all $n \in N$.

13. Prove by induction for all $n \in N$:

$$5 + 25 + 125 + \ldots + 5^n = \frac{5}{4}(5n - 1)$$

14. Prove by induction for all positive integers n:

$$4 + 16 + 64 + \ldots + 4^n = \frac{4}{3}(4^n - 1)$$

15. Prove by induction for all $n \in N$:

$$3 + 3^2 + 3^3 + \ldots + 3^n = \frac{3}{2}(3^n - 1)$$

16. Prove by induction that:

$$\sum_{r=1}^{n} 2^{r-1} = 2^n - 1 \text{ for all } n \in N.$$

17. Prove by induction that:

$$\sum_{r=1}^{n} x^{r-1} = \frac{1 - x^n}{1 - x} \text{ for all } n \in N, x \notin \{0, 1\}.$$

18. Prove by induction that

$$(1)(3) + 2(4) + 3(5) + \ldots + (n-1)(n+1)$$

$$= \frac{n}{6}(n-1)(2n+5) \text{ for all } n > 1, n \in N.$$

19. Prove by induction for all $n \in N$:

$$(1)(1!) + 2(2!) + 3(3!) + \ldots + n(n!) = (n+1)! - 1$$

11.5 Proofs Involving Divisibility

In this section we will use induction to prove statements involving divisibility.

Worked Example 11.4

Prove by induction that 3 is a factor of $4^n - 1$, for all $n \in N$.

Solution

$P(n)$: 3 is a factor of $4^n - 1$

Step 1 Show that $P(1)$ is true.

$P(1)$: $4^1 - 1 = 3$

3 is a factor of 3.

$\therefore P(1)$ is true.

Step 2 Assume that $P(k)$ is true, i.e. that the proposition is true for $n = k$.

$P(k)$: 3 is a factor of $4^k - 1$ is assumed true.

i.e. $4^k - 1 = 3A, A \in Z$

$\Rightarrow 4^k = 3A + 1$

Step 3 Prove that $P(k + 1)$ is true, i.e. that the proposition is true for $n = k + 1$, given that it is true for $n = k$.

$P(k + 1)$: 3 is a factor of $4^{k+1} - 1$

$4^{k+1} - 1 = (4)(4^k) - 1$

$= 4(3A + 1) - 1$

$= 12A + 4 - 1$

$= 12A + 3$

$= 3(4A + 1)$

$= 3B, B \in Z$

$\therefore P(k + 1)$ is divisible by 3, having assumed $P(k)$ is true.

Step 4 $P(1)$ is true.

If $P(k)$ is true then $P(k + 1)$ is true.

$\therefore$ By induction, $P(n)$ is true for all $n \in N$.

Worked Example 11.5

Prove by induction that $10^n - 7^n$ is divisible by 3, for all $n \in N$.

Solution

$P(n)$: $10^n - 7^n$ is divisible by 3, $n \in N$.

Step 1   Show that $P(1)$ is true.

$P(1)$: $10^1 - 7^1$

$= 10 - 7 = 3$

3 is divisible by 3.

$\therefore P(1)$ is true.

Step 2   Assume that $P(k)$ is true, i.e. that the proposition is true for $n = k$.

$P(k)$: $10^k - 7^k$ is assumed to be divisible by 3.

i.e. $10^k - 7^k = 3A$, $A \in Z$.

$\Rightarrow 10^k = 3A + 7^k$

Step 3   Prove that $P(k + 1)$ is true, i.e. that the proposition is true for $n = k + 1$, given that it is true for $n = k$.

$P(k + 1)$: $10^{k+1} - 7^{k+1}$

$= (10)(10^k) - (7)(7^k)$

$= 10[3A + 7^k] - (7)(7^k)$

$= 30A + (10)(7^k) - (7)(7^k)$

$= 30A + (3)(7^k)$

$= 3[10A + 7^k] = 3B$, $B \in Z$

$\therefore P(k + 1)$ is divisible by 3.

$\therefore$ The proposition is true for $n = k + 1$, given that it is true for $n = k$.

Step 4 $P(1)$ is true.

If $P(k)$ is true then $P(k + 1)$ is true.

$\therefore$ By induction, $P(n)$ is true for all $n \in N$.

Worked Example 11.6

Prove by induction that $n^2 + 3n$ is divisible by 2 for all $n \in N$.

Solution

$P(n)$: $n^2 + 3n$ is divisible by 2 for all $n \in N$.

Step 1   Show that the proposition is true for $n = 1$.

$P(1)$: $1^2 + 3(1) = 1 + 3 = 4$

4 is divisible by 2.

$\therefore P(1)$ is true.

Step 2   Assume that $P(k)$ is true, i.e. that the proposition is true for $n = k$.

$P(k)$: $k^2 + 3k$ is assumed to be divisible by 2.

i.e. $k^2 + 3k = 2A$, $A \in Z$

$\therefore k^2 = 2A - 3k$

Step 3   Prove that $P(k + 1)$ is true, i.e. that the proposition is true for $n = k + 1$, given that it is true for $n = k$.

$P(k + 1)$: $(k + 1)^2 + 3(k + 1)$

$= k^2 + 2k + 1 + 3k + 3$

$= k^2 + 5k + 4$

$= (2A - 3k) + 5k + 4$

$= 2A + 2k + 4$

$= 2[A + k + 2] = 2B$, $B \in Z$

$\therefore P(k + 1)$ is true, having assumed $P(k)$ is true.

Step 4 $P(1)$ is true.

If $P(k)$ is true then $P(k + 1)$ is true.

$\therefore$ By induction, $P(n)$ is true for all $n \in N$.

Exercise 11.3

1. Prove that $P(n)$: $7^n - 1$ is divisible by 6, for all $n \in N$.

2. Prove by induction that $5^n - 1$ is divisible by 4 for all $n \in N$.

3. Prove by induction that $9^n - 1$ is divisible by 8 for all $n \in N$.

4. Prove by induction that $11^n - 1$ is divisible by 10 for all $n \in N$.

5. Prove that $3^{2n} - 1$ is divisible by 8, for all $n \in N$.

6. Prove by induction that $2^{2n} - 1$ is divisible by 3 for all $n \in N$.

7. Prove by induction that $7^{2n+1} + 1$ is divisible by 8, for all $n \in N$.

8. Prove by induction that $2^{3n} - 1$ is divisible by 7, for all $n \in N$.

9. Prove by induction that $7^n - 3^n$ is divisible by 4, for all $n \in N$.

10. Prove by induction that $5^{2n} + 12^{n-1}$ is divisible by 13, for all $n \in N$.

11. Prove by induction that $13^n - 6^{n-2}$ is divisible by 7 for all $n > 1$, $n \in N$.

12. Prove by induction that $n^2 + n$ is divisible by 2, for all $n \in N$.

13. Prove by induction that $n^2 + 15n + 4$ is an even number for all $n \in N$.

14. Prove by induction that $n^3 - n$ is divisible by 3, for all $n \in N$.

15. Prove by induction that $n(n + 1)(2n + 1)$ is divisible by 3, for all $n \in N$.

11.6 Inequalities

When dealing with **inequalities**, it is important to know the rules of inequalities.

If $a, b, c \in R$ then:

1. If $a \neq b$, then either $a < b$ or $b < a$.
2. If $a < b$ and $b < c$, then $a < c$.
3. If $a < b$, then $a + c < b + c$.
4. If $a < b$ and $c > 0$, then $ac < bc$.
5. If $a < b$ and $c < 0$, then $ac > bc$.
6. $a^2 \geqslant 0$

Worked Example 11.7

Prove by induction that $4^n > 4n + 1$, $n \geqslant 2$, $n \in N$.

Solution

$P(n)$: $4^n > 4n + 1$, $n \geqslant 2$, $n \in N$

Step 1 Show that $P(2)$ is true, i.e. that the proposition is true for $n = 2$.

LHS: $(4)^2 = 16$

RHS: $4(2) + 1 = 9$

> Be careful with the base case. It does not have to be $n = 1$.

$16 > 9$

Hence, $P(2)$ is true.

Step 2 Assume that $P(k)$ is true, i.e. that the proposition is true for $n = k$.

$P(k)$: $4^k > 4k + 1$

Step 3 Prove that $P(k + 1)$ is true, i.e. that the proposition is true for $n = k + 1$, given that it is true for $n = k$.

$P(k + 1)$: $4^{k+1} > 4(k + 1) + 1$

LHS $= 4^{k+1}$

$= 4 \cdot 4^k$

$> 4(4k + 1)$ [assumption from $P(k)$]

$= 16k + 4$

For LHS > RHS we need $16k + 4 \geqslant$ RHS.

Is $16k + 4 \geqslant 4(k + 1) + 1$?

$16k + 4 \geqslant 4k + 5$

$12k \geqslant 1$

$k \geqslant \dfrac{1}{12}$

Yes, if $k \geqslant \dfrac{1}{12}$.

$\therefore$ The proposition is true for $n = k + 1$, given that it is true for $n = k$, where $k \geqslant 2$.

Step 4 $P(2)$ is true.

If $P(k)$ is true then $P(k + 1)$ is true.

By induction, $P(n)$ is true for $n \geqslant 2$, $n \in N$.

Exercise 11.4

1. Prove by induction that $2^n \geqslant 1 + n$, for all $n \in N$.

2. Prove by induction that $3^n > 2n$, for all $n \in N$.

3. Prove by induction that $3^n > n^2$ for $n \geqslant 2$, $n \in N$.

4. Prove by induction that $2^n > 3n$ for $n \geqslant 4$, $n \in N$.

5. Prove by induction that $4^n > 30n$ for $n \geqslant 4$, $n \in N$.

6. Prove by induction that
$5^n > 25n + 20$ for $n \geqslant 3$, $n \in N$.

7. Prove by induction that $n! > 2^n$, $n \geqslant 4$, $n \in N$.

8. Prove by induction that $(1 + x)^n \geqslant 1 + nx$,
$x > -1$, $n \in N$.

9. Prove by induction that
$(n + 1)! \geqslant 2^n$ for all $n \in N$.

10. Prove by induction that
$(n - 1)! \geqslant 2^{n-1}$ for all $n \in N$.

11. Prove by induction that $n^2 > 4n + 3$, $n \geqslant 5$, $n \in N$.

12. (i) Prove that $4n + 2 > n^2$, $n \geqslant 5$, $n \in N$.

    (ii) Prove that $n^2 < 2^n$, $n \geqslant 5$, $n \in N$.

    (iii) Hence, show that $4n + 2 < n^2 < 2^n$, $n \geqslant 5$,
    $n \in N$.

13. Prove that $(1 + 3x)^n \geqslant 1 + 3nx$ for $x > 0$ and $n \in N$.

14. Prove by induction that
$(1 + ax)^n \geqslant 1 + anx$, for $a > 0$, $x > 0$ and all $n \in N$.

15. (i) Complete the following table:

n	1	2	3	4	5	6	7	8
2^n	2	4						
$4n + 2$	6							

   (ii) From the table find the smallest value of
   $n \in N$ for which $2^n \geqslant 4n + 2$.

   (iii) Complete the following statement:
   $2^n \geqslant 4n + 2$, for $n \geqslant$ __, $n \in$ __.

   (iv) Use induction to prove the statement in (iii).

16. (i) Complete the following table:

n	1	2	3	4	5	6	7
3^n	3	9					
$10n + 100$	110						

   (ii) From the table find the smallest value of
   $n \in N$ for which $3^n \geqslant 10n + 100$.

   (iii) Complete the following statement:
   $3^n \geqslant 10n + 100$, for $n \geqslant$ __, $n \in$ __.

   (iv) Use induction to prove the statement in (iii).

PROOF BY INDUCTION

Revision Exercises

1. Find the value of each of the following sums:

   (i) $\displaystyle\sum_{r=4}^{8} (r^2 - 2)$ (iii) $\displaystyle\sum_{r=1}^{6} (r + 2)!$

   (ii) $\displaystyle\sum_{r=2}^{7} (2r - 2)^3$ (iv) $\displaystyle\sum_{r=3}^{9} r(r^2 + 1)$

2. (i) Evaluate $\displaystyle\sum_{r=1}^{6} 10r$.

   (ii) Prove using induction that:

   $$\sum_{r=1}^{n} 10r = 5n(n + 1), \text{ for all } n \in N.$$

   (iii) Hence, evaluate $\displaystyle\sum_{r=1}^{40} 10r$.

3. Prove each of these statements using induction:

   (i) $1 + 4 + 7 + \ldots + (3n - 2) = \dfrac{n(3n - 1)}{2}$, $n \in N$

   (ii) $3 + 6 + 9 + \ldots + (3n) = \dfrac{3n}{2}(n + 1)$, $n \in N$

   (iii) $12 + 12^2 + 12^3 + \ldots + 12^n = \dfrac{12}{11}(12^n - 1)$, $n \in N$

4. Prove each of these statements using induction:

   (i) $13^n - 1$ is divisible by 12 for all $n \in N$.

   (ii) $13^n - 2^n$ is divisible by 11 for all $n \in N$.

   (iii) $3^{2n} - 1$ is divisible by 4 for all $n \in N$.

5. Prove each of these statements using induction.

   (i) $5^n \geqslant 5n + 15$ for all $n \geqslant 2, n \in N$.

   (ii) $3^n \geqslant n^3$ for all $n \geqslant 3, n \in N$.

   (iii) $n! \geqslant n^2 + n$ for all $n \geqslant 4, n \in N$.

6. (i) Prove that:

   $$1^2 + 3^2 + 5^2 + \ldots + (2n - 1)^2 = \frac{n}{3}(4n^2 - 1),$$
   for all $n \in N$.

   (ii) Prove that:

   $$2^2 + 4^2 + 6^2 + \ldots + (2n)^2$$

   $$= \frac{2n}{3}(2n^2 + 3n + 1), \text{ for all } n \in N.$$

   (iii) Using only your results from (i) and (ii), explain why:

   $$\sum_{r=1}^{2n} r^2 = \frac{n}{3}(8n^2 + 6n + 1), \text{ for all } n \in N.$$

7. Use induction to prove the following statements on divisibility:

   (i) $8^n - 3^n$ is divisible by 5, for all $n \in N$.

   (ii) $5^n - 4n + 3$ is divisible by 4, for all $n \in N$.

   (iii) $4n^3 - n$ is divisible by 3, for all $n \in N$.

   (iv) $2^{3n-1} + 3$ is divisible by 7, for all $n \in N$.

8. (i) Using induction, prove that

   $$(1 + px)^n \geqslant 1 + pnx \text{ for } x > 0, p > 0 \text{ and } n \in N.$$

   (ii) If a and b are positive real numbers with $a \geqslant b$, show that $\dfrac{1}{a} \leqslant \dfrac{1}{b}$.

   (iii) Using the results from (i) and (ii), deduce that

   $$\frac{1}{(1 + px)^n} \leqslant \frac{1}{1 + pnx} \text{ for } x > 0, p > 0 \text{ and } n \in N.$$

Exam Questions

1. Use induction to prove that $2 + (2 \times 3) + (2 \times 3^2) + (2 \times 3^3) + \ldots + (2 \times 3^{n-1}) = 3^n - 1$,

   where n is a positive integer.

   SEC Leaving Certificate Higher Level, Paper 1, 2010

2. (a) Prove, by induction, the formula for the sum of the first n terms of a geometric series. That is, prove that, for $r \neq 1$:

   $$a + ar + ar^2 + \ldots + ar^{n-1} = \frac{a(1 - r^n)}{1 - r}.$$

   (b) By writing the recurring part as an infinite geometric series, express the following number as a fraction of integers:

   $$5 \cdot 2\dot{1} = 5 \cdot 2121212121\ldots$$

   SEC Leaving Certificate Higher Level, Paper 1, 2012

 Solutions and chapter summary available online

12

Complex Numbers

✱ In this chapter you will:

- Investigate the operations of addition, multiplication, subtraction and division with complex numbers C in rectangular form $a + ib$

- Illustrate complex numbers on an Argand diagram

- Interpret the modulus as distance from the origin on an Argand diagram and calculate the complex conjugate.

- Calculate conjugates of sums and products of complex numbers

- Use the Conjugate Root Theorem to find the roots of polynomials

- Work with complex numbers to solve quadratic and other equations including those in the form $z^n = a$, where $n \in Z$ and $z = r(\cos\theta + i\sin\theta)$

- Use De Moivre's Theorem

- Prove De Moivre's Theorem by induction for $n \in N$

- Use applications such as the nth roots of unity, $n \in N$, and identities such as $\cos 3\theta = 4\cos^3 \theta - 3\cos \theta$

❗ You should remember...

- The rules of indices

- The distributive property of the real numbers

- How to use the quadratic formula to solve equations

- How to evaluate the sine, cosine and tangent of angles

Key words

- Complex number
- Argand diagram
- Real part
- Imaginary part
- Translation
- Dilation
- Modulus
- Conjugate
- Polynomial
- Degree of a polynomial
- Polar form
- Argument
- De Moivre's Theorem
- General polar form

12.1 Introduction

The Italian mathematicians Gerolamo Cardano (1501–1576) and Niccolò Tartaglia (1500–1557) were the first to encounter complex numbers.

While working on the solutions to cubic equations, they came upon some unusual solutions involving the square root of −1. Today we call such solutions **complex** solutions.

Complex numbers have many applications in the modern world in such diverse areas as electronic engineering, aircraft design, computer-generated imaging in the film industry and medicine.

Gerolamo Cardano (1501–1576)

Niccolò Tartaglia (1500–1557)

Complex numbers have been introduced to allow for the solutions of certain equations that have no real solutions.

Consider the graph of the function, $f(x) = x^2 - 1$, $x \in R$.

When $f(x) = 0$, $x = -1$ or $x = 1$. Therefore, the solution set of the equation $x^2 - 1 = 0$ is $\{-1, 1\}$. You learned in Chapter 3 that the real solution(s) to $f(x) = 0$ are the value(s) of x, for which the graph of $y = f(x)$ intersects the x-axis.

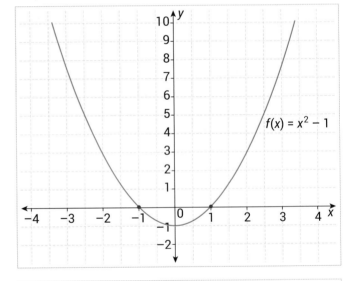

Now consider the graph of the function, $g(x) = x^2 + 1$, $x \in R$.

The graph of $y = g(x)$ does not intersect the x-axis, therefore the equation $x^2 + 1 = 0$ has no real solutions.

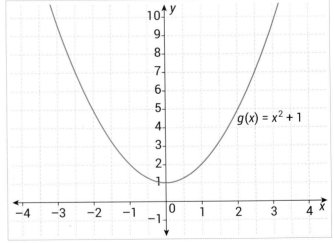

To find a solution to the equation $x^2 + 1 = 0$ we need to introduce a new number whose square is -1. We call this number i (the Greek letter **iota**). So $i^2 = -1$.

Let us check that i is a solution to $x^2 + 1 = 0$.

$i^2 = -1$

By convention the imaginary unit i is defined as $i = \sqrt{-1}$.

Substitute i into the equation:

$(i)^2 + 1 = 0$

$-1 + 1 = 0$

$\quad 0 = 0 \quad$ True

$\therefore\ i$ is a solution.

If both $a < 0$ and $b < 0$, then $\sqrt{a}.\sqrt{b} \neq \sqrt{ab}$ $(a, b \in R)$.
But if $a < 0$ and $b > 0$, or if $a > 0$ and $b < 0$, then $\sqrt{a}.\sqrt{b} = \sqrt{ab}$ $(a, b \in R)$.

Worked Example 12.1

Simplify: (i) $\sqrt{-9}$ (ii) $\sqrt{-72}$

Solution

(i) $\sqrt{-9} = \sqrt{9}\,\sqrt{-1}$

$\quad = 3i$

(ii) $\sqrt{-72} = \sqrt{72} \cdot \sqrt{-1}$

$\quad\quad\quad = \sqrt{36}\,\sqrt{2}\,\sqrt{-1}$

$\quad\quad\quad = 6\sqrt{2}\,i$

Worked Example 12.2

Solve the equation $z^2 + 36 = 0$.

Solution

$z^2 + 36 = 0$

$z^2 = -36$

$z = \pm\sqrt{-36}$

$z = \pm\sqrt{36}\,\sqrt{-1}$

$\therefore\ z = \pm 6i$

$i = \sqrt{-1}$
$i^2 = -1$
$i^3 = -i$
$i^4 = 1$

Worked Example 12.3

Simplify the following:

(i) i^3 (ii) i^4 (iii) i^{49}

Solution

(i) $\quad i^3 = (i^2)(i)$

$\quad\quad = (-1)(i)$

$\quad \therefore i^3 = -i$

(ii) $\quad i^4 = (i^2)^2$

$\quad\quad = (-1)^2$

$\quad \therefore i^4 = 1$

(iii) $\quad i^{49} = (i^{48})(i)$ **OR** $i^{49} = (i^4)^{12}i$

$\quad\quad\quad = (i^2)^{24}(i)$ $= 1^{12}(i)$

$\quad\quad\quad = (-1)^{24}(i)$ $= i$

$\quad\quad\quad = (1)i$

$\quad\quad \therefore i^{49} = i$

Exercise 12.1

1. Write the following in the form ki, $k \in R$, $i^2 = -1$:

    (i) $\sqrt{-100}$ (iv) $\sqrt{-36}$

    (ii) $\sqrt{-81}$ (v) $\sqrt{-121}$

    (iii) $\sqrt{-25}$ (vi) $\sqrt{-64}$

2. Write the following in the form $a\sqrt{b}$, $a, b \in Z$ and b is square free.

    (i) $\sqrt{32}$ (v) $\sqrt{200}$

    (ii) $\sqrt{48}$ (vi) $\sqrt{27}$

    (iii) $\sqrt{50}$ (vii) $\sqrt{162}$

    (iv) $\sqrt{75}$ (viii) $\sqrt{54}$

3. Write the following in the form $a\sqrt{b}i$, $a, b \in R$, b is square free and $i^2 = -1$:

(i) $\sqrt{-8}$ (iv) $\sqrt{-300}$

(ii) $\sqrt{-98}$ (v) $\sqrt{-12}$

(iii) $\sqrt{-45}$ (vi) $\sqrt{-125}$

4. Solve the following equations, giving your answers in the form $\pm pi$ $p \in R$, $i^2 = -1$:

(i) $z^2 + 9 = 0$ (v) $z^2 + 7 = 0$

(ii) $z^2 + 4 = 0$ (vi) $z^2 + 17 = 0$

(iii) $z^2 + 25 = 0$ (vii) $z^2 + 14 = 0$

(iv) $z^2 + 49 = 0$ (viii) $z^2 + \dfrac{9}{4} = 0$

5. Simplify each of the following:

(i) i^6 (iv) i^{12}

(ii) i^5 (v) i^{13}

(iii) i^9 (vi) i^{59}

6. Simplify each of the following:

(i) $7i^{12}$ (v) $5i^{27} + 3i^{57}$

(ii) $5i^{36}$ (vi) $24i^{93} - 23i^{27}$

(iii) $6i^{29}$ (vii) $2i^{18} + 3i^{24}$

(iv) $8i^{31}$ (viii) $7i^{20} - 13i^{40}$

7. Match the numbers in Column A with those in Column B.

A	B
i^4	$1 - i$
$2i^3$	-3
$i^8 + i^3$	$-128i$
i^{98}	$1 + i$
$3(i)^2$	0
$i^4 - i^8$	$-64i$
$(2i)^7$	1
$i^4 - i^7$	$9i$
$(4i)^3$	$-2i$
$5i + 4i$	-1

8. The spinner has eight equal sectors and on each sector is a different power of i.

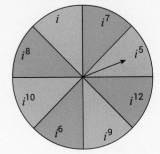

i	-1	$-i$	1
$-$ €5	€2	€10	€2

The table gives possible winnings or losses for one spin of the spinner. By simplifying the powers of i on the spinner, find the probability of:

(i) Losing €5 on one spin

(ii) Winning €10 on one spin

12.2 The Argand Diagram and the Modulus of a Complex Number

The set of real numbers is a subset of the set of complex numbers.

A complex number, z, is any number of the form $z = a + bi$, $a, b \in R$, $i^2 = -1$.

a is called the real part of z, Re(z), and
b is called the imaginary part of z, Im(z).

$2 + 3i$, $5 - 2i$, $\dfrac{1}{2} + \dfrac{3}{4}i$ and $\sqrt{2} - 3i$ are all examples of complex numbers. The number 7 is also a complex number since $7 = 7 + 0i$.

The complex numbers $z_1 = a + bi$ and $z_2 = c + di$ are equal if, and only if, $a = c$ and $b = d$.

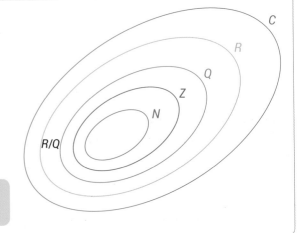

The Argand Diagram

Just as a real number can be represented on a real numberline, a complex number can be represented on a diagram called the **Argand diagram**, also known as the **complex plane**. The Argand diagram is a two-dimensional plane with two perpendicular axes. The horizontal axis is the real axis and the vertical axis is the imaginary axis.

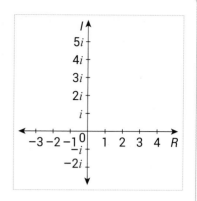

Here is the complex number $3 + 2i$ represented on an Argand diagram.

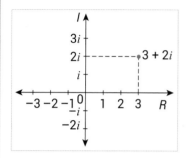 **OR**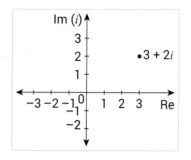

The vertical axis may be labelled $\{..., -2i, -i, 0, i, 2i, ...\}$ or $\{..., -2, -1, 0, 1, 2, ...\}$.

> The Argand diagram was devised by the Swiss mathematician Jean-Robert Argand (1768–1822).

Worked Example 12.4

Represent the following numbers on an Argand diagram:

(i) $-1 + 2i$

(ii) $2 + 3i$

(iii) $-3 - 2i$

(iv) $3 - i$

Solution

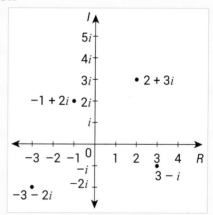

The Modulus of a Complex Number

The **modulus** of a complex number, $a + bi$, is its distance from the origin on the Argand diagram.

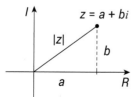

The modulus of a complex number z is denoted by $|z|$.

By the theorem of Pythagoras:

$$|z|^2 = a^2 + b^2$$

$$|z| = \sqrt{a^2 + b^2}$$

$$\boxed{|a + bi| = \sqrt{a^2 + b^2}}$$

Worked Example 12.5

$z_1 = 7 + 24i$ and $z_2 = -20 + 21i$.

Find: (i) $|z_1|$ (ii) $|z_2|$ (iii) $|z_1 + z_2|$

Hence, show that $|z_1 + z_2| < |z_1| + |z_2|$.

Solution

(i) $|z_1| = \sqrt{(7)^2 + (24)^2}$

       $= \sqrt{49 + 576}$

       $= \sqrt{625}$

   $\therefore |z_1| = 25$

(ii) $|z_2| = \sqrt{(-20)^2 + (21)^2}$

       $= \sqrt{400 + 441}$

       $= \sqrt{881}$

   $\therefore |z_2| = 29$

(iii) $|z_1 + z_2| = |(7 + 24i) + (-20 + 21i)|$

          $= |-13 + 45i|$

          $= \sqrt{(-13)^2 + (45)^2}$

          $= \sqrt{2{,}194}$

          ≈ 46.84

  $|z_1| + |z_2| = 25 + 29$

          $= 54$

     $\sqrt{2{,}194} < 54$

   $\therefore |z_1 + z_2| < |z_1| + |z_2|$

Exercise 12.2

1. Plot the following complex numbers on an Argand diagram:

   (i) $3 + 2i$ (ii) $5 - 2i$ (iii) $-6 + 2i$ (iv) -2 (v) $3i$ (vi) 4 (vii) $-5i$ (viii) $2 + 0i$

2. Study the Argand diagram below and complete the grid to spell the name of a famous composer.

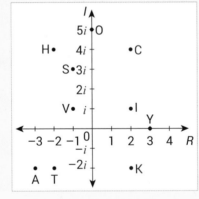

$-2 - 2i$	$2 + 4i$	$-2 + 4i$	$-3 - 2i$	$2 + i$	$2 - 2i$	$5i$	$-1 + i$	$-1 + 3i$	$2 - 2i$	$3 + 0i$

3. Show the following numbers on the complex plane:

   (i) $1 - \sqrt{-144}$ (ii) $-4 - \sqrt{-1}$ (iii) $7 - \sqrt{-81}$ (iv) $2 + \sqrt{-1}$ (v) $4 + \sqrt{-49}$ (vi) $-3 - \sqrt{-36}$

4. Using all the data in the box, form 12 different complex numbers of the form $a + bi$, where $a, b \in z$ and $a \neq b$.

0,   3,   4,   5, i,
+,   −

   Plot these complex numbers on an Argand diagram.

5. Evaluate each of the following. Give your answer in surd form where necessary.

   (i) $|1 + 2i|$ (vi) $|4 - 3i|$

   (ii) $|2 + 2i|$ (vii) $|1 - i|$

   (iii) $|3 - i|$ (viii) $|3 - 10i|$

   (iv) $|3 - 2i|$ (ix) $|2 + 7i|$

   (v) $|1 + 8i|$ (x) $|3 - 5i|$

6. Evaluate each of the following. Give your answer in surd form where necessary.

   (i) $|3 + \sqrt{2}i|$ (v) $|2\sqrt{6} - i|$

   (ii) $|1 + \sqrt{8}i|$ (vi) $|\sqrt{13} + 6i|$

   (iii) $|3 + 2\sqrt{10}i|$ (vii) $|5 + \sqrt{11}i|$

   (iv) $|3 - \sqrt{7}i|$ (viii) $|\sqrt{7} - \sqrt{2}i|$

7. For each of the following equations, find two possible values of k, where $k \in R$:

   (i) $|3 + ki| = 5$

   (ii) $|k + 12i| = 13$

   (iii) $|7 + ki| = 25$

   (iv) $|k + ki| = 2$

   (v) $|(k + 1) + ki| = 29$

   (vi) $|(k + 7) + ki| = 13$

8. If $\frac{1}{2}|6 - 8i| = |4 + ki|$, find two possible values of k, where $k \in R$.

9. If $|p + pi| = |7 - i|$, find two possible values of p, where $p \in R$.

10. Show that $|3 + 4i| = |0 + 5i|$.

11. Plot the complex number $5 + 12i$. Write down three complex numbers that have the same modulus as $5 + 12i$.

12. $z_1 = 6 + i$ and $z_2 = 4 - 2i$.

    (a) Find:

         (i) $|z_1|$ (ii) $|z_2|$ (iii) $|z_1 + z_2|$

    (b) Hence, show that $|z_1 + z_2| < |z_1| + |z_2|$.

13. $z_1 = 1 + 2i$ and $z_2 = 2 + i$.

    (a) Find:

         (i) $|z_1|$ (ii) $|z_2|$ (iii) $|z_1 z_2|$

    (b) Hence, show that $|z_1||z_2| = |z_1 z_2|$.

12.3 Addition and Subtraction of Complex Numbers; Multiplication by a Real Number

Can we add, subtract, multiply and divide complex numbers, as we can real numbers?
The answer is yes. In this section you will learn how to add and subtract complex numbers.

Addition of Complex Numbers

If $z_1 = a + bi$ and $z_2 = c + di$ then we define addition of the complex numbers z_1 and z_2 as follows:

$z_1 + z_2 = (a + bi) + (c + di)$

       $= (a + c) + (b + d)i$

If z_1, z_2 and z_3 are complex numbers, then using the definitions above, the following properties can be proved:

(a) $z_1 + z_2 = z_2 + z_1$ (Commutative property)

(b) $(z_1 + z_2) + z_3 = z_1 + (z_2 + z_3)$ (Associative property)

So, to add two complex numbers we add the real parts to the real parts and the imaginary parts to the imaginary parts.

> If z_1 and z_2 are two complex numbers, then $z_1 + z_2 = [\text{Re}(z_1) + \text{Re}(z_2)] + [\text{Im}(z_1) + \text{Im}(z_2)]i$

Worked Example 12.6

$z_1 = 2 - 3i$ and $z_2 = 11 + 5i$. Evaluate $z_1 + z_2$.

Solution

$$z_1 + z_2 = (2 - 3i) + (11 + 5i)$$
$$= (2 + 11) + (-3 + 5)i$$
$$\therefore z_1 + z_2 = 13 + 2i$$

Subtraction of Complex Numbers

If $z_1 = a + bi$ and $z_2 = c + di$ then we define subtraction of the complex numbers z_1 and z_2 as follows:

$$z_1 - z_2 = (a + bi) - (c + di)$$
$$= (a - c) + (b - d)i$$

If z_1 and z_2 are two complex numbers, then $z_1 - z_2 = [\text{Re}(z_1) - \text{Re}(z_2)] + [\text{Im}(z_1) - \text{Im}(z_2)]i$.

Worked Example 12.7

$z_1 = 18 + 16i$ and $z_2 = 14 - 2i$. Find $z_1 - z_2$.

Solution

$$z_1 - z_2 = (18 + 16i) - (14 - 2i)$$
$$= (18 - 14) + (16 - (-2))i$$
$$\therefore z_1 - z_2 = 4 + 18i$$

Multiplying a Complex Number by a Real Number

While this section focuses on addition and subtraction, we will also deal with multiplying a complex number by a real number now.

If z is a complex number and a is a real number, then $az = a\,\text{Re}(z) + a\,\text{Im}(z)i$.

Worked Example 12.8

If $z = 10 - 2i$, find $5z$.

Solution

$$5z = 5(10 - 2i)$$
$$= 5(10) + 5(-2i)$$
$$\therefore 5z = 50 - 10i$$

Transformations I

Consider the complex numbers $z_1 = 2 + 3i$ and $z_2 = 1 + i$. Adding z_2 to z_1 can be interpreted as a transformation that moves z_1 to a new position on the complex plane. This transformation is equivalent to a translation that moves z_1 one unit to the right and one unit upwards.

$$f(z_1) = z_1 + z_2$$
$$= (2 + 3i) + (1 + i)$$
$$= 3 + 4i$$

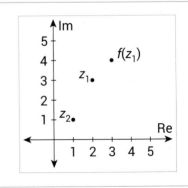

Adding $z_2 = 1 + i$ to any complex number will translate the complex number one unit to the right and one unit upwards. If z is any complex number and $z_1 = x + yi$, then the table below summarises how z is translated by the operation $z + z_1$.

$+ x + yi$	$x < 0$	$x > 0$
$y < 0$	x units left y units down	x units right y units down
$y > 0$	x units left y units up	x units right y units up

Worked Example 12.9

$z_1 = 2 + 4i$, $z_2 = 2 + 3i$, $z_3 = -1 + 2i$ and $\omega = 1 + i$.

(i) Plot z_1, z_2, and z_3 on an Argand diagram.

(ii) Evaluate $z_1 + \omega$, $z_2 + \omega$, and $z_3 + \omega$.

(iii) Plot the answers to part (ii) on an Argand diagram.

(iv) Describe the transformation that is the addition of ω.

Solution

(i)

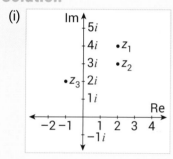

(ii) $z_1 + \omega = (2 + 4i) + (1 + i)$

$= 3 + 5i$

$z_2 + \omega = (2 + 3i) + (1 + i)$

$= 3 + 4i$

$z_3 + \omega = (-1 + 2i) + (1 + i)$

$= 0 + 3i$

(iii)

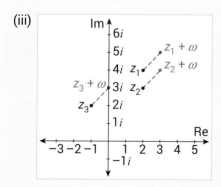

(iv) From the Argand diagram, the numbers z_1, z_2 and z_3 are moved one unit right and one unit up. This is a distance of $\sqrt{2}$ ($|\omega|$) in a north-east direction. We call such a transformation a **translation**.

Worked Example 12.10

$z_1 = 1 + 3i$, $z_2 = 4 + 2i$.

(i) Plot z_1 and z_2 on an Argand diagram.

(ii) Evaluate $z_3 = z_1 + z_2$.

(iii) Construct on the Argand diagram the quadrilateral $Oz_1z_3z_2$ where $O = 0 + 0i$.

(iv) Describe the quadrilateral $Oz_1z_3z_2$.

Solution

(i)

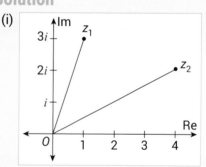

(ii) $z_3 = (1 + 3i) + (4 + 2i)$

$= 5 + 5i$

(iii)

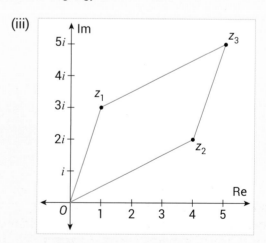

(iv) The quadrilateral $Oz_1z_3z_2$ is a parallelogram.

COMPLEX NUMBERS

Consider the complex number $z = 2 + 3i$ and the ray $[Oz]$ on the complex plane.

Multiplying z by the real number 2 is the equivalent of a dilation (stretching) of $[Oz]$, by a factor of 2.

$f(z) = 2(2 + 3i)$

$\quad = 4 + 6i$

Multiplying z by the real number $\frac{1}{2}$ is the equivalent of a dilation of $[Oz]$ by a factor of $\frac{1}{2}$.

$g(z) = \frac{1}{2}(2 + 3i)$

$\quad = 1 + \frac{3}{2}i$

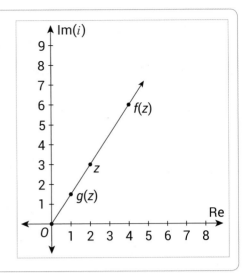

Worked Example 12.11

$z_1 = 2 + 4i$, $z_2 = 2 + 3i$, $z_3 = -1 + 2i$ and $a = 2$.

(i) Plot z_1, z_2 and z_3 on an Argand diagram.

(ii) Evaluate az_1, az_2 and az_3.

(iii) Plot the answers to part (ii) on an Argand diagram.

(iv) Describe the transformation that is multiplication by a.

Solution

(i)

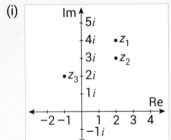

(ii) $az_1 = 2(2 + 4i)$

$\quad = 4 + 8i$

$az_2 = 2(2 + 3i)$

$\quad = 4 + 6i$

$az_3 = 2(-1 + 2i)$

$\quad = -2 + 4i$

(iii)

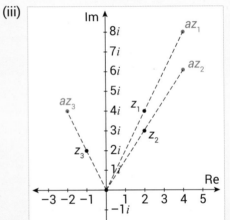

(iv) From the diagram we can see that all the points are moved further from the origin by a factor of 2. We call such a transformation a dilation by a factor of 2.

- If F is the dilation factor and if $F > 1$ or $F < -1$, the dilation is sometimes referred to as a **stretching** on the complex plane.
- If $-1 < F < 1$, then the dilation is sometimes referred to as a **contraction** on the complex plane.

Exercise 12.3

1. Write each of the following in the form $a + bi$, where $a, b \in R$:

   (i) $(2 + 3i) + (5 + i)$ (iii) $(3 + i) - (2 - i)$ (v) $2(6 - 3i) - (5 - i)$

   (ii) $(5 + 2i) + (6 + 3i)$ (iv) $5(2 + i) + 3(1 - i)$ (vi) $2(1 - i) - 3(2 + i)$

(vii) $\frac{1}{2}(8 - 2i) + \frac{1}{3}(3 - 9i)$

(viii) $\frac{2}{3}(27 - 9i) + \frac{3}{5}(25 - 50i)$

(ix) $\sqrt{2}(2\sqrt{2} - i) + \sqrt{2}(\sqrt{2} + i)$

(x) $\frac{1}{2}(6 - 4i) + \frac{1}{4}(16 - 8i)$

2. $z_1 = 2 + 3i$ and $z_2 = 5 - 4i$. Find:

(i) $z_1 + z_2$ (v) $3z_2$

(ii) $z_1 - z_2$ (vi) $2z_1 + 3z_2$

(iii) $z_2 - z_1$ (vii) $5z_1 - 6z_2$

(iv) $2z_1$ (viii) $\frac{1}{2}z_1 + \frac{1}{5}z_2$

3. Let $z = 2 + i$. Find:

(i) $z + 3$ (iii) $z - 3z$ (v) $2z + 3 - 3i$

(ii) $z + 3i$ (iv) $2z + 5z$ (vi) $-4z + i$

4. Let $z = 2 - 3i$. Show the following on an Argand diagram.

(i) $z + 3$ (iii) $1 - z$

(ii) $2z + 6i$ (iv) $\frac{1}{2}(z + i)$

5. Let $z = 1 + i$. Show the following on an Argand diagram:

(i) z (iii) $3z$ (v) $5z$ (vii) $-4z$

(ii) $2z$ (iv) $4z$ (vi) $-3z$ (viii) $-5z$

Describe the transformation of z in parts (ii) to (viii) above.

6. Let $z = -24 + 48i$.
   (a) Show the following on an Argand diagram:

(i) z (iii) $\frac{1}{3}z$ (v) $\frac{1}{6}z$

(ii) $\frac{1}{2}z$ (iv) $\frac{1}{4}z$

(b) Describe the transformation of z in parts (ii) to (v) above.

7. $z_1 = 2 + 3i$, $z_2 = -2 + 5i$, $z_3 = -1 + 4i$ and $\omega = 1 + i$.

(i) Plot z_1, z_2 and z_3 on an Argand diagram.

(ii) Evaluate $z_1 + \omega$, $z_2 + \omega$ and $z_3 + \omega$.

(iii) Plot the answers to part (ii) on an Argand diagram.

(iv) Describe the transformation that is the addition of ω.

8. $z_1 = 3 + 2i$, $z_2 = -1 + 4i$, $z_3 = -3 + 5i$ and $\omega = 1 - i$.

(i) Plot z_1, z_2 and z_3 on an Argand diagram.

(ii) Evaluate $z_1 + \omega$, $z_2 + \omega$ and $z_3 + \omega$.

(iii) Plot the answers to part (ii) on an Argand diagram.

(iv) Describe the transformation that is the addition of ω.

9. $z_1 = 5 + 2i$ and $z_2 = -2 + i$.

(i) Plot z_1 and z_2 on the Argand diagram.

(ii) Evaluate $z_3 = z_1 + z_2$.

(iii) Construct on the Argand diagram the quadrilateral $Oz_1z_3z_2$ where O is $0 + 0i$.

(iv) Describe the quadrilateral $Oz_1z_3z_2$.

10. Consider the Argand diagram below. Label the complex numbers z_1, z_2, z_3, z_4 and z_5, using the information given below.

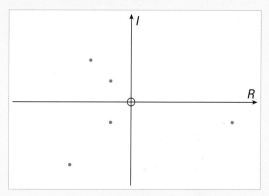

(i) $z_1 = 2z_2$ (ii) $z_4 = \frac{1}{3}z_3$ (iii) $\mathrm{Re}(z_5) > 0$

11. Consider the Argand diagram below. Label the complex numbers z_1, z_2, z_3 and z_4, using the information given below.

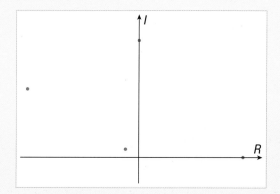

(i) $z_2 = 10z_1$

(ii) $\mathrm{Re}(z_3) = 0$

(iii) $\mathrm{Im}(z_4) = 0$

12. Consider the Argand diagram below. Label the complex numbers z_1, z_2, z_3, z_4 and z_5, using the information given below.

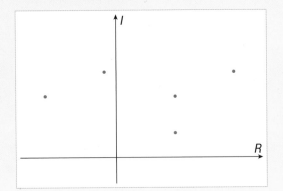

  (i) $\text{Re}(z_1) = \text{Re}(z_5)$

  (ii) $z_2 = z_1 + z_3$

  (iii) $z_4 = z_1 + z_5$

13. Consider the Argand diagram below. Label the complex numbers z_1, z_2, z_3 and z_4, using the information given below.

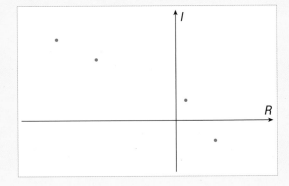

  (i) $z_4 = z_3 - z_2$

  (ii) $|z_2| = 2|z_1|$

14. Given that $z = 2 + 3i$, find the real number k such that $z^2 + kz$ is real.

15. Given that $z = -3 + 4i$, find the real number k such that $z^2 + kz$ is real.

16. If $z_1 = 2 + 3i$ and $z_2 = -2 + 5i$, verify that $|z_1 + z_2| < |z_1| + |z_2|$.

17. If $\omega = a + bi$, find two solutions to the equation $\sqrt{5}|\omega| + i\omega = 3 + i$.

12.4 Multiplication of Complex Numbers

Firstly, we will look at multiplication by a complex number whose real part is zero, i.e. a number of the form qi, $q \in R$. Such a number is called an imaginary number.

Worked Example 12.12

If $z = 4 + i$, find iz.

Solution

$$iz = i(4 + i)$$
$$= 4i + i^2$$
$$= 4i - 1$$
$$\therefore iz = -1 + 4i$$

Transformations II

You are about to see what effect multiplication by i or $-i$ has on a complex number.

Worked Example 12.13

$z_1 = 2 + i$

(i) Find z_2, if $z_2 = iz_1$.

(ii) Plot z_1 and z_2 on an Argand diagram.

(iii) Describe the transformation that maps z_1 onto z_2.

Solution

(i) $z_2 = i(2 + i)$

      $= 2i + i^2$

    $\therefore z_2 = -1 + 2i$

(ii)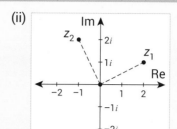

(iii) z_1 is mapped onto z_2 by an anti-clockwise rotation of 90° about the origin.

Worked Example 12.14

$z_1 = 2 + i$

(i) Find z_2, if $z_2 = -iz_1$.

(ii) Plot z_1 and z_2 on the Argand diagram.

(iii) Describe the transformation that maps z_1 onto z_2.

Solution

(i) $z_2 = -i(2 + i)$

      $= -2i - i^2$

      $= -2i - (-1)$

    $\therefore z_2 = 1 - 2i$

(ii)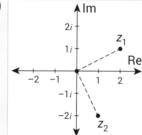

(iii) z_1 is mapped onto z_2 by a clockwise rotation of 90° about the origin.

If z_1 is of the form $x_1 + y_1 i$ and z_2 is of the form $x_2 + y_2 i$, then to evaluate $z_1 z_2$ we make use of the distributive property. Multiplication of complex numbers distributes over addition of complex numbers.

$z_1 z_2 = (x_1 + y_1 i)(x_2 + y_2 i)$

     $= x_1(x_2 + y_2 i) + y_1 i(x_2 + y_2 i)$

     $= x_1 x_2 + x_1 y_2 i + y_1 x_2 i + y_1 y_2 i^2$

     $= (x_1 x_2 - y_1 y_2) + (x_1 y_2 + x_2 y_1)i$

Worked Example 12.15

$z_1 = 2 - 7i$ and $z_2 = 3 + 7i$. Find $z_1 z_2$.

Solution

$z_1 z_2 = (2 - 7i)(3 + 7i)$

     $= 2(3 + 7i) - 7i(3 + 7i)$

     $= 6 + 14i - 21i - 49i^2$ **OR**

     $= 6 - 7i - 49(-1)$

$\therefore z_1 z_2 = 55 - 7i$

	2	$-7i$
3	6	$-21i$
$7i$	$14i$	$-49i^2$

$\therefore z_1 z_2 = 55 - 7i$

Closure is preserved under multiplication. The product of any two complex numbers is itself a complex number.

Exercise 12.4

1. $z_1 = -3 + 2i$

   (i) Find z_2, if $z_2 = iz_1$.

   (ii) Plot z_1 and z_2 on an Argand diagram.

   (iii) Describe the transformation that maps z_1 onto z_2.

2. $z_1 = -3 + 4i$

   (i) Find z_2, if $z_2 = -iz_1$.

   (ii) Plot z_1 and z_2 on an Argand diagram.

   (iii) Describe the transformation that maps z_1 onto z_2.

3. $z_1 = -2 - 3i$

   (i) Find z_2, if $z_2 = -iz_1$.

   (ii) Plot z_1 and z_2 on an Argand diagram.

   (iii) Describe the transformation that maps z_1 onto z_2.

4. Write these products in the form $a + bi$:

   (i) $(2 + 7i)(3 - 5i)$

   (ii) $(1 + 4i)(2 + 5i)$

   (iii) $(6 + i)(-2 + 3i)$

   (iv) $(2 + 3i)(2 - 3i)$

   (v) $(3 + 4i)(3 - 4i)$

   (vi) $3i(2 + 4i)$

   (vii) $(1 - i)(1 + i)$

   (viii) $5(6 - i)$

   (ix) $(-2 - 2i)(-2 + 2i)$

   (x) $(7 + 5i)(2 + i)$

5. Write these products in the form $a + bi$:

   (i) $\left(\dfrac{1}{2} + \dfrac{3}{2}i\right)\left(\dfrac{1}{2} - \dfrac{1}{4}i\right)$

   (ii) $\left(\dfrac{3}{8} - \dfrac{2}{11}i\right)\left(\dfrac{1}{4} - \dfrac{2}{5}i\right)$

   (iii) $\left(\dfrac{2}{9} + \dfrac{3}{5}i\right)\left(\dfrac{3}{4} - \dfrac{1}{5}i\right)$

   (iv) $\left(3\sqrt{7} + 5i\right)\left(3\sqrt{7} - 5i\right)$

   (v) $\left(5 - \sqrt{2}i\right)\left(5 + \sqrt{2}i\right)$

6. $z_1 = 3 + i$

   (i) Find z_2, if $z_2 = iz_1$.

   (ii) Plot z_1 and z_2 on an Argand diagram.

   (iii) Describe the transformation that maps z_1 onto z_2.

7. Copy the diagram below.

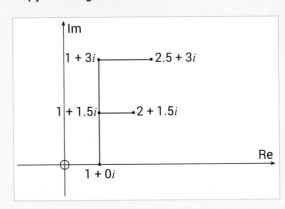

   (i) Multiply each complex number on the diagram by i.

   (ii) Plot your answers from part (i).

   (iii) Describe the transformation of the shape.

8. Copy the diagram below.

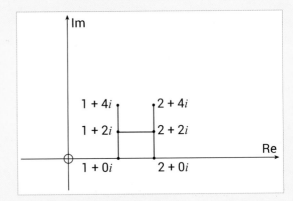

   (i) Multiply each complex number on the diagram by $-i$.

   (ii) Plot your answers from part (i).

   (iii) Describe the transformation of the shape.

12.5 Division of Complex Numbers

In the real number system, if $a \div b = c$, then $a = b \times c$, where $a, b, c \in R$.

Similarly, in the complex number system, if $a \div b = c$, then $a = b \times c$, where $a, b, c \in C$.

However, in the complex number system, we need to follow certain well-defined steps to divide one complex number by another.

Worked Example 12.16

Calculate $\dfrac{15 + 10i}{5}$.

Solution

When we multiply a complex number z by a real number a, we multiply a by $\text{Re}(z)$ and a by $\text{Im}(z)$. Similarly, when we divide a complex number by a real number a, we divide $\text{Re}(z)$ and $\text{Im}(z)$ by a.

$$\frac{15 + 10i}{5} = \frac{15}{5} + \frac{10}{5}i$$

$$= 3 + 2i$$

Conjugate of a Complex Number

> If $z = a + bi$, $a, b \in R$ and $i^2 = -1$, then the conjugate of z (written as $\bar{z}$) is $a - bi$.

Rule: Change the sign of the imaginary part.

For example, if $z = -2 - 12i$, then $\bar{z} = -2 + 12i$.

Two Important Rules on Conjugates

For any complex number, $z = x + yi$, the following two results hold:

(i) $z + \bar{z} = k$, for some $k \in R$.

(ii) $z\bar{z} = l$, for some $l \in R$.

Proof:

(i) $z + \bar{z} = (x + yi) + (x - yi)$

$\qquad = 2x$

$\qquad$ is real

$\qquad \therefore k = 2x$

(ii) $z\bar{z} = (x + yi)(x - yi)$

$\qquad = x(x - yi) + yi(x - yi)$

$\qquad = x^2 - xyi + xyi - y^2 i^2$

$\qquad = x^2 - y^2(-1)$

$\qquad = x^2 + y^2$

$\qquad$ is real

$\qquad \therefore l = x^2 + y^2$

Worked Example 12.17

$z = 2 - 2i$

(i) Find $\bar{z}$.

(ii) Plot z and $\bar{z}$ on the Argand diagram.

(iii) Describe the transformation that maps z to $\bar{z}$.

Solution

(i) $\bar{z} = 2 + 2i$

(ii)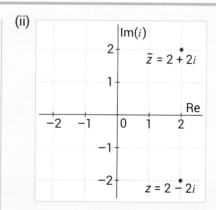

(iii) $\bar{z}$ is the image of z by an axial symmetry in the real axis.

When dealing with division by a complex number, multiply both the numerator and the denominator by the conjugate of the denominator.

Worked Example 12.18

Calculate $\dfrac{2 + 11i}{2 + i}$.

Solution

In this question, we are dividing a complex number by a complex number. If we could reduce the denominator to a real number, then our task would be much easier, as we know how to divide a complex number by a real number. Fortunately, if we multiply a complex number by its conjugate, the result is a real number.

Step 1

Write down the conjugate of the denominator: $\overline{2 + i} = 2 - i$.

Step 2

Multiply the denominator by $2 - i$.

$(2 + i)(2 - i) = 2(2 - i) + i(2 - i)$

$\qquad\qquad = 4 - 2i + 2i - i^2$

$\qquad\qquad = 4 + 1$

$\qquad\qquad = 5$

The difference of two squares could also be used to rationalise the denominator.

$(a + bi)(a - bi) = a^2 - (bi)^2$

$\qquad\qquad\quad = a^2 - b^2i^2$

$\qquad\qquad\quad = a^2 + b^2$

Step 3

Multiply the numerator by $2 - i$.

$(2 + 11i)(2 - i) = 2(2 - i) + 11i(2 - i)$

$\qquad\qquad\quad = 4 - 2i + 22i - 11i^2$

$\qquad\qquad\quad = 4 + 20i + 11$

$\qquad\qquad\quad = 15 + 20i$

Step 4

$\dfrac{2 + 11i}{2 + i} = \dfrac{15 + 20i}{5}$

$\qquad\quad = \dfrac{15}{5} + \dfrac{20}{5}i$

$\qquad\quad = 3 + 4i$

Worked Example 12.19

Simplify the following:

(i) i^{-16} (ii) i^{-31} (iii) $2i^{-49}$

Give your answer in the form $a + bi$, $a, b \in Z$.

Solution

(i) $i^{-16} = \dfrac{1}{i^{16}}$

$\qquad = \dfrac{1}{(i^2)^8}$

$\qquad = \dfrac{1}{(-1)^8}$

$\qquad = \dfrac{1}{1}$

$\qquad = 1$

$\therefore i^{-16} = 1 + 0i$

(ii) $i^{-31} = \dfrac{1}{i^{31}}$

$\qquad = \dfrac{1}{i^{30}(i)}$

$\qquad = \dfrac{1}{(i^2)^{15}(i)}$

$\qquad = \dfrac{1}{(-1)^{15}(i)}$

$\qquad = \dfrac{1}{-i}$

$\qquad = \dfrac{1(i)}{(-i)(i)}$ (The conjugate of $-i = 0 - i$ is $0 + i = i$.)

$\qquad = \dfrac{i}{-i^2}$

$\qquad = \dfrac{i}{1}$

$\qquad = i$

$\therefore i^{-31} = 0 + i$

(iii) $2i^{-49} = \dfrac{2}{i^{49}}$

$\qquad = \dfrac{2}{i^{48}\, i}$

$\qquad = \dfrac{2}{(i^2)^{24}\, i}$

$\qquad = \dfrac{2}{(-1)^{24}\, i}$

$\qquad = \dfrac{2}{i}$

$\qquad = \dfrac{2(-i)}{i(-i)}$ (The conjugate of $i = 0 + i$ is $0 - i = -i$.)

$\qquad = \dfrac{-2i}{1}$

$\qquad = -2i$

$\therefore 2i^{-49} = 0 - 2i$

Exercise 12.5

1. Write down the conjugate of each of the following complex numbers:

   (i) $3 + 4i$ (vi) $3 - \frac{1}{3}i$

   (ii) $3 - 4i$

   (iii) $-3 + 4i$ (vii) $-\frac{1}{4} - \frac{1}{4}i$

   (iv) $-3 - 4i$

   (v) $-\frac{1}{2} + 2i$ (viii) $-\frac{1}{5} + \frac{1}{5}i$

2. Write down the conjugate of each of the following:

   (i) $0 + 5i$ (v) $3i$

   (ii) $5 + 0i$ (vi) 3

   (iii) $0 - 5i$ (vii) $-3i$

   (iv) $-5 + 0i$ (viii) -3

3. Write in the form $p + qi$, $p, q \in Q$:

   (i) $\frac{10 + 25i}{5}$ (iii) $\frac{25 + 10i}{10}$

   (ii) $\frac{16 + 8i}{4}$ (iv) $\frac{3 + 5i}{2}$

4. Write in the form $p + qi$, $p, q \in Q$:

   (i) $\frac{10 + 3i}{i}$ (iii) $\frac{24 + 8i}{4i}$

   (ii) $\frac{15 + 6i}{3i}$ (iv) $\frac{15 + 25i}{5i}$

5. $z_1 = 3 + 4i$ and $z_2 = 5 - 12i$. Find:

   (i) $z_1 + z_2$ (iv) $\overline{z_2}$

   (ii) $z_1 z_2$ (v) $\overline{z_1} + \overline{z_2}$

   (iii) $\overline{z_1}$ (vi) $(\overline{z_1})(\overline{z_2})$

6. Write in the form $p + qi$, $p, q \in Q$:

   (i) $\frac{16 - 8i}{8}$ (iv) $\frac{-16 + 48i}{-4i}$

   (ii) $\frac{5 + 12i}{7}$ (v) $\frac{1 + i}{5i}$

   (iii) $\frac{27 - 18i}{3i}$ (vi) $\frac{33}{12i}$

7. Write in the form $p + qi$, $p, q \in R$:

   (i) $\frac{5 + 5i}{1 + 2i}$ (iv) $\frac{5}{1 + 2i}$

   (ii) $\frac{1 - 5i}{1 - i}$ (v) $\frac{1 + 3i}{1 + i}$

   (iii) $\frac{10}{1 - 3i}$

8. Write in the form $p + qi$, $p, q \in R$:

   (i) $\frac{5 - 5i}{2 + i}$ (v) $\frac{1}{1 + i}$

   (ii) $\frac{6}{1 - i}$ (vi) $\frac{11 + 10i}{2(2 + 3i)}$

   (iii) $\frac{1 + 5i}{i}$ (vii) $\frac{1 - 9i}{2i}$

   (iv) $\frac{6 + 8i}{2i}$

9. $z_1 = a + bi$ and $z_2 = c - di$, where $a, b, c, d \in R$. Write, in terms of a, b, c, and d:

   (i) $\overline{z_1}$

   (ii) $\overline{z_2}$

   (iii) $\overline{z_1} + \overline{z_2}$

   (iv) $z_1 + z_2$

   (v) $\overline{z_1 + z_2}$

   (vi) Verify that $\overline{z_1 + z_2} = \overline{z_1} + \overline{z_2}$.

10. If $z = 1 - 3i$, write $\frac{\overline{z}}{z}$ in the form $a + bi$, $a, b \in Q$.

11. Let $z_1 = -1 + 5i$ and let $z_2 = 2 + 3i$.

    Investigate if $\overline{\left(\frac{z_1}{z_2}\right)} = \frac{\overline{z_1}}{\overline{z_2}}$.

12. Let $z_1 = 11 - 10i$ and let $z_2 = 4 + i$.

    (i) Find $\frac{z_1}{z_2}$.

    (ii) Calculate $|z_1|$ and $|z_2|$.

    (iii) Investigate if $\left|\frac{z_1}{z_2}\right| = \frac{|z_1|}{|z_2|}$.

13. Identify z_1, z_2, z_3, z_4 and z_5 on the Argand diagram, given the information below.

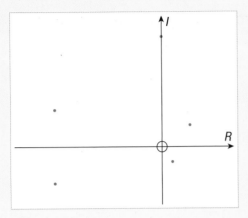

  (i) $z_5 = \overline{z_2}$

  (ii) $\text{Im}(z_5) > 0$

  (iii) $\text{Re}(z_3) = 0$

  (iv) $z_1 = 2iz_4$

14. Identify z_1, z_2, z_3, z_4 and z_5 on the Argand diagram, given the information below.

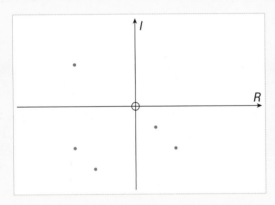

  (i) $z_1 = 2z_2$ (iii) $z_5 = \overline{z_3}$

  (ii) $z_3 = -iz_4$

15. Identify z_1, z_2 and z_3, given the information below.

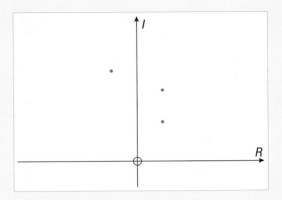

  (i) $\text{Im}(z_2) < \text{Im}(z_3)$ (ii) $z_1 = z_2 z_3$

16. Identify z_1, z_2, z_3 and z_4, given the information below.

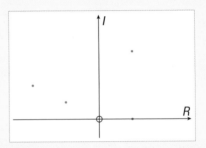

  (i) $z_2 = 2z_1$ (iii) $z_4 = \text{Re}(z_3)$

  (ii) $z_3 = -iz_2$

17. Simplify each of the following, giving your answer in the form $a + bi$, $a, b \in Q$:

  (i) i^{-18} (iv) $2i^{-19} + 3i^{-20}$

  (ii) i^{-33} (v) $10i^{-25} - 15i^{-98}$

  (iii) $3i^{-51}$ (vi) $\dfrac{5i^{47}}{2i^3}$

12.6 Quadratic Equations with Complex Roots

From your knowledge of algebra, you know that the solution to a quadratic equation

$$ax^2 + bx + c = 0, \; a, b, c \in R, \; a \neq 0$$

is given by the formula:

$$x = \frac{-b \pm \sqrt{b^2 - 4ac}}{2a}$$

In this formula, we refer to $b^2 - 4ac$ as the **discriminant**.

If $b^2 - 4ac < 0$, then the solutions (roots) will not be real.

Make sure to revise Chapter 3 Section 3.6 to aid your understanding of this topic.

Properties of the Discriminant

- $b^2 - 4ac \geqslant 0 \rightarrow$ Real roots
- $b^2 - 4ac > 0 \rightarrow$ Real and distinct roots
- $b^2 - 4ac = 0 \rightarrow$ Equal real roots
- $b^2 - 4ac < 0 \rightarrow$ Complex (non-real) roots

Worked Example 12.20

(i) Solve the equation $z^2 - 6z + 13 = 0$ and show the roots on an Argand diagram.

(ii) What do you notice about the roots to the given equation?

Solution

(i) $z = \dfrac{6 \pm \sqrt{(-6)^2 - 4(1)(13)}}{2(1)}$

$= \dfrac{6 \pm \sqrt{-16}}{2}$

$= \dfrac{6 \pm \sqrt{16}\sqrt{-1}}{2}$

$= \dfrac{6 \pm 4i}{2}$

$= \dfrac{6}{2} \pm \dfrac{4i}{2}$

$\therefore z = 3 \pm 2i$

Here are the roots on an Argand diagram.

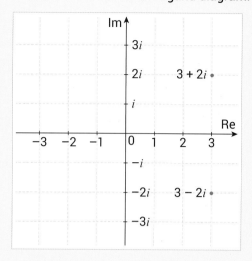

(ii) The roots are not real, and they occur in conjugate pairs, i.e. the roots are conjugates of each other.

Exercise 12.6

1. Solve the equation $z^2 + 4z + 13 = 0$, giving your answer in the form $a + bi$, $a, b \in R$.

2. Solve the following quadratic equations, giving your answer in the form $a + bi$, $a, b \in R$.

    (i) $z^2 + 4z + 5 = 0$

    (ii) $z^2 - 10z + 26 = 0$

    (iii) $z^2 - 6z + 25 = 0$

    (iv) $z^2 - 14z + 50 = 0$

    (v) $z^2 - 6z + 10 = 0$

    (vi) $z^2 - 16z + 68 = 0$

3. Evaluate the following:

    (i) $(1 - 2i)^2$ (ii) $-2(1 - 2i)$

    Hence, show that $1 - 2i$ is a root of the equation $z^2 - 2z + 5 = 0$.

4. Show that the roots of the equation $z^2 - 2z + 10 = 0$ are not real.

5. Solve the equation $z^2 - 8z + 17 = 0$, giving your answer in the form $a + bi$, $a, b \in R$.

6. Show that the roots of the equation $z^2 + 6z + 25 = 0$ are not real.

7. Evaluate the following:

    (i) $(-7 + i)^2$ (ii) $14(-7 + i)$

    Hence, show that $-7 + i$ is a root of the equation $z^2 + 14z + 50 = 0$.

8. Solve the equation $z^2 - 12z + 40 = 0$. Give your answer in the form $a + bi$, $a, b \in R$.

9. Find the roots of the equation $z^2 = -2(5z + 17)$.

10. Solve the following equations and show your solutions on an Argand diagram:

    (i) $z^2 - 4z + 5 = 0$ (iii) $z^2 + 2z + 17 = 0$

    (ii) $z^2 - 8z + 25 = 0$ (iv) $z^2 + 4z + 40 = 0$

11. Form a quadratic equation with each pair of roots, giving your answer in the form $z^2 + bz + c = 0$, where $b, c \in Z$.

    (i) $2 \pm 3i$ (v) $8 \pm i$

    (ii) $5 \pm i$ (vi) $-5 \pm 12i$

    (iii) $3 \pm 2i$ (vii) $-3 \pm 8i$

    (iv) $6 \pm 4i$ (viii) $-4 \pm 7i$

12. Form a quadratic equation with each pair of roots, giving your answer in the form $az^2 + bz + c$, where $a, b, c \in Z$.

(i) $\dfrac{1}{2} \pm \dfrac{1}{2}i$ (iii) $\dfrac{1}{2} \pm \dfrac{1}{3}i$ (v) $-\dfrac{3}{8} \pm \dfrac{1}{4}i$ (vii) $-\dfrac{3}{4} \pm \dfrac{3}{5}i$

(ii) $\dfrac{1}{3} \pm \dfrac{1}{3}i$ (iv) $\dfrac{1}{2} \pm 2i$ (vi) $-\dfrac{2}{5} \pm \dfrac{3}{10}i$ (viii) $-\dfrac{3}{5} \pm \dfrac{2}{3}i$

13. Solve the following equations and show your solutions on an Argand diagram:

(i) $z^2 + 16 = 0$ (ii) $4z^2 - 12z + 25 = 0$ (iii) $9z^2 - 6z + 5 = 0$ (iv) $z^2 - 4z + 53 = 0$

14. (i) Write $\dfrac{14 + 5i}{4 - i}$ as $x + yi$.

     (ii) Hence, show that $\dfrac{14 + 5i}{4 - i}$ is a root of the equation $z^2 - 6z + 13 = 0$.

     (iii) Find the other root of $z^2 - 6z + 13 = 0$.

12.7 Polynomials with Complex Roots

In this section we will find the complex roots of single variable polynomials with real coefficients.

In Chapter 1 we had the following definition:

A **single variable polynomial with real coefficients** is of the form:

$$f(x) = a_n x^n + a_{n-1} x^{n-1} + a_{n-2} x^{n-2} + \ldots + a_2 x^2 + a_1 x + a_0$$

where x is the single variable and each of $a_n, a_{n-1}, \ldots, a_2, a_1, a_0$ are real numbers.

For example, $f(x) = 4x^5 + 3x^3 - 2$ is a single variable polynomial with real coefficients.

In 1799, the German mathematician Carl Friedrich Gauss proved a very important theorem, known as the **Fundamental Theorem of Algebra**.
A consequence of this theorem is that every single variable polynomial of degree n will have exactly n roots ($n \in N$).

The **degree** of a single variable polynomial is the **highest power** of the variable in the polynomial.

For example, the equation $z^5 + z - 5 = 0$ has exactly five solutions, as the polynomial $z^5 + z - 5$ is of **degree** 5.

Worked Example 12.21

The polynomial $f(z) = 3z^3 - 5z^2 + 18z + 12$ has n roots. What is the value of n?

Solution

The highest power of z in the polynomial is 3. By the Fundamental Theorem of Algebra, the polynomial will have three roots, therefore $n = 3$.

The Conjugate Root Theorem

If the complex number $z = a + bi$, where $a, b \in R$, is a root of the polynomial $f(z)$ with **real coefficients**, then $\bar{z} = a - bi$ (the conjugate of z) is also a root.

Worked Example 12.22

Prove the following results for $z, z_1, z_2 \in C$ and $a, b, c \in R$:

  (i) $\overline{az_1 + bz_2} = \overline{az_1} + \overline{bz_2}$

  (ii) $\overline{az} = a\overline{z}$

  (iii) $\overline{az^2} = a\overline{z}^2$

  (iv) $\overline{z^2} = \overline{z}^2$

Hence, show that if z_1 is a root of the polynomial

$$f(z) = az^2 + bz + c,$$

then $\overline{z_1}$, the conjugate of z_1, is also a root.

Solution

  (i) To prove: $\overline{az_1 + bz_2} = \overline{az_1} + \overline{bz_2}$

    Let $z_1 = x_1 + y_1 i$ and $z_2 = x_2 + y_2 i$, $x_1, y_1, x_2, y_2 \in R$.

    LHS $az_1 + bz_2 = a(x_1 + y_1 i) + b(x_2 + y_2 i)$

              $= (ax_1 + bx_2) + (ay_1 + by_2)i$

    $\therefore \overline{az_1 + bz_2} = (ax_1 + bx_2) - (ay_1 + by_2)i$

    RHS $\overline{az_1} + \overline{bz_2} = a(x_1 - y_1 i) + b(x_2 - y_2 i)$

              $= (ax_1 + bx_2) - (ay_1 + by_2)i$

              $= \overline{az_1 + bz_2}$

    $\therefore \overline{az_1 + bz_2} = \overline{az_1} + \overline{bz_2}$

  (ii) To prove: $\overline{az} = a\overline{z}$

    Let $z = x + yi$, $x, y \in R$.

    LHS $az = ax + ayi$

        $\overline{az} = ax - ayi$

RHS $a\overline{z} = a(x - yi)$

       $= ax - ayi$

       $= \overline{az}$

  $\therefore \overline{az} = a\overline{z}$

 (iii) To prove: $\overline{az^2} = a\overline{z}^2$

    From part (ii), $\overline{az} = a\overline{z}$ where $a \in R, z \in C$.

    $\therefore \overline{az^2} = a\overline{z}^2$ as $z^2 \in C$

 (iv) To prove: $\overline{z^2} = \overline{z}^2$

    Let $z = x + yi$, $x, y \in R$.

    LHS $z^2 = x^2 - y^2 + 2xyi$

        $\overline{z^2} = x^2 - y^2 - 2xyi$

    RHS $\overline{z} = x - yi$

        $\overline{z}^2 = (x - yi)(x - yi)$

            $= x(x - yi) - yi(x - yi)$

            $= x^2 - y^2 - 2xyi$

            $= \overline{z^2}$

  $\therefore \overline{z^2} = \overline{z}^2$

$f(z) = az^2 + bz + c$

z_1 a root $\Rightarrow f(z_1) = az_1^2 + bz_1 + c = 0$

$\overline{az_1^2 + bz_1 + c} = \overline{0}$

$\overline{az_1^2} + \overline{bz_1} + \overline{c} = 0$ (part (i))

$a\overline{z_1}^2 + b\overline{z_1} + c = 0$ (parts (ii) and (iii))

$a\overline{z_1}^2 + b\overline{z_1} + c = 0$ (part (iv))

$\therefore \overline{z_1}$, the conjugate of z_1, is also a root of $f(z)$.

Worked Example 12.23

If $z = 4 + 3i$ is a root of the polynomial $f(z) = z^2 - 8z + 25$, then show that $\overline{z} = 4 - 3i$ is also a root.

Solution

$f(4 - 3i) = (4 - 3i)^2 - 8(4 - 3i) + 25$

          $= 4(4 - 3i) - 3i(4 - 3i) - 8(4 - 3i) + 25$

          $= 16 - 12i - 12i + 9i^2 - 32 + 24i + 25$

          $= 16 + 9(-1) - 32 + 25$

          $= 41 - 41$

          $= 0$

$\therefore \overline{z} = 4 - 3i$ is also a root of $f(z)$.

Worked Example 12.24

The polynomial $f(z) = 3z^3 - 5z^2 + 13z + 5$ has n roots.

(i) What is the value of n?

(ii) If $1 + 2i$ is a root of $f(z)$, write down another root of $f(z)$.

(iii) Explain why $f(z)$ must have a real root.

(iv) Find the real root of $f(z)$.

Solution

(i) $f(z)$ is a polynomial of degree 3, therefore it has three roots.

$n = 3$

(ii) Since the coefficients of the polynomial are real, we can use the Conjugate Root Theorem. Therefore, another root of $f(z)$ is $1 - 2i$.

(iii) $f(z)$ has three roots. We have already identified two complex roots, and since complex roots come in pairs, the one remaining root has to be real.

You should revise Chapter 2, Section 2.6 to enhance your understanding of solving polynomials with complex roots.

(iv) **Step 1** Form a quadratic polynomial $g(z)$, with roots $1 + 2i$ and $1 - 2i$.

Sum of the roots $= 1 + 2i + 1 - 2i = 2$

Product of the roots $= (1 + 2i)(1 - 2i)$
$= 5$

$\therefore g(z) = z^2 - 2z + 5$

Step 2 Divide $f(z)$ by $g(z)$.

$$
\begin{array}{r}
3z + 1 \\
z^2 - 2z + 5 \overline{)3z^3 - 5z^2 + 13z + 5} \\
-(3z^3 - 6z^2 + 15z) \\
\hline
z^2 - 2z + 5 \\
-(z^2 - 2z + 5) \\
\hline
0
\end{array}
$$

Step 3 $3z + 1$ is a linear factor of $f(z)$.

Therefore, the solution to the equation $3z + 1 = 0$ gives the real root of $f(z)$.

$3z + 1 = 0$

$\Rightarrow z = -\dfrac{1}{3}$

Exercise 12.7

1. $f(z) = z^2 - 10z + 26$ is a quadratic polynomial.

   (i) Verify that $z = 5 + i$ is a root of the equation $z^2 - 10z + 26 = 0$.

   (ii) Write down the other root of $z^2 - 10z + 26 = 0$.

2. $f(z) = z^2 + 6z + 25$ is a quadratic polynomial.

   (i) Verify that $z = -3 - 4i$ is a root of $f(z)$.

   (ii) Write down the other root of $f(z)$.

3. $f(z) = z^3 - z^2 - 4z - 6$ is a cubic polynomial.

   (i) Show that $z = -1 + i$ is a solution to the equation $f(z) = 0$.

   (ii) Write down another solution to $f(z) = 0$.

4. Show that $z = -1$ is a root of the equation $z^3 - 5z^2 + 4z + 10 = 0$. Show that the other two roots are complex.

5. The polynomial $f(z) = 2z^3 - 3z^2 + 18z + 10$ has n roots.

   (i) What is the value of n?

   (ii) If $1 - 3i$ is a root of $f(z) = 0$, write down another root of $f(z) = 0$.

   (iii) Find the real root of $f(z)$.

6. $2 + 3i$ is a root of the equation $z^4 + 40z + k = 0$.

 (i) Find the value of k.

 (ii) Write down another root of the equation.

7. The graph of $f(z) = z^3 + z - k$, over the domain $-2 < z < 2.4$, is shown.

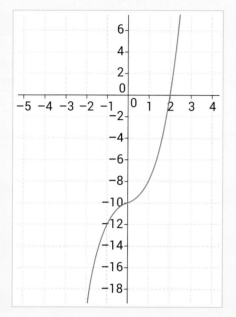

 (i) The co-ordinates of the x- and y-intercepts are $(a,0)$ and $(0,b)$, $a, b \in Z$. Write down the value of each of a and b.

 (ii) What is the value of the real root of $f(z)$?

 (iii) What is the value of k?

 (iv) $h(z) = z + c$ is a linear polynomial and $h(z)$ divides $f(z)$. Find $h(z)$.

 (v) Find the non-real roots of $f(z)$.

8. Part of the graph of $f(z) = z^3 - 11z + k$ is shown.

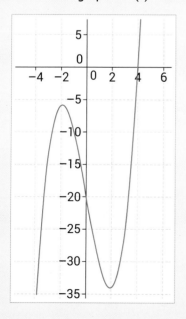

 (i) If $k \in Z$, find the value of k.

 (ii) Verify that the co-ordinates of the x-intercept are $(4,0)$.

 (iii) $(z - 4)(Q(z)) = f(z)$. $Q(z)$ is a polynomial. Find $Q(z)$.

 (iv) Solve $f(z) = 0$.

9. The equation $z^4 - 2z^3 - 2z^2 - 2z - 3 = 0$ has two **integer** roots.

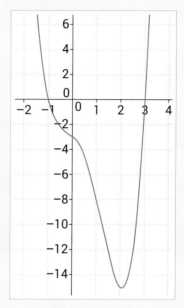

 (i) Using the graph of $f(z) = z^4 - 2z^3 - 2z^2 - 2z - 3$, find the value of the real roots of $f(z) = 0$.

 (ii) Show that $g(z) = z^2 - 2z - 3$ is a factor of $f(z)$.

 (iii) Hence, find the two non-real roots of $f(z)$.

10. $f(z) = z^3 - 1, z \in C$

 (i) Verify that $z = 1$ is a solution to the equation $z^3 - 1 = 0$.

 (ii) Show that $z^3 - 1 = (z - 1)(z^2 + z + 1)$.

 (iii) Show that the roots of $z^3 - 1 = 0$ are of the form 1, ω and ω^2.

 (iv) Show that $1 + \omega + \omega^2 = 0$.

11. -2, z_1 and z_2 are the roots of the cubic equation $z^3 + 8 = 0$.

 (i) Find z_1 and z_2 in the form $a + bi$, $a, b \in R$.

 (ii) Show that $z_1 + z_2 = 2$ and find the value of z_1z_2.

 (iii) Write down a cubic equation whose roots are -2, $z_1 + z_2$ and z_1z_2.

12. $z_1 = a + bi$, $a, b \in R$, $b \neq 0$ is a complex root of the equation $z^2 - 2z + 25 = 0$. Without evaluating the roots, answer the following questions:

(i) Show that $\overline{z_1}$, the conjugate of z_1, is also a root of $z^2 - 2z + 25 = 0$.

(ii) What is the value of $z_1 + \overline{z_1}$?

(iii) What is the value of $z_1\overline{z_1}$?

(iv) Find an equation with roots $4z_1$ and $4\overline{z_1}$.

13. $z_1 = a + bi$, $a, b \in R$, is a complex root of the equation $z^2 - 3z + 32 = 0$. Without evaluating the roots, answer the following questions:

(i) Is $\overline{z_1}$, the conjugate of z_1, also a root of $z^2 - 3z + 32 = 0$?

(ii) What is the value of $z_1 + \overline{z_1}$?

(iii) What is the value of $z_1\overline{z_1}$?

(iv) Find an equation with roots $-z_1$ and $-\overline{z_1}$.

14. $z_1 = a + bi$, $a, b \in R$, is a complex root of the equation $z^2 - 4z + 64 = 0$. Without evaluating the roots, answer the following questions:

(i) Is $\overline{z_1}$, the conjugate of z_1, also a root of $z^2 - 4z + 64 = 0$?

(ii) What is the value of $z_1 + \overline{z_1}$?

(iii) What is the value of $z_1\overline{z_1}$?

(iv) Find an equation with roots $\frac{1}{4}z_1$ and $\frac{1}{4}\overline{z_1}$.

15. $f(z) = a_3z^3 + a_2z^2 + a_1z + a_0$ is a cubic polynomial.

$g(z) = b_2z^2 + b_1z + b_0$ is a quadratic polynomial.

(i) If the roots of $g(z) = 0$ are $1 + i$ and $1 - i$, find a possible set of values for b_0, b_1 and b_2.

(ii) If the roots of $f(z) = 0$ are $1 + i$, $1 - i$ and 5, find a possible set of values for a_0, a_1, a_2 and a_3.

12.8 Polar Form of a Complex Number

The complex number $z = x + yi$ is represented on the Argand diagram below.

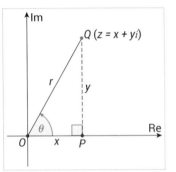

The line segment OQ makes an angle θ with the positive x-axis.

The angle, θ, between the line segment joining a complex number, z, to the origin and the positive x-axis is called the **argument** of z or **arg(z)**. (The angle θ is anti-clockwise.)

The length, r, of the line segment joining a complex number, z, to the origin is called the **modulus** of z.

The **polar form** of a complex number is $r(\cos\theta + i\sin\theta)$, where r is the modulus of the complex number and θ is its argument.

Note: By convention, $-\pi < \theta \leq \pi$.

The **rectangular form** or **Cartesian form** of a complex number is

$$x + iy$$

where $x, y \in R$ and $i = \sqrt{-1}$.

In the triangle OPQ:

$\sin\theta = \dfrac{y}{r}$

$\therefore\ y = r\sin\theta$

$\cos\theta = \dfrac{x}{r}$

$\therefore\ x = r\cos\theta$

$\Rightarrow z = x + yi$ (Cartesian form or rectangular form)

$= r\cos\theta + r\sin\theta i$

$\therefore z = r(\cos\theta + i\sin\theta)$ (Polar form)

 A review of Book 2, Section 7.2 is important before the following Worked Example.

Worked Example 12.25

Write the complex number $-\sqrt{3} + i$ in polar form.

Solution

Step 1   Show $-\sqrt{3} + i$ on an Argand diagram.

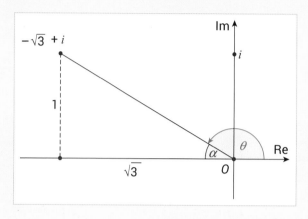

Step 2   Find the modulus of the complex number.

$$r = \sqrt{(-\sqrt{3})^2 + (1)^2}$$
$$r = \sqrt{4}$$
$$\therefore r = 2$$

Step 3   Find the argument of the complex number.

$$\tan \alpha = \frac{1}{\sqrt{3}}$$
$$\therefore \alpha = \frac{\pi}{6}$$
$$\therefore \theta = \pi - \frac{\pi}{6}$$
$$\Rightarrow \quad \theta = \frac{5\pi}{6}$$

Step 4   Write the complex number in polar form, $r(\cos \theta + i \sin \theta)$.

$$-\sqrt{3} + i = 2\left(\cos \frac{5\pi}{6} + i \sin \frac{5\pi}{6}\right)$$

Note: Now a calculator should be used to check the solution.

Worked Example 12.26

Write the complex number $-\sqrt{2} - \sqrt{2}i$ in polar form.

Solution

Step 1   Show $-\sqrt{2} - \sqrt{2}\,i$ on an Argand diagram.

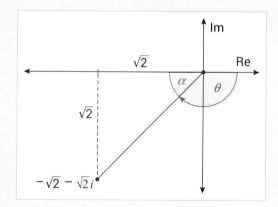

Step 2   Find the modulus of the complex number.

$$r = \sqrt{(-\sqrt{2})^2 + (-\sqrt{2})^2}$$
$$r = \sqrt{2 + 2}$$
$$r = \sqrt{4}$$
$$r = 2$$

Step 3   Find the argument of the complex number.

$$\tan \alpha = \frac{\sqrt{2}}{\sqrt{2}} = 1$$
$$\therefore \alpha = \frac{\pi}{4}$$
$$\therefore \theta = -\pi + \frac{\pi}{4}$$
$$\theta = -\frac{3\pi}{4}$$

Step 4   Write the complex number in the form $r(\cos \theta + i \sin \theta)$.

$$-\sqrt{2} - \sqrt{2}\,i = 2\left(\cos\left(-\frac{3\pi}{4}\right) + i \sin\left(-\frac{3\pi}{4}\right)\right)$$

COMPLEX NUMBERS

Worked Example 12.27

Write the complex number $z = 2\left(\cos\left(\dfrac{5\pi}{4}\right) + i\sin\left(\dfrac{5\pi}{4}\right)\right)$ in rectangular form.

Solution

$z = 2\left(\cos\left(\dfrac{5\pi}{4}\right) + i\sin\left(\dfrac{5\pi}{4}\right)\right)$

$ = 2\left(-\dfrac{1}{\sqrt{2}} + i\left(-\dfrac{1}{\sqrt{2}}\right)\right)$

$ = -\dfrac{2}{\sqrt{2}} - \dfrac{2}{\sqrt{2}}\,i$

$ = -\dfrac{2\sqrt{2}}{2} - \dfrac{2\sqrt{2}}{2}\,i$ (multiplying each term by $\dfrac{\sqrt{2}}{\sqrt{2}}$)

$ = -\sqrt{2} - \sqrt{2}\,i$

Multiplying and Dividing Numbers in Polar Form

Consider the complex numbers $z_1 = r_1(\cos\theta_1 + i\sin\theta_1)$ and $z_2 = r_2(\cos\theta_2 + i\sin\theta_2)$.

$z_1 z_2 = r_1(\cos\theta_1 + i\sin\theta_1)\,r_2(\cos\theta_2 + i\sin\theta_2)$

$ = r_1 r_2(\cos\theta_1 + i\sin\theta_1)\,(\cos\theta_2 + i\sin\theta_2)$

$ = r_1 r_2[\cos\theta_1\,(\cos\theta_2 + i\sin\theta_2) + i\sin\theta_1(\cos\theta_2 + i\sin\theta_2)]$

$ = r_1 r_2[\cos\theta_1\cos\theta_2 + i\cos\theta_1\sin\theta_2 + i\sin\theta_1\cos\theta_2 + i^2\sin\theta_1\,\sin\theta_2)]$

$ = r_1 r_2[\cos\theta_1\cos\theta_2 - \sin\theta_1\sin\theta_2 + (\cos\theta_1\sin\theta_2 + \sin\theta_1\cos\theta_2)i]$

$ = r_1 r_2[\cos(\theta_1 + \theta_2) + i\sin(\theta_1 + \theta_2)]$

See Book 2, Section 7.19.

> If $z_1 = r_1(\cos\theta_1 + i\sin\theta_1)$ and $z_2 = r_2(\cos\theta_2 + i\sin\theta_2)$, then
>
> $z_1 z_2 = r_1 r_2(\cos(\theta_1 + \theta_2) + i\sin(\theta_1 + \theta_2))$.
>
> In words: multiply the moduli and add the arguments.

$\dfrac{z_1}{z_2} = \dfrac{r_1(\cos\theta_1 + i\sin\theta_1)}{r_2(\cos\theta_2 + i\sin\theta_2)} = \dfrac{r_1(\cos\theta_1 + i\sin\theta_1)(\cos\theta_2 - i\sin\theta_2)}{r_2(\cos\theta_2 + i\sin\theta_2)(\cos\theta_2 - i\sin\theta_2)}$

$\phantom{\dfrac{z_1}{z_2}} = \dfrac{r_1(\cos\theta_1\cos\theta_2 + \sin\theta_1\sin\theta_2 + i(\sin\theta_1\cos\theta_2 - \cos\theta_1\sin\theta_2)}{r_2(\cos^2\theta_2 + \sin^2\theta_2)}$

$\phantom{\dfrac{z_1}{z_2}} = \dfrac{r_1[\cos(\theta_1 - \theta_2) + i\sin(\theta_1 - \theta_2)]}{r_2(1)}$

$\phantom{\dfrac{z_1}{z_2}} = \dfrac{r_1}{r_2}[\cos(\theta_1 - \theta_2) + i\sin(\theta_1 - \theta_2)]$

> If $z_1 = r_1(\cos\theta_1 + i\sin\theta_1)$ and $z_2 = r_2(\cos\theta_2 + i\sin\theta_2)$,
>
> then $\dfrac{z_1}{z_2} = \dfrac{r_1}{r_2}[\cos(\theta_1 - \theta_2) + i\sin(\theta_1 - \theta_2)]$.
>
> In words: divide the moduli and subtract the arguments.

Worked Example 12.28

$z_1 = 3\left(\cos \frac{\pi}{6} + i \sin \frac{\pi}{6}\right)$ and $z_2 = 4\left(\cos \frac{\pi}{3} + i \sin \frac{\pi}{3}\right)$. Find, in the form $x + yi$:

(i) $z_1 z_2$ (ii) $\dfrac{z_1}{z_2}$

Solution

(i)
$$z_1 z_2 = 3\left(\cos \frac{\pi}{6} + i \sin \frac{\pi}{6}\right)4\left(\cos \frac{\pi}{3} + i \sin \frac{\pi}{3}\right)$$
$$= (3)(4)\left[\cos\left(\frac{\pi}{6} + \frac{\pi}{3}\right) + i \sin\left(\frac{\pi}{6} + \frac{\pi}{3}\right)\right]$$
$$= 12\left[\cos \frac{\pi}{2} + i \sin \frac{\pi}{2}\right]$$
$$= 12[0 + i]$$
$$\Rightarrow z_1 z_2 = 0 + 12i$$

(ii)
$$\frac{z_1}{z_2} = \frac{3\left(\cos \frac{\pi}{6} + i \sin \frac{\pi}{6}\right)}{4\left(\cos \frac{\pi}{3} + i \sin \frac{\pi}{3}\right)}$$
$$= \frac{3}{4}\left[\cos\left(\frac{\pi}{6} - \frac{\pi}{3}\right) + i \sin\left(\frac{\pi}{6} - \frac{\pi}{3}\right)\right]$$
$$= \frac{3}{4}\left[\cos\left(-\frac{\pi}{6}\right) + i \sin\left(-\frac{\pi}{6}\right)\right]$$
$$= \frac{3}{4}\left[\cos \frac{\pi}{6} - i \sin \frac{\pi}{6}\right]$$
$$= \frac{3}{4}\left[\frac{\sqrt{3}}{2} - \frac{1}{2}i\right]$$
$$\Rightarrow \frac{z_1}{z_2} = \frac{3\sqrt{3}}{8} - \frac{3}{8}i$$

$\cos(-A) = \cos A$
$\sin(-A) = -\sin A$

Worked Example 12.29

The complex numbers z and ω are such that:

$z = 1 + 2\sqrt{3}i$ and $z\omega = \dfrac{3\sqrt{3}}{2} + \dfrac{5}{2}i.$

(i) Find ω in the form $a + bi$, $a, b \in R$.

(ii) Find $|\omega|$ and $\arg(\omega)$.

(iii) Write ω in polar form.

Solution

(i)
$$z\omega = \frac{3\sqrt{3}}{2} + \frac{5}{2}i$$
$$(1 + 2\sqrt{3}i)\,\omega = \frac{3\sqrt{3}}{2} + \frac{5}{2}i$$
$$\therefore \omega = \frac{\frac{3\sqrt{3}}{2} + \frac{5}{2}i}{1 + 2\sqrt{3}i}$$
$$\omega = \frac{\left(\frac{3\sqrt{3}}{2} + \frac{5}{2}i\right)(1 - 2\sqrt{3}i)}{(1 + 2\sqrt{3}i)(1 - 2\sqrt{3}i)}$$
$$= \frac{\frac{3\sqrt{3}}{2}(1 - 2\sqrt{3}i) + \frac{5}{2}i(1 - 2\sqrt{3}i)}{13}$$
$$= \frac{\frac{3\sqrt{3}}{2} - 9i + \frac{5}{2}i + 5\sqrt{3}}{13}$$

$$= \frac{\frac{13\sqrt{3}}{2} - \frac{13}{2}i}{13}$$
$$\therefore \omega = \frac{\sqrt{3}}{2} - \frac{1}{2}i$$

(ii)
$$|\omega| = \sqrt{\left(\frac{\sqrt{3}}{2}\right)^2 + \left(-\frac{1}{2}\right)^2}$$
$$= \sqrt{\frac{3}{4} + \frac{1}{4}}$$
$$= \sqrt{1}$$
$$\therefore |\omega| = 1$$

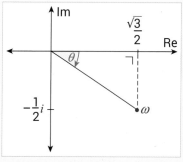

$\tan \theta = \dfrac{\frac{1}{2}}{\frac{\sqrt{3}}{2}} = \dfrac{1}{\sqrt{3}}$

$\therefore \theta = \dfrac{\pi}{6}$

$\Rightarrow \arg(\omega) = -\dfrac{\pi}{6}$

(iii) $\omega = 1\left(\cos\left(-\dfrac{\pi}{6}\right) + i \sin\left(-\dfrac{\pi}{6}\right)\right)$

12

Exercise 12.8

COMPLEX NUMBERS

1. Write the following complex numbers in polar form, $r(\cos \theta + i \sin \theta)$:

   (i) $3 + 3i$ (iii) $2 + 2\sqrt{3}\,i$

   (ii) $1 + i$ (iv) $\sqrt{3} + i$

2. Write the following complex numbers in polar form, $r(\cos \theta + i \sin \theta)$:

   (i) $-4 + 4i$ (iii) $-5 + 5\sqrt{3}\,i$

   (ii) $-3 + 3i$ (iv) $-\sqrt{3} + i$

3. Write the following complex numbers in polar form, $r(\cos \theta + i \sin \theta)$:

   (i) $-\sqrt{3} - i$ (iii) $-1 - \sqrt{3}\,i$

   (ii) $-7 - 7i$ (iv) $-2 - 2\sqrt{3}\,i$

4. Write the following complex numbers in polar form, $r(\cos \theta + i \sin \theta)$:

   (i) $2 - 2i$ (iii) $1 - \sqrt{3}\,i$

   (ii) $3 - 3i$ (iv) $2 - 2\sqrt{3}\,i$

5. Write the following complex numbers in polar form, $r(\cos \theta + i \sin \theta)$:

   (i) $1 + \sqrt{3}\,i$ (iii) $-1 + i$

   (ii) $2 + 2i$ (iv) $2\sqrt{3} - 2i$

6. Write the following in rectangular form:

   (i) $\sqrt{2}\left(\cos\left(\frac{\pi}{4}\right) + i\sin\left(\frac{\pi}{4}\right)\right)$

   (ii) $\sqrt{3}\left(\cos\left(\frac{\pi}{6}\right) + i\sin\left(\frac{\pi}{6}\right)\right)$

   (iii) $\sqrt{3}\left(\cos\left(\frac{\pi}{3}\right) + i\sin\left(\frac{\pi}{3}\right)\right)$

   (iv) $\sqrt{2}\left(\cos\left(\frac{3\pi}{4}\right) + i\sin\left(\frac{3\pi}{4}\right)\right)$

   (v) $\sqrt{3}\left(\cos\left(\frac{7\pi}{6}\right) + i\sin\left(\frac{7\pi}{6}\right)\right)$

   (vi) $\sqrt{3}\left(\cos\left(\frac{5\pi}{3}\right) + i\sin\left(\frac{5\pi}{3}\right)\right)$

7. Write the following in rectangular form:

   (i) $\sqrt{32}\left(\cos\frac{\pi}{4} + i\sin\frac{\pi}{4}\right)$

   (ii) $3(\cos \pi + i \sin \pi)$

   (iii) $2\left(\cos\frac{\pi}{2} + i\sin\frac{\pi}{2}\right)$

   (iv) $2\left(\cos\frac{11\pi}{6} + i\sin\frac{11\pi}{6}\right)$

   (v) $100(\cos 25\pi + i \sin 25\pi)$

8. Given that $z = -2 + 2i$, evaluate:

   (i) $\arg(z)$ (ii) $-\arg(z)$ (iii) $-\arg\left(\frac{1}{z}\right)$

9. $z_1 = r_1(\cos \theta_1 + i \sin \theta_1)$ and $z_2 = r_2(\cos \theta_2 + i \sin \theta_2)$.

   Show that $z_1 z_2 = r_1 r_2 (\cos (\theta_1 + \theta_2) + i \sin (\theta_1 + \theta_2))$.

10. Write the following in polar form:

    (i) $\left[5\left(\cos\frac{\pi}{3} + i\sin\frac{\pi}{3}\right)\right]\left[2\left(\cos\frac{\pi}{6} + i\sin\frac{\pi}{6}\right)\right]$

    (ii) $\left[3\left(\cos\left(\frac{\pi}{7}\right) + i\sin\left(\frac{\pi}{7}\right)\right)\right]\left[5\left(\cos\frac{\pi}{9} + i\sin\frac{\pi}{9}\right)\right]$

    (iii) $\left[2\left(\cos\left(\frac{\pi}{4}\right) + i\sin\left(\frac{\pi}{4}\right)\right)\right]\left[7\left(\cos\left(\frac{\pi}{8}\right) + i\sin\left(\frac{\pi}{8}\right)\right)\right]$

    (iv) $\left[7\left(\cos\left(\frac{\pi}{8}\right) + i\sin\left(\frac{\pi}{8}\right)\right)\right]\left[9\left(\cos\left(\frac{\pi}{3}\right) + i\sin\left(\frac{\pi}{3}\right)\right)\right]$

    (v) $\left[9\left(\cos\frac{\pi}{2} + i\sin\frac{\pi}{2}\right)\right]\left[3\left(\cos\left(\frac{\pi}{5}\right) + i\sin\left(\frac{\pi}{5}\right)\right)\right]$

11. Write the following in polar form:

    (i) $\dfrac{2\left(\cos\frac{\pi}{3} + i\sin\frac{\pi}{3}\right)}{\left(\cos\frac{\pi}{6} + i\sin\frac{\pi}{6}\right)}$

    (ii) $\dfrac{10\left(\cos\frac{\pi}{2} + i\sin\frac{\pi}{2}\right)}{5\left(\cos\frac{\pi}{4} + i\sin\frac{\pi}{4}\right)}$

    (iii) $\dfrac{12\left(\cos\frac{\pi}{5} + i\sin\frac{\pi}{5}\right)}{6\left(\cos\frac{\pi}{10} + i\sin\frac{\pi}{10}\right)}$

    (iv) $\dfrac{18\left(\cos\frac{\pi}{3} + i\sin\frac{\pi}{3}\right)}{6\left(\cos\frac{\pi}{2} + i\sin\frac{\pi}{2}\right)}$

    (v) $\dfrac{55\left(\cos\frac{\pi}{20} + i\sin\frac{\pi}{20}\right)}{5\left(\cos\frac{\pi}{2} + i\sin\frac{\pi}{2}\right)}$

12. Write the following in polar form:

(i) $\left[2\left(\cos\frac{\pi}{8}+i\sin\frac{\pi}{8}\right)\right]\left[3\left(\cos\frac{\pi}{12}+i\sin\frac{\pi}{12}\right)\right]$

(ii) $\left[10\left(\cos\frac{\pi}{5}+i\sin\frac{\pi}{5}\right)\right]\left[5\left(\cos\frac{\pi}{10}+i\sin\frac{\pi}{10}\right)\right]$

(iii) $\dfrac{9\left(\cos\frac{\pi}{8}+i\sin\frac{\pi}{8}\right)}{3\left(\cos\frac{\pi}{16}+i\sin\frac{\pi}{16}\right)}$

(iv) $\dfrac{12\left(\cos\frac{\pi}{7}+i\sin\frac{\pi}{7}\right)}{4\left(\cos\frac{\pi}{14}+i\sin\frac{\pi}{14}\right)}$

13. $z_1=\sqrt{3}+i$ and $z_2=-1+\sqrt{3}i$

(i) Plot z_1 and z_2 on an Argand diagram.

(ii) Write z_1z_2 in the form $x+yi$.

(iii) Show that $\arg(z_1)+\arg(z_2)=\arg(z_1z_2)$.

(iv) Show that $|z_1||z_2|=|z_1z_2|$.

14. For each of the following, find suitable values for r and θ.

Note: In each case there is an infinite number of possible values for θ.

(i) $[r(\cos\theta+i\sin\theta)]\left[2\left(\cos\left(\frac{\pi}{4}\right)+i\sin\left(\frac{\pi}{4}\right)\right)\right]$

$=8\left(\cos\frac{\pi}{2}+i\sin\frac{\pi}{2}\right)$

(ii) $[r(\cos\theta+i\sin\theta)]\left[\frac{5}{6}\left(\cos\frac{\pi}{6}+i\sin\frac{\pi}{6}\right)\right]$

$=3\left(\cos\frac{\pi}{8}+i\sin\frac{\pi}{8}\right)$

(iii) $\dfrac{r(\cos\theta+i\sin\theta)}{5\left(\cos\frac{\pi}{3}+i\sin\frac{\pi}{3}\right)}=2\left(\cos\left(\frac{2\pi}{5}\right)+i\sin\left(\frac{2\pi}{5}\right)\right)$

(iv) $\dfrac{3\left(\cos\frac{\pi}{8}+i\sin\frac{\pi}{8}\right)}{r(\cos\theta+i\sin\theta)}=\frac{3}{2}\left(\cos\left(\frac{2\pi}{3}\right)+i\sin\left(\frac{2\pi}{3}\right)\right)$

15. Write each of the following in polar form:

(i) $(\sqrt{3}+i)\left(\frac{1}{2}-\frac{\sqrt{3}}{2}i\right)$

(ii) $2i(1-i)$

(iii) $\dfrac{2}{-1+i}$

16. Solve the following quadratic equations and write the solutions in polar form.

(i) $x^2-2x+2=0$

(ii) $x^2+2x+4=0$

(iii) $x^2+2\sqrt{3}x+4=0$

(iv) $x^2-4x+8=0$

17. The complex numbers z and ω are such that

$$z=-\frac{1}{2}+\frac{\sqrt{3}}{2}i \text{ and } z\omega=14+23i.$$

(i) Find ω in the form $a+bi$, where a and b are real.

(ii) Show z and ω on an Argand diagram.

(iii) Find $|z|$ and $\arg(z)$.

(iv) Write z in polar form.

(v) Multiplication by z rotates a complex number in _____ direction, through ____°.

18. $z=\cos\theta+i\sin\theta$ is a complex number in polar form. Show that:

(i) $\cos\theta=\frac{1}{2}\left(z+\frac{1}{z}\right)$

(ii) $\sin\theta=-\frac{i}{2}\left(z-\frac{1}{z}\right)$

19. The set $\{z_1,z_2,z_3,z_4,z_5,z_6,z_7,z_8\}$ of complex numbers is shown on the Argand diagram. z_{n+1} is an anti-clockwise rotation of z_n through $\frac{\pi}{4}$ radians, $1\leqslant n\leqslant 7, n\in N$.

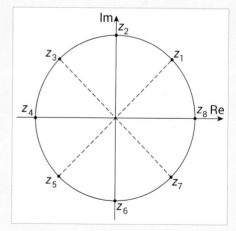

(i) Write z_1 in the form $r(\cos\theta+i\sin\theta)$ given that $|z_1|=1$.

(ii) Write z_4 in the form $r(\cos\theta+i\sin\theta)$.

(iii) $z_5=a+bi$. Find the real numbers a and b.

12.9 De Moivre's Theorem and Applications

Abraham de Moivre was a French mathematician. He was born in the Champagne region of France in 1667 and died in London in 1754. He is most famous for the theorem named after him, which links complex numbers and trigonometry. He also made contributions to probability and wrote a book, *The Doctrine of Chances*, on the subject.

Abraham de Moivre
(1667–1754)

De Moivre's Theorem

If $z = r(\cos \theta + i \sin \theta)$, then $z^n = r^n(\cos n\theta + i \sin n\theta)$, for $n \in Z$, i.e. $[r(\cos \theta + i \sin \theta)]^n = r^n(\cos n\theta + i \sin n\theta)$.

Note: De Moivre's Theorem is on page 20 of *Formulae and Tables*.

De Moivre's Theorem for $n \in N$

Proof by Induction

This is a formal proof and may be asked in the exam.

Step 1 Is de Moivre's Theorem true for $n = 1$?

LHS: $z^1 = [r(\cos \theta + i \sin \theta)]^1 = r(\cos \theta + i \sin \theta)$

RHS: $r^1(\cos(1)\theta + i \sin(1)\theta) = r(\cos \theta + i \sin \theta)$

$\therefore$ True for $n = 1$.

Step 2 Given that the theorem is true for $n = k$, prove that it is true for $n = k + 1$.

Given: $[r(\cos \theta + i \sin \theta)]^k = r^k(\cos k\theta + i \sin k\theta)$ $(k \in N)$

To prove: $[r(\cos \theta + i \sin \theta)]^{k+1} = r^{k+1}(\cos(k+1)\theta + i \sin(k+1)\theta)$

Proof:

$\begin{aligned}
\text{LHS} &= [r(\cos \theta + i \sin \theta)]^{k+1} \\
&= [r(\cos \theta + i \sin \theta)]^k [r(\cos \theta + i \sin \theta)] \\
&= [r^k(\cos k\theta + i \sin k\theta)][r(\cos \theta + i \sin \theta)] \quad \text{[Given]} \\
&= r^k \cdot r \cdot (\cos k\theta + i \sin k\theta)(\cos \theta + i \sin \theta) \\
&= r^{k+1}[\cos k\theta \cos \theta + i \sin k\theta \cos \theta + i \cos k\theta \sin \theta - \sin k\theta \sin \theta] \\
&= r^{k+1}[(\cos k\theta \cos \theta - \sin k\theta \sin \theta) + i(\sin k\theta \cos \theta + \cos k\theta \sin \theta)] \\
&= r^{k+1}[\cos(k\theta + \theta) + i \sin(k\theta + \theta)] \\
&= r^{k+1}(\cos(k+1)\theta + i \sin(k+1)\theta) \\
&= \text{RHS}
\end{aligned}$

$(\cos(A + B) = \cos A \cos B - \sin A \sin B,$
$\sin(A + B) = \sin A \cos B + \cos A \sin B)$

Step 3 By induction, de Moivre's Theorem is true for all $n \in N$.

De Moivre's Theorem, $n \in Q$

De Moivre's Theorem is in fact true for all $n \in Q$. We prove the case only for natural numbers, but we make use of the fact that it is true for all $n \in Q$.

Worked Example 12.30

Use de Moivre's Theorem to write $(1 + i)^{10}$ in the form $x + yi$, $x, y \in R$.

Solution

Step 1 Write $1 + i$ in polar form, $r(\cos \theta + i \sin \theta)$.

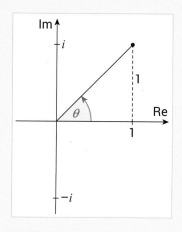

$r = \sqrt{1^2 + 1^2} = \sqrt{2}$

$\tan \theta = 1$

$\therefore \theta = \dfrac{\pi}{4}$

$1 + i = \sqrt{2}\left(\cos \dfrac{\pi}{4} + i \sin \dfrac{\pi}{4}\right)$

Step 2 Apply de Moivre's Theorem.

$$(1 + i)^{10} = \left(\sqrt{2}\left(\cos \dfrac{\pi}{4} + i \sin \dfrac{\pi}{4}\right)\right)^{10}$$

$$= \sqrt{2}^{10}\left(\cos 10\left(\dfrac{\pi}{4}\right) + i \sin 10\left(\dfrac{\pi}{4}\right)\right)$$

$$= 32\left(\cos \dfrac{5\pi}{2} + i \sin \dfrac{5\pi}{2}\right)$$

$$= 32(0 + 1i)$$

$$\therefore (1 + i)^{10} = 0 + 32i$$

Worked Example 12.31

Use de Moivre's Theorem to prove the identity $\sin 3\theta = 3 \sin \theta - 4 \sin^3 \theta$.

Solution

Binomial expansion:

$$(\cos \theta + i \sin \theta)^3 = \binom{3}{0}\cos^3 \theta + \binom{3}{1}(\cos^2 \theta)(i \sin \theta) + \binom{3}{2}(\cos \theta)(i \sin \theta)^2 + \binom{3}{3}(i \sin \theta)^3$$

$$= \cos^3 \theta + (3\cos^2 \theta \sin \theta)i - 3\cos \theta \sin^2 \theta - (\sin^3 \theta)i$$

$$= \cos^3 \theta - 3\cos \theta \sin^2 \theta + (3\cos^2 \theta \sin \theta - \sin^3 \theta)i$$

> Revise Chapter 1, Section 1.5 on binomial expansions.

De Moivre's Theorem: $(\cos \theta + i \sin \theta)^3 = \cos 3\theta + i \sin 3\theta$

Equate imaginary parts: $\sin 3\theta = 3\cos^2 \theta \sin \theta - \sin^3 \theta$

$$= 3(1 - \sin^2 \theta)(\sin \theta) - \sin^3 \theta \qquad \text{(As } \cos^2\theta + \sin^2\theta = 1 \therefore \cos^2\theta = 1 - \sin^2 \theta.)$$

$$= 3\sin \theta - 3\sin^3 \theta - \sin^3 \theta$$

$$= 3\sin \theta - 4\sin^3 \theta$$

Worked Example 12.32

Use de Moivre's Theorem to write $\left[2\left(\cos\dfrac{\pi}{4} - i\sin\dfrac{\pi}{4}\right)\right]^6$ in rectangular form.

Solution

Step 1

Write $2\left(\cos\dfrac{\pi}{4} - i\sin\dfrac{\pi}{4}\right)$ in polar form, $r(\cos\theta + i\sin\theta)$.

$\cos\left(\dfrac{\pi}{4}\right) = \cos\left(-\dfrac{\pi}{4}\right)$ and $-\sin\left(\dfrac{\pi}{4}\right) = \sin\left(-\dfrac{\pi}{4}\right)$.

$2\left(\cos\dfrac{\pi}{4} - i\sin\dfrac{\pi}{4}\right) = 2\left(\cos\left(-\dfrac{\pi}{4}\right) + i\sin\left(-\dfrac{\pi}{4}\right)\right)$

Step 2

Apply de Moivre's Theorem.

$\left[2\left(\cos\dfrac{\pi}{4} - i\sin\dfrac{\pi}{4}\right)\right]^6 = \left[2\left(\cos\left(-\dfrac{\pi}{4}\right) + i\sin\left(-\dfrac{\pi}{4}\right)\right)\right]^6$

$\qquad = 2^6\left(\cos 6\left(-\dfrac{\pi}{4}\right) + i\sin 6\left(-\dfrac{\pi}{4}\right)\right)$

$\qquad = 2^6\left(\cos\left(-\dfrac{3\pi}{2}\right) + i\sin\left(-\dfrac{3\pi}{2}\right)\right)$

$\qquad = 2^6\left(\cos\left(\dfrac{3\pi}{2}\right) - i\sin\left(\dfrac{3\pi}{2}\right)\right)$

$\qquad = 64(0 - i(-1))$

$\qquad = 0 + 64i$

Exercise 12.9

1. Use de Moivre's Theorem to write the following in the form $a + bi$:

   (i) $\left(\cos\dfrac{\pi}{32} + i\sin\dfrac{\pi}{32}\right)^8$

   (ii) $\left(\cos\dfrac{\pi}{36} + i\sin\dfrac{\pi}{36}\right)^9$

   (iii) $\left(\cos\dfrac{\pi}{6} + i\sin\dfrac{\pi}{6}\right)^2$

   (iv) $\left(\cos\dfrac{\pi}{3} + i\sin\dfrac{\pi}{3}\right)^6$

   (v) $\left(\cos\dfrac{\pi}{3} + i\sin\dfrac{\pi}{3}\right)^5$

   (vi) $\left[5\left(\cos\dfrac{\pi}{3} + i\sin\dfrac{\pi}{3}\right)\right]^6$

   (vii) $\left[\sqrt{2}\left(\cos\dfrac{\pi}{4} + i\sin\dfrac{\pi}{4}\right)\right]^4$

   (viii) $\left[\sqrt{3}\left(\cos\dfrac{\pi}{12} + i\sin\dfrac{\pi}{12}\right)\right]^8$

2. The complex number $z = \sqrt{3} + i$ is shown on the Argand diagram.

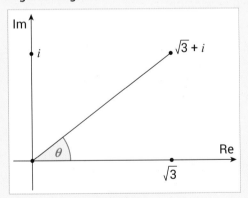

   (i) Find θ, the argument of z.

   (ii) Calculate r, the modulus of z.

   (iii) Write z in polar form.

   (iv) Use the theorem of de Moivre to write $(\sqrt{3} + i)^{10}$ in the form $a + bi$.

3. Let $z = 1 - i$.

   (i) Plot z on an Argand diagram.

   (ii) Find arg(z) and |z|.

   (iii) Hence, write z in polar form.

   (iv) Use the theorem of de Moivre to evaluate z^9.

4. Let $z = -1 + i$.

   (i) Find θ, the argument of z.

   (ii) Calculate r, the modulus of z.

   (iii) Write z in polar form.

   (iv) Use the theorem of de Moivre to evaluate z^5 and z^9.

   (v) Show that $z^5 + z^9 = 12z$.

5. Use de Moivre's Theorem to write the following in the form $a + bi$.

   (i) $(2 + 2i)^8$

   (ii) $(1 - i)^{16}$

   (iii) $\left(\frac{1}{2} + \frac{\sqrt{3}}{2}i\right)^{13}$

   (iv) $\left(\frac{1}{\sqrt{2}} + \frac{1}{\sqrt{2}}i\right)^{11}$

   (v) $\left(-\frac{1}{2} - \frac{\sqrt{3}}{2}i\right)^{60}$

   (vi) $\left(-\frac{\sqrt{3}}{2} + \frac{1}{2}i\right)^{6}$

   (vii) $(-2 - 2i)^9$

   (viii) $(-1 + i)^{13}$

6. Let $z = \frac{1}{\sqrt{2}} + \frac{1}{\sqrt{2}}i$.

   (i) Plot z on an Argand diagram.

   (ii) Find arg(z) and |z|.

   (iii) Write z in polar form.

   (iv) Use the theorem of de Moivre to evaluate z^6.

   (v) Find the least value of $n \in N$ for which $z^n = z$.

7. Let $\omega = \cos \theta + i \sin \theta$.

   (i) Use de Moivre's Theorem to write ω^3 in the form $\cos n\theta + i \sin n\theta$.

   (ii) Expand $(\cos \theta + i \sin \theta)^3$ using the binomial theorem.

   (iii) Equate Re(ω^3) from part (i) with Re(ω^3) from part (ii) to prove the identity
   $$\cos 3\theta = 4 \cos^3 \theta - 3 \cos \theta.$$

   (iv) Find the period and range of the function
   $f(\theta) = 4 \cos^3 \theta - 3 \cos \theta.$

8. Let $z = \cos A + i \sin A$.

   (i) If $z^4 = \cos B + i \sin B$, then use de Moivre's Theorem to write B in terms of A.

   (ii) Expand $(\cos A + i \sin A)^4$ using the binomial theorem.

   (iii) Equate Re(z^4) from part (i) with Re(z^4) from part (ii) to prove the identity
   $$\cos 4A = 8 \cos^4 A - 8 \cos^2 A + 1.$$

   (iv) Solve, for A, the equation
   $8 \cos^4 A = 8 \cos^2 A - 1.$

9. Let $z = \cos \theta + i \sin \theta$.
   Use de Moivre's Theorem to show that:

   (i) $z + \frac{1}{z} = 2 \cos \theta$

   (ii) $z^n + \frac{1}{z^n} = 2 \cos n\theta$

10. Prove that, if $z = r(\cos \theta + i \sin \theta)$, then $z^n = r^n(\cos(n\theta) + i \sin(n\theta))$, for $n \in N$.

11. Let $z = \cos \theta + i \sin \theta$.
    Use de Moivre's Theorem to show that:

    (i) $z - \frac{1}{z} = 2i \sin \theta$

    (ii) $z^n - \frac{1}{z^n} = 2i \sin n\theta$

    (iii) $\sin^3 \theta = \frac{1}{4}[3 \sin \theta - \sin 3\theta]$

12. Use de Moivre's Theorem to write each of the following in rectangular form:

    (i) $\left[3\left(\cos \frac{\pi}{6} - i \sin \frac{\pi}{6}\right)\right]^5$

    (ii) $\left[2\left(\cos \frac{\pi}{3} - i \sin \frac{\pi}{3}\right)\right]^{10}$

    (iii) $\left[5\left(\cos \frac{5\pi}{4} - i \sin \frac{5\pi}{4}\right)\right]^3$

12.10 De Moivre's Theorem for $n \in Q$

De Moivre's Theorem is also used to find the roots of equations. When de Moivre's Theorem is applied to finding solutions to equations, then the **general polar form** of a complex number is used.

The **general polar form** of a complex number is $r[(\cos(\theta + 2n\pi) + i\sin(\theta + 2n\pi)]$, where $n \in Z$.

Why is it necessary to use general polar form when finding the roots of equations?
Consider the following argument:

$\cos(\theta + 2n\pi) = \cos\theta, n \in Z$ ($\cos x$ is periodic with period 2π)

$\sin(\theta + 2n\pi) = \sin\theta, n \in Z$ ($\sin x$ is periodic with period 2π)

$\cos m(\theta + 2n\pi) = \cos(m\theta + 2mn\pi) = \cos(m\theta)$, if $m, n \in Z$

$\sin m(\theta + 2n\pi) = \sin(m\theta + 2mn\pi) = \sin(m\theta)$, if $m, n \in Z$

> Revise Book 2, Section 7.9 on graphing trigonometric functions.

By de Moivre's Theorem

$[\cos(\theta + 2n\pi) + i\sin(\theta + 2n\pi)]^m = \cos m(\theta + 2n\pi) + i\sin m(\theta + 2n\pi), m, n \in Z$

$\qquad\qquad\qquad\qquad = \cos(m\theta) + i\sin(m\theta)$

$\qquad\qquad\qquad\qquad = (\cos\theta + i\sin\theta)^m$ (de Moivre)

This shows that if m is an integer, then it is not necessary to use general polar form when applying de Moivre's Theorem. However, if $m \in Q$ and $m \notin Z$ then:

$\cos m(\theta + 2n\pi) = \cos(m\theta + 2mn\pi)$

and $\sin m(\theta + 2n\pi) = \sin(m\theta + 2mn\pi)$

Here $2mn\pi$ is not a multiple of 2π, for all values of $n \in Z$, as m is a fraction.

Hence, $\cos m(\theta + 2n\pi) \neq \cos m\theta$ and $\sin m(\theta + 2n\pi) \neq \sin m\theta$, so general polar form is required.

Worked Example 12.33

Let $\omega = -2 - 2\sqrt{3}i$.

(i) Plot ω on an Argand diagram.

(ii) Find $\arg(\omega)$ and $|\omega|$.

(iii) Write ω in general polar form.

(iv) What is the number of solutions to the equation $z^4 - \omega = 0$?

(v) Solve the equation $z^4 - \omega = 0$.
Plot your solutions on an Argand diagram.

Solution

(i)

(ii) $\arg(\omega)$ $\tan\alpha = \dfrac{2\sqrt{3}}{2} = \sqrt{3}$

$\qquad\qquad\qquad \therefore \alpha = \dfrac{\pi}{3}$

$\theta = \arg(\omega)$

$\qquad \therefore \theta = \left(-\pi + \dfrac{\pi}{3}\right)$

$\qquad \Rightarrow \arg(\omega) = -\dfrac{2\pi}{3}$

$\qquad |\omega| = \sqrt{(-2)^2 + (-2\sqrt{3})^2}$

$\qquad\qquad = \sqrt{4 + 12}$

$\qquad\qquad = \sqrt{16}$

$\qquad \therefore |\omega| = 4$

(iii) $\omega = 4\left[\cos\left(-\dfrac{2\pi}{3} + 2n\pi\right) + i\sin\left(-\dfrac{2\pi}{3} + 2n\pi\right)\right]$

(iv) $z^4 - \omega$ is a degree 4 polynomial. By the Fundamental Theorem of Algebra, there will be four roots.

(v) $z^4 - \omega = 0$

$\Rightarrow z^4 = \omega$

Express in general polar form:

$$z^4 = 4\left[\cos\left(-\frac{2\pi}{3} + 2n\pi\right) + i\sin\left(-\frac{2\pi}{3} + 2n\pi\right)\right]$$

$$\therefore z = \left[4\left[\cos\left(-\frac{2\pi}{3} + 2n\pi\right) + i\sin\left(-\frac{2\pi}{3} + 2n\pi\right)\right]\right]^{\frac{1}{4}}$$

Apply the theorem of de Moivre:

$$z = 4^{\frac{1}{4}}\left[\cos\frac{1}{4}\left(-\frac{2\pi}{3} + 2n\pi\right) + i\sin\frac{1}{4}\left(-\frac{2\pi}{3} + 2n\pi\right)\right]$$

$$z = \sqrt{2}\left[\cos\left(\frac{n\pi}{2} - \frac{\pi}{6}\right) + i\sin\left(\frac{n\pi}{2} - \frac{\pi}{6}\right)\right]$$

Find the four solutions:

For $n = 0$	For $n = 1$
$z_1 = \sqrt{2}\left[\cos\left(-\frac{\pi}{6}\right) + i\sin\left(-\frac{\pi}{6}\right)\right]$	$z_2 = \sqrt{2}\left[\cos\left(\frac{\pi}{2} - \frac{\pi}{6}\right) + i\sin\left(\frac{\pi}{2} - \frac{\pi}{6}\right)\right]$
$= \sqrt{2}\left[\frac{\sqrt{3}}{2} - \frac{1}{2}i\right]$	$= \sqrt{2}\left[\cos\frac{\pi}{3} + i\sin\frac{\pi}{3}\right]$
$z_1 = \frac{\sqrt{6}}{2} - \frac{\sqrt{2}}{2}i$	$= \sqrt{2}\left[\frac{1}{2} + \frac{\sqrt{3}}{2}i\right]$
	$= \frac{\sqrt{2}}{2} + \frac{\sqrt{6}}{2}i$

For $n = 2$	For $n = 3$
$z_3 = \sqrt{2}\left[\cos\left(\pi - \frac{\pi}{6}\right) + i\sin\left(\pi - \frac{\pi}{6}\right)\right]$	$z_4 = \sqrt{2}\left[\cos\left(\frac{3\pi}{2} - \frac{\pi}{6}\right) + i\sin\left(\frac{3\pi}{2} - \frac{\pi}{6}\right)\right]$
$= \sqrt{2}\left[\cos\frac{5\pi}{6} + i\sin\frac{5\pi}{6}\right]$	$= \sqrt{2}\left[\cos\frac{4\pi}{3} + i\sin\frac{4\pi}{3}\right]$
$= \sqrt{2}\left[-\frac{\sqrt{3}}{2} + \frac{1}{2}i\right]$	$= \sqrt{2}\left[-\frac{1}{2} - \frac{\sqrt{3}}{2}i\right]$
$= -\frac{\sqrt{6}}{2} + \frac{\sqrt{2}}{2}i$	$= -\frac{\sqrt{2}}{2} - \frac{\sqrt{6}}{2}i$

By the Fundamental Theorem of Algebra, there are no more solutions. If we substitute $n = 4$, then we will get the same solution as for $n = 0$.

Also, note that each solution can be found by rotating the previous solution anti-clockwise through $\frac{1}{4}$ of 2π. To see why this is so, consider the argument $\frac{1}{4}\left(-\frac{2\pi}{3} + 2n\pi\right)$ of each root.

$\frac{1}{4}\left(-\frac{2\pi}{3} + 2n\pi\right) = -\frac{\pi}{6} + \frac{2n\pi}{4}$, $0 \leqslant n \leqslant 3$. As n goes through the integers 0, 1, 2, 3, the term $\frac{2n\pi}{4}$ produces the sequence 0, $\frac{\pi}{2}, \pi, \frac{3\pi}{2}$. Hence, each solution can be found by rotating the previous solution anti-clockwise through $\frac{1}{4}$ of 2π.

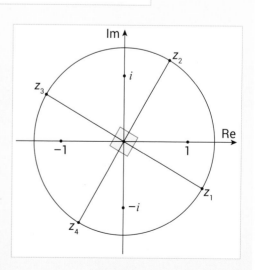

Worked Example 12.34

$f(z) = z^3 + 27, z \in C$ is a polynomial of degree 3.

(i) Show that $f(-3) = 0$.

(ii) The root $z_1 = -3$ is plotted on the Argand diagram.

Locate the other roots on the diagram.

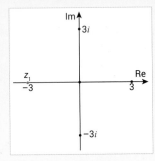

(iii) Find all three roots.

(iv) Verify that your solutions to part (iii) satisfy $z^3 + 27 = 0$.

Solution

(i) $f(-3) = (-3)^3 + 27$

$\quad = -27 + 27$

$\therefore f(-3) = 0$

(ii) By the Fundamental Theorem of Algebra, there are three solutions to the equation. We label these solutions z_1, z_2 and z_3. From de Moivre, we know that z_2 is an anti-clockwise rotation of z_1 through $\frac{1}{3}$ of 2π. Similarly, z_3 is an anti-clockwise rotation of z_2 through $\frac{1}{3}$ of 2π.

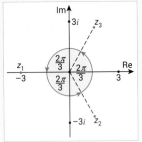

(iii) $z_1 = 3(\cos \pi + i \sin \pi)$

$\quad = 3(-1 + 0i)$

$\quad = -3 + 0i$

$z_2 = 3\left(\cos\left(\pi + \frac{2\pi}{3}\right) + i \sin\left(\pi + \frac{2\pi}{3}\right)\right)$

$\quad = 3\left(\cos\left(\frac{5\pi}{3}\right) + i \sin\left(\frac{5\pi}{3}\right)\right)$

$\quad = 3\left(\frac{1}{2} - i\left(\frac{\sqrt{3}}{2}\right)\right)$

$\therefore z_2 = \frac{3}{2} - \frac{3\sqrt{3}}{2}i$

$z_3 = 3\left(\cos\left(\frac{5\pi}{3} + \frac{2\pi}{3}\right) + i \sin\left(\frac{5\pi}{3} + \frac{2\pi}{3}\right)\right)$

$\quad = 3\left(\cos\left(\frac{7\pi}{3}\right) + i \sin\left(\frac{7\pi}{3}\right)\right)$

$\quad = 3\left(\cos\frac{\pi}{3} + i \sin\frac{\pi}{3}\right)$

$\quad = 3\left(\frac{1}{2} + i\left(\frac{\sqrt{3}}{2}\right)\right)$

$\therefore z_3 = \frac{3}{2} + \frac{3\sqrt{3}}{2}i$

(iv) $\quad z_1 = -3 + 0i$

$\qquad = -3$

$z_1^3 + 27 = (-3)^3 + 27$

$\qquad = -27 + 27$

$\qquad = 0$

$\therefore z_1 = -3 + 0i$ is a solution.

$z_2 = \frac{3}{2} - \frac{3\sqrt{3}}{2}i$

$z_2^3 + 27 = \left(\frac{3}{2} - \frac{3\sqrt{3}}{2}i\right)^3 + 27$

$\quad = \left(\frac{3}{2} - \frac{3\sqrt{3}}{2}i\right)\left(\frac{3}{2} - \frac{3\sqrt{3}}{2}i\right)^2 + 27$

$\quad = \left(\frac{3}{2} - \frac{3\sqrt{3}}{2}i\right)\left(\frac{9}{4} - \frac{9\sqrt{3}}{2}i - \frac{27}{4}\right) + 27$

$\quad = \left(\frac{3}{2} - \frac{3\sqrt{3}}{2}i\right)\left(-\frac{9}{2} - \frac{9\sqrt{3}}{2}i\right) + 27$

$\quad = -\frac{27}{4} - \frac{27\sqrt{3}}{4}i + \frac{27\sqrt{3}}{4}i - \frac{81}{4} + 27$

$\quad = -\frac{108}{4} + 27$

$\quad = -27 + 27$

$\quad = 0$

$\therefore z_2 = \frac{3}{2} - \frac{3\sqrt{3}}{2}i$ is a solution.

$z_3 = \frac{3}{2} + \frac{3\sqrt{3}}{2}i$

$z_3^3 + 27 = \left(\frac{3}{2} + \frac{3\sqrt{3}}{2}i\right)^3 + 27$

$\quad = \left(\frac{3}{2} + \frac{3\sqrt{3}}{2}i\right)\left(\frac{3}{2} + \frac{3\sqrt{3}}{2}i\right)^2 + 27$

$\quad = \left(\frac{3}{2} + \frac{3\sqrt{3}}{2}i\right)\left(-\frac{9}{2} + \frac{9\sqrt{3}}{2}i\right) + 27$

$\quad = -\frac{27}{4} + \frac{27\sqrt{3}}{4}i - \frac{27\sqrt{3}}{4}i - \frac{81}{4} + 27$

$\quad = -\frac{108}{4} + 27$

$\quad = -27 + 27$

$\quad = 0$

$\therefore z_3 = \frac{3}{2} + \frac{3\sqrt{3}}{2}i$ is a solution.

At top right:

$\quad = 3\left(\cos\frac{\pi}{3} + i \sin\frac{\pi}{3}\right)$

$\quad = 3\left(\frac{1}{2} + i\left(\frac{\sqrt{3}}{2}\right)\right)$

$\therefore z_3 = \frac{3}{2} + \frac{3\sqrt{3}}{2}i$

Exercise 12.10

1. Let $\omega = 1 - \sqrt{3}i$.

   (i) Plot ω on an Argand diagram.

   (ii) Find $\arg(\omega)$ and $|\omega|$.

   (iii) Write ω in general polar form.

   (iv) What is the number of solutions to the equation $z^2 - \omega = 0$?

   (v) Solve the equation $z^2 - \omega = 0$. Plot your solutions on an Argand diagram.

2. Use de Moivre's Theorem to solve each of these equations. Plot your solutions on the complex plane.

   (i) $z^2 = 4i$

   (ii) $z^2 + 1 + \sqrt{3}i = 0$

   (iii) $z^2 = 1 + \sqrt{3}i$

   (iv) $z^2 = \dfrac{1}{2} - \dfrac{\sqrt{3}}{2}i$

   (v) $z^3 = 8$

   (vi) $z^3 + 1 = 0$

   (vii) $z^4 + 2 + 2\sqrt{3}i = 0$

   (viii) $z^3 = -64i$

3. Let $\alpha = -64i$.

   (i) Write α in general polar form.

   (ii) Find the solutions, z_1, z_2, z_3, z_4, z_5 and z_6 to the equation $z^6 = \alpha$.

   (iii) Plot the solutions on an Argand diagram.

   (iv) Write down the measure of $\angle z_2 O z_1$, where O is the origin.

   (v) Join $z_1 \rightarrow z_2 \rightarrow z_3 \rightarrow z_4 \rightarrow z_5 \rightarrow z_6 \rightarrow z_1$, with a straight edge. Name the shape thus formed.

4. Two roots, z_1 and z_2, of the equation $z^3 - 8 = 0$ are shown on the diagram.

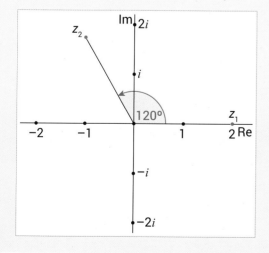

   (i) Copy the diagram and plot z_3, the third root of the equation. Explain, using a geometric argument, how you located the third root.

   (ii) Write z_2 and z_3 in the form $x + yi$, where x and y are real.

5. The solutions to the equation $z^4 = 1 + \sqrt{3}i$ are plotted on the complex plane.

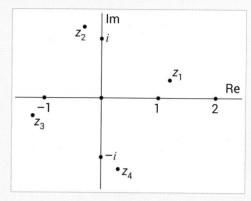

   (i) $z_1 = 2^{\frac{1}{4}}\left(\cos\dfrac{\pi}{12} + i\sin\dfrac{\pi}{12}\right)$
   What are $|z_1|, |z_2|, |z_3|$ and $|z_4|$?

   (ii) Find, in the form $r(\cos\theta + i\sin\theta)$, z_2, z_3 and z_4. Explain, using a geometric argument, how you found the other three roots.

6. $f(z) = z^3 + 8$, $z \in C$ is a polynomial of degree 3.

   (i) Show that $f(-2) = 0$.

   (ii) The root $z_1 = -2$ is plotted on the Argand diagram.

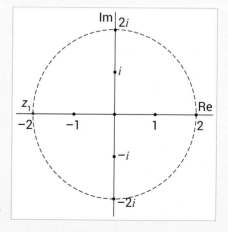

   Locate the other roots on the diagram.

7. $f(z) = z^4 + 4$, $z \in C$ is a polynomial of degree 4.

   (i) Show that $f(z_1) = 0$, where $z_1 = 1 + i$.

   (ii) Plot z_1 on an Argand diagram.

   (iii) How many other roots does the equation $f(z) = 0$ have?

   (iv) Locate these roots on the Argand diagram.

   (v) Explain why $f(i\omega) = 0$, where ω is any root of $f(z) = 0$.

8. Write $P(z) = z^5 - 1$ as a product of linear factors.

9. The solutions to the equation $z^3 - 1 = 0$ are known as the cube roots of unity.

   (i) Use de Moivre's Theorem to solve the equation $z^3 - 1 = 0$.

   (ii) If one complex solution to $z^3 - 1 = 0$ is ω, then show that the other complex solution is ω^2.

   (iii) Evaluate $1 + \omega + \omega^2$, the sum of the cube roots of unity.

   (iv) Explain why $\omega^3 = 1$.

   (v) Show that $\overline{\omega} = \omega^2$ and $(\overline{\omega})^2 = \omega$.

10. The solutions to the equation $z^4 - 1 = 0$ are known as the fourth roots of unity.

   (i) Use de Moivre's Theorem to solve the equation $z^4 - 1 = 0$.

   (ii) Show that the roots are of the form $(1, \omega, \omega^2, \omega^3)$.

   (iii) Show that $1 + \omega + \omega^2 + \omega^3 = 0$.

   (iv) Explain why $\omega^4 = 1$.

Revision Exercises

1. $z_1 = 1 + 3i$, $z_2 = -2 - 3i$ and $z_3 = 1 + i$.

   (a) Evaluate each of the following:

     (i) $z_1 + z_2$ (v) $3z_1 + 2z_2$

     (ii) $z_2 + z_3$ (vi) $2z_1 - 3z_3$

     (iii) $z_1 - z_2$ (vii) $2z_3 - 3z_2$

     (iv) $z_3 - z_2$ (viii) $z_3 + 2z_2$

   (b) On the Argand diagram, plot z_1, z_2 and z_4, where $z_4 = z_1 + z_2$.

   (c) On the Argand diagram, construct the quadrilateral $Oz_1z_4z_2$, where $O = 0 + 0i$.

   (d) Describe the quadrilateral in part (c).

2. (a) Simplify:

     (i) $\sqrt{-144}$ (iii) i^{72} (v) $2i^{-8} + 3i^{-7}$

     (ii) i^{65} (iv) i^{-13}

   (b) Simplify and plot on an Argand diagram:

     (i) $(3 + i)(5 - 2i)$

     (ii) $(8 + 4i) + (2 - i)$

     (iii) $\dfrac{7 - i}{2 + i}$

3. $z_1 = 2 + i$, $z_2 = -3 + 2i$, $z_3 = -5 + 2i$, and $\theta = 1 + i$.

   (i) Plot z_1, z_2 and z_3 on an Argand diagram.

   (ii) Evaluate $z_1 + \theta$, $z_2 + \theta$ and $z_3 + \theta$.

   (iii) Plot the answers to part (ii) on an Argand diagram.

   (iv) Describe the transformation that is the addition of θ.

4. Let $z_1 = 2 - i$ and let $z_2 = 6 + i$.

   (i) Find $\dfrac{z_1}{z_2}$.

   (ii) Calculate $|z_1|$ and $|z_2|$.

   (iii) Investigate if $\left|\dfrac{z_1}{z_2}\right| = \dfrac{|z_1|}{|z_2|}$.

5. Solve the following cubic equations, given that each equation has one integer root:

   (i) $z^3 + 11z^2 + 49z - 61 = 0$

   (ii) $z^3 - 5z^2 + 16z - 30 = 0$

   (iii) $z^3 + 8z^2 + 70z + 116 = 0$

   (iv) $z^3 - 2z + 4 = 0$

6. $z_1 = -4 - 5i$

   (i) Find z_2, if $z_2 = -iz_1$.

   (ii) Plot z_1, and z_2 on an Argand diagram.

   (iii) Describe the transformation that maps z_1 onto z_2.

7. Write the following in polar form:

(i) $\left[3\left(\cos\dfrac{\pi}{15}+i\sin\dfrac{\pi}{15}\right)\right]\left[2\left(\cos\dfrac{\pi}{12}+i\sin\dfrac{\pi}{12}\right)\right]$

(ii) $\left[5\left(\cos\dfrac{\pi}{9}+i\sin\dfrac{\pi}{9}\right)\right]\left[6\left(\cos\dfrac{\pi}{11}+i\sin\dfrac{\pi}{11}\right)\right]$

(iii) $\dfrac{10\left(\cos\dfrac{\pi}{8}+i\sin\dfrac{\pi}{8}\right)}{2\left(\cos\dfrac{\pi}{18}+i\sin\dfrac{\pi}{18}\right)}$

(iv) $\dfrac{18\left(\cos\dfrac{\pi}{3}+i\sin\dfrac{\pi}{3}\right)}{9\left(\cos\dfrac{\pi}{27}+i\sin\dfrac{\pi}{27}\right)}$

8. $z = r(\cos\theta + i\sin\theta)$

Prove that $z^n = r^n(\cos n\theta + i\sin n\theta)$, for $n \in N$.

9. $z_1 = -2 + 3i$ and $z_2 = 3 + 2i$.

(i) Simplify $\dfrac{z_1}{z_2}$ and, hence, find the value of $\left(\dfrac{z_1}{z_2}\right)^9$.

(ii) Show that $\dfrac{|z_1|}{|z_2|} = \left|\dfrac{z_1}{z_2}\right|$.

10. Use the theorem of de Moivre to prove the identity

$$\sin 4\theta = 4\cos^3\theta\sin\theta - 4\cos\theta\sin^3\theta$$

11. $z = \dfrac{1}{\sqrt{3}} + i$

(i) Write z in polar form.

(ii) Use the theorem of de Moivre to write $\left(\dfrac{1}{\sqrt{3}} + i\right)^{20}$ in the form $a + bi$.

12. (i) Use de Moivre's Theorem to find the three roots of the equation $z^3 + 64 = 0$.

(ii) ω is a complex number such that $\omega\overline{\omega} - 2i\omega = 7 - 4i$, where $\overline{\omega}$ is the complex conjugate of ω.

Find the two possible values of ω. Express each in the form $p + qi$, $p, q \in R$.

Exam Questions

1. The complex number z satisfies the equation $|z| = |z + 2|$.

(i) Show that the real part of z is -1.

(ii) The complex number z also satisfies $|z| = 2$. Find the two possible values of the imaginary part of z and show these on an Argand diagram.

(iii) Write these two possible values of z in polar form.

NCCA Project Maths Pre-Leaving Certificate Sample Paper, February 2011

2. (a) $W = -1 + \sqrt{3}i$ is a complex number, where $i^2 = -1$.

(i) Write W in polar form.

(ii) Use de Moivre's Theorem to solve the equation $z^2 = -1 + \sqrt{3}i$, giving your answer(s) in rectangular form.

(b) Four complex numbers, z_1, z_2, z_3 and z_4, are shown on the Argand diagram.

They satisfy the following conditions:

$$z_2 = iz_1$$
$$z_3 = kz_1, \text{ where } k \in R$$
$$z_4 = z_2 + z_3$$

The same scale is used on both axes.

(i) Identify which number is which, by labelling the points on the diagram.

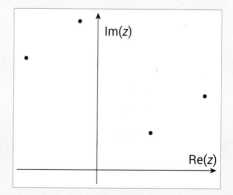

(ii) Write down the approximate value of k.

SEC Project Maths Leaving Certificate Higher Level, Sample Paper 1, 2011

3. $z = \dfrac{4}{1 + \sqrt{3}i}$ is a complex number, where $i^2 = -1$.

   (a) Verify that z can be written as $1 - \sqrt{3}i$.

   (b) Plot z on an Argand diagram and write z in polar form.

   (c) Use de Moivre's Theorem to show that $z^{10} = -2^9(1 - \sqrt{3}i)$.

   SEC Leaving Certificate Higher Level, Paper 1, 2013

4. (a) The complex numbers z_1, z_2 and z_3 are such that $\dfrac{2}{z_1} = \dfrac{1}{z_2} + \dfrac{1}{z_3}$, $z_2 = 2 + 3i$ and $z_3 = 3 - 2i$, where $i^2 = -1$. Write z_1 in the form $a + bi$, where $a, b \in Z$.

   (b) Let ω be a complex number such that $\omega^n = 1$, $\omega \neq 1$, and $S = 1 + \omega + \omega^2 + \ldots + \omega^{n-1}$. Use the formula for the sum of a finite geometric series to write the value of S in its simplest form.

   SEC Leaving Certificate Higher Level, Paper 1, 2015

5. Let G be the set $\{x + yi \mid x, y \in Z, i^2 = -1\}$. Consider the Venn diagram below.

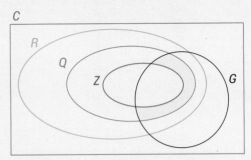

   (a) There are three regions in the diagram that represent empty sets. One of these is shaded. Shade in the other two.

   (b) Insert each of the following numbers in its correct region on the diagram:

   $\sqrt{2}$ 7 $\sqrt{3} - i$

   $4 + 3i$ $\dfrac{1}{2}$ $\dfrac{1}{2} + 2i$

   (c) Consider the product ab, where $a \in G$ and $b \in Q$. There is a non-empty region in the diagram where ab cannot be. Write the word 'here' in this region.

   SEC Project Maths Leaving Certificate Higher Level, Paper 1, 2012

Solutions and chapter summary available online

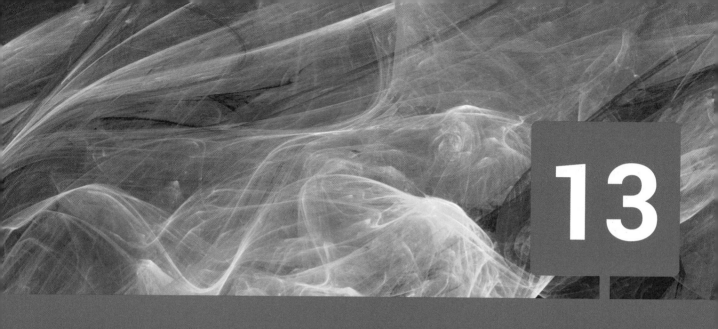

13

Differential Calculus I

In this chapter you will learn about:

- Limits and continuity
- Differentiation of linear and quadratic functions from first principles
- Differentiation of polynomials by rule
- Differentiation of functions with rational powers
- The Chain Rule for differentiation of composite functions
- Differentiation of products and quotients
- Differentiation of trigonometric functions
- Differentiation of inverse trigonometric functions
- Differentiation of exponential functions
- Differentiation of logarithmic functions
- Differentiating to find the slope of a tangent to a circle

You should remember...

- How to solve linear and quadratic equations
- How to find the equation of a line

Key words

- Derivative
- First principles
- Slope
- Constant
- Product Rule
- Quotient Rule
- Chain Rule
- Polynomial

It is important to have studied the trigonometry in Book 2, Sections 7.1–7.9 before proceeding with this chapter.

13.1 Calculus

Over three hundred years ago, the branch of mathematics known as calculus was first developed.

Isaac Newton (1642–1727) was an English physicist and mathematician. In his twenties, he started work on a new mathematics – the 'mathematics of moving things' or 'calculus'. He described this new mathematics to friends but did not publish any account of how he did it.

Isaac Newton
(1642–1727)

Gottfried Leibniz
(1646–1716)

At the same time, a young German mathematician called Gottfried Leibniz (1646–1716), working independently of Newton, came up with a different version of the same thing.

Both men are now acknowledged as having invented this vital branch of mathematics.

13.2 Limits and Continuity

Consider the function $f(x) = \dfrac{x^2}{x}$, with real inputs. What value does $f(x)$ tend towards as x gets closer to zero? Let us complete an input–output table to investigate.

x	$f(x)$
−1	−1
−0.5	−0.5
−0.25	−0.25
−0.125	−0.125
−0.0625	−0.0625

Approaching from the left

x	$f(x)$
1	1
0.5	0.5
0.25	0.25
0.125	0.125
0.0625	0.0625

Approaching from the right

We can see that, as x gets closer and closer to zero (approaching from either side), $f(x)$ tends towards a value of zero.

In words, we say: 'The limit of the function $f(x) = \dfrac{x^2}{x}$ as x tends to 0 is equal to 0.'

In notation, we write: $\displaystyle\lim_{x \to 0} f(x) = \lim_{x \to 0} \dfrac{x^2}{x} = 0$.

If $\displaystyle\lim_{x \to a} f(x)$ exists, then $\displaystyle\lim_{x \to a^+} f(x) = \lim_{x \to a^-} f(x)$.

- The notation $\displaystyle\lim_{x \to a^-} f(x)$ indicates that a is being approached from the left.

- The notation $\displaystyle\lim_{x \to a^+} f(x)$ indicates that a is being approached from the right.

- The notation $\displaystyle\lim_{x \to a} f(x)$ indicates that a is being approached from either side.

Continuity

What would a graph of the function $f(x) = \dfrac{x^2}{x}$, with real inputs, look like?

It would have a 'break' in it at $x = 0$, since $f(x)$ is not defined at $x = 0$.

The reason is that $f(0) = \dfrac{(0)^2}{0} = \dfrac{0}{0}$, which is indeterminate.

We say that f is not continuous at $x = 0$, since there is a 'break' in the graph at $x = 0$. To draw a graph of this function, your pen would have to leave the page at $x = 0$. On the other hand:

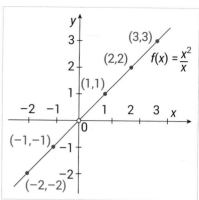

> If a function $g(x)$ is continuous at a particular input value, $x = c$, then $\lim\limits_{x \to c} g(x) = g(c)$. The converse is also true.

Note that with the previous function $f(x) = \dfrac{x^2}{x}$, although $\lim\limits_{x \to 0} f(x) = 0$, $f(0)$ was indeterminate. Therefore, $\lim\limits_{x \to 0} f(x) \neq f(0)$, so f was not continuous at $x = 0$.

Worked Example 13.1

Consider the function H given by:

$$H(x) = \begin{cases} 3x + 2, & \text{for } x < 1 \\ 3x - 3, & \text{for } x \geq 1 \end{cases}$$

Graph the function H and find each of the following limits, if they exist.

(i) $\lim\limits_{x \to 3} H(x)$ (ii) $\lim\limits_{x \to 1} H(x)$

Solution

(i) We can check the limits from the left and the right both numerically (using a table) and graphically.

$x \to 3^- \ (x < 3)$	$H(x)$	$x \to 3^+ \ (x > 3)$	$H(x)$
2	3	4	9
2.5	4.5	3.5	7.5
2.9	5.7	3.1	6.3
2.99	5.97	3.01	6.03
2.999	5.997	3.001	6.003

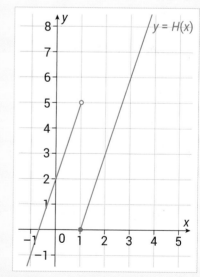

From the table, we can see that $\lim\limits_{x \to 3^+} H(x) = \lim\limits_{x \to 3^-} H(x) = 6$.

Therefore, $\lim\limits_{x \to 3} H(x) = 6$.

(ii)

$x \to 1^- \ (x < 1)$	$H(x)$	$x \to 1^+ \ (x > 1)$	$H(x)$
0	2	2	3
0.5	3.5	1.5	1.5
0.9	4.7	1.1	0.3
0.99	4.97	1.01	0.03
0.999	4.997	1.001	0.003

From the table, we can see that $\lim\limits_{x \to 1^+} H(x) = 0$ and $\lim\limits_{x \to 1^-} H(x) = 5$.

Therefore, $\lim\limits_{x \to 1} H(x)$ does not exist.

$H(x)$ is a **piecewise function**. This is a function whose definition changes depending on the value of the independent variable x.

$H(x)$ is defined differently for $x < 1$ and for $x \geq 1$, hence the split in the graph of $H(x)$.

Worked Example 13.2

The function $f(x) = \dfrac{1}{x - 2}$ is graphed in the domain $-4 \leqslant x \leqslant 7$, $x \neq 2$, $x \in R$.

Explain why the function f is not continuous at $x = 2$.

Solution

$x = 2$ is not in the domain of this function. Therefore, $f(2)$ does not exist. This implies that $\lim\limits_{x \to 2} f(x) \neq f(2)$. Hence, the function is not continuous at $x = 2$.

Alternative Method

$f(2) = \dfrac{1}{2 - 2}$

$= \dfrac{1}{0}$, which is not defined.

$\therefore$ f is not continuous at $x = 2$.

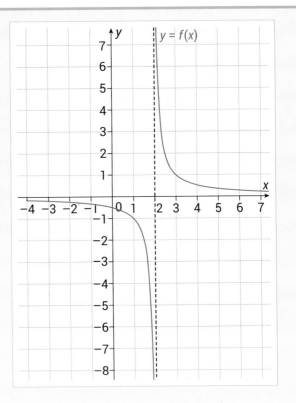

The line $x = 2$ shown on the graph is called an **asymptote**.

An asymptote is a line whose distance to a given curve tends to zero.

Worked Example 13.3

Show that the function $f(x) = 2x + 3$, $x \in R$, is continuous at $x = 2$.

Solution

Looking at the algebraic form of $f(x) = 2x + 3$, we can see that the function is defined over all $x \in R$ and is a linear function.

So f is continuous at $x = 2$.

Alternatively, using an input–output table:

x	$f(x)$	x	$f(x)$
1.0	5	3.0	9
1.5	6	2.5	8
1.8	6.6	2.2	7.4
1.9	6.8	2.1	7.2
1.95	6.9	2.05	7.1
1.99	6.98	2.01	7.02
1.995	6.99	2.005	7.01
1.999	6.998	2.001	7.002

$\left.\begin{array}{l} \lim\limits_{x \to 2^-} f(x) = 7 \\[2mm] \lim\limits_{x \to 2^+} f(x) = 7 \end{array}\right\}$ $\therefore$ $\lim\limits_{x \to 2} f(x)$ exists and equals 7.

Also, $f(2) = 2(2) + 3$
$= 4 + 3$
$= 7$

As $\lim\limits_{x \to 2} f(x) = f(2)$, f is continuous at $x = 2$.

Worked Example 13.4

Evaluate the following limits. (Assume that the limits exist.)

(i) $\lim\limits_{x \to 5} \dfrac{x^2 - 25}{x - 5}$ (ii) $\lim\limits_{x \to 2} \dfrac{x^3 - 8}{x - 2}$

Solution

(i) We can check the limits from the left and the right numerically (using a table) and/or graphically.

$$\text{Let } f(x) = \frac{x^2 - 25}{x - 5}.$$

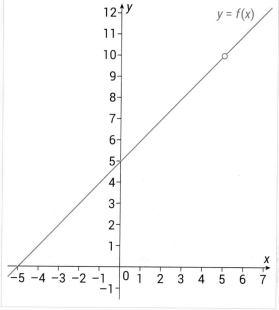

$x \to 5^- \ (x < 5)$	$f(x)$	$x \to 5^+ \ (x > 5)$	$f(x)$
4	9	6	11
4.5	9.5	5.5	10.5
4.9	9.9	5.1	10.1
4.99	9.99	5.01	10.01
4.999	9.999	5.001	10.001

From the table and/or graph, it is clear that:

$$\lim_{x \to 5} \frac{x^2 - 25}{x - 5} = 10$$

Algebraic Approach

We can shorten our work as follows:

$$\lim_{x \to 5} \frac{x^2 - 25}{x - 5} = \lim_{x \to 5} \frac{(x + 5)(x - 5)}{x - 5}$$
$$= \lim_{x \to 5} (x + 5)$$
$$= 5 + 5$$
$$= 10$$

(ii) Again, we can check the limits from the left and the right numerically (using a table) and/or graphically.

$$\text{Let } f(x) = \frac{x^3 - 8}{x - 2}.$$

From the table and/or graph, it is clear that:

$$\lim_{x \to 2} \frac{x^3 - 8}{x - 2} = 12$$

$x \to 2^- \ (x < 2)$	$f(x)$	$x \to 2^+ \ (x > 2)$	$f(x)$
1	7	3	19
1.5	9.25	2.5	15.25
1.9	11.41	2.1	12.61
1.99	11.9401	2.01	12.0601
1.999	11.994001	2.001	12.006001

Algebraic Approach

$$\lim_{x \to 2} \frac{x^3 - 8}{x - 2} = \lim_{x \to 2} \frac{(x - 2)(x^2 + 2x + 4)}{x - 2}$$
$$= \lim_{x \to 2} (x^2 + 2x + 4)$$
$$= (2)^2 + 2(2) + 4$$
$$= 12$$

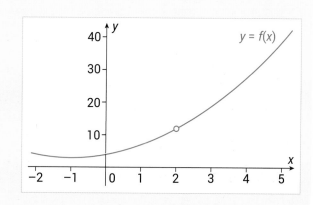

Exercise 13.1

1. Copy and complete the table to give values of the function $f(x) = 3x - 4$, $x \in R$, for x close to 2.

x	$f(x)$	x	$f(x)$
1.0		3.0	
1.5		2.5	
1.9		2.1	
1.99		2.01	

   (i) Use the table to evaluate $\lim_{x \to 2^+} f(x)$ and $\lim_{x \to 2^-} f(x)$.

   (ii) Hence, write down $\lim_{x \to 2} f(x)$.

2. Copy and complete the table to give the values of the function $f(x) = 5 - 2x$, $x \in R$, for x close to 3.

x	$f(x)$	x	$f(x)$
2.0		4.0	
2.5		3.5	
2.85		3.15	
2.995		3.005	

   (i) Use the table to evaluate $\lim_{x \to 3^+} f(x)$ and $\lim_{x \to 3^-} f(x)$.

   (ii) Hence, write down $\lim_{x \to 3} f(x)$.

3. Use an input–output table to evaluate $\lim_{x \to 4^+} f(x)$ and $\lim_{x \to 4^-} f(x)$, where $f(x) = 2x - 3$, $x \in R$.

   Does $\lim_{x \to 4} f(x)$ exist? Explain.

4. Use an input–output table to evaluate $\lim_{x \to 1^+} f(x)$ and $\lim_{x \to 1^-} f(x)$, where $f(x) = x^2 - 2x + 1$.

   Does $\lim_{x \to 1} f(x)$ exist? Explain.

5. Consider the function H given by:

   $$H(x) = \begin{cases} 2x + 2, & \text{for } x < 1 \\ 2x - 3, & \text{for } x \geq 1 \end{cases}$$

   Graph the function and find each of the following limits, if they exist:

   (i) $\lim_{x \to 3} H(x)$ (ii) $\lim_{x \to 1} H(x)$

6. Consider the function f given by

   $$f(x) = \begin{cases} 2x + 2, & \text{for } x < 0 \\ x^2, & \text{for } x \geq 0 \end{cases}$$

   Graph the function and find each of the following limits, if they exist:

   (i) $\lim_{x \to 2} f(x)$ (ii) $\lim_{x \to 0} f(x)$

7. An object falls through the air until it reaches a maximum speed, called its terminal velocity. The object then continues to fall at this terminal velocity. The distance, s metres, it falls is given by

   $$s(t) = \begin{cases} 6t + 0.3t^2 - 0.01t^3, & 0 \leq t \leq 10 \\ 80 + 3.6(t - 10), & t > 10 \end{cases}$$

   Graph the function $s(t)$ and find each of the following limits, if they exist:

   (i) $\lim_{t \to 11} s(t)$ (ii) $\lim_{t \to 10} s(t)$

8. A sprinter's velocity over the course of a particular 100 m race is approximated by the following model, where V is the velocity in metres per second, and t is the time in seconds from the starting signal:

   $$V(t) = \begin{cases} 0, & 0 \leq t < 0.2 \\ -0.5t^2 + 5t - 0.98, & 0.2 \leq t < 5 \\ 11.52, & t \geq 5 \end{cases}$$

   (a) Sketch the graph of V as a function of t for the first 7 seconds of the race.

   (b) Find each of the following limits, if they exist.

   (i) $\lim_{t \to 0.2} V$ (ii) $\lim_{t \to 5} V$ (iii) $\lim_{t \to 6} V$

9. Find the following limits (you may assume the limit exists in each case):

   (i) $\lim_{x \to 1} (3x + 4)$ (iv) $\lim_{x \to 5} \dfrac{x^2 - 25}{x - 5}$

   (ii) $\lim_{x \to 3} (3x^2 - 2)$ (v) $\lim_{x \to 2} \dfrac{x^3 - 8}{x - 2}$

   (iii) $\lim_{x \to 4} \dfrac{x^2 - 16}{x - 4}$

10. Find the following limits (you may assume the limit exists in each case):

   (i) $\lim_{x \to 2} \dfrac{x^2 - 4}{x^2 - x - 2}$ (iv) $\lim_{x \to 0} \dfrac{2x}{5x}$

   (ii) $\lim_{x \to 3} \dfrac{x^2 - 9}{x^2 + x - 12}$ (v) $\lim_{x \to 0} \dfrac{3x^2}{4x^2}$

   (iii) $\lim_{x \to 5} \dfrac{x^2 - 25}{x^3 - 125}$

13.3 Differentiation from First Principles

Unlike the slope of a line, the slope of a curve is constantly changing. We define the slope of a curve at a point P on the curve to be the slope of the tangent to the curve at the point P. On the curve shown, the slope of the tangent increases as x increases (or as the point P moves up the curve). We say the slope of the tangent is the instantaneous rate of change of y with respect to x.

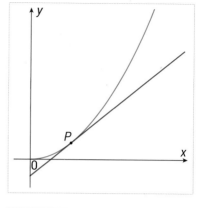

We can approximate the slope of a curve at a given point by taking a nearby point on the curve and finding the slope of the line joining this point to the given point. Such a line is called a secant line.

The slope of the secant line PQ is given by:

$$m = \frac{f(x + h) - f(x)}{x + h - x}, \text{ where } h \text{ is a small change in the input variable } x.$$

$$\therefore m = \frac{f(x + h) - f(x)}{h}$$

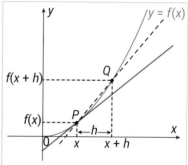

If we let h become smaller and smaller, the slope of PQ becomes closer and closer to the slope of the tangent to the curve at the given point P.

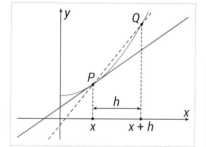 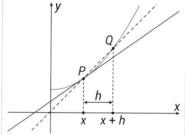 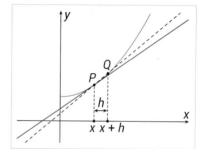

We say that the slope of the tangent is given by:

$$\frac{f(x + h) - f(x)}{h} \text{ as } h \text{ approaches zero,}$$

or more formally as:

$$\lim_{h \to 0} \frac{f(x + h) - f(x)}{h}$$

If $y = f(x)$, the slope of the tangent to the curve $y = f(x)$ at the point $(x, f(x))$ is:

$$\frac{dy}{dx} = f'(x) = \lim_{h \to 0} \frac{f(x + h) - f(x)}{h}$$

Both $\dfrac{dy}{dx}$ and $f'(x)$ stand for the slope of the tangent to the curve, or the gradient of the curve, $y = f(x)$.

$\dfrac{dy}{dx}$ is pronounced 'dee y dee x'.

$f'(x)$ is pronounced 'f prime of x'.

Differentiation is the process of finding this slope or gradient. Differentiation 'from first principles' involves calculating the difference between $f(x + h)$ and $f(x)$, dividing by h, and then taking the limit as h approaches zero.

$\dfrac{dy}{dx}$ or $f'(x)$ is called the **derivative** of the function $y = f(x)$ with respect to x.

DIFFERENTIAL CALCULUS I

Worked Example 13.5

Differentiate $f(x) = 2x + 3$, with respect to x, from first principles.

Solution

$$f(x) = 2x + 3$$

$$f(x + h) = 2(x + h) + 3$$

$$= 2x + 2h + 3$$

$$f(x + h) - f(x) = 2x + 2h + 3 - 2x - 3$$

$$= 2h$$

$$\frac{f(x + h) - f(x)}{h} = \frac{2h}{h}$$

$$= 2$$

$$\lim_{h \to 0} \frac{f(x + h) - f(x)}{h} = \lim_{h \to 0} 2$$

$$= 2$$

$$\therefore \frac{dy}{dx} = f'(x) = 2$$

> You can write
> $$\frac{dy}{dx} = 2 \text{ or } f'(x) = 2.$$

Worked Example 13.6

Differentiate $f(x) = 3 + 2x - x^2$, with respect to x, from first principles.

Solution

$$f(x) = 3 + 2x - x^2$$

$$f(x + h) = 3 + 2(x + h) - (x + h)^2$$

$$= 3 + 2x + 2h - (x^2 + 2hx + h^2)$$

$$= 3 + 2x + 2h - x^2 - 2hx - h^2$$

$$f(x + h) - f(x) = 3 + 2x + 2h - x^2 - 2hx - h^2 - (3 + 2x - x^2)$$

$$= 2h - 2hx - h^2$$

$$\frac{f(x + h) - f(x)}{h} = \frac{2h - 2hx - h^2}{h}$$

$$= 2 - 2x - h$$

$$\lim_{h \to 0} \frac{f(x + h) - f(x)}{h} = \lim_{h \to 0} (2 - 2x - h)$$

$$= 2 - 2x - 0$$

$$\therefore f'(x) = 2 - 2x$$

Exercise 13.2

1. $f(x) = 3x - 2, x \in R$

   (i) Graph $f(x)$ in the domain $-2 \leqslant x \leqslant 3$.

   (ii) Differentiate $f(x)$ with respect to x from first principles.

   (iii) Explain why the derivative of $f(x)$ is constant for all $x \in R$.

2. $f(x) = 5 - 6x, x \in R$

   (i) Graph $f(x)$ in the domain $-1 \leqslant x \leqslant 4$.

   (ii) Differentiate $f(x)$ with respect to x from first principles.

3. Differentiate the following functions with respect to x from first principles:

   (i) $f(x) = x^2$ (vi) $f(x) = 1 + 2x - x^2$

   (ii) $f(x) = x^2 + 2x$ (vii) $f(x) = -2x^2$

   (iii) $f(x) = x^2 + 2x + 1$ (viii) $f(x) = 5 - 2x^2$

   (iv) $f(x) = -x^2$ (ix) $f(x) = 5 - 3x - 2x^2$

   (v) $f(x) = 2x - x^2$

   > From page 18 in *Formulae and Tables*, the equation of a line may be found using
   > $$y - y_1 = m(x - x_1) \text{ or } y = mx + c.$$

4. The function $g(x) = 3x^2$ is defined for all $x \in R$.

   (i) Differentiate $g(x)$, with respect to x, from first principles.

   (ii) Hence, find the slope of the tangent to the curve $g(x) = 3x^2$ at the point $(1,3)$.

   (iii) Find the equation of the tangent to the graph of $g(x) = 3x^2$ at the point $(1,3)$. Write your answer in the form $y = mx + c$.

5. The function $h(x) = x^2 + 2x$ is defined for all $x \in R$.

   (i) Differentiate $h(x)$, with respect to x, from first principles.

   (ii) Find the equation of the tangent to the graph of $h(x) = x^2 + 2x$ at the point $(2,8)$. Write your answer in the form $ax + by + c = 0$.

6. The function $f(x) = 2 + 3x - x^2$ is defined for all $x \in R$.

   (i) Differentiate $f(x)$ with respect to x from first principles.

   (ii) Hence, find the slope of the tangent to the curve $f(x) = 2 + 3x - x^2$ at the point $(1,4)$.

   (iii) Write in the form $ax + by + c = 0$ the equation of the tangent to the graph of $f(x) = 2 + 3x - x^2$ at the point $(1,4)$.

7. Show from first principles that the derivative of $f(x) = 5x^2$ at $x = 1$ is 10.

8. Show from first principles that the derivative of $f(x) = 5x^2 - 2x + 5$ at $x = 2$ is 18.

9. The function $g(x) = 1 + 6x - 2x^2$ is defined for all $x \in R$.

   (i) Differentiate $g(x)$ with respect to x from first principles.

   (ii) Hence, find the co-ordinates of the point A on the graph of $g(x)$ where the tangent at A has a slope of 14.

13.4 Differentiating Polynomial Functions and Functions with Rational Powers

A polynomial function in x is a function of the form:

$$f(x) = a_n x^n + a_{n-1} x^{n-1} + \ldots + a_2 x^2 + a_1 x + a_0$$

where n is a non-negative integer and $a_0, a_1, \ldots, a_n$ are constant coefficients.

The following are examples of polynomial functions:

(i) $f(x) = 4x^4 + 5x^3 + 2x^2 + 3x - 8$ (iii) $h(x) = 3x + 4$

(ii) $g(x) = x^{100} - 99$ (iv) $p(x) = 5$

In this section we learn how to differentiate polynomial functions and functions with rational powers.

The Derivative of x^n

It is possible to derive the following rules using differentiation from first principles and the method of proof by induction:

Rule 1

If $y = x^n$, $n \in N$, then $\dfrac{dy}{dx} = nx^{n-1}$.

Rule 2

If $y = a$, where a is any constant, then $\dfrac{dy}{dx} = 0$.

Rule 3

If $y = ax^n$, where a is any constant and $n \in N$, then $\dfrac{dy}{dx} = anx^{n-1}$.

Rules for differentiating can be found on page 25 of *Formulae and Tables*.

Worked Example 13.7

Differentiate the following with respect to x:

(i) $f(x) = x^2$

(ii) $g(x) = 2x$

(iii) $y = 4$

Solution

(i) $f'(x) = 2x$

(ii) $g'(x) = 2$

(iii) $\dfrac{dy}{dx} = 0$

To differentiate a power of x, multiply by the power and reduce the power by 1.

DIFFERENTIAL CALCULUS I

Properties of Limits

The following are some important properties of limits:

Suppose that $\lim_{x \to a} f(x) = L$ and $\lim_{x \to a} g(x) = M$, where $L, M \in R$. Then the following properties apply:

(1) $\lim_{x \to a}[f(x) + g(x)] = \lim_{x \to a} f(x) + \lim_{x \to a} g(x)$ (Sum property)

(2) $\lim_{x \to a}[f(x) \times g(x)] = \lim_{x \to a} f(x) \times \lim_{x \to a} g(x)$ (Product property)

(3) $\lim_{x \to a} \dfrac{f(x)}{g(x)} = \dfrac{\lim_{x \to a} f(x)}{\lim_{x \to a} g(x)}$ $\left[\lim_{x \to a} g(x) \neq 0\right]$ (Quotient property)

(4) $\lim_{x \to a} \sqrt{f(x)} = \sqrt{\lim_{x \to a} f(x)}$ (Root property)

The Sum Rule

Rule 4

If $y = f(x) + g(x)$, then $\dfrac{dy}{dx} = \dfrac{df}{dx} + \dfrac{dg}{dx}$.

Worked Example 13.8

(i) If $f(x) = x^3 + 5x^2 - 6x + 7$, find $f'(x)$.

(ii) If $y = x^2 - 3x + 11$, find the value of $\dfrac{dy}{dx}$ when $x = 1$.

Solution

(i) $f'(x) = 3x^2 + 10x - 6$ (Differentiate term by term.)

(ii) $\dfrac{dy}{dx} = 2x - 3$

$\dfrac{dy}{dx}\Big|_{x=1} = 2(1) - 3$

$= 2 - 3$

$= -1$

Rational Powers

Rule 5

If $y = x^n, n \in Q$,   (Q is the set of rationals)

then $\dfrac{dy}{dx} = nx^{n-1}$.

The power rule for rational powers can be proved using the binomial theorem.

Worked Example 13.9

If $f(x) = \sqrt{x} - \sqrt{x^3} - 8x$, find $f'(x)$.

Solution

Step 1   Write all terms of the expression in index form.

$f(x) = x^{\frac{1}{2}} - x^{\frac{3}{2}} - 8x$

Step 2   Differentiate the expression.

$f'(x) = \dfrac{1}{2}x^{-\frac{1}{2}} - \dfrac{3}{2}x^{\frac{1}{2}} - 8$

$f'(x) = \dfrac{1}{2\sqrt{x}} - \dfrac{3}{2}\sqrt{x} - 8$

Worked Example 13.10

A graph of the cubic function $f(x) = 2x^3 + 5x^2 + x - 3$ is shown.
The tangent to $y = f(x)$ at the point $(0, -3)$ is also shown on the diagram.

  (i) Write down $f'(x)$, the derivative of $f(x)$.

 (ii) Hence, find the slope of the tangent to $y = f(x)$ at $(0, -3)$.

(iii) Find the equation of the tangent to the curve at $(0, -3)$.

(iv) Calculate the area enclosed between the tangent, the x-axis and the y-axis.

Solution

  (i) $f(x) = 2x^3 + 5x^2 + x - 3$

      $f'(x) = 6x^2 + 10x + 1$

 (ii) To find the slope of the tangent to $y = f(x)$ at $(0, -3)$,
we need to find $f'(0)$.

      $f'(0) = 6(0)^2 + 10(0) + 1$

          $= 1$

     Therefore, the slope of the tangent to the curve at $(0, -3)$ is 1.

(iii) $y - y_1 = m(x - x_1)$ Point $(0, -3)$ $m = 1$

      $y + 3 = 1(x - 0)$

        $\therefore y = x - 3$

(iv) $y = x - 3$

$x = 0$	$y = 0$
$y = -3$	$0 = x - 3$
	$3 = x$

    $\therefore$ Intersects the x-axis at $(3, 0)$ and y-axis at $(0, -3)$.

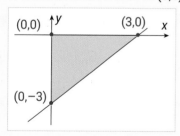

Area of shaded triangle $= \dfrac{1}{2}$ base × perpendicular height

$$= \frac{1}{2}(3) \times 3$$

$$= 4.5 \text{ units}^2$$

Exercise 13.3

1. Differentiate the following with respect to x:

  (i) $y = 4x^2 + 2x + 6$ (vi) $y = 2 - x$

 (ii) $y = x^{12} + 9x + 12$ (vii) $y = 4$

(iii) $y = 3x^3 + 4x^2 - 3x + 8$ (viii) $y = \dfrac{1}{2}$

(iv) $y = 3x$ (ix) $y = -\sqrt{2}$

 (v) $y = 5 - 2x$

2. $f(x) = x^2 - 2x + 12$

  (i) Find $f'(x)$.

 (ii) Evaluate $f'(100)$.

3. $g(x) = x^3 - x^2 + 4$

  (i) Find $g'(x)$.

 (ii) Evaluate $g'(-5)$.

4. $f(x) = 12x^8 + 12x^4 + 12x^2 + 12$

(i) Find $f'(x)$.

(ii) Evaluate $f'(1)$.

5. $f(x) = ax^3 + bx^2 + cx + d$, where a, b, c, and d are constant.

(i) Find $f'(x)$.

(ii) Find in terms of a, b, and c, $f'(1)$.

6. $g(x) = ax^3 + ax^2 + a$, where a is constant.

(i) Find $g'(x)$.

(ii) Show that $g(1 + \sqrt{2}) = g'(1 + \sqrt{2}) - a\sqrt{2}$.

7. $f(x) = x^p + 2x^{p-1}$, where $p \in N$.

(i) Find $f'(x)$.

(ii) Show that $f(1) = f'(1) + 5 - 3p$.

8. $f(x) = ax^q + a(1 - q)x^2$, where a, $q \in N$.

(i) Find $f'(x)$.

(ii) Show that $f(1) = f'(1)$.

9. The function $f(x) = 5 + 2x - 2x^2$ is shown, together with the tangent to $y = f(x)$ at the point $(2,1)$.

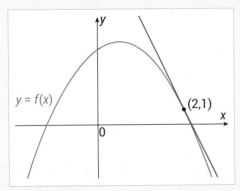

(i) Write down $f'(x)$, the derivative of $f(x)$ with respect to x.

(ii) Hence, find the slope of the tangent to $y = f(x)$ at $(2,1)$.

(iii) Find the equation of the tangent to the curve at $(2,1)$.

(iv) Find the co-ordinates of the point where this tangent intersects the y-axis.

10. The function $f(x) = x^2 + 2x + 1$ is shown together with the tangent to $f(x)$ at the point $(0,1)$.

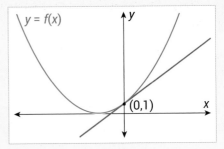

(i) Find $f'(x)$.

(ii) Find the slope of the tangent to $f(x)$ at $(0,1)$.

(iii) Find the equation of the tangent to $f(x)$ at $(0,1)$.

(iv) Find the co-ordinates of the point where this tangent intersects the x-axis.

11. For each of the following curves, find the equation of the tangent to the curve at the given point.

(i) $f(x) = x^2 - 2x - 1$ $(0,1)$

(ii) $f(x) = 2x^2 + 3x - 2$ $(1,3)$

(iii) $g(x) = 5 - x - x^2$ $(2,-1)$

(iv) $h(x) = 5x - 3x^2$ $(0,0)$

12. A graph of the cubic function $h(x) = x^3 + 5x^2 + 5x + 1$ is shown. The tangent to $y = h(x)$ at the point $(0,1)$ is also shown on the diagram.

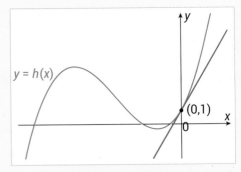

(i) Write down $h'(x)$, the derivative of $h(x)$ with respect to x.

(ii) Hence, find the slope of the tangent to $y = h(x)$ at $(0,1)$.

(iii) Find the equation of the tangent to the curve at $(0,1)$.

(iv) Find the co-ordinates of the point where the tangent intersects the x-axis.

(v) Hence, calculate the area enclosed between the tangent, the x-axis and the y-axis.

13. A graph of the cubic function
$g(x) = 1 + 2x + 3x^2 - x^3$ is shown. The tangent
to $y = g(x)$ at the point $(0,1)$ is also shown on the
diagram.

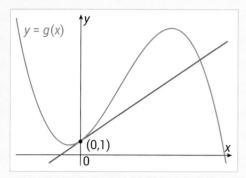

(i) Find $g'(x)$, the derivative of $g(x)$ with
respect to x.

(ii) Hence, find the slope of the tangent to
$y = g(x)$ at $(0,1)$.

(iii) Find the equation of the tangent to the
curve at $(0,1)$.

(iv) Find the co-ordinates of the point where
the tangent intersects the x-axis.

(v) Hence, calculate the area enclosed between
the tangent, the x-axis and the y-axis.

(vi) Show that the tangent also intersects the
graph of $y = g(x)$ at the point $(3,7)$.

14. Show that the tangent to the curve
$y = x^2 - 2x + 5$ at $(1,4)$ has a slope equal to 0.

15. Find the point on the curve $f(x) = x^2 - 6x + 11$
where the tangent is parallel to the x-axis.

16. Find $f'(x)$ for each of the following:

(i) $f(x) = x^{\frac{1}{2}}$

(ii) $f(x) = x^{\frac{1}{3}}$

(iii) $f(x) = x^{\frac{1}{4}}$

(iv) $f(x) = x^{\frac{3}{2}}$

(v) $f(x) = x^{-\frac{1}{2}}$

(vi) $f(x) = x^{-\frac{1}{3}}$

(vii) $f(x) = x^{-\frac{2}{5}}$

(viii) $f(x) = 2x^{\frac{1}{2}}$

(ix) $f(x) = 3x^{\frac{1}{3}}$

(x) $f(x) = 2x^{-\frac{1}{2}}$

(xi) $f(x) = -3x^{-\frac{1}{3}}$

(xii) $f(x) = 5x^{\frac{2}{5}}$

17. Write the following in the form kx^n, $k \in R$,
$n \in Q$ and hence find their derivatives:

(i) $\sqrt{x}$

(ii) $\sqrt[4]{x}$

(iii) $\sqrt[5]{x}$

(iv) $\sqrt[6]{x}$

(v) $\sqrt[9]{x}$

(vi) $\dfrac{1}{x^5}$

(vii) $\dfrac{1}{x^7}$

(viii) $\dfrac{1}{x^9}$

(ix) $\dfrac{1}{x^{10}}$

(x) $\sqrt{x}\,\sqrt[5]{x}$

(xi) $\sqrt[9]{x}\,\sqrt[5]{x}$

(xii) $\sqrt[p]{x}$

(xiii) $\dfrac{3}{x^3}$

(xiv) $\dfrac{2}{x^2}$

(xv) $\dfrac{3}{\sqrt{x}}$

(xvi) $\dfrac{2}{\sqrt[3]{x}}$

(xvii) $\dfrac{\sqrt{x}}{x^3}$

18. Differentiate the following with respect to x:

(i) $\dfrac{6x^2 + x^3 - 2x}{2x}$

(ii) $\dfrac{x^2 + x}{\sqrt{x}}$

(iii) $\dfrac{x^{\frac{1}{3}} + \sqrt{x} - x}{x}$

(iv) $\dfrac{x + 1}{\sqrt[3]{x}}$

19. Simplify the following expressions and then
differentiate with respect to x:

(i) $\dfrac{x^2 - 16}{x - 4}$

(ii) $\dfrac{x^3 - 1}{x - 1}$

(iii) $\dfrac{x^3 + 1}{x + 1}$

(iv) $\dfrac{x^4 - 16}{x - 2}$

20. The curve $y = ax^2 + bx$ passes through the point
$(2,4)$ with gradient 8. Find the values of a and b.

21. The curve $y = cx + \dfrac{d}{x}$ has gradient 6 at the point
$\left(\frac{1}{2},1\right)$. Find the values of c and d.

13.5 The Chain Rule

Consider the function $f(x) = \sqrt{x^2 + 5x - 2}$.

$f(x)$ is said to be a composite function. It consists of two functions composed together: an **INSIDE** function
$v(x) = x^2 + 5x - 2$ and an **OUTSIDE** function $u(x) = \sqrt{x}$. Therefore, we can write $f(x)$ as:

$$f(x) = u(v(x))$$

How do we find $f'(x)$, the derivative of this composite function $f(x)$, with respect to x?
To answer this question, consider the following problem:

If a car is going four times as fast as a bicycle and the bicycle is going three times as fast as a
runner, how many times as fast as the runner is the car going?

The car is going 4 × 3 = 12 times as fast as the runner.

If $\dfrac{dC}{dR}$ is the rate of change of the car with respect to the runner, $\dfrac{dC}{dB}$ the rate of change of the car with respect to the bicycle and $\dfrac{dB}{dR}$ the rate of change of the bicycle with respect to the runner, then we have the following formula:

$$\frac{dC}{dR} = \frac{dC}{dB} \times \frac{dB}{dR}$$

This is known as the **Chain Rule**.

> ### The Chain Rule
>
> u and v are both functions and f is the composite function defined by $f(x) = u(v(x))$.
>
> In this case, $f'(x) = \dfrac{du}{dv} \times \dfrac{dv}{dx}$.

The Chain Rule is on page 25 of *Formulae and Tables*.

Put loosely, the Chain Rule tells us to multiply the derivative of the OUTSIDE function by the derivative of the INSIDE function.

We can now differentiate $f(x) = \sqrt{x^2 + 5x - 2}$ with respect to x.

Worked Example 13.11

Differentiate the function $f(x) = \sqrt{x^2 + 5x - 2}$ with respect to x.

Solution

OUTSIDE function:

$u(v) = \sqrt{v}$

$\quad = v^{\frac{1}{2}}$

$\dfrac{du}{dv} = \dfrac{1}{2}v^{-\frac{1}{2}}$

$\quad = \dfrac{1}{2\sqrt{v}}$

INSIDE function:

$v(x) = x^2 + 5x - 2$

$\dfrac{dv}{dx} = 2x + 5$

By the Chain Rule:

$f'(x) = \dfrac{du}{dv} \cdot \dfrac{dv}{dx}$

$\quad = \dfrac{1}{2\sqrt{v}} \cdot (2x + 5)$

$\therefore f'(x) = \dfrac{2x + 5}{2\sqrt{x^2 + 5x - 2}}$

Worked Example 13.12

Differentiate $f(x) = (3x + 1)^3$, $x \in R$, with respect to x using the Chain Rule.

Solution

Let $y = v^3$ and let $v = 3x + 1$.

By the Chain Rule:

$f'(x) = \dfrac{dy}{dx} = \dfrac{dy}{dv} \times \dfrac{dv}{dx}$

$\quad y = v^3 \qquad\qquad v = 3x + 1$

$\quad \dfrac{dy}{dv} = 3v^2 \qquad\quad \dfrac{dv}{dx} = 3$

$\dfrac{dy}{dx} = \dfrac{dy}{dv} \times \dfrac{dv}{dx}$

$\therefore \dfrac{dy}{dx} = (3v^2)(3)$

$\quad = 9v^2$

$\therefore f'(x) = 9(3x + 1)^2$

After much practice, the Chain Rule can be applied directly to questions of the form $f(x) = [g(x)]^{power}$.

Step 1 Bring down power. **Step 3** Reduce power by 1.

Step 2 Write down 'bracket'. **Step 4** Differentiate bracket.

Worked Example 13.13

Differentiate $y = (x^2 + 3x)^3$ with respect to x.

Solution

$y = (x^2 + 3x)^3$

Using the Chain Rule:

$\dfrac{dy}{dx} = \boxed{3(x^2 + 3x)^2(2x + 3)}$

$= (6x + 9)(x^2 + 3x)^2$

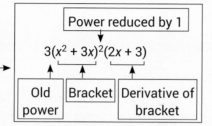

Power reduced by 1

$3(x^2 + 3x)^2(2x + 3)$

Old power | Bracket | Derivative of bracket

Exercise 13.4

1. Complete the table below. An example has been done for you.

Function $f(x)$	Inside Function $v(x)$	Outside Function $u(x)$
$\cos 3x$	$3x$	$\cos x$
$e^{6x - 5}$		
$\sqrt{4x^3}$		
$\ln(\tan x)$		
	$2x + 1$	$\sqrt{x}$
	$2x^2 + x$	x^3
$(4x - 5)^5$		

2. Differentiate, with respect to x, the following functions using the Chain Rule:

   (i) $y = (3x + 1)^3$ (iv) $y = (8x + 3)^3$

   (ii) $y = (x^2 + 7)^3$ (v) $y = (x^3 - 25)^2$

   (iii) $y = (3x^3 - 8)^5$ (vi) $y = (x^3 - 3x^2 + 2)^2$

3. Differentiate, with respect to x, the following functions using the Chain Rule:

   (i) $(7x + 1)^2$ (iv) $(x^2 + 1)^3$

   (ii) $(3 - x)^4$ (v) $(2 + 3x)^7$

   (iii) $(4x - 5)^5$ (vi) $(9 - 3x^2)^6$

4. Differentiate, with respect to x, the following functions using the Chain Rule:

   (i) $(x^2 + 2x)^{\frac{1}{2}}$ (v) $\sqrt{x^2 - 8}$

   (ii) $(2x^2 + x)^{\frac{1}{2}}$ (vi) $\sqrt[3]{2x^2 + 4}$

   (iii) $(x^2 - 2x + 4)^{\frac{1}{3}}$ (vii) $\sqrt[4]{x^2 + 8x}$

   (iv) $(x^2 + 2x)^{\frac{1}{4}}$

5. Differentiate, with respect to x, the following functions using the Chain Rule:

   (i) $\sqrt[5]{x^2 + 2x + 4}$ (vi) $\dfrac{1}{(x + 2)^2}$

   (ii) $(x^2 + 2x + 1)^{-1}$

   (iii) $(2x^2 - 3x + 4)^{-2}$ (vii) $\dfrac{1}{(x + 2)^3}$

   (iv) $(5x^2 + 3x + 8)^{-4}$

   (v) $\dfrac{1}{x + 2}$ (viii) $\dfrac{1}{(x^2 + 2x + 3)^5}$

6. Differentiate, with respect to x, the following functions using the Chain Rule:

   (i) $(2 - 6x)^3$ (iv) $\sqrt{4x^3 - 5}$

   (ii) $(2x^4 - 5)^{\frac{1}{2}}$

   (iii) $(x^2 + 3)^{-1}$ (v) $\dfrac{1}{\sqrt{x} + 7x}$

7. Differentiate, with respect to x, the following functions using the Chain Rule:

(i) $\dfrac{6}{\sqrt{8 - x^2}}$

(ii) $\dfrac{-3}{(x^3 + 6x)^{\frac{1}{3}}}$

(iii) $(2 + x^2)^{\frac{3}{4}}$

(iv) $(4 - x^2)^{-3}$

(v) $(x^7 - 6)^{-\frac{1}{2}}$

8. Differentiate, with respect to x, the following functions using the Chain Rule:

(i) $\sqrt[4]{6 - \sqrt{x}}$

(ii) $\left(1 + \dfrac{1}{x}\right)^{\frac{1}{2}}$

(iii) $\sqrt[3]{x^2 + \dfrac{1}{x^2}}$

(iv) $\sqrt{\dfrac{x + 1}{x^2}}$

(v) $\dfrac{1}{\sqrt{x^2 + 7x}}$

(vi) $\sqrt{\dfrac{8x^3 + 27}{2x + 3}}$

9. A tangent is drawn to the curve $y = \sqrt{x^3 + 1}$, $x \geq -1$, $x \in R$, at the point (2,3).

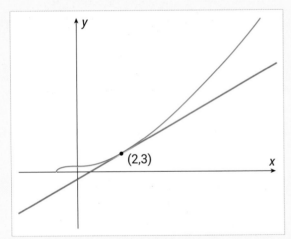

(i) Find the value of $\dfrac{dy}{dx}$ at $x = 2$.

(ii) Hence, find the equation of the tangent to the curve at (2,3).

(iii) Find the co-ordinates of the points where the tangent intersects the x-axis and y-axis.

(iv) Find the area of the triangle bounded by the tangent, the x-axis and the y-axis.

10. A tangent is drawn to the curve,
$y = \sqrt[4]{15x + 1}$, $x \geq -\dfrac{1}{15}$, $x \in R$, at the point (1,2).

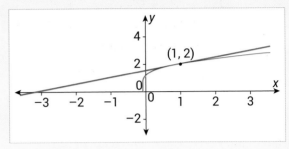

(i) Find the value of $\dfrac{dy}{dx}$ at $x = 1$.

(ii) Find the equation of the tangent to the curve at (1,2).

11. The function $f(x) = (2 - x^2)^5$ is defined for all values of $x \in R$.

(i) Find the equation of the tangent t_1 to the graph of $f(x)$ at the point (1,1).

(ii) $g(x)$ is the image of $f(x)$ by a horizontal translation and $g(x) = (2 - (x + a)^2)^5$ for some constant a. Find the value of a.

(iii) If t_2 is parallel to t_1, find the equation of t_2.

(iv) Find the distance between t_1 and t_2.

(v) Hence, find the area of the trapezoid bounded between the x-axis, the y-axis, t_1 and t_2.

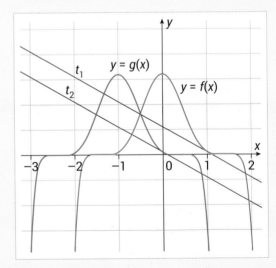

12. Let $y = [f(x)]^4$, where $f(x)$ is some function in x.

If $f(1) = 5$ and $\dfrac{dy}{dx} = -160$ at $x = 1$, find $f'(1)$.

13. Let $y = [g(x) + 3x^2]^3$, where $g(x)$ is a function in x.

What is the value of $g'(-1)$, given that $\dfrac{dy}{dx} = 3$ at $x = -1$ and $g(-1) = -5$?

14. Consider the function H given by

$$H(x) = \begin{cases} -x - 1, & \text{for } -3 \leqslant x < -1 \\ (x+1)^2, & \text{for } -1 \leqslant x < 0 \\ (x^2 - 1)^4, & \text{for } 0 \leqslant x < 1.2 \end{cases} \quad (x \in R)$$

Evaluate the following derivatives:

(i) $H'(-2)$ (ii) $H'(-0.5)$ (iii) $H'(0.5)$

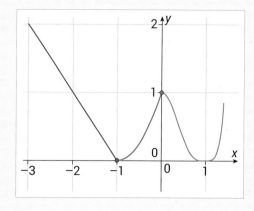

13.6 The Product Rule and Quotient Rule

We have already seen that the derivative of a sum is the sum of the derivatives.

However, the derivative of a product is **not** the product of the derivatives.

Similarly, the derivative of a quotient is **not** the quotient of the derivatives.

The Product Rule

If $u(x)$ and $v(x)$ are two functions
and $f(x) = u(x)v(x)$, then

$$f'(x) = u(x)v'(x) + v(x)u'(x)$$

OR

$$\frac{df}{dx} = u\frac{dv}{dx} + v\frac{du}{dx}$$

The Quotient Rule

If $u(x)$ and $v(x)$ are two functions
and $f(x) = \dfrac{u(x)}{v(x)}$, then

$$f'(x) = \frac{v(x)u'(x) - u(x)v'(x)}{(v(x))^2}$$

OR

$$\frac{df}{dx} = \frac{v\dfrac{du}{dx} - u\dfrac{dv}{dx}}{v^2}$$

These rules can be found on page 25 of *Formulae and Tables*. Both rules can be derived from first principles.

Worked Example 13.14

Differentiate the following functions with respect to x:

(i) $f(x) = (x^2 - 4)(3x^3 - x^2 + 9)$

(ii) $g(x) = \dfrac{2x - 3}{x^2 - 4}$

Solution

(i) Let $u = x^2 - 4$ and $v = 3x^3 - x^2 + 9$.

$$\frac{du}{dx} = 2x \quad \text{and} \quad \frac{dv}{dx} = 9x^2 - 2x$$

$$f'(x) = u\frac{dv}{dx} + v\frac{du}{dx}$$

$$= (x^2 - 4)(9x^2 - 2x) + (3x^3 - x^2 + 9)(2x)$$

$$= 9x^4 - 2x^3 - 36x^2 + 8x + 6x^4 - 2x^3 + 18x$$

$$\therefore f'(x) = 15x^4 - 4x^3 - 36x^2 + 26x$$

(ii) Let $u = 2x - 3$ and $v = x^2 - 4$.

$$\frac{du}{dx} = 2 \quad \text{and} \quad \frac{dv}{dx} = 2x$$

$$g'(x) = \frac{v\dfrac{du}{dx} - u\dfrac{dv}{dx}}{v^2}$$

$$= \frac{(x^2 - 4)(2) - (2x - 3)(2x)}{(x^2 - 4)^2}$$

$$= \frac{2x^2 - 8 - 4x^2 + 6x}{(x^2 - 4)^2}$$

$$\therefore g'(x) = \frac{-2x^2 + 6x - 8}{(x^2 - 4)^2}$$

Evaluate the derivative of each of the following functions at $x = 0$:

(i) $f(x) = \dfrac{(2x + 5)(x - 2)}{x + 3}$

(ii) $h(x) = \dfrac{(3x^2 + 4x + 2)^7}{x + 9}$

Solution

(i) **Step 1**

We begin by differentiating the numerator, as it is in the form of a product.

Let $u = (2x + 5)(x - 2)$.

$\dfrac{du}{dx} = (2x + 5)(1) + (x - 2)(2)$

(Product Rule)

$= 2x + 5 + 2x - 4$

$= 4x + 1$

Step 2

Let $v = x + 3$.

$\dfrac{dv}{dx} = 1$

$f'(x) = \dfrac{v\dfrac{du}{dx} - u\dfrac{dv}{dx}}{v^2}$

$f'(x) = \dfrac{(x + 3)(4x + 1) - (2x + 5)(x - 2)(1)}{(x + 3)^2}$

$= \dfrac{4x^2 + 13x + 3 - (2x^2 + x - 10)}{(x + 3)^2}$

$\therefore f'(x) = \dfrac{2x^2 + 12x + 13}{(x + 3)^2}$

Step 3

$f'(0) = \dfrac{2(0)^2 + 12(0) + 13}{(0 + 3)^2}$

$= \dfrac{13}{9}$

(ii) **Step 1**

Use the chain rule to differentiate the numerator.

Let $u = (3x^2 + 4x + 2)^7$.

$\dfrac{du}{dx} = 7(3x^2 + 4x + 2)^6(6x + 4)$

$= (42x + 28)(3x^2 + 4x + 2)^6$

Step 2

Let $v = x + 9$.

$\dfrac{dv}{dx} = 1$

$h'(x) = \dfrac{v\dfrac{du}{dx} - u\dfrac{dv}{dx}}{v^2}$

$h'(x) = \dfrac{(x + 9)(42x + 28)(3x^2 + 4x + 2)^6 - (3x^2 + 4x + 2)^7(1)}{(x + 9)^2}$

$= \dfrac{(3x^2 + 4x + 2)^6[(x + 9)(42x + 28) - (3x^2 + 4x + 2)]}{(x + 9)^2}$

$= \dfrac{(3x^2 + 4x + 2)^6(42x^2 + 406x + 252 - 3x^2 - 4x - 2)}{(x + 9)^2}$

$\therefore h'(x) = \dfrac{(3x^2 + 4x + 2)^6(39x^2 + 402x + 250)}{(x + 9)^2}$

Step 3

$h'(0) = \dfrac{(3(0)^2 + 4(0) + 2)^6(39(0)^2 + 402(0) + 250)}{(0 + 9)^2}$

$= \dfrac{2^6(250)}{9^2}$

$= \dfrac{16,000}{81}$

Exercise 13.5

1. Differentiate, with respect to x, the following functions in two ways:

   (a) Using the Product Rule

   (b) By multiplying the expressions before differentiating
   Compare your results as a check.

   (i) $y = (x^5)(x^{10})$

   (ii) $y = (x^9)(x^6)$

   (iii) $y = (3x + 2)(4x - 5)$

   (iv) $y = (x - 9)(x + 9)$

   (v) $y = x^2(x^3 + 5)$

2. Differentiate, with respect to x, the following functions in two ways:

   (a) Using the Product Rule

   (b) By multiplying the expressions before differentiating
   Compare your results as a check.

   (i) $f(x) = (4\sqrt{x} + 3)(x^2)$

   (ii) $g(x) = (5\sqrt{x} + 3)(x^3)$

   (iii) $h(x) = (2x - 3)(3x^2 + 2x + 5)$

   (iv) $y = (\sqrt{x} + 3)(3x - 2\sqrt{x} + 8)$

   (v) $f(x) = (2x + 3\sqrt{x} + 5)(\sqrt{x} + 4)$

3. Differentiate, with respect to x, the following functions in two ways:

   (a) Using the Quotient Rule

   (b) By dividing the expressions before differentiating
   Compare your results as a check.

   (i) $y = \dfrac{x^8}{x^2}$

   (ii) $y = \dfrac{x^2 - 9}{x + 3}$

   (iii) $f(x) = \dfrac{3x^5 + x^2}{x}$

   (iv) $g(x) = \dfrac{x^2 - 16}{x + 4}$

   (v) $y = \dfrac{3x^7 - x^3}{x^2}$

   (vi) $h(x) = \dfrac{x^3 + 27}{x + 3}$

4. Use the Product Rule to differentiate each of the following functions with respect to x:

   (i) $f(x) = (3x + 1)(5x + 2)$

   (ii) $g(x) = (x^2 - 1)(5x - 2)$

   (iii) $h(x) = (1 - x^2)(x^2 + 5x + 3)$

   (iv) $F(x) = \sqrt{x}(2x + 4)$

5. Use the Quotient Rule to differentiate each of the following functions with respect to x:

   (i) $f(x) = \dfrac{3x + 1}{7x + 2}$ (iv) $F(x) = \dfrac{2x + 1}{x^2 - 5}$

   (ii) $g(x) = \dfrac{5x + 2}{9x + 1}$ (v) $G(x) = \dfrac{1}{x + 2}$

   (iii) $h(x) = \dfrac{x}{x^2 + 1}$

   What other rule could you have used to differentiate the function in part (v)?

6. Find the value of the derivative of $g(x) = (x^2 + 2x - 3)(x^4 + 3x^2)$ at $x = 1$.

7. Find the value of the derivative of $h(x) = (x^8 - 9x^6 + 12)(x + 4)$ at $x = -1$.

8. Find the value of the derivative of
   $$f(x) = \frac{3x^2 + 4}{x^2 + 2} \text{ at } x = 1.$$

9. Find the value of the derivative of
   $$g(x) = \frac{3x + 4}{4x + 3} \text{ at } x = 0.$$

10. The graph of $F(x) = (5x^2 + 4x - 3)(2x^2 - 3x + 1)$, $x \in R$, is shown.

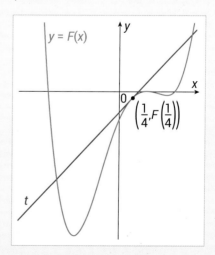

   (i) Find $F'(x)$, the derivative of $F(x)$.

(ii) t is a tangent to the graph at $x = \frac{1}{4}$.
Find the slope of t.

(iii) Find the equation of t.

11. The graph of $F(x) = \dfrac{3x^2 - 5x}{x^2 - 1}$, $-3 \leqslant x \leqslant 3$,

$x \in R$, is shown.

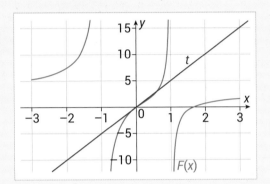

(i) t is a tangent to the graph at $x = 0$.
Use your graph to find the slope of t.

(ii) Use differentiation to find the slope of t.

(iii) Find, in the form $y = mx + c$, the equation of t.

12. The function $F(x) = \dfrac{x^2 - 1}{\sqrt{x}(x + 3)}$ is defined for all

$x > 0$, $x \in R$, and the function $h(x) = \sqrt{x}(x + 3)$ is
defined for all $x \geqslant 0$, $x \in R$.

(i) Find the derivative of $h(x)$.

(ii) Hence, find the derivative of $F(x)$.

(iii) What is the slope of the tangent to the
graph of $F(x)$ at $x = 1$?

13. The function $G(x) = \dfrac{(x^2 - 3x)(3x^3 - 8x^2 + 7x)}{x^2 - 9}$

is defined for $x \in R$, $x \neq \pm 3$.

(i) If $h(x) = (x^2 - 3x)(3x^3 - 8x^2 + 7x)$, find $h'(x)$,
the derivative of $h(x)$.

(ii) Hence, find $G'(1)$.

14. The function $H(x) = \dfrac{x^2 + 4}{(3x^3 - x^2)^{10}}$ is defined for

$x \in R$, $x \neq 0$, $x \neq \frac{1}{3}$.

(i) If $g(x) = (3x^3 - x^2)^{10}$, find $g'(x)$, the
derivative of $g(x)$.

(ii) Hence, find $H'(x)$, the derivative of $H(x)$.

13.7 Trigonometric Functions

If we sketch the graph of $f(x) = \sin x$, $0 \leqslant x \leqslant 5\pi$, and use the interpretation of $f'(x)$ as the slope of the
tangent to the sine curve in order to sketch the graph $f'(x)$, then it looks as if the resulting graph may be
the same as the cosine curve.

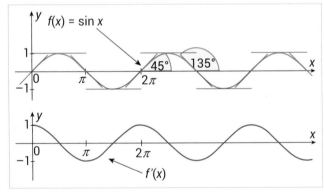

x	0	$\dfrac{\pi}{2}$	π	$\dfrac{3\pi}{2}$	2π	$\dfrac{5\pi}{2}$	3π	$\dfrac{7\pi}{2}$	4π	$\dfrac{9\pi}{2}$	5π
Slope of tangent	1	0	−1	0	1	0	−1	0	1	0	−1

Indeed, the following can be proved from first principles:

$f(x)$	$f'(x)$
$\sin x$	$\cos x$
$\cos x$	$-\sin x$
$\tan x$	$\sec^2 x$

- The derivative of $\sin x$ is $\cos x$.
- The derivative of $\cos x$ is $-\sin x$.
- The derivative of $\tan x$ is $\sec^2 x$.

The derivatives of $\sin x$, $\cos x$ and $\tan x$ are given on page 25 of *Formulae and Tables*.

Worked Example 13.16

Use the Chain Rule to differentiate each of the following functions with respect to x:

(i) $f(x) = \cos 4x$ (iii) $h(x) = \sqrt{\sin x}$

(ii) $g(x) = \tan^4 3x$

Solution

(i) $f(x) = \cos 4x$

$$y = \cos v \qquad v = 4x$$
$$\frac{dy}{dv} = -\sin v \text{ and } \frac{dv}{dx} = 4$$

By the Chain Rule:
$$\frac{dy}{dx} = \frac{dy}{dv} \times \frac{dv}{dx}$$
$$\therefore f'(x) = (-\sin v) \times 4$$
$$= -4\sin 4x \quad \text{(replacing } v \text{ with } 4x\text{)}$$

(ii) $g(x) = \tan^4 3x = (\tan 3x)^4$

$$y = v^4 \qquad v = \tan 3x$$

$$\frac{dy}{dv} = 4v^3 \qquad \frac{dv}{dx} = 3\sec^2 3x \quad \text{(We use the Chain Rule to get } \frac{dv}{dx}.\text{)}$$

By the Chain Rule:
$$\frac{dy}{dx} = \frac{dy}{dv} \times \frac{dv}{dx}$$
$$\therefore g'(x) = 4v^3 \times 3\sec^2 3x$$
$$= 12(\tan 3x)^3 \sec^2 3x$$
$$= 12\tan^3 3x \sec^2 3x$$

(iii) $h(x) = \sqrt{\sin x}$
$$= (\sin x)^{\frac{1}{2}}$$
$$y = v^{\frac{1}{2}} \qquad v = \sin x$$
$$\frac{dy}{dv} = \frac{1}{2}v^{-\frac{1}{2}} \qquad \frac{dv}{dx} = \cos x$$

By the Chain Rule:
$$\frac{dy}{dx} = \frac{dy}{dv} \times \frac{dv}{dx}$$
$$\therefore h'(x) = \frac{1}{2}v^{-\frac{1}{2}} \times \cos x$$
$$= \frac{1}{2}(\sin x)^{-\frac{1}{2}}\cos x$$
$$= \frac{\cos x}{2\sqrt{\sin x}}$$

To differentiate functions of the form $f(x) = \sin^n(mx)$, it is often useful to use the following shortened version of the Chain Rule:

$$f'(x) = \underbrace{n\sin^{n-1}(mx)}_{\substack{\text{Differentiate} \\ \text{"power term"}}} \underbrace{(\cos mx)}_{\substack{\text{Differentiate} \\ \text{trigonometric} \\ \text{function}}} \underbrace{(m)}_{\substack{\text{Differentiate} \\ \text{angle}}}$$

A similar approach can be taken if another trigonometric function is used.

Worked Example 13.17

Differentiate the function $g(x) = \cos^4 3x$ with respect to x.

Solution
$$g'(x) = \underbrace{4(\cos 3x)^3}_{\substack{\text{Power} \\ \text{term}}} \underbrace{(-\sin 3x)}_{\substack{\text{Trigonometric} \\ \text{function}}} \underbrace{(3)}_{\text{Angle}}$$

$$= -12\cos^3 3x \sin 3x$$

Worked Example 13.18

Differentiate the function $f(x) = x \sin x$ with respect to x.

Hence, find the slope of the tangent to the curve $f(x) = x \sin x$ at the point $(\pi, 0)$.

Solution

$f(x)$ is a product of two other functions of x, namely $u(x) = x$ and $v(x) = \sin x$.

Therefore, the Product Rule can be used to differentiate $f(x)$.

Let $u = x$ and $v = \sin x$.

$$\frac{du}{dx} = 1 \text{ and } \frac{dv}{dx} = \cos x$$

$$\frac{df}{dx} = u\frac{dv}{dx} + v\frac{du}{dx}$$

$$\therefore f'(x) = (x)(\cos x) + (\sin x)(1)$$

$$= x \cos x + \sin x$$

$$f'(\pi) = (\pi)(\cos \pi) + \sin \pi$$

$$= (\pi)(-1) + 0$$

$$= -\pi$$

Hence, the slope of the tangent to the curve at the point $(\pi, 0)$ is $-\pi$.

Sometimes it is necessary to use some of the trigonometric identities on pages 13 to 15 of *Formulae and Tables*.

Worked Example 13.19

Let $f(x) = \sin^4 x + \cos^4 x$.

Find $f'(x)$, the derivative of $f(x)$ and express it in the form $k \sin px$, where $k, p \in Z$.

Solution

$$f'(x) = 4 \sin^3 x \cos x - 4 \cos^3 x \sin x$$

$$= 4 \sin x \cos x(\sin^2 x - \cos^2 x)$$

$$= 2(2 \sin x \cos x)(-\cos 2x) \quad \text{(Formulae and Tables, page 14)}$$

$$= -2 \sin 2x \cos 2x \quad \text{(Formulae and Tables, page 14)}$$

$$= -\sin 4x \quad (\sin 2A = 2 \sin A \cos A$$

$$\Rightarrow \sin 4x = 2 \sin 2x \cos 2x)$$

Exercise 13.6

1. Write down the derivative of each of the following expressions (with respect to the variable concerned):

   (i) $\sin x + \cos x$

   (ii) $3 \cos \theta$

   (iii) $\sin \theta + 5$

   (iv) $4 \sin \theta - 8$

   (v) $2 \cos x - 3 \sin x$

   (vi) $3 \tan \theta$

2. Find the gradient of each curve at the point whose x co-ordinate is given:

   (i) $y = \sin x, x = \frac{\pi}{2}$

   (ii) $y = \sin x, x = 0$

   (iii) $y = \cos x, x = \pi$

   (iv) $y = -2 \sin x, x = \frac{\pi}{4}$

   (v) $y = x - \sin x, x = \frac{\pi}{2}$

3. Find the equation of the tangent to the curve $y = \cos \theta + 3 \sin \theta$, at the point where $\theta = \frac{\pi}{2}$.

4. Use the Product Rule to differentiate the following expressions:

   (i) $x \sin x$

   (ii) $x \cos x$

   (iii) $x^2 \tan x$

   (iv) $(x^2 + 1) \sin x$

   (v) $(x^3 + 1) \cos x$

   (vi) $\sin x \cos x$

   (vii) $\sin x \tan x$

   (viii) $\cos x \tan x$

   (ix) $(x + \sin x) \cos x$

5. Use the Quotient Rule to differentiate the following expressions:

(i) $\dfrac{2x}{\sin x}$

(vi) $\dfrac{\tan x}{x^2 + 1}$

(ii) $\dfrac{x}{\cos x}$

(vii) $\dfrac{\tan x}{\sin x}$

(iii) $\dfrac{x}{\tan x}$

(viii) $\dfrac{\sin x}{\cos x}$

(iv) $\dfrac{x^2 + 1}{\sin x}$

(ix) $\dfrac{\cos x}{\tan x}$

(v) $\dfrac{\cos x}{x + 1}$

6. Use the Product or Quotient Rules to differentiate the following functions with respect to x:

(i) $F(x) = 2x \cos x$

(iv) $g(x) = \dfrac{x}{\sin x}$

(ii) $G(x) = x^2 \sin x$

(iii) $f(x) = x \tan x$

(v) $H(x) = \dfrac{4x}{\cos x}$

7. Use the Chain Rule to find the derivative of each of the following expressions:

(i) $\sin 3x$

(v) $\cos (8x - 2)$

(ii) $\cos 4x$

(vi) $\tan (3x + 4)$

(iii) $\tan 5x$

(vii) $2 \sin 5x$

(iv) $\sin (3x + 4)$

(viii) $3 \cos 4x$

8. Find the derivative of each of the following functions with respect to x:

(i) $F(x) = \sin 5x$

(ii) $G(x) = 3 \cos 3x$

(iii) $H(x) = 7 \tan 5x$

(iv) $f(x) = 2 \sin 3x + 5 \cos 2x$

(v) $g(x) = \tan 2x + \tan 3x$

9. Find the derivative of each of the following functions with respect to x:

(i) $f(x) = \sin^3 x$

(iv) $f(x) = \sin^5 x$

(ii) $f(x) = \cos^2 x$

(v) $f(x) = \cos^6 x$

(iii) $f(x) = \tan^4 x$

(vi) $f(x) = \tan^7 x$

10. Find the derivative of each of the following functions with respect to x:

(i) $f(x) = \sin^3 2x$

(iv) $f(x) = \sin^5 3x$

(ii) $f(x) = \cos^2 3x$

(v) $f(x) = \cos^6 4x$

(iii) $f(x) = \tan^4 5x$

(vi) $f(x) = \tan^8 2x$

11. Find the derivative of each of the following functions with respect to x:

(i) $F(x) = \sin^2 x$

(iv) $f(x) = \sin^2 2x + \cos^2 3x$

(ii) $G(x) = \tan^2 x$

(v) $g(x) = \tan^4 3x + \tan^5 4x$

(iii) $H(x) = \cos^3 5x$

12. The function $f(x) = x \cos x$ is defined for all $x \in R$.

(i) Find $f'(x)$, the derivative of $f(x)$.

(ii) Hence, find the equation of the tangent to $f(x) = x \cos x$ at $x = \dfrac{3\pi}{2}$.

13. $\dfrac{d(\sin x)}{dx} = \cos x$ and $\dfrac{d(\cos x)}{dx} = -\sin x$

Use the Chain or Quotient Rule to differentiate the following with respect to x:

(i) $\sec x$ (ii) $\operatorname{cosec} x$ (iii) $\cot x$

14. The graph of the function $f(x) = \cos x \sin x$, $0 \leqslant x \leqslant 2\pi$ is shown.

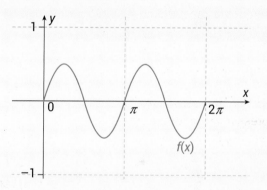

(i) Show that $f'(x) = \cos 2x$.

(ii) Hence, find the equation of the tangent to $y = f(x)$ at $x = \dfrac{11\pi}{8}$.

(iii) $g(x) = x f(x)$ is defined for $0 \leqslant x \leqslant 2\pi$.

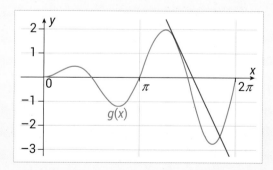

Find the equation of the tangent to $y = g(x)$ at $x = \dfrac{11\pi}{8}$.

15. The function $f(\theta) = \frac{1}{3} \sin 3\theta + 3 \sin \theta$ is defined for all $\theta \in R$.

   (i) Find $f'(\theta)$, the derivative of $f(\theta)$.

   (ii) Hence, find positive integers a and b such that $f'(\theta) = a \cos^b \theta$.

16. Given that $f(\theta) = \sin(\theta + \pi) \cos(\theta - \pi)$, find the derivative of $f(\theta)$ and express it in the form $\cos n\theta$, where $n \in Z$.

13.8 Differentiation of Inverse Trigonometric Functions

The functions $\sin^{-1} x$, $\cos^{-1} x$ and $\tan^{-1} x$, can also be differentiated.

$f(x)$	$f'(x)$
$\cos^{-1} \dfrac{x}{a}$	$-\dfrac{1}{\sqrt{a^2 - x^2}}$
$\sin^{-1} \dfrac{x}{a}$	$\dfrac{1}{\sqrt{a^2 - x^2}}$
$\tan^{-1} \dfrac{x}{a}$	$\dfrac{a}{a^2 + x^2}$

These rules are on page 25 of *Formulae and Tables*.

Worked Example 13.20

Differentiate the function $y = \sin^{-1} \dfrac{x}{a}$ with respect to x, where $x \in R$ and a is a non-zero constant.

Solution

$y = \sin^{-1} \dfrac{x}{a}$

$\Rightarrow \sin y = \dfrac{x}{a}$

$\Rightarrow x = a \sin y$

So, $\dfrac{dx}{dy} = a \cos y$.

$\Rightarrow \dfrac{dy}{dx} = \dfrac{1}{a \cos y}$

$\dfrac{dy}{dx} = \dfrac{1}{a \left[\dfrac{\sqrt{a^2 - x^2}}{a} \right]}$ (see work on right side)

$\therefore \dfrac{dy}{dx} = \dfrac{1}{\sqrt{a^2 - x^2}}$

When using the $\sin^{-1}$ function, we limit ourselves to the principal value. The principal value is discussed in more detail in Book 2, Chapter 7.

So, for $y = \sin^{-1} \dfrac{x}{a}$, $y \in \left[-\dfrac{\pi}{2}, \dfrac{\pi}{2} \right]$.

If $0 < y < \dfrac{\pi}{2}$, we can construct a right-angled triangle containing y.

Let us assume that $x, a > 0$.

$\sin y = \dfrac{x}{a}$

By Pythagoras' theorem, the third side is of length $\sqrt{a^2 - x^2}$.

$\therefore \cos y = \dfrac{\sqrt{a^2 - x^2}}{a}$

Worked Example 13.21

Find the domain of each of the following functions:

   (i) $y = \sin^{-1} x$

   (ii) $y = \sin^{-1}(x + 2)$

   (iii) $y = \sin^{-1}(3x - 2)$

Solution

(i) $y = \sin^{-1} x \Rightarrow x = \sin y$

Since $-1 \leqslant \sin y \leqslant 1, \Rightarrow -1 \leqslant x \leqslant 1$.

Domain $[-1, 1]$

(ii) $y = \sin^{-1}(x + 2)$

$-1 \leqslant x + 2 \leqslant 1$

$-1 \leqslant x + 2$	$x + 2 \leqslant 1$
$-3 \leqslant x$	$x \leqslant -1$

$-3 \leqslant x \leqslant -1$

Domain: $[-3, -1]$

(iii) $y = \sin^{-1}(3x - 2)$

$-1 \leqslant 3x - 2 \leqslant 1$

$-1 \leqslant 3x - 2$	$3x - 2 \leqslant 1$
$1 \leqslant 3x$	$3x \leqslant 3$
$\dfrac{1}{3} \leqslant x$	$x \leqslant 1$

$\dfrac{1}{3} \leqslant x \leqslant 1$

Domain: $\left[\dfrac{1}{3}, 1\right]$

Worked Example 13.22

Differentiate the function $y = \sin^{-1}\left(\dfrac{1}{x^2}\right)$ with respect to x $(x > 1, x \in R)$.

Solution

$y = \sin^{-1}\left(\dfrac{1}{x^2}\right)$

Let $y = \sin^{-1} v$. $v = \dfrac{1}{x^2} = x^{-2}$

$\dfrac{dy}{dv} = \dfrac{1}{\sqrt{1 - v^2}}$ $\dfrac{dv}{dx} = -2x^{-3} = -\dfrac{2}{x^3}$

By the Chain Rule:

$\dfrac{dy}{dx} = \dfrac{dy}{dv} \times \dfrac{dv}{dx}$

$\therefore \dfrac{dy}{dx} = \dfrac{1}{\sqrt{1 - v^2}} \times -\dfrac{2}{x^3}$

$= -\dfrac{2}{x^3 \sqrt{1 - \left(\dfrac{1}{x^2}\right)^2}}$

$= -\dfrac{2}{x^3 \sqrt{1 - \dfrac{1}{x^4}}}$

$= -\dfrac{2}{x^3 \sqrt{\dfrac{x^4 - 1}{x^4}}}$

$= -\dfrac{2}{x \sqrt{x^4 - 1}}$

Exercise 13.7

1. Differentiate each of the following with respect to x:

   (i) $f(x) = \sin^{-1} \dfrac{x}{3}$

   (ii) $g(x) = \cos^{-1} \dfrac{x}{4}$

   (iii) $h(x) = \tan^{-1} \dfrac{x}{5}$

   (iv) $F(x) = \sin^{-1} \dfrac{x}{7} + \sin^{-1} \dfrac{x}{9}$

   (v) $H(x) = \sin^{-1} \dfrac{x}{8} + \cos^{-1} \dfrac{x}{11}$

2. Use the Product Rule to differentiate each of the following:

   (i) $y = 2x \sin^{-1} \dfrac{x}{4}$

   (ii) $y = x \cos^{-1} \dfrac{x}{3}$

   (iii) $y = 2x \tan^{-1} \dfrac{x}{4}$

   (iv) $y = (x + 2) \sin^{-1} \dfrac{x}{3}$

   (v) $y = (x^2 + 2x) \cos^{-1} \dfrac{x}{5}$

   (vi) $y = x^3 \tan^{-1} \dfrac{x}{3}$

3. Use the Quotient Rule to differentiate each of the following:

(i) $y = \dfrac{x}{\sin^{-1}\frac{x}{2}}$

(ii) $y = \dfrac{x^2}{\cos^{-1}\frac{x}{3}}$

(iii) $y = \dfrac{x}{\tan^{-1}\frac{x}{4}}$

(iv) $y = \dfrac{x^3}{\sin^{-1}\frac{x}{3}}$

(v) $y = \dfrac{\sin^{-1}\frac{x}{2}}{x+1}$

(vi) $y = \dfrac{\tan^{-1}\frac{x}{3}}{x^3}$

4. Differentiate each of the following with respect to x:

(i) $y = x\sin^{-1}x$

(ii) $y = (x+4)\cos^{-1}\dfrac{x}{3}$

(iii) $y = \left(x^2 + \dfrac{1}{x}\right)\tan^{-1}\dfrac{x}{4}$

(iv) $y = \dfrac{1}{x}\sin^{-1}\dfrac{x}{2}$

5. Differentiate each of the following with respect to x:

(i) $F(x) = \dfrac{\sin^{-1}x}{x^2}$

(ii) $G(x) = \dfrac{\cos^{-1}\frac{x}{2}}{x-1}$

(iii) $H(x) = \dfrac{\tan^{-1}x}{x^4 - 1}$

(iv) $f(x) = \dfrac{\cos^{-1}\frac{x}{3}}{x^2 + 1}$

6. Use the Chain Rule to differentiate each of the following with respect to x:

(i) $f(x) = \sin^{-1}4x$

(ii) $f(x) = \sin^{-1}5x$

(iii) $f(x) = \sin^{-1}x^2$

(iv) $f(x) = \sin^{-1}(x^2 + 1)$

(v) $f(x) = \tan^{-1}2x$

(vi) $f(x) = \tan^{-1}x^3$

(vii) $f(x) = \cos^{-1}(x^3 + 3)$

(viii) $f(x) = \sin^{-1}\left(\dfrac{2}{x}\right)$

7. Differentiate, with respect to x, each of the following:

(i) $f(x) = \sin^{-1}2x$

(ii) $g(x) = \sin^{-1}x^3$

(iii) $h(x) = \tan^{-1}(2x - \pi)$

(iv) $F(x) = \cos^{-1}\left(5x + \dfrac{\pi}{2}\right)$

8. Find the derivative of each of these functions at the given value of x:

(i) $\sin^{-1}x^3$ at $x = \dfrac{1}{4}$

(ii) $\tan^{-1}3x$ at $x = \dfrac{1}{5}$

(iii) $\cos^{-1}2x$ at $x = \dfrac{3}{8}$

(iv) $\cos^{-1}x^2$ at $x = \dfrac{1}{3}$

9. A graph of the function $f(x) = 2\tan^{-1}\sqrt{x}$, $x \in R, x \geqslant 0$, is shown.

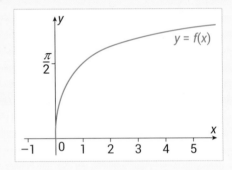

(i) Find $f'(x)$, the derivative of $f(x)$.

(ii) Hence, find the equation of the tangent to $y = f(x)$ at $\left(1, \dfrac{\pi}{2}\right)$.

10. A graph of the function, $f(x) = \sin^{-1}(3x - 1)$, $x \in R, x \in \left[0, \dfrac{2}{3}\right]$, is shown below.

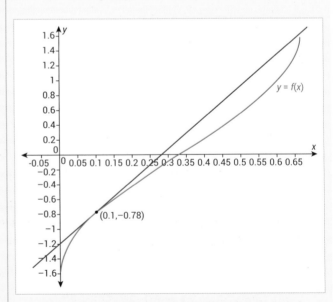

(i) Find $f'(x)$, the derivative of $f(x)$.

(ii) Find the equation of the tangent to $y = f(x)$ at $(0.1, -0.78)$.

11. A function, $f(x) = \sin^{-1}\left(x + \frac{\sqrt{3}}{2}\right)$ is defined on the domain $\left[\frac{-2 - \sqrt{3}}{2}, \frac{2 - \sqrt{3}}{2}\right]$.

   (i) Find $f(0)$.

   (ii) Using the chain rule find $f'(x)$.

   (iii) Evaluate $f'(0)$.

   (iv) Hence, find the equation of the tangent to $f(x)$ at $x = 0$.

12. Find the equation of the tangent to the curve $y = \tan^{-1}(2x + 1)$ at $x = 0$.

13. If $y = \sin^{-1}(\cos x)$, show that $\frac{dy}{dx} = \pm 1$ for all x, $x \in R$, where $\cos x \neq \pm 1$.

14. Find the domain of each of the following functions:

   (i) $y = \sin^{-1}(x + 8)$ (iii) $y = \sin^{-1}(x^2)$

   (ii) $y = \sin^{-1}(2x - 3)$ (iv) $y = \sin^{-1}\left(\frac{1}{x}\right)$

15. $g(x) = \frac{x}{1 + x}$, $x \in R$, $x \neq -1$, and

   $f(x) = \tan^{-1} x$, $x \in R$.

   (i) Write in terms of x the composite function $F(x) = f(g(x))$.

   (ii) Find $g'(x)$, the derivative of $g(x)$.

   (iii) Hence, using the Chain Rule, show that

   $$F'(x) = \frac{1}{2x^2 + 2x + 1}.$$

16. The graph of the function $f(x) = \frac{1}{x}\sin^{-1}\frac{1}{x}$, $x \in R$, $x \leq -1$ or $x \geq 1$, and the tangent to the graph at $x = \sqrt{2}$ are shown.

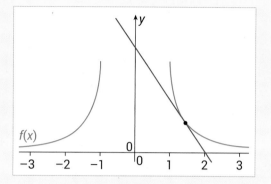

   (i) Explain why the domain of $f(x)$ cannot include values in the range $-1 < x < 1$.

   (ii) Using the Chain Rule, differentiate the following function:

   $$h(x) = \sin^{-1}\frac{1}{x}, \; x \in R, \; x \leq -1 \text{ or } x \geq 1.$$

   (iii) Hence, find $f'(x)$, the derivative of $f(x)$.

   (iv) Show that $f'(\sqrt{2}) = -\frac{1}{2} - \frac{\pi}{8}$.

17. Let $f(x) = \tan^{-1}\frac{x}{2}$ and $g(x) = \tan^{-1}\frac{2}{x}$, $x \in R$, $x > 0$.

   (i) Find $f'(x)$ and $g'(x)$.

   (ii) Hence, show that $f(x) + g(x)$ is constant.

   (iii) Find the value of $f(x) + g(x)$.

13.9 The Exponential Function and the Natural Logarithm Function

The Exponential Function

The irrational number e has a special property: if you draw the graph of e^x, you will find that the slope of the tangent to the graph at any point is equal to the y co-ordinate at that point.

So, if $f(x) = e^x$, then $f'(x) = e^x$.

Consider the graph of $f(x) = e^x$ shown on the right and the tangent to this graph at the point $(2, e^2)$.

The slope of this tangent is e^2.

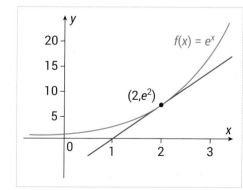

The Natural Logarithm Function

The function $f(x) = \log_e x = \ln x$ is the **natural logarithm function** in x. The natural logarithm function is the inverse of the exponential function.

If $f(x) = \ln x$, how would we find $f'(x)$?

If $y = \ln x$

$\Rightarrow \ x = e^y$

$\Rightarrow \dfrac{dx}{dy} = e^y$

$\Rightarrow \dfrac{dy}{dx} = \dfrac{1}{e^y}$

So, $\dfrac{dy}{dx} = \dfrac{1}{x}$. (as $e^y = x$)

$f(x)$	$f'(x)$
$\ln x$	$\dfrac{1}{x}$
e^x	e^x
e^{ax}	ae^{ax}
a^x	$a^x \ln a$

The rules for differentiating e^x and $\ln x$ with respect to x are shown on page 25 of *Formulae and Tables*.

Worked Example 13.23

Differentiate the following with respect to x:

(i) e^{3x} (ii) e^{-7x}

Solution

(i) $f(x) = e^{3x}$

$\quad y = e^v \qquad v = 3x$

$\quad \dfrac{dy}{dv} = e^v \qquad \dfrac{dv}{dx} = 3$

By the Chain Rule:

$\quad \dfrac{dy}{dx} = \dfrac{dy}{dv} \cdot \dfrac{dv}{dx}$

$\therefore f'(x) = e^v \cdot 3$

$\qquad = 3e^{3x}$

On page 25 of *Formulae and Tables*, a formula for the derivative of e^{ax} is given:

$\dfrac{d(e^{ax})}{dx} = ae^{ax}$, where a is some constant.

(ii) $f(x) = e^{-7x}$

$\therefore f'(x) = -7e^{-7x}$ (using formula)

Worked Example 13.24

Differentiate the following with respect to x:

(i) $\log_e ax \ (a, x > 0)$ (iii) $\log_e(x^2 + 1)$

(ii) $\log_e 3x \ (x > 0)$

Solution

(i) $f(x) = \log_e ax$

$\quad y = \log_e v \qquad v = ax$

$\quad \dfrac{dy}{dv} = \dfrac{1}{v} \qquad \dfrac{dv}{dx} = a$

By the Chain Rule:

$\quad \dfrac{dy}{dx} = \dfrac{dy}{dv} \times \dfrac{dv}{dx}$

$\therefore f'(x) = \left(\dfrac{1}{v}\right)(a)$

$\qquad = \dfrac{a}{ax}$

$\quad f'(x) = \dfrac{1}{x}$

(ii) $f(x) = \log_e 3x$

$\therefore f'(x) = \dfrac{1}{x}$ (from part (i))

(iii) $f(x) = \log_e(x^2 + 1)$

$\quad y = \log_e v \qquad v = x^2 + 1$

$\quad \dfrac{dy}{dv} = \dfrac{1}{v} \qquad \dfrac{dv}{dx} = 2x$

$\quad \dfrac{dy}{dx} = \dfrac{dy}{dv} \cdot \dfrac{dv}{dx}$

$\therefore f'(x) = \left(\dfrac{1}{v}\right)(2x)$

$\quad f'(x) = \dfrac{2x}{x^2 + 1}$

It should now be clear that if $f(x) = \log_e g(x)$,

then $f'(x) = \dfrac{g'(x)}{g(x)}$.

Sometimes, it is better to apply one or more laws of logarithms before differentiating.

Remember

Law 1 $\quad \log_a xy = \log_a x + \log_a y$

Law 2 $\quad \log_a \dfrac{x}{y} = \log_a x - \log_a y$

Law 3 $\quad \log_a x^q = q \log_a x$

These laws are on page 21 of *Formulae and Tables*.

Worked Example 13.25

$y = a^x$, where $a > 0$.

(i) Find $\dfrac{dy}{dx}$.

(ii) Hence, find the derivative of 2^x with respect to x.

Solution

(i) $y = a^x$

$\log_e y = \log_e a^x \quad$ (Find log to the base e of both sides.)

$\log_e y = x \log_e a \quad$ (Law 3 of Logarithms)

$\therefore x = \dfrac{1}{\log_e a} \log_e y$

$\dfrac{dx}{dy} = \left(\dfrac{1}{\log_e a}\right)\left(\dfrac{1}{y}\right)$

$\quad = \dfrac{1}{(\log_e a)y}$

$\therefore \dfrac{dy}{dx} = (\log_e a)y$

$\quad = a^x \log_e a$

(ii) $y = 2^x$

$\dfrac{dy}{dx} = 2^x(\log_e 2) \quad$ (from part (i))

$f(x) = a^x$

$\therefore f'(x) = a^x \ln a$

Formulae and Tables, page 25

Worked Example 13.26

Differentiate the function $f(x) = \log_e \sqrt{\dfrac{x^2}{x^2 + 1}}$ with respect to x.

Give your answer in the form $\dfrac{1}{ax^3 + ax}$, $a \in N$.

Solution

$f(x) = \log_e \sqrt{\dfrac{x^2}{x^2 + 1}}$

$= \log_e \left(\dfrac{x^2}{x^2 + 1}\right)^{\frac{1}{2}}$

$= \dfrac{1}{2} \log_e \dfrac{x^2}{x^2 + 1}$

$= \dfrac{1}{2}\left[\log_e x^2 - \log_e (x^2 + 1)\right]$

$= \dfrac{1}{2}\left[2 \log_e x - \log_e(x^2 + 1)\right]$

$\therefore f(x) = \log_e x - \dfrac{1}{2}\log_e (x^2 + 1)$

$\therefore f'(x) = \dfrac{1}{x} - \dfrac{1}{2} \cdot \dfrac{2x}{x^2 + 1}$

$= \dfrac{1}{x} - \dfrac{x}{x^2 + 1}$

$= \dfrac{x^2 + 1 - x^2}{x(x^2 + 1)}$

$= \dfrac{1}{x^3 + x}$

Exercise 13.8

1. Differentiate each of the following with respect to x:

   (i) e^{2x} (iv) e^{-2x} (vii) $e^{x^2 + 2x + 1}$

   (ii) e^{5x} (v) $e^{\cos x}$ (viii) $e^{\tan x}$

   (iii) e^{4x} (vi) $e^{5x - 4}$

2. Differentiate each of the following with respect to x:

   (i) $\ln(3x + 2)$ (vi) $\ln(x^2 - 2x + 1)$

   (ii) $\ln(x^2 - 8)$ (vii) $\ln(\tan x)$

   (iii) $\ln(4x - 5)$ (viii) $\ln(1 - 4x)$

   (iv) $\ln(\sin x)$ (ix) $\ln(3 - x^3)$

   (v) $\ln(x^4 - 5)$ (x) $\ln 3x$

3. Differentiate each of the following with respect to x:

   (i) $x \ln x$ (iv) $x^2 e^x$

   (ii) $x e^{2x}$ (v) $x^4 e^{3x}$

   (iii) $x^3 \ln x$ (vi) $x^2 \ln e^x$

4. Differentiate each of the following with respect to x:

   (i) $\dfrac{e^{2x}}{x}$ (iv) $\ln \dfrac{2x}{x}$

   (ii) $\dfrac{\ln x^2}{e^x}$ (v) $\dfrac{e^{x^2}}{x^3}$

   (iii) $\dfrac{e^{-2x} - 1}{e^x + 1}$ (vi) $\dfrac{x}{e^x}$

5. Differentiate each of the following with respect to x:

   (i) $\ln \dfrac{3}{x}$ (iv) $\ln \dfrac{3x + 2}{2x - 3}$

   (ii) $\ln \sqrt[5]{x}$ (v) $\ln \sqrt{5x + 2}$

   (iii) $\ln(3x + 9)^3$ (vi) $\ln e^{5x}$

6. Differentiate each of the following with respect to x:

   (i) 3^x (iv) $\dfrac{5^x}{2}$

   (ii) $3(2^x)$

   (iii) $2^{2x - 3}$ (v) $\dfrac{7^x}{8^x}$

   (vi) $3^x 5^x$

7. Find the value of the derivative of each of the following functions at the given value of x:

   (i) $\ln(x^3 + 2)$ at $x = \dfrac{3}{4}$

   (ii) $e^{2\sin x - 1}$ at $x = \dfrac{\pi}{2}$

   (iii) $\dfrac{\ln x}{x}$ at $x = e$

   (iv) $3x\, e^{5x}$ at $x = 0$

   (v) $\dfrac{1}{\ln x}$ at $x = e$

   (vi) e^x at $x = \ln 2$

8. Show that the equation of the tangent to the curve $y = e^{\left(\frac{x}{x+1}\right)}$ at the point where $x = 0$ is $y = x + 1$.

9. Show that the derivative of $\log_e \dfrac{\sin x}{1 + \sin x}$ is $2 - \sqrt{2}$ when $x = \dfrac{\pi}{4}$.

10. The function $f(x) = (1 + x)\log_e(1 + x)$ is defined for $x > -1$.

    Find the value of $f'(x)$ at $x = \dfrac{1 - e}{e}$.

13.10 Implicit Differentiation

The functions that we have met so far can be described by expressing one variable explicitly in terms of another variable, for example:

$$y = \sqrt{x^2 + 5} \text{ or } y = 2x^2 \cos x$$

Sometimes, we deal with equations in x and y in which the relation between x and y is implicit.

Eq. (1) $x^2 + y^2 = 36$ **OR**   **Eq. (2)** $x^2 + y^2 + 2x + 2y - 34 = 0$

The graph of Eq. (1) above is a circle with centre (0,0) and radius length 6, while the graph of Eq. (2) is a circle with centre (−1,−1) and radius length 6 (see Book 2, Chapter 9).

On our course we need to be able to use differentiation to find the slope of a tangent to a circle. Therefore, we will need to know how to differentiate equations such as Eq. (1) and Eq. (2) above.

Worked Example 13.27

Use differentiation to find the slope of the tangent to the circle $x^2 + y^2 = 25$ at the point (3,4).

Solution

Differentiate both sides of the equation $x^2 + y^2 = 25$ with respect to x.

$$\frac{d(x^2 + y^2)}{dx} = \frac{d(25)}{dx}$$

$$\frac{d(x^2)}{dx} + \frac{d(y^2)}{dx} = \frac{d(25)}{dx}$$

$$\frac{d(x^2)}{dx} = 2x$$

$$\frac{d(25)}{dx} = 0 \quad \text{(as 25 is a constant)}$$

What about $\frac{d(y^2)}{dx}$?

Use the Chain Rule here:

Write $\dfrac{d(y^2)}{dx} = \dfrac{d(y^2)}{d(\cdot)} \times \dfrac{d(\cdot)}{dx}$.

Replace $(\cdot)$ with y.

$$\frac{d(y^2)}{dx} = \frac{d(y^2)}{d(y)} \times \frac{dy}{dx}$$

$$= 2y\frac{dy}{dx}$$

Therefore:

$$2x + 2y\frac{dy}{dx} = 0$$

Make $\dfrac{dy}{dx}$ the subject of the formula:

$$2y\frac{dy}{dx} = -2x$$

$$\frac{dy}{dx} = -\frac{2x}{2y}$$

$$\frac{dy}{dx} = -\frac{x}{y}$$

Now find the value of $\dfrac{dy}{dx}$ at (3,4). This will be the required slope.

$$\frac{dy}{dx}\bigg|_{(3,4)} = -\frac{3}{4}$$

Alternative Method

Write y explicitly in terms of x.

$$x^2 + y^2 = 25$$

$$y^2 = 25 - x^2$$

$$y = \pm\sqrt{25 - x^2}$$

$y = \sqrt{25 - x^2}$ is the semicircle of radius 5 units and centre (0,0) on or above the x-axis.

$y = -\sqrt{25 - x^2}$ is the semicircle of radius 5 units and centre (0,0) on or below the x-axis.

As we are looking for the slope of the tangent at the point (3,4), we will use $y = \sqrt{25 - x^2}$.

$$y = (25 - x^2)^{\frac{1}{2}}$$

Use the Chain Rule:

$$y = v^{\frac{1}{2}} \qquad\qquad v = 25 - x^2$$

$$\frac{dy}{dv} = \frac{1}{2}v^{-\frac{1}{2}} \qquad\qquad \frac{dv}{dx} = -2x$$

$$\frac{dy}{dx} = \frac{dy}{dv} \cdot \frac{dv}{dx}$$

$$= \frac{1}{2}v^{-\frac{1}{2}} \cdot (-2x)$$

$$= -\frac{x}{v^{\frac{1}{2}}}$$

$$= -\frac{x}{y}$$

The required slope is $\dfrac{dy}{dx}\bigg|_{(3,4)} = -\dfrac{3}{4}$.

Worked Example 13.28

(i) Use differentiation to find the slope of the tangent t to the circle $x^2 + y^2 + 6x - 2y - 15 = 0$ at the point $(-6, -3)$.

(ii) Hence, find the equation of t.

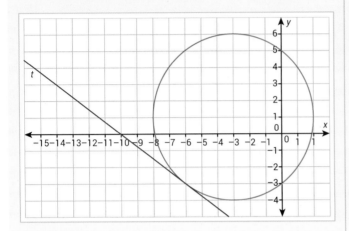

Solution

(i) $x^2 + y^2 + 6x - 2y - 15 = 0$

$$2x + 2y\frac{dy}{dx} + 6 - 2\frac{dy}{dx} + 0 = 0$$

$$(2y - 2)\frac{dy}{dx} = -2x - 6$$

$$(y - 1)\frac{dy}{dx} = -x - 3$$

$$\frac{dy}{dx} = \frac{-x - 3}{y - 1}$$

$$\therefore \frac{dy}{dx}\Big|_{(-6,-3)} = \frac{-(-6) - 3}{-3 - 1}$$

$$= \frac{6 - 3}{-4}$$

$$= \frac{3}{-4}$$

$$\text{Slope} = -\frac{3}{4}$$

(ii) Point $(-6, -3)$ Slope $= -\frac{3}{4}$

$$y - (-3) = -\frac{3}{4}(x - (-6))$$

$$4(y + 3) = -3(x + 6)$$

$$4y + 12 = -3x - 18$$

$$t: 3x + 4y + 30 = 0$$

Exercise 13.9

1. For each of the following circles, express $\frac{dy}{dx}$ in terms of x and y:

    (i) $x^2 + y^2 = 16$

    (ii) $x^2 + y^2 = 49$

    (iii) $2x^2 + 2y^2 = 81$

    (iv) $3x^2 + 3y^2 = 64$

    (v) $ax^2 + ay^2 = b$ (where a, b are of equal sign)

2. For each of the following circles, express $\frac{dy}{dx}$ in terms of x and y:

    (i) $x^2 + y^2 + 2x - 2y + 1 = 0$

    (ii) $x^2 + y^2 + 4x - 6y + 11 = 0$

    (iii) $2x^2 + 2y^2 - 2x - 8y - 1 = 0$

    (iv) $5x^2 + 5y^2 + 2x - 2y - 1 = 0$

    (v) $7x^2 + 7y^2 + 2x - 2y - 3 = 0$

3. For each of the following circles, express $\frac{dy}{dx}$ in terms of x and y:

    (i) $(x - 3)^2 + (y + 2)^2 = 14$

    (ii) $(x - 8)^2 + (y - 2)^2 = 36$

    (iii) $(x + 3)^2 + (y - 9)^2 = 24$

    (iv) $(x - 5)^2 + (y + 3)^2 = 25$

    (v) $(x - 7)^2 + (y + 6)^2 = 49$

4. Use differentiation to find the slope of the tangent to the circle $x^2 + y^2 = 100$ at the point $(-6, -8)$.

5. Use differentiation to find the slope of the tangent to the circle $x^2 + y^2 - 6x - 2y - 3 = 0$ at the point $(5, 4)$.

6. Use differentiation to find the slope of the tangent to the circle $(x - 1)^2 + (y + 2)^2 = 5$ at the point $(3, -3)$. Hence, find the equation of the tangent to the circle containing the point $(3, -3)$.

7. The graphs of the function $f(x) = x^2 + 2x - 3$ and the circle $(x - 7)^2 + (y - 1)^2 = 20$ are shown. AC is a tangent to the circle at $A(3,3)$ and a tangent to $f(x)$ at C. B is the centre of the circle.

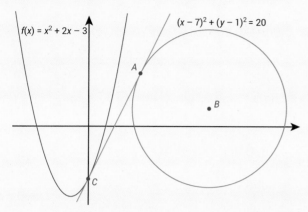

(i) Use differentiation to find the slope of the tangent AC.

(ii) Find the equation of AC.

(iii) Use two different methods to find the co-ordinates of the point C.

(iv) Show that $|AC| : |AB| = 3:2$.

(v) Show that the area of the circle is more than four times greater than the area of the triangle ABC.

8. c is the circle $x^2 + y^2 + 8x + 14 = 0$, and d is the circle $x^2 + y^2 - 4x - 8y - 30 = 0$. a is a tangent to c at the point $F(-3,-1)$.

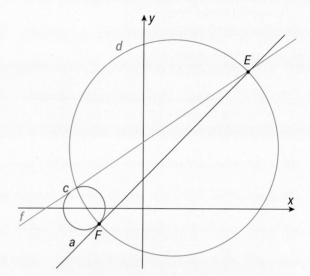

(i) Use differentiation to find the slope of a.

(ii) Find the equation of a.

(iii) Show that a contains the centre of d.

(iv) Find the co-ordinates of E, if E is an endpoint of the diameter $[EF]$.

(v) A tangent f is drawn from E to the circle c. Show that the equation of f is $79x - 119y + 518 = 0$.

(vi) Find, to the nearest degree, the measure of the acute angle between the tangents a and f.

Revision Exercises

1. Use an input–output table to evaluate $\lim\limits_{x \to 4^+} f(x)$ and $\lim\limits_{x \to 4^-} f(x)$, where $f(x) = 5x + 2$, $x \in R$. Does the $\lim\limits_{x \to 4} f(x)$ exist?

2. Consider the function G given by

$$G(x) = \begin{cases} x + 4, & \text{for } x < 2 \\ 3x - 6, & \text{for } x \geqslant 2 \end{cases}$$

Graph the function and find each of the following limits, if they exist:

(i) $\lim\limits_{x \to 4} G(x)$ (ii) $\lim\limits_{x \to 0} G(x)$ (iii) $\lim\limits_{x \to 2} G(x)$

3. Evaluate the following limits. You may assume each limit exists.

(i) $\lim\limits_{x \to 10} 5x - 8$

(ii) $\lim\limits_{x \to 2} \dfrac{x - 2}{x^2 + x - 6}$

(iii) $\lim\limits_{x \to 9} \dfrac{x - 9}{\sqrt{x} - 3}$

(iv) $\lim\limits_{x \to -2} \dfrac{x^3 + 8}{x^2 - 4}$

4. Determine if each of the following functions are continuous at the given value of x:

(i) $f(x) = 5x - 2$, $x = 1$

(ii) $f(x) = \dfrac{2}{x - 3}$, $x = 4$

(iii) $f(x) = \dfrac{5}{x - 2}$, $x = 2$

(iv) $f(x) = \dfrac{x^2 - 25}{x - 5}$, $x = 5$

5. Differentiate each of the following functions from first principles:

(i) $f(x) = 2x - 1$ (iv) $f(x) = 2x^2 + 3x$

(ii) $f(x) = x^2 - 1$ (v) $f(x) = 2 - 3x - 5x^2$

(iii) $f(x) = 5 - x^2$

6. The function $g(x) = x^2 - 3x$ is defined for all $x \in R$.

   (i) Differentiate $g(x)$ with respect to x from first principles.

   (ii) Hence, find the slope of the tangent to the curve $g(x) = x^2 - 3x$ at the point $(2, -2)$.

   (iii) Write in the form $y = mx + c$ the equation of the tangent to the graph of $g(x)$ at the point $(2, -2)$.

7. Differentiate the following with respect to x:

   (i) $y = 2x^2 + 12x + 16$

   (ii) $y = 15x^2 + 10x - 12$

   (iii) $f(x) = x^4 - 19x + 120$

   (iv) $g(x) = 3x^7 - 12x^2 - 4x + 12$

   (v) $h(x) = 4x^3 + 4$

8. A graph of the cubic function $g(x) = x^3 - 3x^2 - 10x + 24$ is shown. The tangent to the graph of $g(x)$ at the point $(3.5, -4.875)$ is also shown on the diagram.

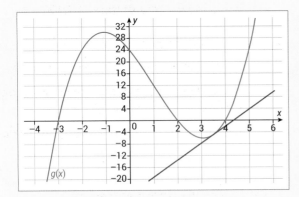

Find the equation of the tangent to $g(x)$ at $x = 3.5$.

9. Differentiate each of the following functions with respect to x (use the Product Rule):

   (i) $f(x) = (3x + 4)(2x - 2)$

   (ii) $f(x) = (x^2 + 2x)(3x - 8)$

   (iii) $f(x) = (5x - 8)(x^2 + 2x + 1)$

   (iv) $f(x) = (x - 1)(x^3 - 1)$

10. Differentiate each of the following functions with respect to x (use the Quotient Rule):

   (i) $f(x) = \dfrac{x - 1}{x + 8}$ (iii) $f(x) = \dfrac{x^2 + 4}{x^2 - 2}$

   (ii) $f(x) = \dfrac{x^2 - 1}{x + 9}$ (iv) $f(x) = \dfrac{x^2 - 25}{x - 5}$

11. Differentiate each of the following functions with respect to x (use the Chain Rule):

   (i) $f(x) = (x + 2)^{10}$

   (ii) $f(x) = (x^2 + 2)^{\frac{1}{2}}$

   (iii) $f(x) = \sqrt{x^3 + 1}$

   (iv) $f(x) = \sqrt[4]{x^2 - 8}$

12. Differentiate each of the following functions with respect to x:

   (i) $f(x) = (2x + 4)(6x - 3)$

   (ii) $f(x) = \dfrac{2x - 1}{5x + 2}$

   (iii) $f(x) = \left[\dfrac{x - 4}{x + 3}\right]^3$

   (iv) $g(x) = (x^2 - 5)(3x - 2)$

13. Differentiate each of the following trigonometric functions:

   (i) $g(x) = \sin x$ (iii) $g(x) = \tan x$

   (ii) $g(x) = \cos x$ (iv) $g(x) = 2\sin x$

14. Use the Product Rule to differentiate the following functions with respect to x:

   (i) $F(x) = 2x^2 \cos x$

   (ii) $G(x) = (x^2 + 1)\sin x$

   (iii) $g(x) = 2 \sin x \cos x$

   (iv) $f(x) = x \sec x$

15. Evaluate the derivatives of each of the following functions at $x = \dfrac{\pi}{2}$:

   (i) $\sin 5x$ (iii) $\tan^2 6x$

   (ii) $\cos^2 2x$ (iv) $\sin^3 4x$

16. Differentiate each of the following with respect to the letter indicated:

   (i) $F(x) = \sqrt{x}(3x - 11)$ $[x]$

   (ii) $G(x) = \dfrac{1}{2x - 3}$ $[x]$

   (iii) $s(t) = \sqrt[5]{\dfrac{t^3 + 1}{t + 1}}$ $[t]$

   (iv) $f(x) = \dfrac{2x}{\sqrt{x^2 + 1}}$ $[x]$

17. Differentiate each of the following functions with respect to x:

    (i) $f(x) = e^{10x}$

    (ii) $f(x) = e^{9x^2 - 4}$

    (iii) $f(x) = e^{15x^3 - 3x^2}$

    (iv) $f(x) = \ln 18x$

    (v) $f(x) = \ln(3x^2 + 4x - 2)$

    (vi) $f(x) = \ln(x^3 - 8x^2)$

18. Differentiate each of the following functions with respect to x:

    (i) $f(x) = \sin^{-1} \dfrac{x}{9}$ (iv) $f(x) = \sin^{-1}(2x)$

    (ii) $f(x) = \cos^{-1} \dfrac{x}{5}$ (v) $f(x) = \cos^{-1} 7x$

    (iii) $f(x) = \tan^{-1} \dfrac{x}{15}$ (vi) $f(x) = \tan^{-1} 9x$

19. $f(x) = \ln \dfrac{3x + 1}{2x - 5}, x \in R, x > \dfrac{5}{2}$

    (i) Find $f'(x)$, the derivative of $f(x)$.

    (ii) Hence, find the slope of the tangent to

         the curve $y = \ln \dfrac{3x + 1}{2x - 5}$ at $x = 5$.

20. Find the derivative of each of these functions at the given value of x (answers to four decimal places where necessary):

    (i) $F(x) = 4x\, e^{-4x}$ at $x = 0$

    (ii) $h(x) = \cos^{-1} 3x^2,\ x = \dfrac{1}{4}$

    (iii) $G(x) = \dfrac{x}{\ln x}$ at $x = e$

    (iv) $k(x) = \sin^{-1} \dfrac{1 + x}{1 + 2x},\ x = 2$

21. (i) Find the derivative of the function

         $f(\theta) = \dfrac{\sin 2\theta}{1 + \cos 2\theta}$.

    (ii) Show that $f'(\theta)$, the derivative of $f(\theta)$, can be written in the form $f'(\theta) = \sec^a b\theta$, where a and b are positive integers.

 Solutions and chapter summary available online

22.

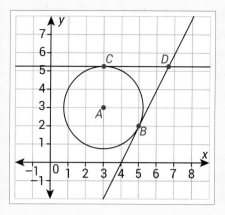

The circle $(x - 3)^2 + (y - 3)^2 = 5$ has centre A and contains the points B and C.

    (i) Write the equation of this circle in the form $x^2 + y^2 + ex + fy + g = 0$, where $e, f, g \in R$.

    (ii) Express the slope of a tangent to this circle at a point on the circle in terms of x and y.

    (iii) Hence, calculate the slope of the tangent BD.

    (iv) The point C is vertically above the centre point A. Find the slope of the tangent CD.

    (v) Find the co-ordinates of the point D.

    (vi) Calculate the radius of the circle. Hence, calculate the area of the kite $ABDC$.

23. c is the circle $x^2 + y^2 - 4x - 2y + 1 = 0$.

    (i) Verify that the point $A(3, 1 + \sqrt{3})$ lies on c.

    (ii) Use differentiation to find the slope of the tangent to c at the point A.

    (iii) Show that the equation of the tangent at A can be written as $y = -\dfrac{1}{\sqrt{3}}x + 2\sqrt{3} + 1$.

    (iv) Sketch the circle and tangent.

    (v) Find the area of the triangle enclosed between the tangent at A and the x and y axes.

Exam Questions

1. (a) Differentiate the function $2x^2 - 3x - 6$ with respect to x from first principles.

    (b) Let $f(x) = \dfrac{2x}{x + 2},\ x \neq -2, x \in R$. Find the co-ordinates of the points at which the slope of the tangent to the curve

         $y = f(x)$ is $\dfrac{1}{4}$.

SEC Leaving Certificate Higher Level, Paper 1, 2014

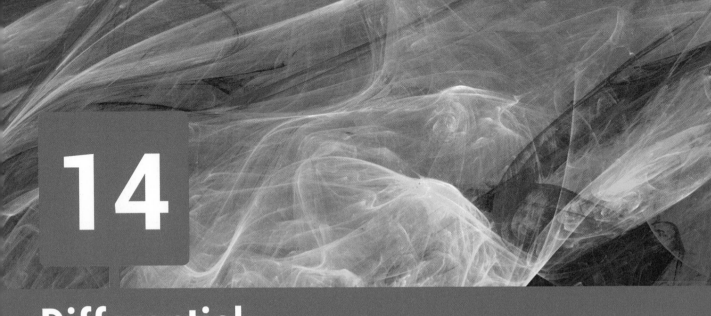

14

Differential Calculus II

In this chapter you will learn about:

- ⊙ Second derivatives
- ⊙ Increasing and decreasing functions

- ⊙ Stationary points and points of inflection
- ⊙ Applying the differentiation of functions to solve problems

You should remember...

- ⊙ How to differentiate polynomials and rational functions
- ⊙ The Sum Rule, the Product Rule, the Quotient Rule and the Chain Rule
- ⊙ How to differentiate trigonometric functions
- ⊙ How to differentiate inverse trigonometric functions
- ⊙ How to differentiate exponential functions and logarithmic functions

Key words

- ⊙ Chain Rule
- ⊙ Second derivative
- ⊙ Differential equation

- ⊙ Increasing function
- ⊙ Decreasing function
- ⊙ Stationary point

- ⊙ Local maximum
- ⊙ Local minimum
- ⊙ Point of inflection

14.1 The Second Derivative

When a function $y = f(x)$ is differentiated with respect to x, the first-order derivative is written as $\frac{dy}{dx}$ or $f'(x)$. If the first-order derivative is itself differentiated with respect to x, the second-order derivative is obtained and is written as $\frac{d^2y}{dx^2}$ or $f''(x)$.

For example:

$$y = x^3 - 7x$$

$$\frac{dy}{dx} = 3x^2 - 7$$

$$\frac{d^2y}{dx^2} = 6x$$

Second derivatives will be used later to help us classify the stationary points of various functions.

- $\frac{d^2y}{dx^2}$ is read as 'dee squared y dee x squared'.

- $f''(x)$ is read as 'f double prime of x'.

Worked Example 14.1

For each of the following functions, find $\frac{d^2y}{dx^2}$.

(i) $y = 5x^2 + 2x - 6$ (iii) $y = (3x^3 - 2x^2)(5x + 4)$

(ii) $y = \cos x$

Solution

(i) $y = 5x^2 + 2x - 6$ (ii) $y = \cos x$

$\quad \dfrac{dy}{dx} = 10x + 2$ $\dfrac{dy}{dx} = -\sin x$

$\quad \dfrac{d^2y}{dx^2} = 10$ $\dfrac{d^2y}{dx^2} = -\cos x$

(iii) $y = (3x^3 - 2x^2)(5x + 4)$

$\quad \dfrac{dy}{dx} = (3x^3 - 2x^2)(5) + (5x + 4)(9x^2 - 4x)$

$\hfill \text{(Product Rule)}$

$\quad = 15x^3 - 10x^2 + 45x^3 + 16x^2 - 16x$

$\quad = 60x^3 + 6x^2 - 16x$

$\quad \dfrac{d^2y}{dx^2} = 180x^2 + 12x - 16$

Differential Equations

A differential equation is an equation containing derivatives. If the highest-order derivative in the differential equation is a first-order derivative, then the equation is called a **first-order differential equation**.

> **First-order differential equation**
>
> Example: $x\dfrac{dy}{dx} = 10$

If the highest-order derivative in the differential equation is a second-order derivative, then the equation is called a **second-order differential equation**.

> **Second-order differential equation**
>
> Example: $\dfrac{d^2y}{dx^2} - 6\dfrac{dy}{dx} + 9y = 0$

On our course, we need to know how to verify solutions to differential equations.

Differential equations can be used to represent real-life phenomena. For example, the first-order differential equation below describes the rate of growth $\left(\frac{dN}{dt}\right)$ in the level of fish stocks (N) over time (t) for a particular population of fish.

$$\left(\frac{dN}{dt}\right) - 0.12N + 0.008N^2 = 0$$

Worked Example 14.2

Show that $y = xe^{-2x}$ is a solution to the differential equation $\frac{d^2y}{dx^2} + 4\frac{dy}{dx} + 4y = 0$.

Solution

Step 1 $y = xe^{-2x}$

$$\frac{dy}{dx} = x(-2e^{-2x}) + e^{-2x}(1) \quad \text{(Product Rule)}$$

$$\therefore \frac{dy}{dx} = e^{-2x}(1 - 2x)$$

$u = x$	$v = e^{-2x}$
$\frac{du}{dx} = 1$	$\frac{dv}{dx} = -2e^{-2x}$

Step 2 $\frac{d^2y}{dx^2} = e^{-2x}(-2) + (1 - 2x)(-2e^{-2x}) \quad \text{(Product Rule)}$

$$= -2e^{-2x}(1 + 1 - 2x)$$

$$= -2e^{-2x}(2 - 2x)$$

$$\therefore \frac{d^2y}{dx^2} = -4e^{-2x}(1 - x)$$

$u = e^{-2x}$	$v = 1 - 2x$
$\frac{du}{dx} = -2e^{-2x}$	$\frac{dv}{dx} = -2$

Step 3 $\frac{d^2y}{dx^2} + 4\frac{dy}{dx} + 4y = -4e^{-2x}(1 - x) + 4[e^{-2x}(1 - 2x)] + 4xe^{-2x}$ $\left(\text{Substitute for } \frac{d^2y}{dx^2}, \frac{dy}{dx} \text{ and } y.\right)$

$$= 4e^{-2x}(-1 + x + 1 - 2x + x) \quad \text{(Factorise out } 4e^{-2x}.\text{)}$$

$$= 4e^{-2x}(0)$$

$$= 0$$

$\therefore y = xe^{-2x}$ is a solution.

Exercise 14.1

1. For each of the following functions, find $\frac{d^2y}{dx^2}$:

   (i) $y = x^2$

   (ii) $y = x^2 + 2x + 1$

   (iii) $y = x^3 - 3x^2 + 4x + 2$

   (iv) $y = e^{2x}$

   (v) $y = e^{4x + 2}$

   (vi) $y = \cos x$

   (vii) $y = 3 \sin x$

   (viii) $y = -2 \cos x$

   (ix) $y = x^2 + e^{2x} + \cos x$

   (x) $y = x^2 + e^{2x - 3} + 3 \sin x$

2. For each of the following functions, find $\frac{d^2y}{dx^2}$:

   (i) $y = (x + 4)(x - 2)$ (iv) $y = (x^2 + 2)(x - 3)$

   (ii) $y = (3x + 2)(x - 4)$ (v) $y = (3x^2 - 4)(x + 2)$

   (iii) $y = (x - 1)(x + 1)$ (vi) $y = (x^2 - 3)(x + 2)$

3. Using a combination of the Quotient Rule and Chain Rule find $\frac{d^2y}{dx^2}$ for each of the following functions:

   (i) $y = \dfrac{3}{x + 2}$ (iv) $y = \dfrac{5}{x + 5}$

   (ii) $y = \dfrac{2}{x + 4}$ (v) $y = -\dfrac{3}{x + 2}$

   (iii) $y = -\dfrac{3}{x - 2}$ (vi) $y = \dfrac{8}{x^2 - 3}$

4. For each of the following functions, find $\dfrac{d^2y}{dx^2}$:

    (i) $y = \ln(x + 5)$ (iv) $y = \ln(2x + 3)$

    (ii) $y = \ln(3x - 2)$ (v) $y = \ln(x^2 + 4)$

    (iii) $y = \ln(5x + 4)$ (vi) $y = \ln(x^2 - 8)$

5. For each of the following functions, find $\dfrac{d^2y}{dx^2}$:

    (i) $y = \sin 3x$ (iv) $y = \cos(2x - 8)$

    (ii) $y = \cos 3x$ (v) $y = \sin(\sqrt{2}x^2 - 8)$

    (iii) $y = \sin(2x + 4)$ (vi) $y = \cos(\sqrt{3}x^2 - 9)$

6. Find the second derivative of each of the following functions:

    (i) $f(t) = \sin t$ (iv) $F(t) = \ln t$

    (ii) $g(x) = \tan^{-1}\dfrac{x}{2}$ (v) $h(x) = e^x \sin x$

    (iii) $A(r) = \dfrac{2}{3}\pi r^2$

7. Show that $y = \cos 3x$ is a solution to the differential equation $\dfrac{d^2y}{dx^2} + 9y = 0$.

8. Show that $f(t) = e^{3t}$ is a solution to the differential equation $f''(t) - 6f'(t) + 9f(t) = 0$.

9. If $y = xe^{-x}$, show that $\dfrac{d^2y}{dx^2} + 2\dfrac{dy}{dx} + y = 0$.

10. If $f(t) = (\sin^{-1} t)^2$, show that $(1 - t^2)\, f''(t) - t f'(t) = 2$.

11. If $y = Axe^{-3x}$, where A is any constant, show that y is a solution to the differential equation $\dfrac{d^2y}{dx^2} + 6\dfrac{dy}{dx} + 9y = 0$.

If $y = Be^{mx}$ is also a solution to this equation, where B and m are non-zero real numbers, find the value of m.

12. The rate of growth of a population of bacteria, if left unchecked, is modelled by the differential equation $\dfrac{dP}{dt} = kP$, where k is a constant. $\dfrac{dP}{dt}$ is the rate of change of the population at time t and P is the population size at time t. t is measured in minutes.

    (i) Show that $P = Ce^{kt}$ is a solution to the differential equation $\dfrac{dP}{dt} = kP$. (C is a constant.)

    (ii) Show that C is the population size at the initial time, $t = 0$.

    (iii) If the initial size of the population is 1,000 and the population has grown to a size of 32,000 in 60 minutes, find the value of the constant k.

13. x is the displacement of a particle, measured in metres, from a fixed point O. The particle has a mass of m kilograms. t is the time elapsed in seconds.

    (i) Explain why the velocity of the particle is given by the differential coefficient $\dfrac{dx}{dt}$.

    (ii) Hence, say why its acceleration is $\dfrac{d^2x}{dt^2}$.

    (iii) The particle's motion can be modelled by the differential equation $\dfrac{d^2x}{dt^2} = -\left[\dfrac{k}{m}\right]x$, where m is the mass of the particle and k is a positive constant.

    Show that $x = \sin\left(\sqrt{\dfrac{k}{m}}\, t\right)$ is a solution to this differential equation.

    (iv) If $k = \pi^2$ and $m = 9$, find the distance of the particle from O after 1 second.

14.2 Increasing and Decreasing Functions

A function $f(x)$ increases on an interval, I, if $f(b) \geqslant f(a)$ for all $b > a$, where $a, b \in I$. If $f(b) > f(a)$ for all $b > a$, the function is said to be **strictly increasing** on the interval I.

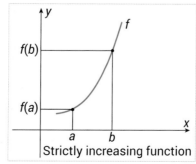

Strictly increasing function

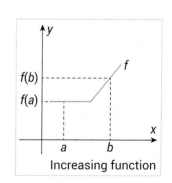

Increasing function

A function $f(x)$ **decreases** on an interval, I, if $f(b) \leqslant f(a)$ for all $b > a$, where $a, b \in I$. If $f(b) < f(a)$ for all $b > a$, the function is said to be **strictly decreasing** on the interval I.

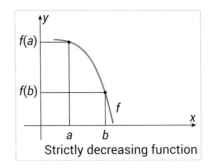

Strictly decreasing function

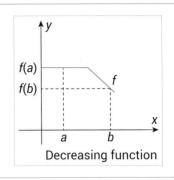

Decreasing function

Worked Example 14.3

A is the closed interval $[1, 5]$. The function f is defined on A by $f: A \rightarrow R: x \rightarrow (x - 4)^2$.

The graph of f is shown.

(i) Explain why f is strictly increasing on the interval $(4, 5]$.

> Note: $(4, 5]$ means 4 is not included but 5 is.
>
> See Chapter 6 for a more detailed explanation of intervals.

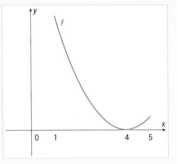

(ii) Define the largest closed interval on A on which the function f is decreasing.

Solution

(i) As $f(x_2) > f(x_1)$ for each $x_1, x_2 \in (4, 5]$, where $x_1 < x_2$, f is strictly increasing on $(4, 5]$.

(ii) The largest closed interval on A on which the function f is decreasing is $[1, 4]$, since $f(x_2) \leqslant f(x_1)$ for each $x_1, x_2 \in [1, 4]$, where $x_1 < x_2$. No wider closed interval on A has this property.

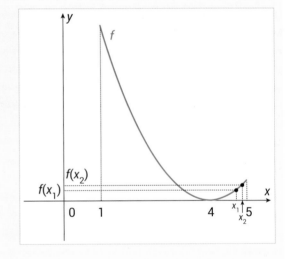

Tangents

In Chapter 13, we learned that the derivative of a function f gives us the slope of each tangent to the curve f. Evaluating the derivative at a particular point on the curve gives us the slope of the tangent to the curve at that particular point.

Consider a function $f(x)$ that is differentiable at each point on a given interval, I. If this function f is strictly increasing on the interval I, then $f'(x) > 0$ for all $x \in I$. If this function f is increasing on the interval I, then $f'(x) \geqslant 0$ for all $x \in I$.

> If $f'(x) > 0$ for all x in an interval I, then f is **strictly increasing** on that interval. If $f'(x) \geqslant 0$ for all x in an interval I, then f is **increasing** on I.

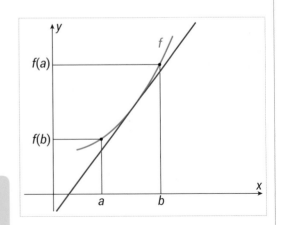

Consider a function $f(x)$ that is differentiable at each point on a given interval, I. If this function f is strictly decreasing on the interval I, then $f'(x) < 0$ for all $x \in I$. If this function f is decreasing on the interval I, then $f'(x) \leq 0$ for all $x \in I$.

> If $f'(x) < 0$ for all x in an interval I, then f is **strictly decreasing** on that interval. If $f'(x) \leq 0$ for all x in an interval I, then f is **decreasing** on I.

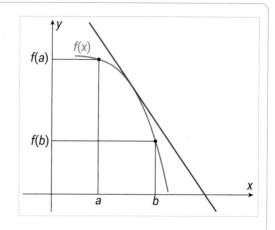

Worked Example 14.4

Investigate the values of x for which the function $f: R \rightarrow R: x \rightarrow x^3 - 4x^2$ is decreasing.

Solution

We need to find the values of x for which $f'(x) \leq 0$.

Step 1 Find $f'(x)$, the derivative of $f(x)$.

$$f'(x) = 3x^2 - 8x$$

Step 2 Solve $f'(x) \leq 0$, i.e. solve $3x^2 - 8x \leq 0$.

Let $3x^2 - 8x = 0$.

$$x(3x - 8) = 0$$

$$x = 0 \quad \textbf{OR} \quad x = \frac{8}{3}$$

> Setting $f'(x) \leq 0$ gives us the interval on which f is decreasing.

Step 3

Sketch the graph of $f'(x)$, the derivative (slope) function.

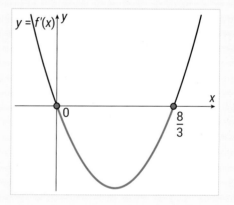

From the sketch, we can see that $f'(x) \leq 0$ when $0 \leq x \leq \frac{8}{3}$.

Therefore, f is decreasing on the interval $0 \leq x \leq \frac{8}{3}$, $x \in R$.

Worked Example 14.5

The function f is defined on $R \setminus \{2\}$ by $f: R \setminus \{2\} \rightarrow R: x \rightarrow \dfrac{x}{x - 2}$.

Show that f is a strictly decreasing function on $R \setminus \{2\}$.

Solution

Find the derivative of $f(x)$.

$$f'(x) = \frac{(x - 2)(1) - x(1)}{(x - 2)^2} \quad \text{(Quotient Rule)}$$

$$\therefore f'(x) = -\frac{2}{(x - 2)^2}$$

$(x - 2)^2 > 0$ for all values of $x \in R \setminus \{2\}$

$$\therefore -\frac{2}{(x - 2)^2} < 0 \text{ for all values of } x \in R \setminus \{2\}$$

As $f'(x) < 0$ for $x \in R \setminus \{2\}$, f is a strictly decreasing function on the interval $R \setminus \{2\}$.

Exercise 14.2

1. For each of the following functions, state:

(a) The range of values of *x* for which the function is defined

(b) The range of values of *x* for which the function is strictly increasing

(c) The range of values of *x* for which the function is strictly decreasing

2. For each of the following functions, state:

(a) The range of values of *x* for which the function is defined

(b) The range of values of *x* for which the function is strictly decreasing

(c) The range of values of *x* for which the function is strictly increasing

(i)

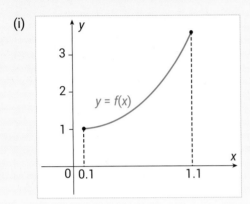

(ii)

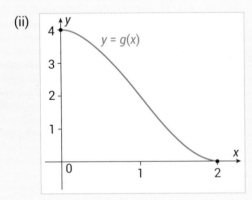

(iii)

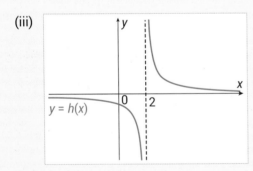

(iv)

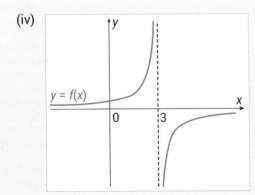

(i)

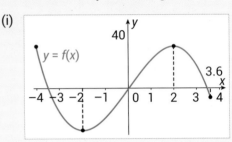

(ii)

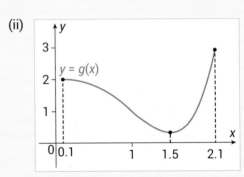

(iii)

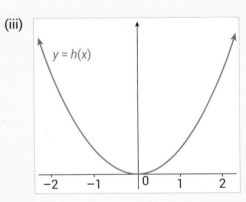

(iv)

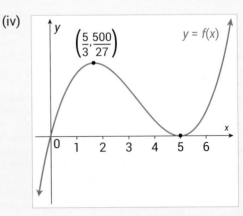

3. The function f is defined on R by
$f: R \rightarrow R: x \rightarrow x^3 - 6x^2$.

   (i) Find $f'(x)$, the derivative of $f(x)$.

   (ii) Solve the equation $f'(x) = 0$.

   (iii) Sketch a graph of $f'(x)$, indicating clearly the x and y intercepts.

   (iv) Find the range of values of x for which $f'(x) \leqslant 0$.

   (v) Complete the sentence:

      A function is d _____ on an interval if $f'(x) \leqslant$ _____ for all values of x on that interval.

   (vi) Hence, find the range of values of x for which $f(x)$ is decreasing.

4. The function g is defined on R by
$g: R \rightarrow R: x \rightarrow 3x^2 - 2x^3$.

   (i) Find $g'(x)$, the derivative of $g(x)$.

   (ii) Solve the equation $g'(x) = 0$.

   (iii) Sketch a graph of $g'(x)$, indicating clearly the x and y intercepts.

   (iv) Find the range of values of x for which $g'(x) \geqslant 0$.

   (v) Complete the sentence:

      A function is i _____ on an interval if $g'(x) \geqslant$ _____ for all values of x on that interval.

   (vi) Hence, find the range of values of x for which $g(x)$ is increasing.

5. The function f is defined on R by
$f: R \rightarrow R: x \rightarrow 2x^3 - 3x^2 - 36x + 10$.

   (i) Find $f'(x)$, the derivative of $f(x)$.

   (ii) Solve the equation $f'(x) = 0$.

   (iii) Sketch a graph of $f'(x)$, indicating clearly the x and y intercepts.

   (iv) Find the range of values of x for which $f'(x) < 0$.

   (v) Find the range of values of x for which $f'(x) > 0$.

   (vi) Find the range of values of x for which $f(x)$ is strictly decreasing.

   (vii) Find the range of values of x for which $f(x)$ is strictly increasing.

6. Using the method of Question 5, find the range of values of x for which the function $f(x)$ is increasing and the range of values of x for which the function $f(x)$ is decreasing for each of the following functions:

   (i) $f(x) = x^3 - x^2 - x + 12$

   (ii) $f(x) = 2x^3 - 2x^2 - 2x - 11$

   (iii) $f(x) = 4x^2 - 2x^3$

   (iv) $f(x) = 8x^2 - x^3$

7. A is the closed interval $[1, 16]$.
The function f is defined on A by
$f: A \rightarrow R: x \rightarrow 2x^3 - 45x^2 + 216x + 128$.

The graphs of f and f', the derivative of f, are shown below.

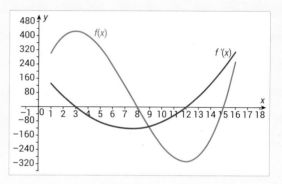

   (i) Find, in the form $f': A \rightarrow R: x \rightarrow ax^2 + bx + c$, the function f', the derivative of f.

   (ii) What are the roots of the function $f'(x)$?

   (iii) For what range of values of x is $f(x)$ decreasing?

   (iv) For what range of values of x is $f(x)$ strictly increasing?

8. B is the closed interval $[0, 5]$. The function f is defined on B by
$f: B \rightarrow R: x \rightarrow x^3 - 5x^2 + 3x + 5$.

   (i) Find, in the form $f': B \rightarrow R: x \rightarrow ax^2 + bx + c$, the function f', the derivative of f.

   (ii) Hence, find the range of values of x for which the function, f, is strictly decreasing.

   (iii) For what range of values of x is the function, f, strictly increasing?

9. Let *f* be any function defined on some interval of real values. The graphs of the derivatives of some functions of this kind are shown below. In each case, find:

(a) The range of values of *x* for which the function, *f*, is strictly increasing

(b) The range of values of *x* for which the function, *f*, is strictly decreasing

(i)
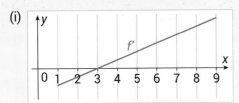

(ii)
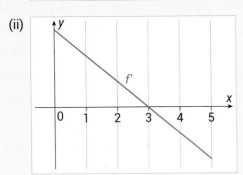

(iii)
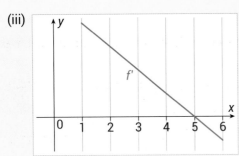

(iv)
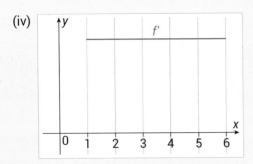

10. Let *f* be any function defined on some interval of real values. The graphs of the derivatives of some functions of this kind are shown. In each case, find:

(a) The range of values of *x* for which the function, *f*, is strictly increasing

(b) The range of values of *x* for which the function, *f*, is strictly decreasing

(i)
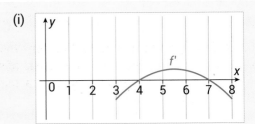

(ii)
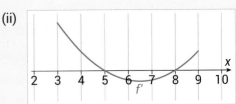

(iii)
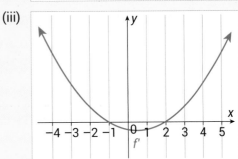

(iv)
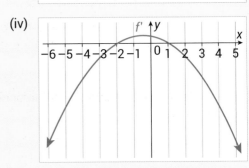

11. The function *f* is defined on $R\backslash\{1\}$ by:

$$f: R\backslash\{1\} \rightarrow R: x \rightarrow \frac{x}{1-x}$$

(i) Explain the meaning of the following statement:

'The function $f: R\backslash\{1\} \rightarrow R: x \rightarrow \dfrac{x}{1-x}$

increases for all values of *x* on $R\backslash\{1\}$.'

(ii) Show that *f* is an increasing function on $R\backslash\{1\}$.

12. The function *f* is defined for all $x \in R$.

$$f: R \rightarrow R: x \rightarrow x^3 + 6x^2 + 15x + 36$$

(i) Find, in the form $f': R \rightarrow R: x \rightarrow ax^2 + bx + c$, the function f', the derivative of *f*.

Write f' in the form
$f': R \rightarrow R: x \rightarrow 3[(x + a)^2 + b]$.

(ii) Hence, say if *f* is an increasing function for all $x \in R$. Explain your answer.

14.3 Turning Points and Points of Inflection

At a **stationary point** on a curve, the slope (gradient) of the tangent to the curve is zero. There are three types of stationary point that we consider: local maximum points, local minimum points and horizontal points of inflection.

> At a stationary point, $\dfrac{dy}{dx} = 0$.

Local Maximum and Local Minimum Points

At a **turning point** on a curve, the gradient or slope of the curve at that point is zero. The derivative immediately to one side of a turning point has a different sign to the derivative immediately to the other side. Maximum and minimum points are called turning points because the graph turns at these points.

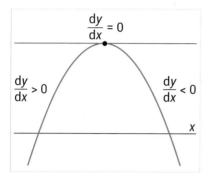

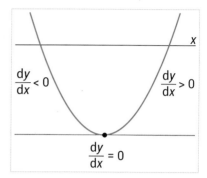

Maximum points – 'humps'

As x increases, the gradient or slope goes from positive → zero → negative.

Minimum points – 'troughs'

As x increases, the gradient or slope goes from negative → zero → positive.

Classifying Turning Points: The Second Derivative Test

The second derivative test can be useful for determining whether a given turning point is a local maximum or a local minimum.

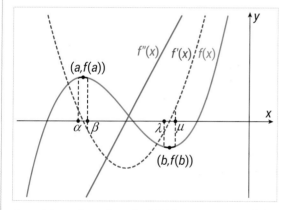

> Given a stationary point (x_0, y_0) of a function, $f(x)$, if:
>
> - $\dfrac{d^2y}{dx^2} < 0$ at (x_0) then (x_0, y_0) is a local maximum
>
> - $\dfrac{d^2y}{dx^2} > 0$ at (x_0) then (x_0, y_0) is a local minimum
>
> - $\dfrac{d^2y}{dx^2} = 0$ no conclusion can be drawn so test the slope on either side of (x_0, y_0) to determine the nature of the stationary point

Consider a function, f. If $f'(x) = 0$ at $x = c$, then:

- If $f''(c) < 0$, then f has a local maximum at $x = c$.
- If $f''(c) > 0$, then f has a local minimum at $x = c$.
- If $f''(c) = 0$, then the second derivative test fails. For example, the function $y = x^4$ has a local minimum at $x = 0$, yet $y''(0) = 0$.

The diagram shows graphs of $f(x)$ (a cubic function), $f'(x)$ (a quadratic function) and $f''(x)$ (a linear function).

$f(x)$ has a local maximum at $(a, f(a))$ and a local minimum at $(b, f(b))$.

- In the interval (α, β), $f'(x)$ is strictly decreasing as the slope of the tangent to the graph of $f(x)$ becomes more negative. Therefore, for any $c \in (\alpha, \beta)$, $f''(c) < 0$. Hence, $f''(a) < 0$, as $a \in (\alpha, \beta)$.
- In the interval (λ, μ), $f'(x)$ is strictly increasing as the slope of the tangent to the graph of $f(x)$ becomes more positive. Therefore, for any $c \in (\lambda, \mu)$, $f''(c) > 0$. Hence, $f''(b) > 0$, as $b \in (\lambda, \mu)$.

Worked Example 14.6

Find the co-ordinates of the turning points of the function $f: R \rightarrow R: x \rightarrow 8x^2 - 4x^3$ and determine their nature.

Solution

$f(x) = 8x^2 - 4x^3$

$\Rightarrow f'(x) = 16x - 12x^2$ and $f''(x) = 16 - 24x$

Solve $f'(x) = 0$, to find the stationary points.

$16x - 12x^2 = 0$

$4x - 3x^2 = 0$

$x(4 - 3x) = 0$

$\therefore x = 0$ **OR** $4 - 3x = 0$

$x = \frac{4}{3}$

> Never divide such an equation by x. Doing this results in the stationary point at $x = 0$ being lost. Instead, factorise out x.

Find the corresponding y-values.

When $x = 0$, $y = 8(0)^2 - 4(0)^3 = 0$ When $x = \frac{4}{3}$, $y = 8\left(\frac{4}{3}\right)^2 - 4\left(\frac{4}{3}\right)^3 = 4\frac{20}{27}$.

Therefore, the co-ordinates of the stationary points are $(0,0)$ and $\left(\frac{4}{3}, 4\frac{20}{27}\right)$.

Second derivative test to investigate the nature of stationary points $(0,0)$ and $\left(\frac{4}{3}, 4\frac{20}{27}\right)$

$f''(x) = 16 - 24x$

Test $x = 0$:

$f''(0) = 16 - 24(0)$

$= 16$

> 0

At $x = 0$ there is a local minimum, as $f''(0) > 0$. Therefore, $(0,0)$ are the co-ordinates of the local minimum.

Test $x = \frac{4}{3}$:

$f''\left(\frac{4}{3}\right) = 16 - 24\left(\frac{4}{3}\right)$

$= -16$

< 0

At $x = \frac{4}{3}$ there is a local maximum, as $f''\left(\frac{4}{3}\right) < 0$. Therefore, $\left(\frac{4}{3}, 4\frac{20}{27}\right)$ are the co-ordinates of the local maximum.

An alternative to the second derivative test (or to be used when second derivative test fails)

Work out the sign of the gradient on either side of the stationary point.

Left of point	At point	Right of point	
$+$ ╱	___ 0	╲ $-$	$\Rightarrow$ Local maximum
$-$ ╲	___ 0	╱ $+$	$\Rightarrow$ Local minimum

When using this test, it is important to choose points in the neighbourhood of the stationary points. If you choose points that are too far away, you may jump over a turning point.

Test $x = 0$:

	Left of point	At point	Right of point
	$x = -0.1$	$x = 0$	$x = 0.1$
	$\dfrac{dy}{dx} = 16(-0.1) - 12(-0.1)^2$ $= -1.72$	$\dfrac{dy}{dx} = 0$	$\dfrac{dy}{dx} = 16(0.1) - 12(0.1)^2$ $= 1.48$
	$< 0,$ i.e. −		$> 0,$ i.e. +
	Negative slope	Zero slope	Positive slope

Therefore, $(0,0)$ is a local minimum.

Test $x = \dfrac{4}{3}$:

	Left of point	At point	Right of point
	$x = 1$	$x = \dfrac{4}{3}$	$x = 1.6$
	$\dfrac{dy}{dx} = 16(1) - 12(1)^2 = 4$	$\dfrac{dy}{dx} = 0$	$\dfrac{dy}{dx} = 16(1.6) - 12(1.6)^2 = -5.12$
	$> 0,$ i.e. +		$< 0,$ i.e. −
	Positive slope	Zero slope	Negative slope

Therefore, $\left(\dfrac{4}{3}, 4\dfrac{20}{27}\right)$ is a local maximum.

Points of Inflection

The graphs of two functions are shown.

In Graph A, the slopes of the tangent lines increase as you move from left to right. In this case we say that the curve is **concave up** on the interval. Notice also that the tangent lines are below the curve.

In Graph B, the slopes of the tangent lines decrease as you move from left to right. In this case, we say that the curve is **concave down** on the interval. If a curve is concave down on an interval, then the tangent lines are above the curve.

Graph A

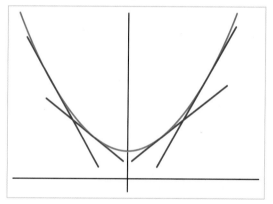

Graph B

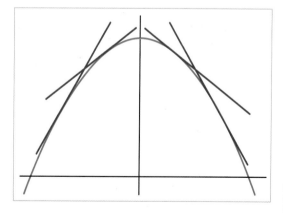

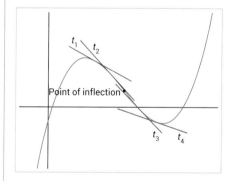

The point where the concavity of a curve changes from concave up to concave down or from concave down to concave up is called a **point of inflection**.

Consider the point of inflection C shown in the diagram overleaf. As we move along the curve to the right through C, tangent lines to the curve go from being above the curve to being below the curve. The same thing happens as we move rightwards along the curve through the point of inflection F. Moving rightwards through the other point of inflection E, tangent lines to the curve go from being below the curve to being above the curve.

> If a function f has a point of inflection at $x = c$, then $f''(c) = 0$.

In the diagram, the point F is a point of inflection and is also a stationary point (since the slope of the tangent to the curve here is zero). Such a point is known as a horizontal point of inflection. Notice how the sign of the first derivative is the same either side of a horizontal point of inflection.

If a function f has a horizontal point of inflection at $x = c$, then $f'(c) = f''(c) = 0$.

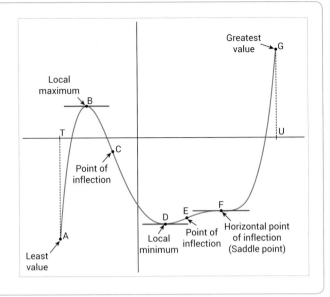

Worked Example 14.7

The function f is defined on R by $f: R \rightarrow R: x \rightarrow x^4 - 4x^3$.

(i) Find $f'(x)$, the derivative of $f(x)$.

(ii) Find the co-ordinates of the stationary points of $f(x)$.

(iii) Determine the nature of the stationary points.

(iv) Find the x- and y-intercepts of the graph of $f(x)$.

(v) Hence, draw a graph of $f(x)$ in the domain $-1 \leqslant x \leqslant 4, x \in R$.

(vi) What is the maximum value of $f(x)$ on $-1 \leqslant x \leqslant 4, x \in R$?

Solution

(i) $f(x) = x^4 - 4x^3$

$\Rightarrow f'(x) = 4x^3 - 12x^2$

(ii) $f'(x) = 0$ (to find stationary points)

$4x^3 - 12x^2 = 0$

$x^3 - 3x^2 = 0$

$x^2(x - 3) = 0$

$x^2 = 0$ **OR** $x - 3 = 0$

$\therefore x = 0$ **OR** $x = 3$

$f(0) = (0)^4 - 4(0)^3$ and $f(3) = (3)^4 - 4(3)^3$

$= 0$ $= 27$

Therefore, $(0,0)$ and $(3,-27)$ are the two stationary points.

(iii) $f'(x) = 4x^3 - 12x^2$

$\Rightarrow f''(x) = 12x^2 - 24x$

$f''(0) = 12(0) - 24(0)$

$= 0$ ... Test fails.

Work out the sign of the gradient on either side of the stationary point.

$f'(-0.1) = 4(-0.1)^3 - 12(-0.1)^2 = -0.124 < 0$

$f'(0.1) = 4(0.1)^3 - 12(0.1)^2 = -0.116 < 0$

As the signs are the same either side of $x = 0$, there is a horizontal point of inflection.

$f''(3) = 12(3)^2 - 24(3)$

$= 108 - 72$

$= 36$

> 0

$\Rightarrow$ At $x = 3$, there is a local minimum.

(iv) x-intercepts:

Let $f(x) = 0$.

$x^4 - 4x^3 = 0$

$x^3(x - 4) = 0$

$x^3 = 0$ **OR** $x - 4 = 0$

$\therefore x = 0$ **OR** $x = 4$

$(0,0)$ and $(4,0)$ are the x-intercepts.

y-intercepts:

Let $x = 0$.

$\therefore f(0) = (0)^4 - 4(0)^3$

$= 0$

$(0,0)$ is the y-intercept.

(v) $f(-1) = (-1)^4 - 4(-1)^3$

$\therefore f(-1) = 5$

So $(-1,5)$ is on the graph of f.

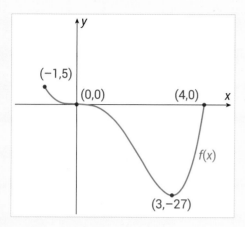

(vi) The maximum value of $f(x)$ on $-1 \leqslant x \leqslant 4$ is 5. Note how the maximum value occurs at an endpoint.

If asked to find the maximum or minimum value of a function on a finite domain, note that it may not be the local maximum or local minimum value. It could be the value taken at an endpoint.

Worked Example 14.8

The graph of a cubic function f is shown.

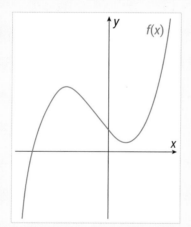

One of the four diagrams A, B, C and D below, shows the graph of the derivative of f. State which one it is and justify your answer.

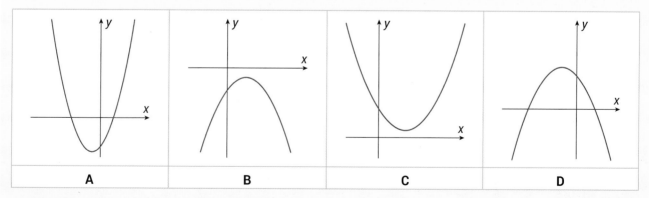

Solution

Graphs B and C can be eliminated for the following reasons:

- Graph B lies entirely below the x-axis, which implies that the derivative is negative for all values of x. If the derivative is always negative, then the function is a strictly decreasing function. f is not a strictly decreasing function.

- Graph C lies entirely above the x-axis, which implies that the derivative is positive for all values of x. If the derivative is always positive, then the function is a strictly increasing function. f is not a strictly increasing function.

Graph D can also be eliminated for the following reason:

- Graph D begins below the x-axis, i.e. the function is decreasing initially. However, the function f shown is increasing initially.

Graph A is the correct solution:

- The graph begins above the x-axis. Therefore, the function is increasing initially. The graph of the derivative then crosses the x-axis. The x-value of this intercept corresponds to the value of x for which f has a local maximum point. The derivative then becomes negative, showing that f is strictly decreasing here. The graph then cuts the x-axis once more. The x-value here corresponds to the x-value for which f has a local minimum point. The derivative then becomes positive once more, so f is strictly increasing here.

Exercise 14.3

1. For each of the following curves:

   (a) Find $\dfrac{dy}{dx}$

   (b) Solve $\dfrac{dy}{dx} = 0$

   (c) Find the co-ordinates of the point on the curve where $\dfrac{dy}{dx} = 0$

      (i) $y = x^2 + 2x - 3$

      (ii) $y = 2x^2 + 3x - 5$

      (iii) $y = x^2 - x - 12$

      (iv) $y = 3x^2 + 4x - 5$

      (v) $y = 3x^2 - x - 1$

2. For each of the following curves:

   (a) Find $\dfrac{dy}{dx}$

   (b) Solve $\dfrac{dy}{dx} = 0$

   (c) Find the co-ordinates of the points on the curve where $\dfrac{dy}{dx} = 0$

      (i) $y = x^3 - x^2 - 5x + 17$

      (ii) $y = 2x^3 - 2x^2 - 2x + 3$

      (iii) $y = 3x^3 - 2x^2 - 5x - 7$

      (iv) $y = 2x^3 - 5x^2 - 4x + 9$

      (v) $y = x^3 - 2x^2 - 4x + 1$

3. Find the co-ordinates of the points on the curves below where the slope is zero.

   (i) $y = x^2 + 2x - 8$

   (ii) $y = x^2 + 8x + 12$

   (iii) $y = 9 + 27x - x^3$

   (iv) $y = \sqrt{x} + \dfrac{1}{\sqrt{x}}$

4. $y = x^2 - 4x - 5$

   (i) Show that $\dfrac{dy}{dx} = 0$ when $x = 2$.

   (ii) Find $\dfrac{dy}{dx}$ when $x = 1.9$.

   (iii) Find $\dfrac{dy}{dx}$ when $x = 2.1$.

   (iv) Explain why $x = 2$ gives the local minimum value of y.

5. $y = 2x^2 - 8x - 3$

   (i) Show that $\dfrac{dy}{dx} = 0$ when $x = 2$.

   (ii) Find $\dfrac{dy}{dx}$ when $x = 1.95$.

   (iii) Find $\dfrac{dy}{dx}$ when $x = 2.01$.

   (iv) Explain why $x = 2$ gives the local minimum value of y.

6. $y = 12 - 27x - 3x^2$

(i) Show that $\frac{dy}{dx} = 0$ when $x = -4.5$.

(ii) Find $\frac{dy}{dx}$ when $x = -4.6$.

(iii) Find $\frac{dy}{dx}$ when $x = -4.4$.

(iv) Explain why $x = -4.5$ gives the local minimum value of y.

7. $y = x^3 + 5x^2 - 8x + 2$

(i) Show that $\frac{dy}{dx} = 0$ when $x = -4$ and $x = \frac{2}{3}$.

(ii) Show that $\frac{dy}{dx} > 0$ when $x = -4.1$ and $\frac{dy}{dx} < 0$ when $x = -3.9$.

(iii) Explain why the curve has a local maximum at $x = -4$.

(iv) Verify that $\frac{dy}{dx} < 0$ when $x = \frac{1}{2}$ and $\frac{dy}{dx} > 0$ when $x = \frac{5}{6}$.

(v) Explain why the curve has a local minimum at $x = \frac{2}{3}$.

8. $y = x^2 - 5x - 2$

(i) Show that $\frac{dy}{dx} = 0$ when $x = \frac{5}{2}$.

(ii) By considering the sign of $\frac{dy}{dx}$ for two values of x, one less than $\frac{5}{2}$ and one greater than $\frac{5}{2}$, show that $x = \frac{5}{2}$ gives a local minimum value of y.

(iii) Find the co-ordinates of the local minimum point on the curve $y = x^2 - 5x - 2$.

9. $y = x^3 - 75x$

(i) Show that $\frac{dy}{dx} = 0$ when $x = \pm 5$.

(ii) By considering the sign of $\frac{dy}{dx}$ for two values of x, one less than -5 and one greater than -5, show that $x = -5$ gives a local maximum value of y.

(iii) Similarly, show that $x = 5$ gives a local minimum value of y.

(iv) Find the co-ordinates of the local maximum and the local minimum point on the curve $y = x^3 - 75x$.

10. The diagram below shows the graph of the function $f(x) = x^2 - 6x + 17$.

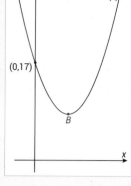

(i) Find a, the value of x for which $f'(x) = 0$.

(ii) Show that $f''(a) > 0$.

(iii) Hence, find the co-ordinates of the point B, the minimum point on the curve.

11. The function f is defined on R by $f : R \to R : x \to 3 + 10x - x^2$.

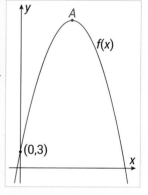

(i) Find a, the value of x for which $f'(x) = 0$.

(ii) Show that $f''(a) < 0$.

(iii) Hence, find the co-ordinates of the point A, the maximum point on the curve.

12. Let $f(x) = x^3 - 12x$, $x \in R$. The graph of $f(x)$ is shown below. x_1 and x_2 are the x-values of the turning points of the curve of $f(x)$.

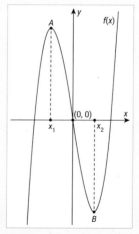

(i) Solve the quadratic equation $f'(x) = 0$.

(ii) Explain why the solutions to $f'(x) = 0$ are x_1 and x_2.

(iii) Find the co-ordinates of A and B.

(iv) Show that $f''(x_1) < 0$ and $f''(x_2) > 0$.

13. Find the co-ordinates of the local maximum point and the local minimum point on the curve $y = 2x^3 - 3x^2 - 36x + 10$.

14. The function f is defined on R by
   $f : R \rightarrow R : x \rightarrow (x + 1)^2(2 - x)$.

   (i) Find the co-ordinates of the local maximum point and the local minimum point on the curve of $f(x)$.

   (ii) Find the co-ordinates of the points where the curve intersects the x-axis and the y-axis.

   (iii) Find the co-ordinates of the point of inflection on the curve.

   (iv) Draw a rough sketch of the curve.

   (v) Hence, write down the range of values of x for which $f(x)$ is increasing.

15. A is the closed interval $[0, 3\pi]$. The function f is defined on A by $f : A \rightarrow R : x \rightarrow x - 2\sin x$.

   A graph of f is shown below.

   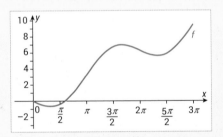

   (i) Find all stationary points and determine their nature.

   (ii) Use the graph to find the maximum value of f on the interval, A.

   (iii) Use algebra to find the actual maximum value of f on the given interval.

16. The function f is defined on R^+ by
   $f : R^+ \rightarrow R : x \rightarrow x \ln x$.

   (i) Show that f has no points of inflection.

   (ii) Find the minimum value of $f(x)$.

17. The graph of a quadratic function h is shown.

   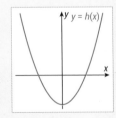

One of the two diagrams A and B below shows the graph of the derivative of h. State which one it is and justify your answer.

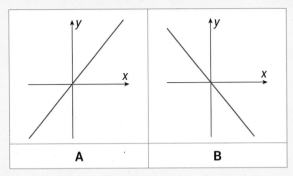

18. The graph of a cubic function f is shown.

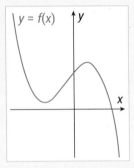

One of the four diagrams A, B, C and D below shows the graph of the derivative of f. State which one it is and justify your answer.

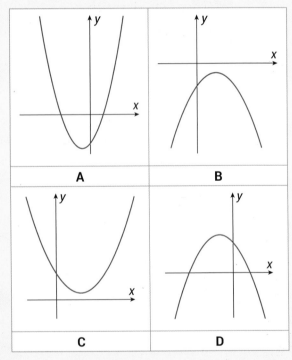

19. The function $f: x \rightarrow ax^3 - bx^2$ is defined for all $x \in R$. Graphs of $f'(x)$ and $f''(x)$, the first and second derivatives of $f(x)$, are shown below.

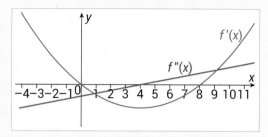

  (i) Use the diagram to explain why the function does not have a horizontal point of inflection.

  (ii) Write down the x-values of the local maximum, local minimum and point of inflection of the function, given that all exist.

  (iii) Write, in terms of a and b, the co-ordinates of the local minimum point and the point of inflection of $f(x)$.

  (iv) If $(8, -256)$ is a point on the graph of f, find the value of a and the value of b.

  (v) Find the co-ordinates of the local maximum, local minimum and point of inflection of the function.

  (vi) Draw a sketch of the function.

20. The function $f(x) = (1 + x)\log_e(1 + x)$ is defined for $x > -1$.

  (i) Show that the curve $y = f(x)$ has a stationary point at $\left(\dfrac{1-e}{e}, -\dfrac{1}{e}\right)$.

  (ii) Determine whether this point is a local maximum or a local minimum.

21. $f(x) = \log_e(3x) - 3x, \ x > 0$

  (i) Show that $\left(\dfrac{1}{3}, -1\right)$ is a local maximum point of $f(x)$.

  (ii) Explain why $f(x)$ is continuous for all $x > 0$.

  (iii) Hence, deduce that the graph of $f(x)$ does not intersect the x-axis.

22. The function $f: x \rightarrow e^{x^2}$ is defined for all $x \in R$.

  (i) Find $f'(x)$ and $f''(x)$.

  (ii) Find the turning point of the curve $y = e^{x^2}$.

  (iii) Determine whether this turning point is a local maximum or a local minimum.

23. $f(x) = \dfrac{\ln x}{x}, \ x > 0$

  (i) Show that the maximum point on the graph of $y = f(x)$ occurs at the point $\left(e, \dfrac{1}{e}\right)$.

  (ii) Hence, show that $x^e \leqslant e^x$ for all $x > 0$.

  (iii) Which is bigger, π^e or e^π? Explain.

14.4 Maximum and Minimum Problems

Calculus is an important tool in solving maximum–minimum problems. We can use an analysis of stationary points to solve real-life problems in fields such as economics, engineering, physics, meteorology – in fact, any area of life in which there is movement or change.

To find the maximum and minimum values of a continuous function f on a closed interval $[a, b]$:

1. Find the values of f at the endpoints of the interval, i.e. find $f(a)$ and $f(b)$.

2. Find the local maximum and local minimum values of f in $[a, b]$.

3. The largest of the values from Steps 1 and 2 is the maximum, and the smallest of these values is the minimum.

Worked Example 14.9

From a 30 cm × 30 cm sheet of cardboard, square corners are cut out so that the sides are folded up to make a box.

  (i) What dimensions will yield a box of maximum volume?

  (ii) What is the maximum volume of the box?

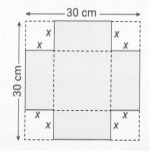

DIFFERENTIAL CALCULUS II

Solution

(i)

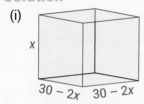

Side length of base = 30 − 2x, height = x.

∴ Volume (V) = (30 − 2x)(30 − 2x)(x)

$\qquad$ = (900 − 120x + 4x²)(x)

∴ V = 900x − 120x² + 4x³

$\dfrac{dV}{dx}$ = 900 − 240x + 12x²

Let $\dfrac{dV}{dx}$ = 0 and solve to find the stationary points.

12x² − 240x + 900 = 0

$\qquad$ x² − 20x + 75 = 0

$\qquad$ (x − 15)(x − 5) = 0

$\qquad$ x = 15 **OR** x = 5

$\dfrac{d²V}{dx²}$ = −240 + 24x

At x = 15, $\dfrac{d²V}{dx²}$ = −240 + 24(15).

$\qquad\qquad$ = −240 + 360

$\qquad\qquad$ = 120

$\qquad\qquad$ > 0

Therefore, there is a local minimum at x = 15.

At x = 5, $\dfrac{d²V}{dx²}$ = −240 + 24(5).

$\qquad\qquad$ = −240 + 120

$\qquad\qquad$ = −120

$\qquad\qquad$ < 0

Therefore, there is a local maximum at x = 5.

The volume function, V(x) = 900x − 120x² + 4x³, has domain 0 ⩽ x ⩽ 15. When x = 0, there are no corner cuts. When x = 15, we get the largest possible corner cuts. V(0) = 0 and V(15) = 0. Therefore, the local maximum value is also the maximum volume.

Required dimensions for maximum volume (using x = 5):

Length = 30 − 2(5) = 20 cm

Width = 30 − 2(5) = 20 cm

Height = 5 cm

(ii) Maximum volume of box = 20 × 20 × 5

$\qquad\qquad\qquad\qquad\qquad$ = 2,000 cm³

OR

Volume = 900x − 120x² + 4x³

So, maximum volume:

$\qquad$ = 900(5) − 120(5)² + 4(5)³

$\qquad$ = 2,000 cm³

Worked Example 14.10

A is the closed interval [−5, 3.5]. The function f is defined on A by f : A → R : x → x³ + 5x² − 8x + 2.

A graph of f is shown.

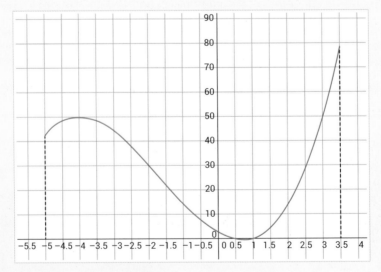

Find the maximum and minimum values of f(x).

Solution

Step 1 Find the values of f at the endpoints of the interval.

$$f(-5) = (-5)^3 + 5(-5)^2 - 8(-5) + 2$$
$$= 42$$

$$f(3.5) = (3.5)^3 + 5(3.5)^2 - 8(3.5) + 2$$
$$= 78.125$$

Step 2 Find the local maximum and local minimum values of f in $[-5, 3.5]$.

$$f'(x) = 3x^2 + 10x - 8$$

$f'(x) = 0$ for stationary points

$$3x^2 + 10x - 8 = 0$$
$$(3x - 2)(x + 4) = 0$$

$$3x - 2 = 0 \quad \Rightarrow \quad x = \frac{2}{3}$$
$$x + 4 = 0 \quad \Rightarrow \quad x = -4$$

$$f\left(\frac{2}{3}\right) = \left(\frac{2}{3}\right)^3 + 5\left(\frac{2}{3}\right)^2 - 8\left(\frac{2}{3}\right) + 2 = -\frac{22}{27}$$
$$f(-4) = (-4)^3 + 5(-4)^2 - 8(-4) + 2 = 50$$

Step 3 Maximum value of $f(x) = $ Max $\left\{42, 78.125, -\frac{22}{27}, 50\right\}$
$$= 78.125$$

Minimum value of $f(x) = $ Min $\left\{42, 78.125, -\frac{22}{27}, 50\right\}$
$$= -\frac{22}{27}$$

Worked Example 14.11

Between 0°C and 30°C (i.e. in the interval $[0, 30]$), the volume V (in cubic centimetres) of 1 kg of water at a temperature T is given approximately by the formula:

$$V = 999.87 - 0.06426T + 0.0085043T^2 - 0.0000679T^3$$

Find:

(i) The rate at which V is changing with respect to T in the interval $[0, 30]$

(ii) $V(0)$ and $V(30)$, the volumes at 0°C and 30°C, respectively

(iii) The temperature at which the water has its minimum volume in the interval $[0, 30]$ and this minimum volume.

(iv) The temperature at which the water has its maximum volume in the interval $[0, 30]$ and this maximum volume.

Solution

(i) $\dfrac{dV}{dT} = -0.06426 + 0.0170086T - 0.0002037T^2$

(ii) $V(0) = 999.87$ cm^3

$$V(30) = 999.87 - 0.06426(30) + 0.0085043(30)^2 - 0.0000679(30)^3$$
$$= 1{,}003.76277 \text{ cm}^3$$

(iii) Investigate if the local minimum of V is in the interval $[0, 30]$.

$$\frac{dV}{dT} = 0$$

$$-0.06426 + 0.0170086T - 0.0002037T^2 = 0$$

$$T = \frac{-0.0170086 \pm \sqrt{(0.0170086)^2 - 4(-0.0002037)(-0.06426)}}{2(-0.0002037)}$$

$T \approx 3.967$ **OR** $T \approx 79.532$

We accept $T = 3.967$ only, as $79.532 \notin [0, 30]$.

How do we know we have a local minimum at $T = 3.967$?

$$\frac{d^2V}{dT^2} = 0.0170086 - 0.0004074T$$

$$\left.\frac{d^2V}{dT^2}\right|_{T = 3.967} \approx 0.015$$

$$> 0$$

$\therefore$ We have a local minimum at $T = 3.967$.

$V(3.967) = 999.87 - 0.06426(3.967) + 0.0085043(3.967)^2 - 0.0000679(3.967)^3$

$\qquad = 999.74$

From (ii), $V(0) = 999.87$ and $V(30) = 1{,}003.76$.

Therefore, the temperature at which the water has its minimum volume in the interval $[0, 30]$ is $3.967°C$.

The minimum volume is 999.74 cm^3.

(iv) $V(0) = 999.87$

$V(30) = 1{,}003.76$

Therefore, the temperature at which the water has its maximum value in the interval $[0, 30]$ is $30°C$.

The maximum volume is $1{,}003.76$ cm^3.

Worked Example 14.12

The appropximate length of the day in Galway, measured in hours from sunrise to sunset, may be calculated using the function

$$f(t) = 12.25 + 4.75 \sin\left(\frac{2\pi}{365}t\right)$$

where t is the number of days after March 21st and $\left(\frac{2\pi}{365}t\right)$ is expressed in radians.

(i) Find the length of the day in Galway on June 5th (76 days after March 21st). Give your answer in hours and minutes, correct to the nearest minute.

(ii) Find a date on which the length of the day in Galway is approximately 15 hours.

(iii) Find $f'(t)$, the derivative of $f(t)$.

(iv) Hence, or otherwise, find the length of the longest day in Galway.

Solution

(i) $f(t) = 12.25 + 4.75 \sin\left(\frac{2\pi}{365}t\right)$

$f(76) = 12.25 + 4.75 \sin\left(\frac{2\pi}{365} \times 76\right)$

$= 12.25 + 4.587$

$= 16.837$

$= 16$ hours 50 minutes

(ii) $f(t) = 12.25 + 4.75 \sin\left(\frac{2\pi}{365}t\right) = 15$

$\Rightarrow 4.75 \sin\left(\frac{2\pi}{365}t\right) = 2\frac{3}{4}$

$\Rightarrow \sin\left(\frac{2\pi}{365}t\right) = 0.578947$

$\Rightarrow \frac{2\pi}{365}t = 0.6174371$

$\Rightarrow t = 35.87$

36 days after March 21st is April 26th.

(iii) $f(t) = 12.25 + 4.75 \sin\left(\frac{2\pi}{365}t\right)$

$f'(t) = 0 + 4.75 \times \frac{2\pi}{365} \cos\left(\frac{2\pi}{365}t\right)$

$= \frac{9.5\pi}{365} \cos\left(\frac{2\pi}{365}\right)t$

(iv) $f'(t) = 0 \Rightarrow \frac{9.5\pi}{365} \cos\left(\frac{2\pi}{365}t\right) = 0$

$\Rightarrow \cos\left(\frac{2\pi}{365}t\right) = 0$

$\Rightarrow \frac{2\pi}{365}t = \frac{\pi}{2}$

$\Rightarrow t = \frac{365}{4} = 91.25$

$f(91.25) = 12.25 + 4.75 \sin\left(\frac{2\pi}{365} \times 91.25\right)$

$= 12.25 + 4.75 \sin\frac{\pi}{2}$

$= 17$ hours

Exercise 14.4

1. A rectangle has a perimeter of 100 cm.   x cm

   (i) If the width of the rectangle is x cm, find, in terms of x, the length of the rectangle.

   (ii) Show that the area of the rectangle is given by $A = 50x - x^2$.

   (iii) Find the value of x that maximises the area of the rectangle.

   (iv) Find the maximum area of the rectangle.

2. An enclosure is in the shape of a rectangle. One side of the enclosure is fenced in by a building. 100 m of fencing is available to fence the other three sides

   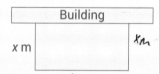
   Building
   x m   xm
   100 − 2x

   (i) If the width of the enclosure is x m, find, in terms of x, the length of the enclosure.

   (ii) Show that the area of the enclosure is given by $A = 100x - 2x^2$.

   (iii) Find the value of x that maximises the area of the enclosure.

   (iv) Find the maximum area of the enclosure.

3. The rectangle shown has an area of 50 m².

   x   50 m²
   y

   (i) Show that $y = \frac{50}{x}$.

   (ii) Show that P, the perimeter of the rectangle, can be written as $P = 2x + 100\,x^{-1}$.

   (iii) Find the value of x that minimises P, the perimeter of the rectangle.

   (iv) What is the minimum length of the perimeter?

4. A farmer wishes to enclose a rectangular section of a field for grazing. She has purchased 200 m of electric fence to construct the enclosure. She designs the rectangular enclosure so that all 200 m of electric fence is just enough to enclose the grazing area.

   (i) If one side of the enclosure is x metres long, explain why the adjacent side is $(100 - x)$ m long.

   (ii) Find, in terms of x, the area of the enclosure.

   (iii) Find the value of x that maximises the area of the enclosure.

(iv) If the farmer decides to use a circular enclosure, find the radius length of such an enclosure. Assume all 200 m of fencing is needed to form this enclosure. Answer correct to two decimal places.

(v) Find the area of the circular enclosure, correct to the nearest square metre.

(vi) If the farmer wants to have a maximum grazing area, which design should she use – rectangular or circular?

5. A farmer wants to enclose two rectangular paddocks, which are equal in area. A river runs along the side of both paddocks. The farmer has 300 m of fencing, all of which is used.

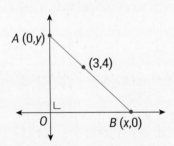

(i) If x represents the length (from the river bank) of each paddock and y represents the width, show that $y = 150 - \frac{3}{2}x$.

(ii) Find, in terms of x, the area of one of the paddocks.

(iii) Find the value of x that maximises the area of each paddock.

(iv) What is the maximum area of the enclosure?

6. A line that passes through the point (3,4) intersects the x-axis at $(x,0)$ and the y-axis at $(0,y)$.

(i) Explain why the slope of the line joining (3,4) and (0,y) is equal to the slope of the line joining (3,4) and (x,0).

(ii) Hence show that $y = 4 - \dfrac{12}{3 - x}$.

(iii) Find, in terms of x, the area of the triangle AOB.

(iv) Use the Quotient Rule to find $\dfrac{dy}{dx}$.

(v) Hence, find the maximum area of the triangle AOB.

7. A Norman window is shaped like a rectangle with a semicircle on top. Suppose that the perimeter of a Norman window is to be 8 m.

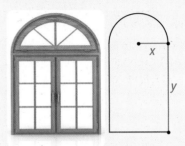

(i) Assume that $2x$ represents the base length of the rectangular part of the window and that y represents the height of the rectangular part. Taking $\pi = 3.14$, show that $y = 4 - 2.57x$.

(ii) Find, in terms of x, the area of the window.

(iii) What dimensions should the window have to allow the maximum amount of light to enter through the window?

8. Two numbers add to give 64.

(i) If the numbers are x and y, write an equation in x and y.

(ii) Using the equation in (i), write y in terms of x.

(iii) Show that the product of the two numbers, in terms of x, is given by $P = 64x - x^2$.

(iv) Find the value of x that maximises the product.

(v) Hence, write two numbers that sum to 64 and whose product is a maximum.

9. Of all the numbers whose sum is 100, find the two that have the maximum product; that is, maximise $P = xy$, where $x + y = 100$.

10. Liffey Appliances is marketing a new washing machine. It determines that in order to sell x machines, the price per machine (in euros) must be $440 - 0.3x$.

It also determines that the cost in euros of producing x washing machines is given by $C(x) = 6,000 + 0.5x^2$.

(i) If x machines are sold, find $R(x)$, the total revenue received. Your answer will be a quadratic expression in x.

(ii) Find $P(x)$, the profit function, if x machines are sold. [$P(x) = R(x) - C(x)$]

(iii) How many machines must be produced to maximise profit?

(iv) What is the maximum profit?

11. The owner of a fast-food shop finds that there is a relationship between the amount of salt S (g/portion) added to the fries and his weekly sales of fries F (measured in 100's of portions).

$$F = 4S + 1 - S^2 \quad 0 \leqslant S \leqslant 4.2$$

(i) Find the amount of salt he should put on his fries to maximise sales.

(ii) The total cost C (€ per portion) associated with the sales of fries is given by:

$$C = 0.3 + 0.2F + 0.1S$$

Find the amount of salt he should add to minimise his costs.

(iii) Given that a portion of fries sells for €1 find the amount of salt he should add to maximise his profit.

12. A computer manufacturer determines that in order to sell x units of a new computer, the price per unit, in euros, must be $p(x) = 1,200 - x$.

The manufacturer also determines that the total cost (in euros) of producing x units is given by $C(x) = 3,500 + 20x$.

(i) Find $R(x)$, the total revenue generated by the sale of x computers.

(ii) Find the total profit, $P(x)$, generated by the sale of x computers.

(iii) How many units must the company produce and sell in order to maximise profit?

(iv) What is the maximum profit?

(v) What price per unit must be charged to make this maximum profit?

13. A cylindrical can is manufactured to hold 1 litre of oil. (1 litre = 1,000 cm³)

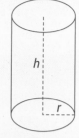

(i) Find the height of the can in terms of the radius, r.

(ii) Find a formula in terms of r for the total surface area of the can.

(iii) Find the dimensions that will minimise the cost of the metal used to manufacture the can.

14. A sector of a circle has area 100 cm².

(i) Show that $\theta = \dfrac{200}{r^2}$

(θ is measured in radians).

(ii) Explain why $r > \sqrt{\dfrac{100}{\pi}}$.

(*Hint*: $\theta < 2\pi$.)

(iii) Show that the perimeter (P) of the sector is given by $P = 2r + \dfrac{200}{r}$.

(iv) Find the value of r that minimises the perimeter.

15. An equilateral triangle of side length 4 cm has a rectangle inscribed in it.

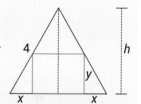

(i) Find h, the height of the triangle.

(ii) Use similar triangles to show that $y = \sqrt{3}x$.

(iii) Find, in terms of x, the area of the rectangle.

(iv) Hence, find the maximum possible area of this rectangle.

(v) What percentage of the triangle is occupied by this rectangle?

14.5 Rates of Change

We can use our knowledge of differentiation to answer questions about the rate at which one variable changes with respect to change in another variable. For example, the displacement (distance in a particular direction) of a car travelling along a road changes as time passes. The rate of change of displacement with respect to time is known as velocity (speed in a particular direction).

$$\dfrac{dy}{dt} = \dfrac{dy}{dx} \cdot \dfrac{dx}{dt}$$

If s is displacement, t is time and v is velocity, then we get the relationship $v = \dfrac{ds}{dt} = s'(t)$.

If displacement is in metres (m) and time is in seconds (s), then velocity is in metres per second (m/s or ms⁻¹).

Similarly, the acceleration of an object (such as a moving car) is defined as the rate of change of velocity with respect to time. If a is acceleration, then we can write acceleration as $a = \dfrac{dv}{dt} = v'(t)$. If velocity is in metres per second and time is in seconds, then acceleration is in metres per second (m/s² or ms⁻²).

$$v = \frac{ds}{dt} = s'(t) \qquad a = \frac{dv}{dt} = v'(t)$$

Velocity is the rate of change of displacement (with respect to time).

Acceleration is the rate of change of velocity (with respect to time).

Worked Example 14.13

The distance s (in metres) of a car from a point P after t seconds ($t \leqslant 5$) is given by:

$$s = 3t^2 \qquad 0 \leqslant t \leqslant 5$$

(i) Find, in terms of t, the velocity of the car.

(ii) Calculate the velocity of the car when $t = 4s$.

(iii) Find the constant acceleration of the car.

Solution

(i) Velocity is the rate of change of displacement with respect to time.

$$v = \frac{ds}{dt} = 6t \text{ (in ms}^{-1})$$

(ii) At $t = 4$, $v = 6(4) = 24$ ms⁻¹.

(iii) Acceleration is the rate of change of velocity with respect to time.

$$a = \frac{dv}{dt} = 6 \text{ ms}^{-2}$$

Worked Example 14.14

The cost of extracting T tonnes of ore from a copper mine is $C = f(T)$ euros; in other words, the cost of extraction is a function of the amount of ore mined.

(i) Explain the meaning of $f'(T)$, the derivative of f with respect to T.

(ii) What are the units of measurement for $f'(T)$?

Solution

(i) $f'(T)$ is the rate of change of C (cost) with respect to the amount of ore mined. For example, if $f'(3,000) = 500$, this means that when 3,000 tonnes has been mined, the cost of mining the next tonne of ore will be €500.

(ii) Euros per tonne.

Worked Example 14.15

According to Boyle's Law, for a given mass of gas at a fixed temperature, $PV = C$, where P is the pressure exerted by the gas and V is the volume of the contained gas. C is a constant that depends on the type of gas. Initially, $V = 100$ cm³ and $P = 2$ atm (atm is an international standard unit of pressure).

(i) Find the value of the constant C.

(ii) If the pressure is decreasing at a rate of 0.01 atm s⁻¹, find the rate at which the gas is expanding when the volume is 125 cm³.

Solution

(i) $PV = C$

$C = 100(2) = 200$

(ii) Pressure is decreasing at a rate of 0.01 atm s⁻¹.

This is written as $\dfrac{dP}{dt} = -0.01$ (derivative is negative as pressure is decreasing).

We are looking to find $\dfrac{dV}{dt}$ at $V = 125$.

The Chain Rule gives:

$$\frac{dV}{dt} = \frac{dV}{dP} \cdot \frac{dP}{dt}$$

We now need to find $\frac{dV}{dP}$.

$$PV = 200$$

$$\Rightarrow V = \frac{200}{P} = 200P^{-1}$$

$$\frac{dV}{dP} = -200P^{-2} = -\frac{200}{P^2}$$

$$\therefore \frac{dV}{dt} = -\frac{200}{P^2} \times -0.01 = \frac{2}{P^2}$$

$$PV = 200$$

$$\therefore P = \frac{200}{V}$$

At $V = 125$, $P = \frac{200}{125}$.

$$\therefore P = 1.6$$

$$\left.\frac{dV}{dt}\right|_{P=1.6} = \frac{2}{(1.6)^2}$$

$$= \frac{25}{32}$$

$$= 0.78125 \text{ cm}^3 \text{ s}^{-1}$$

Worked Example 14.16

The area of a healing wound is given by $A = \pi r^2$, where r is the radius length of the wound.

If the radius length is decreasing at a rate of 0.5 mm per day, how fast is the area decreasing at the instant when the radius length is 10 mm?

Solution

$A = \pi r^2$

$\therefore \frac{dA}{dr} = 2\pi r$ (the rate at which the area of the wound is changing with respect to its radius length)

$$\frac{dr}{dt} = -0.5 \text{ mm/day}$$

We require $\frac{dA}{dt}$, the rate of decrease of the area.

$$\frac{dA}{dt} = \frac{dA}{dr} \cdot \frac{dr}{dt} \quad \text{(Chain Rule)}$$

$$= (2\pi r)(-0.5)$$

$$= -\pi r$$

When $r = 10$, $\frac{dA}{dt} = -10\pi \text{ mm}^2/\text{day}$.

Exercise 14.5

1. The average weight W (in kilograms) of an ash tree is given by the function $W = f(x)$, where x is the height of the tree in metres.

    (i) Explain the meaning of $f'(x)$, the derivative of $f(x)$.

    (ii) Will $f'(x)$ be positive or negative? Explain.

    (iii) What are the units of measurement for $f'(x)$?

2. A loaf of bread has just been taken out of the oven and is cooling off before being eaten. The temperature T of the bread (measured in degrees Celsius) is a function of t (measured in minutes), the length of time the bread has been out of the oven. Therefore, we have $T = T(t)$.

    (i) What is the meaning of $T(5)$?

    (ii) Is $T'(t)$ positive or negative? Explain.

    (iii) What are the units for $T'(t)$?

3. A car accelerates in a straight line so that its distance s (in metres) from its starting point p after t seconds is given by the function $s(t) = t^2$. Find:

    (i) The distance of the car from p after 4 seconds

    (ii) The distance of the car from p after 5 seconds

    (iii) The speed of the car in terms of t

    (iv) The speed of the car after 4 seconds

    (v) What is the constant rate of acceleration of the car?

4. A ball is thrown straight up into the air. The height, h (measured in metres), of the ball after t seconds is given by the function $h(t) = 40t - 5t^2$.

    (i) Find the height of the ball after 1 second.

    (ii) Explain why $h'(t)$ represents the speed of the ball after t seconds.

DIFFERENTIAL CALCULUS II

(iii) Find the speed of the ball after *t* seconds.

(iv) What is the speed of the ball when it reaches its maximum height?

(v) Find the time at which the ball reaches its maximum height.

(vi) Find the maximum height reached.

5. The temperature *T* of a patient during an illness is given by $T(t) = -0.6t^2 + 0.67t + 37$, where *T* is the temperature (in degrees Celsius) at time *t* (in days).

(Time is measured from the onset of the illness.)

(i) Find $T'(t)$, the rate at which the temperature is changing with respect to time.

(ii) Find the rate at which the temperature is changing at *t* = 3 days.

(iii) When will the patient's temperature begin to fall? Answer correct to the nearest hour.

6. The surface area, *S*, of a sphere of radius *r* is given by the formula $S = 4\pi r^2$. The radius of the sphere is increasing at a rate of 2 cms⁻¹.

(i) Find $\dfrac{dS}{dr}$.

(ii) Find $\dfrac{dS}{dt}$, the rate of increase of the surface area, when *r* = 4 cm.

7. The length of the edge of a cube is decreasing at a rate of 4 cm per minute.

(i) What is the value of *n* if *V*, the volume of the cube, is given by $V(x) = x^n$, where *x* is the length of an edge of the cube?

(ii) What is the value of *m* and *n* if *S*, the surface area of the cube, is given by $S(x) = mx^n$, where *x* is the length of an edge of the cube?

(iii) Explain why $x'(t)$ or $\dfrac{dx}{dt}$ is negative.

(iv) Find the rate at which the volume of the cube is decreasing when *x* = 10 cm.

(v) Find the rate at which the surface area of the cube is decreasing when *x* = 10 cm.

8. The length of the radius of a spherical balloon is increasing at a rate of 1 cm per second.

(i) Write down an expression for *V*, the volume of the balloon, in terms of *r*, the radius of the balloon.

(ii) Write down an expression for *S*, the surface area of the balloon, in terms of *r*, the radius of the balloon.

(iii) Explain why $r'(t)$ or $\dfrac{dr}{dt}$ is positive.

(iv) Find the rate at which the volume of the balloon is increasing when *r* = 12 cm.

(v) Find the rate at which the surface area of the balloon is increasing when *r* = 12 cm.

9. The area of a circle is increasing at a rate of 6 cm² s⁻¹.

(i) Find, in terms of *r*, $\dfrac{dC}{dr}$, the rate of change of the circumference with respect to the radius.

(ii) Find, in terms of *r*, $\dfrac{dA}{dr}$, the rate of change of the area with respect to the radius.

(iii) Hence, find $\dfrac{dC}{dA}$ in terms of *r*.

(iv) Find $\dfrac{dC}{dt}$, the rate of increase of the circumference, when the radius is 3 cm.

10. The area and perimeter of the rectangle shown are denoted by *A* and *P*, respectively.

$\dfrac{dA}{dt}$, the rate at which the area of the rectangle is increasing, is 16 cm² s⁻¹.

(i) Find $\dfrac{dP}{dx}$ and $\dfrac{dA}{dx}$.

(ii) Hence, find $\dfrac{dP}{dA}$ in terms of *x*.

(iii) Find $\dfrac{dP}{dt}$ at the instant when *x* = 2 cm.

11. The volume *V* (in m³) of oil in a tank changes with time *t* ($1 \le t \le T$) in hours according to the formula $V = 32 - 10 \ln t$, where *T* represents the time when the tank is empty of oil.

(i) What is the volume of oil in the tank when *t* = 1?

(ii) Find the rate of change, in m³ per hour, of the volume of oil in the tank when *t* = 1.

(iii) Determine the value of *T* in hours correct to one decimal place.

12. A vessel in the shape of a right circular cone is placed so that it is standing on its apex. Water is flowing into the cone at a steady rate of 1 m³ per minute. The vessel has a height of 2 m and a diameter of 2 m.

    (a) (i) Using similar triangles, show that $r = \frac{1}{2}h$, where *r* is the radius of the surface of the water and *h* is the height of the water.

    (ii) Show that the volume of water in the cone is given by $V = \frac{1}{12}\pi h^3$.

(b) When the vessel is one-eighth full, find:

    (i) The rate at which the water is rising

    (ii) The rate at which the free surface of the water is increasing

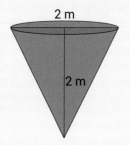

Revision Exercises

1. For each of the following functions, find $f''(x)$ and, hence, $f''(-3)$:

    (i) $f(x) = 3x^3 + 2x^2 + x$

    (ii) $f(x) = 4x^4 - 3x^2 + x$

    (iii) $f(x) = 5x^7 - 3x^5 + 4x^3$

    (iv) $f(x) = 5x^6 + 4x^4 - 3x^2 + 8$

2. For each of the following functions, find $\frac{d^2y}{dx^2}$:

    (i) $y = \cos 2x$

    (ii) $y = \sin 5x$

    (iii) $y = e^{4x+2}$

    (iv) $y = \tan^{-1}\left(\frac{x}{8}\right)$

    (v) $y = \cos^2(9x)$

    (vi) $y = \ln(x^2 + 2x + 1)$

3. Show that $y = \sin 2x$ is a solution to the differential equation $\frac{d^2y}{dx^2} + 4y = 0$.

4. The function *f* is defined on *R* by $f: R \to R: x \to x^3 - 7x^2 + 16x + 15$.

    (i) Find $f'(x)$, the derivative of $f(x)$.

    (ii) Sketch a graph of $f'(x)$, indicating clearly the *x* and *y* intercepts.

    (iii) Find the range of values of *x* for which $f'(x)$ is increasing.

    (iv) Find the range of values of *x* for which $f'(x)$ is decreasing.

5. The function *f* is defined on *R* by $f: R \to R: x \to x^2 - 14x + 3$.

    (i) Show that $\frac{dy}{dx} = 0$ when *x* = 7.

    (ii) Evaluate $\frac{dy}{dx}$ when *x* = 6.9.

    (iii) Evaluate $\frac{dy}{dx}$ when *x* = 7.1.

    (iv) Hence, explain why $f(x)$ is minimised when *x* = 7.

6. The function *f* is defined on *R* by $f: R \to R: x \to x^3 - 108x$.

    (i) Show that $\frac{dy}{dx} = 0$ when *x* = ±6.

    (ii) By considering the sign of $\frac{dy}{dx}$ for two values of *x*, one less than −6 and one greater than −6, show that *x* = −6 gives a local maximum value of *f*.

    (iii) Similarly, show that *x* = 6 gives a local minimum value of the function.

7. The slant height of a cone is 26 cm.

   (i) Use the Theorem of Pythagoras to write r^2 in terms of h.

   (ii) Write down the volume of the cone in terms of h.

   (iii) Find the maximum volume of the cone in terms of π.

8. A solid cylinder has a total surface area of 108π.

   (i) Show that $h = \dfrac{108 - 2r^2}{2r}$.

   (ii) Show that V, the volume of the cylinder, is given by $V = 54\pi r - \pi r^3$.

   (iii) Find the value of r that maximises the volume of the cylinder.

   (iv) Find the maximum volume of the cylinder.

9. A cough is a contraction of the trachea in order to increase the velocity of the air being expelled. The velocity of the outgoing air for a person can be modelled by a function $f(x) = c(a - x)x^2$, where a is the normal radius of the person's trachea (in centimetres), x is the radius while coughing and c is a positive constant.

   (i) What is the unit of measurement for the velocity of outgoing air?

   (ii) What is the radius of the trachea in a person who is not coughing? Answer in terms of a.

   (iii) By what percentage does the radius of the trachea need to contract in order to expel air with maximum volume?

   (iv) What is the maximum velocity with which air can be expelled while coughing, in terms of a and c?

10. A 30 cm piece of wire is cut in two pieces. One piece is used to form a circle and the other to form a square.

    How should the wire be cut so that the sum of the areas is:

    (i) A minimum   (ii) A maximum

11. The force of attraction F (measured in Newtons) between two bodies is a function of the distance r between the two bodies (measured in metres), i.e. $F = F(r)$.

    For two given bodies, A and B:

    w

    (i) Show that $F'(r) = -\dfrac{2{,}000}{r^3}$.

    (ii) What are the units of $F'(r)$?

    (iii) Find the force of attraction F between the two bodies when $r = 10$ m.

    (iv) Find the rate of change of F with respect to r when $r = 10$ m.

12. A pebble is dropped into still water, and circular ripples spread out from the point of entry. The radius of the circles increase at a rate of 10 cms^{-1}.

    (i) If r is the radius of one of the circles, write down the area of the circle.

    (ii) What is $\dfrac{dA}{dr}$ in terms of r?

    (iii) Write down $\dfrac{dr}{dt}$.

    (iv) Explain why $\dfrac{dA}{dt} = \dfrac{dA}{dr} \cdot \dfrac{dr}{dt}$.

    (v) Find the rate at which the area of the circles is increasing when the radius length is 25 cm.

13. The Hubble telescope was deployed in April 1990 by the space shuttle *Discovery*. A model for the velocity (in m/s) of the shuttle from lift-off at $t = 0$ seconds until the rocket boosters were jettisoned at $t = 126$ seconds is given by:

$$v(t) = 0.000396849t^3 - 0.027520392t^2 + 7.1963t + 0.939698$$

(i) Find, in terms of t, the acceleration of the shuttle in the interval $[0, 126]$.

(ii) Find the velocity and acceleration of the shuttle after 10 seconds.

(iii) Find the absolute maximum and absolute minimum values of the acceleration between lift-off and the jettisoning of the boosters.

Exam Questions

1. Each diagram below shows part of the graph of a function. Each of these functions is either quadratic or cubic or trigonometric or exponential (not necessarily in that order).

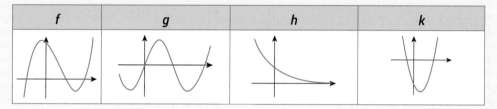

| f | g | h | k |

Each diagram below shows part of the graph of the first derivative of one of the above functions (not necessarily in the same order).

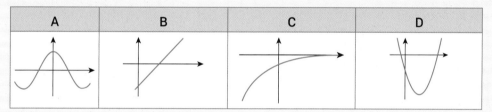

| A | B | C | D |

Each diagram below shows part of the graph of the second derivative of one of the original functions (not necessarily in the same order).

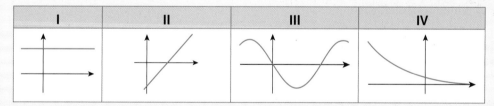

| I | II | III | IV |

(a) Complete the table below by matching the function to its first derivative and its second derivative.

Type of function	Function	First derivative	Second derivative
Quadratic			
Cubic			
Trigonometric			
Exponential			

(b) For **one** row in the table, explain your choice of first derivative and second derivative.

SEC Leaving Certificate Higher Level, Paper 1, 2013

DIFFERENTIAL CALCULUS II

2. (a) Solve the equation $x = \sqrt{x + 6}$, $x \in R$.

   (b) Differentiate $x - \sqrt{x + 6}$ with respect to x.

   (c) Find the co-ordinates of the turning point of the function $y = x - \sqrt{x + 6}$, $x \geqslant -6$.

SEC Leaving Certificate Higher Level, Paper 1, 2015

3. A plane is flying horizontally at P at a height of 150 m above level ground when it begins its descent. P is 5 km, horizontally, from the point of touchdown O. The plane lands horizontally at O.

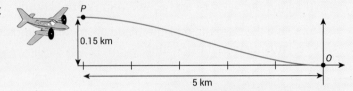

   Taking O as the origin, $(x, f(x))$ approximately describes the path of the plane's descent where $f(x) = 0.0024x^3 + 0.018x^2 + cx + d$, $-5 \leqslant x \leqslant 0$, and both x and $f(x)$ are measured in km.

   (a) (i) Show that $d = 0$.

   (ii) Using the fact that P is the point $(-5, 0.15)$, or otherwise, show that $c = 0$.

   (b) (i) Find the value of $f'(x)$, the derivative of $f(x)$, when $x = -4$.

   (ii) Use your answer to part (b) (i) to find the angle at which the plane is descending when it is 4 km from touchdown. Give your answer correct to the nearest degree.

   (c) Show that $(-2.5, 0.075)$ is the point of inflection of the curve $y = f(x)$.

   (d) (i) If (x, y) is a point on the curve $y = f(x)$, verify that $(-x - 5, -y + 0.15)$ is also a point on $y = f(x)$.

   (ii) Find the image of $(-x - 5, -y + 0.15)$ under symmetry in the point of inflection.

SEC Leaving Certificate Higher Level, Paper 1, 2015

4. An oil spill occurs off-shore in an area of calm water with no currents. The oil is spilling at a rate of 4×10^6 cm^3 per minute. The oil floats on top of the water.

   (a) (i) Complete the table below to show the total volume of oil on the water after each of the first 6 minutes of the oil spill.

Time (minutes)	1	2	3	4	5	6
Volume (10^6 cm^3)		8				

   (ii) Draw a graph to show the total volume of oil on the water over the first 6 minutes.

   (iii) Write an equation for $V(t)$, the volume of oil on the water, in cm^3, after t minutes.

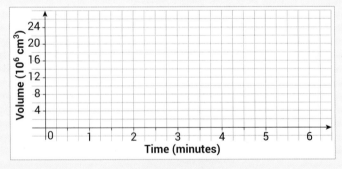

   (b) The spilled oil forms a circular oil slick 1 **millimetre** thick.

   (i) Write an equation for the volume of oil in the slick, in cm^3, when the radius is r cm.

   (ii) Find the rate, in cm per minute, at which the radius of the oil slick is increasing when the radius is 50 m.

   (c) Show that the area of water covered by the oil slick is increasing at a constant rate of 4×10^7 cm^2 per minute.

   (d) The nearest land is 1 km from the point at which the oil spill began. Find how long it will take for the oil slick to reach land. Give your answer correct to the nearest hour.

 Solutions and chapter summary available online

SEC Leaving Certificate Higher Level, Paper 1, 2015

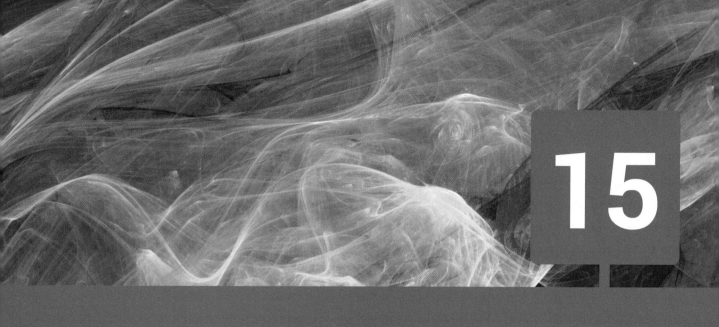

15

Integral Calculus

In this chapter you will learn to:

- Recognise integration as the reverse process of differentiation
- Integrate sums, differences and constant multiples of functions of the form
  - ⊚ x^a where $a \in Q$
  - ⊚ a^x where $a \in R, a > 0$

- ⊚ sin ax where $a \in R$
- ⊚ cos ax where $a \in R$
- Use integration to find the average value of a function over an interval
- Determine the areas of plane regions bounded by polynomial and exponential curves

You should remember...

- Derivatives of polynomials
- Derivatives of trigonometric functions

- Derivatives of exponential and natural logarithm functions
- Derivatives of inverse trigonometric functions

Key words

- Antiderivative
- Indefinite integral
- Definite integral
- Average value of a function
- Bounded area

INTEGRAL CALCULUS

Numerous real-world processes involve rates of change that may be constantly changing – the velocity of a projectile, the rate of temperature change of an object, the growth of money in a bank account.

Knowing these rates of change can be very important. Using a process called **integration** or **antidifferentiation**, we can use a rate of change to gain valuable information about the example at hand.

Microbiologists study the growth rate of microscopic organisms such as viruses and bacteria.

For example, microbiologists know that, for many species of bacterium, the rate of growth of the bacterial population is proportional to the size of the population at that time. That is:

$$\frac{dP}{dt} \qquad \propto \qquad P(t)$$

(rate of change in population with respect to time)

(population size at time t)

So, $\dfrac{dP}{dt} = kP(t)$. (where k is a constant)

By integrating both sides of this equation with respect to time t, we can derive an expression for the population size in terms of t: $P(t) = Ae^{kt}$.

15.1 Antiderivatives and the Indefinite Integral

Suppose that the function $f(x)$ is such that $f'(x) = 5$. Can we find $f(x)$? One possibility for $f(x)$ would be $f(x) = 5x$, since the derivative of $5x$, with respect to (wrt) x is 5. There are many other functions whose derivative is 5. Here are some examples:

$$f(x) = 5x + 2 \qquad\qquad f(x) = 5x - \frac{1}{2}$$

$$f(x) = 5x + 2.4 \qquad\qquad f(x) = 5x - \sqrt{3}$$

We say that any function of the form $5x + c$ is an antiderivative of 5, where c is any constant.

> If two functions in x, f and g, have the same derivative, then $f(x) = g(x) + c$. c is called the constant of integration.

The set of all antiderivatives of a function is a set containing infinitely many parallel curves. The diagram on the right shows graphs of some antiderivatives of $f'(x) = 2x + 4$.

The graphs shown represent the following functions:

- $y = x^2 + 4x$
- $y = x^2 + 4x - 2$
- $y = x^2 + 4x + 2$
- $y = x^2 + 4x + 4$

Remember, these are only four examples of the infinitely many parallel curves where $f'(x) = 2x + 4$.

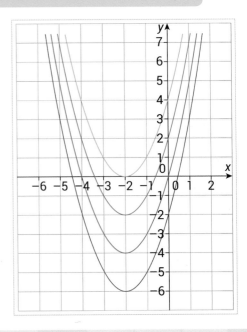

Worked Example 15.1

(i) Differentiate the function $f: R \to R: x \to \frac{1}{3}x^3$.

(ii) Hence, find three antiderivatives of x^2.

Solution

(i) $f(x) = \frac{1}{3}x^3$

$f'(x) = x^2$

(ii) If the derivative of $\frac{1}{3}x^3$ is x^2, then an antiderivative of x^2 is of the form $\frac{1}{3}x^3 + c$, where c is any constant.

So: $\frac{1}{3}x^3 + 5$, $\frac{1}{3}x^3 - 2\pi$ and $\frac{1}{3}x^3$ are three antiderivatives of x^2.

Indefinite Integrals

The general form of an antiderivative is called the **indefinite integral**. To indicate that an antiderivative of x^2 is of the form $\frac{x^3}{3} + c$, we write:

$$\int x^2 \, dx = \frac{x^3}{3} + c$$

This is an indefinite integral. It involves an arbitrary constant of integration, c. (Arbitrary means 'can take any value'.)

We pronounce the above mathematical statement as

'the integral of x^2 with respect to x is $\frac{x^3}{3}$ plus c'.

In general, for any function $f(x)$, we have:

$$\int \frac{d(f(x))}{dx} \, dx = f(x) + c$$

Note

Integration was initially intended for use as a process of summation (adding). The notation for integration evolved from the summation approach.

The sign for integration, the integral sign $\int$, is an elongated S.

Worked Example 15.2

(a) Differentiate the following functions, each with respect to x:

(i) $f(x) = \frac{1}{4}x^4$

(ii) $g(x) = \frac{1}{7}x^7$

(iii) $h(x) = \frac{2}{5}x^5$

(b) Hence find the following indefinite integrals:

(i) $\int x^3 \, dx$

(ii) $\int x^6 \, dx$

(iii) $\int 2x^4 \, dx$

Solution

(a) (i) $f'(x) = x^3$

(ii) $g'(x) = x^6$

(iii) $h'(x) = 2x^4$

(b) (i) $\int f'(x) \, dx = f(x) + c$

$\Rightarrow \int x^3 \, dx = \frac{1}{4}x^4 + c$

(ii) $\int g'(x) \, dx = g(x) + c$

$\Rightarrow \int x^6 \, dx = \frac{1}{7}x^7 + c$

(iii) $\int h'(x) \, dx = h(x) + c$

$\Rightarrow \int 2x^4 \, dx = \frac{2}{5}x + c$

Exercise 15.1

1. For each of the following functions, find $f'(x)$:

   (i) $f(x) = 4x$

   (ii) $f(x) = x^2 + 2x$

   (iii) $f(x) = 2x^2 - 3x - 2$

   (iv) $f(x) = x^3 + 2x^2 + 5x + 8$

   (v) $f(x) = 4x^4 - 16$

   (vi) $f(x) = 5x^5 - 4x^4$

2. Using your results from Question 1, find **two** antiderivatives of each of the following functions:

   (i) $f'(x) = 4$

   (ii) $f'(x) = 2x + 2$

   (iii) $f'(x) = 4x - 3$

   (iv) $f'(x) = 3x^2 + 4x + 5$

   (v) $f'(x) = 16x^3$

   (vi) $f'(x) = 25x^4 - 16x^3$

3. Use either the Product Rule, Quotient Rule or Chain Rule to differentiate each of the following:

   (i) $f(x) = (3x^2 + 4)(5x + 6)$

   (ii) $f(x) = (x + 4)(2x - 8)$

   (iii) $f(x) = \dfrac{x + 2}{x - 3}$

   (iv) $f(x) = \dfrac{x + 1}{x + 4}$

   (v) $f(x) = (3x - 2)^{20}$

   (vi) $f(x) = 5(x - 2)^{12}$

4. Using your results from Question 3, find an antiderivative of each of the following functions:

   (i) $f'(x) = 45x^2 + 36x + 20$

   (ii) $f'(x) = 4x$

   (iii) $f'(x) = -\dfrac{5}{(x - 3)^2}$

   (iv) $f'(x) = \dfrac{3}{(x + 4)^2}$

   (v) $f'(x) = 60(3x - 2)^{19}$

   (vi) $f'(x) = 60(x - 2)^{11}$

5. Write down the derivatives of each of the following functions with respect to the letter in the brackets:

   (i) $f(x) = \sin x$ $[x]$

   (ii) $g(x) = \cos x$ $[x]$

   (iii) $f(t) = \tan t$ $[t]$

   (iv) $h(t) = \ln t$ $[t]$

   (v) $F(x) = e^x$ $[x]$

6. Using your results from Question 5, find an antiderivative of each of the following functions with respect to the variable used before:

   (i) $f'(x) = \cos x$

   (ii) $g'(x) = -\sin x$

   (iii) $f'(t) = \sec^2 t$

   (iv) $h'(t) = \dfrac{1}{t}$

   (v) $F'(x) = e^x$

7. Differentiate each of the following wrt x:

   (i) $y = \cos 2x$

   (ii) $y = 3 \sin 3x$

   (iii) $y = e^{x^2}$

   (iv) $y = 2 \ln x$

   (v) $y = 2^x$

8. Using your results from Question 7, find **two** antiderivatives of each of the following functions:

   (i) $f'(x) = -2 \sin 2x$

   (ii) $f'(x) = 9 \cos 3x$

   (iii) $f'(x) = 2\, xe^{x^2}$

   (iv) $f'(x) = \dfrac{2}{x}$

   (v) $f'(x) = (\ln 2)2^x$

9. Find the derivatives of each of the following functions wrt x:

   (i) $f(x) = \cos^{-1} \dfrac{x}{4}$

   (ii) $g(x) = \sin^{-1} \dfrac{x}{5}$

   (iii) $f(x) = \tan^{-1} \dfrac{x}{6}$

   (iv) $p(x) = \cos^{-1} 3x$

   (v) $h(x) = \tan^{-1} 4x$

10. Using your results from Question 9, find an antiderivative of each of the following functions:

   (i) $f'(t) = -\dfrac{1}{\sqrt{16 - t^2}}$

   (ii) $g'(t) = \dfrac{1}{\sqrt{25 - t^2}}$

   (iii) $h'(t) = \dfrac{6}{36 + t^2}$

   (iv) $f'(t) = \dfrac{-3}{\sqrt{1 - 9t^2}}$

   (v) $q'(t) = \dfrac{4}{1 + 16t^2}$

11. Differentiate each of the following functions wrt x:

   (i) $f(x) = \dfrac{1}{5}x^5$

   (ii) $f(x) = \dfrac{1}{6}x^6$

   (iii) $f(x) = \dfrac{1}{10}x^{10}$

   (iv) $f(x) = \dfrac{1}{500}x^{500}$

   (v) $f(x) = \dfrac{1}{r}x^r$ (r is a non-zero constant)

12. Using your results from Question 11, find an antiderivative of each of the following functions:

  (i) $f'(x) = x^4$ (iii) $f'(x) = x^9$

  (ii) $f'(x) = x^5$ (iv) $f'(x) = x^{499}$

  (v) $f'(x) = x^{r-1}$ (r is a non-zero constant)

13. Find the derivatives of each of the following functions wrt x:

  (i) $f(x) = \dfrac{1}{3}x^3$ (iv) $f(x) = \dfrac{2}{3}x^{\frac{3}{2}}$

  (ii) $f(x) = \dfrac{1}{4}x^4$ (v) $f(x) = \dfrac{2}{5}x^{\frac{5}{2}}$

  (iii) $f(x) = \dfrac{1}{2}x^2$

14. Using your results from Question 13, find each of the following indefinite integrals:

  (i) $\displaystyle\int x^2\, dx$

  (ii) $\displaystyle\int x^3\, dx$

  (iii) $\displaystyle\int x\, dx$

  (iv) $\displaystyle\int x^{\frac{1}{2}}\, dx$

  (v) $\displaystyle\int x^{\frac{3}{2}}\, dx$

15.2 Integrating Sums, Differences and Constant Multiples of Functions of the Form x^a Where $a \in Q$

A single variable polynomial in x of degree n is a function of the following form:

$$f(x) = a_n x^n + a_{n-1} x^{n-1} + \ldots + a_2 x^2 + a_1 x + a_0,\ n \in N \cup \{0\}$$

$f(x) = 4x^3 + 3x^2 + 2x + 8$ is an example of a single variable polynomial function in x.

On our course, we need to know how to integrate single variable polynomial functions.

Consider the function $f(x) = \dfrac{1}{r+1} x^{r+1} + c,\ r \neq -1$. The derivative of $f(x)$ wrt x is $f'(x) = (r+1)\left(\dfrac{1}{r+1}\right) x^r = x^r$.

Therefore, the indefinite integral $\displaystyle\int x^r\, dx = \dfrac{1}{r+1} x^{r+1} + c$.

> **Rule 1** $\displaystyle\int x^r\, dx = \dfrac{x^{r+1}}{r+1} + c,\ r \neq -1$, where c is the constant of integration.

> **Rule 2** $\displaystyle\int kf(x)\, dx = k\int f(x)\, dx$, where k is a constant.

> **Rule 3** $\displaystyle\int (f(x) \pm g(x))\, dx = \int f(x)\, dx \pm \int g(x)\, dx$

$\displaystyle\int x^n\, dx = \dfrac{x^{n+1}}{n+1} + c,\ n \neq -1$

Formulae and Tables, page 26.

Division by zero is not defined, so $n = -1$ is excluded.

Rule in words
To integrate a term in a polynomial, add one to the power and divide by the new power.

The rule $\displaystyle\int x^n\, dx = \dfrac{x^{n+1}}{n+1} + c,\ n \neq -1$ applies only to cases where n is not equal to -1. Does the indefinite integral $\displaystyle\int x^{-1}\, dx = \int \dfrac{1}{x}\, dx$ exist?

If $f(x) = \ln x$, then $f'(x) = \dfrac{1}{x}$. As **integration is the reverse process of differentiation**, $\displaystyle\int \dfrac{1}{x}\, dx = \ln x + c$, where c is the constant of integration.

$\displaystyle\int \dfrac{1}{x}\, dx = \ln x + c$

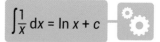

Worked Example 15.3

Find: (i) $\int (2x^2 + 5x^3)\, dx$ (ii) $\int (x + 2)^3\, dx$ (iii) $\int \left(7x - \dfrac{2}{x^3}\right) dx$ (iv) $\int \sqrt{x}\, dx$

Solution

(i) $\int (2x^2 + 5x^3)\, dx = \int 2x^2\, dx + \int 5x^3\, dx$

$\qquad = 2\int x^2\, dx + 5\int x^3\, dx$

$\qquad = \dfrac{2x^3}{3} + \dfrac{5x^4}{4} + c$

(ii) $\qquad (x + 2)^3 = x^3 + 6x^2 + 12x + 8$

$\therefore \int (x + 2)^3\, dx = \int (x^3 + 6x^2 + 12x + 8)\, dx$

$\qquad = \dfrac{x^4}{4} + 2x^3 + 6x^2 + 8x + c$

(iii) $\int \left(7x - \dfrac{2}{x^3}\right) dx = \int (7x - 2x^{-3})\, dx$

$\qquad = \dfrac{7}{2}x^2 + x^{-2} + c$

$\qquad = \dfrac{7}{2}x^2 + \dfrac{1}{x^2} + c$

> The arbitrary constants from each integral can be combined into one constant.

(iv) $\int \sqrt{x}\, dx = \int x^{\frac{1}{2}}\, dx$

$\qquad = \dfrac{x^{\frac{3}{2}}}{\frac{3}{2}} + c$

$\qquad = \dfrac{2}{3}x^{\frac{3}{2}} + c$

Worked Example 15.4

Find an expression for y, given that $\dfrac{dy}{dx} = 3 - 6x$ and $y = 1$ when $x = 2$.

Solution

$y = \int (3 - 6x)\, dx$

$y = 3x - 3x^2 + c$

Now $y = 1$ when $x = 2$.

$\Rightarrow 1 = 3(2) - 3(2)^2 + c$

$1 = 6 - 12 + c$

$c = 6 + 1$

$c = 7$

$\therefore y = 7 + 3x - 3x^2$

Worked Example 15.5

A particle moves in a straight line and has acceleration given by $a(t) = 6t + 40$ cm s^{-2}. Its initial velocity is $v(0) = -60$ cm s^{-1}, and its initial displacement from a fixed point O is $s(0) = 3$ cm.

(i) Find its velocity function $v(t)$ and, hence, its speed after 10 seconds.

(ii) Find its displacement function $s(t)$ and, hence, its distance from O after 10 seconds.

Velocity is the rate of change of displacement with respect to time:

$$s'(t) = v(t) \quad \text{OR} \quad \frac{ds}{dt} = v$$

Velocity is measured in m/s or m s^{-1} (or in cm/s or cm s^{-1}, etc.).

Acceleration is the rate of change of velocity with respect to time:

$$v'(t) = a(t) \quad \text{OR} \quad \frac{dv}{dt} = a$$

Acceleration is measured in m/s^2 or m s^{-2} (or in cm/s^2 or cm s^{-2}, etc.).

Solution

(i) $v'(t) = a(t) = 6t + 40$

$v(t) = \int v'(t)\,dt$, where $v(0) = -60$ cm s^{-1}

$= \int (6t + 40)\,dt$

$= \dfrac{6t^2}{2} + 40t + c$

$v(t) = 3t^2 + 40t + c$

We can now evaluate c, the constant of integration.

$v(0) = 3(0)^2 + 40(0) + c = c$

But we are given that $v(0) = -60$ cm s^{-1}, so $c = -60$.

$\therefore v(t) = 3t^2 + 40t - 60$

$v(10) = 3(10)^2 + 40(10) - 60$

$= 300 + 400 - 60$

$= 640$ cm s^{-1}

(ii) $s'(t) = v(t) = 3t^2 + 40t - 60$, where $s(0) = 3$

$s(t) = \int (3t^2 + 40t - 60)\,dt$

$= \dfrac{3t^3}{3} + \dfrac{40t^2}{2} - 60t + c$

$s(t) = t^3 + 20t^2 - 60t + c$

$s(0) = (0)^3 + 20(0)^2 - 60(0) + c$

$\therefore s(0) = c$

But $s(0) = 3$ cm, so $c = 3$.

$\therefore s(t) = t^3 + 20t^2 - 60t + 3$

$s(10) = 10^3 + 20(10)^2 - 60(10) + 3$

$= 1{,}000 + 2{,}000 - 600 + 3$

$= 2{,}403$ cm

Worked Example 15.6

The slope of the tangent to a curve $y = f(x)$ at each point (x, y) is $3x^2 - 8x - 5$. The curve passes through the origin. Find the function f.

Solution

In Chapter 13 you learned that the derivative, $f'(x)$, of a function represents the slope of the tangent to $f(x)$ at each point, (x,y).

So, $f'(x) = 3x^2 - 8x - 5$.

$\Rightarrow f(x) = \int (3x^2 - 8x - 5)\,dx$

$= x^3 - 4x^2 - 5x + c$

The curve passes through the origin $(0,0)$, therefore $f(0) = 0$.

$f(0) = 0^3 - 4(0)^2 - 5(0) + c = 0$

$\Rightarrow c = 0$

$f(x) = x^3 - 4x^2 - 5x$

Exercise 15.2

1. Find each of the following indefinite integrals:

   (i) $\int x^2\,dx$

   (ii) $\int x^3\,dx$

   (iii) $\int x\,dx$

   (iv) $\int 4\,dx$

2. Find each of the following indefinite integrals:

   (i) $\int x^4\,dx$

   (ii) $\int x^5\,dx$

   (iii) $\int x^8\,dx$

   (iv) $\int x^n\,dx$ $(n \in Q, n \neq -1)$

   (v) $\int x^{-2}\,dx$

   (vi) $\int \dfrac{1}{3x^2}\,dx$

3. Find each of the following indefinite integrals:

   (i) $\int 5x^2\,dx$

   (ii) $\int 3x\,dx$

   (iii) $\int 2\,dx$

   (iv) $\int ax^3\,dx$ (a is a constant)

4. Find each of the following indefinite integrals:

   (i) $\int (x^2 + 2x + 1)\,dx$

   (ii) $\int (x^4 - 6)\,dx$

   (iii) $\int (x^3 + 1)\,dx$

   (iv) $\int (x^3 + 3x^2 - x + 2)\,dx$

INTEGRAL CALCULUS

5. Find each of the following indefinite integrals:

(i) $\int (x^5 + 3x^4 + 2x)\, dx$

(ii) $\int (x^{10} + 9)\, dx$

(iii) $\int (x^8 + x^6 + x^4 + x^2 + 1)\, dx$

(iv) $\int (9x^9 + 7x^7 + 5x^5 + 3x^3 + x)\, dx$

(v) $\int (100x^{99})\, dx$

6. (i) By factorising the numerator and simplifying show that $\dfrac{x^8 + x^4}{x^2} = x^6 + x^2$.

(ii) Hence, find $\int \dfrac{x^8 + x^4}{x^2}\, dx$.

7. (i) Expand $(2x^2 + 5x)^2$.

(ii) Hence, simplify $\dfrac{(2x^2 + 5x)^2}{x}$.

(iii) Find $\int \dfrac{(2x^2 + 5x)^2}{x}\, dx$.

8. (i) Expand $(2x^2 + 3x)(x^4 - x)$.

(ii) Hence, simplify $\dfrac{(2x^2 + 3x)(x^4 - x)}{x^2}$.

(iii) Find $\int \dfrac{(2x^2 + 3x)(x^4 - x)}{x^2}\, dx$.

9. Find $\int y\, dx$ if:

(i) $y = \dfrac{x^5 + x^6}{x^4}$

(ii) $y = \dfrac{(x^2 + 4x)^2}{x}$

(iii) $y = \dfrac{8x^5 - 9x^3}{2x^2}$

(iv) $y = \dfrac{(x^2 + x)(x^3 - x)}{x}$

10. Find each of the following indefinite integrals:

(i) $\int (5t + 3)^2 t^3\, dt$

(ii) $\int (y + 1)^3\, dy$

(iii) $\int (2x - 3)(x + 1)^2\, dx$

(iv) $\int \dfrac{x^2 - 1}{x + 1}\, dx$

11. Find each of the following indefinite integrals:

(i) $\int (\sqrt{x} + 4)\, dx$

(ii) $\int \left(x^2 + \dfrac{1}{x^2}\right) dx$

(iii) $\int \left(\sqrt{x} + \dfrac{1}{\sqrt{x}}\right) dx$

(iv) $\int x^{\frac{1}{3}}\, dx$

(v) $\int \sqrt[4]{x}\, dx$

(vi) $\int \left(x^5 + \dfrac{1}{\sqrt[5]{x}}\right) dx$

12. Find each of the following indefinite integrals:

(i) $\int 3\sqrt{x}\, dx$

(ii) $\int (8 + 5\sqrt[3]{x})\, dx$

(iii) $\int \left(3\sqrt{x} + \dfrac{1}{3\sqrt{x}}\right) dx$

(iv) $\int x^{\frac{2}{5}}\, dx$

(v) $\int \left(3x^{\frac{3}{2}} + 5x^{\frac{1}{2}}\right) dx$

(vi) $\int \left(3x^6 + \dfrac{1}{6\sqrt[6]{x}}\right) dx$

13. Given that $\dfrac{dy}{dx} = 3x + \dfrac{2}{x^2}$:

(i) Find an expression for y in terms of x, given that $y = 8$ when $x = 2$.

(ii) Find the value of y when $x = 1$.

14. The curve $y = f(x)$ passes through the point $(1, -2)$. Given that $f'(x) = 2x - 8$, find the function f.

15. A car moving along a straight road at a speed of 10 ms^{-1} passes a tall building. The speed of the car at time t is given by

$$v = 10 + 3t \qquad 0 \leqslant t < 12$$

where t is the number of seconds that has elapsed since passing the building.

(i) Find the speed of the car when $t = 3$.

(ii) Find t when $v = 40$ ms^{-1}.

(iii) Speed is the rate of change of distance with respect to time $(v = s'(t))$. Use integration to find the distance of the car from the building after t seconds. (Remember $s(0) = 0$.)

(iv) How far is the car from the building when $t = 11$?

16. The acceleration of a particle in metres per second squared moving in a straight line is given by

$$a(t) = 6 + 2t - 3t^2$$

where t (measured in seconds) is the time that has elapsed since the particle was first observed.

(i) What is the acceleration of the particle when $t = 3$?

(ii) Acceleration is the rate of change of velocity with respect to time ($a(t) = v'(t)$). Use integration to find the velocity of the particle after t seconds, given that $v(0) = 1$.

(iii) What is the velocity of the particle when $t = 10$?

17. A particle moves in a straight line and has acceleration given by $a(t) = 5 + 4t - 2t^2$ ms^{-2}. Its initial velocity $v(0) = 3$ ms^{-1}, and its initial displacement from a fixed point is $s(0) = 10$ m.

(i) Find its velocity function $v(t)$ and hence its speed after 10 seconds.

(ii) Find its displacement function $s(t)$ and, hence, its distance from the fixed point after 20 seconds.

18. A ball is thrown upwards with a speed of 16 ms^{-1} from the edge of a cliff 144 m above sea level.

> Any object dropped from a height, will accelerate downwards at a rate of about 9.8 ms^{-2}.

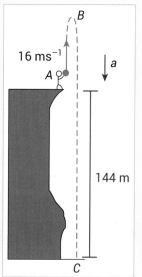

(i) Explain why the acceleration of the ball is $a(t) = -9.8$ ms^{-2}.

(ii) Find $v(t)$, the velocity of the ball t seconds after it is thrown upwards.
(*Hint*: $v(t) = \int a(t)\, dt$, where $v(0) = 16$)

(iii) What is the speed of the ball at the instant it reaches its maximum height?

(iv) How long does it take for the ball to reach its maximum height?

(v) Find $s(t)$, the displacement of the ball from the cliff top t seconds after it is thrown upwards. (*Hint*: $s(t) = \int v(t)\, dt$, where $s(0) = 0$)

(vi) How many seconds after it is thrown upwards does the ball hit the sea? (*Hint*: The displacement of the sea from the top of the cliff is -144 m.)

19. The slope of a curve is given by $\dfrac{dy}{dx} = 8x - 3x^2$. Given that the curve passes through the origin $(0,0)$ find:

(i) The equation of the curve

(ii) Where the curve intersects the x-axis

20. Raindrops grow as they fall, their surface area increases, and therefore the resistance to their falling increases. A raindrop has an initial downward velocity of 10 m s^{-1} and its downward acceleration is given

by $a(t) = \begin{cases} 9 - 0.9t & \text{if } 0 \leqslant t \leqslant 10 \\ 0 & \text{for } t > 10 \end{cases}$

The raindrop is initially 500 m above the ground.

(i) Find the velocity function $v(t)$ of the raindrop after t seconds, $0 \leqslant t \leqslant 10$.

(ii) Find $v(10)$ and, hence, write down the speed at which the raindrop hits the ground.

(iii) Find $s(t)$, the distance travelled by the raindrop in t seconds, $0 \leqslant t \leqslant 10$.

(iv) How long does it take the raindrop to fall to the ground?

21. The slope function of a curve is $\dfrac{dy}{dx} = ax + b$, where a and b are constants.

The curve passes through the points $(0,-1)$ and $(2,-5)$.

At the point $(2,-5)$, the slope of the curve is 1.

Find the equation of the curve.

15.3 Integrating Exponential and Trigonometric Functions

Integrating Exponential Functions

> An **exponential function** is any function of the form $f(x) = a^x$, where a is any positive constant.
> The **natural exponential function** is the function $f(x) = e^x$.

The natural exponential function e^x has the special property that it is its own derivative. That is, if $f(x) = e^x$, then $f'(x) = e^x$ also. As **integration is the reverse process of differentiation**, we get the following important result:

$$\int e^x \, dx = e^x + c$$

where c is an arbitrary constant of integration.

In a similar way, we can calculate the indefinite integral of e^{ax} (where a is a positive constant) with respect to x. From Chapters 13 and 14 on differential calculus we saw that if $f(x) = e^{ax}$, then, by the Chain Rule, $f'(x) = ae^{ax}$. In other words, if $f(x) = \frac{1}{a}e^{ax}$, $f'(x) = e^{ax}$.

This yields the following important result:

$$\int e^{ax} \, dx = \frac{1}{a}e^{ax} + c.$$

Recall from Chapter 7 on indices and logarithms that if $y = a^x$ then $\ln y = (\ln a) \, x$.

Differentiating both sides with respect to x we get $\frac{1}{y}\frac{dy}{dx} = \ln a \Rightarrow \frac{dy}{dx} = y \ln a$.

Therefore, $\frac{dy}{dx} = \frac{d(a^x)}{dx} = a^x \ln a$.

In other words, if $f(x) = \frac{a^x}{\ln a}$, then $f'(x) = a^x$. This yields the important result:

$$\int a^x \, dx = \frac{a^x}{\ln a} + c.$$

These three important indefinite integrals are summarised below, and are on page 26 of *Formulae and Tables*:

$$\int e^x \, dx = e^x + c \qquad \int e^{ax} \, dx = \frac{1}{a}e^{ax} + c \qquad \int a^x \, dx = \frac{a^x}{\ln a} + c$$

Worked Example 15.7

Find the following indefinite integrals:

(i) $\int e^{2x} \, dx$

(ii) $\int e^{-3x} \, dx$

(iii) $\int e^{\frac{x}{3}} \, dx$

(iv) $\int 2^x \, dx$

Solution

(i) $\int e^{2x} \, dx = \frac{e^{2x}}{2} + c$

(ii) $\int e^{-3x} \, dx = \frac{e^{-3x}}{-3} + c$

$$= -\frac{e^{-3x}}{3} + c$$

(iii) $\int e^{\frac{x}{3}} \, dx = \frac{e^{\frac{x}{3}}}{\left(\frac{1}{3}\right)} + c$

$$= e^{\frac{x}{3}} \times 3 + c$$

$$= 3e^{\frac{x}{3}} + c$$

> $\left(\frac{x}{3} = \left(\frac{1}{3}\right)x\right)$
>
> Dividing by $\frac{1}{3}$ is the same as multiplying by 3.

(iv) $\int 2^x \, dx = \frac{2^x}{\ln 2} + c$

Worked Example 15.8

f is the function $f: R \to R: t \to t^2 e^t$.

(i) Find $f'(t)$, the derivative of $f(t)$.

(ii) Hence, find $\int (t^2 + 2t)e^t \, dt$.

Solution

(i) $f(t) = t^2 e^t$

$f'(t) = t^2 e^t + e^t(2t)$ (by the Product Rule)

$= (t^2 + 2t)e^t$

This is because integration is the reverse process of differentiation.

(ii) The derivative (with respect to t) of $f(t) = t^2 e^t$ is $f'(t) = (t^2 + 2t)e^t$.

Therefore, $\int (t^2 + 2t)e^t \, dt = t^2 e^t + c$.

Worked Example 15.9

Find the indefinite integral $\int \dfrac{e^{2t} - e^{-t}}{e^{-t} - 1} \, dt$.

Solution

$\dfrac{e^{2t} - e^{-t}}{e^{-t} - 1} = \dfrac{e^{3t} - e^0}{e^0 - e^t}$ (Multiply numerator and denominator by e^t.)

$= \dfrac{e^{3t} - 1}{1 - e^t}$

$= \dfrac{(e^t)^3 - 1}{1 - e^t}$ (Third law of indices)

$= \dfrac{(e^t - 1)(e^{2t} + e^t + 1)}{1 - e^t}$ (difference of two cubes)

$= \dfrac{-(1 - e^t)(e^{2t} + e^t + 1)}{1 - e^t}$

$= -(e^{2t} + e^t + 1)$

$\int \dfrac{e^{2t} - e^{-t}}{e^{-t} - 1} \, dt = \int -(e^{2t} + e^t + 1) \, dt$

$= -\int (e^{2t} + e^t + 1) \, dt$

$= -\left(\dfrac{e^{2t}}{2} + e^t + t \right) + c$

Integrating Trigonometric Functions

From differentiation we know that if $y = \sin x$ then $\dfrac{dy}{dx} = \cos x$.

Since **integration is the reverse process of differentiation**, the indefinite integral $\int \cos x \, dx = \sin x + c$ where c is an arbitrary constant of integration.

Similarly, $\int \sin x \, dx = -\cos x + c$.

Also, from differentiation we know that if $y = \sin ax$, where a is constant, then $\dfrac{dy}{dx} = a \cos ax$.

This implies that the indefinite integral

$\int a \cos ax \, dx = \sin ax + c$.

$\therefore \int \cos ax \, dx = \dfrac{1}{a} \sin ax + c$

Similarly $\int \sin ax \, dx = -\dfrac{1}{a} \cos ax + c$.

$\int \cos x \, dx = \sin x + c$ $\int \cos ax \, dx = \dfrac{1}{a} \sin ax + c$

$\int \sin x \, dx = -\cos x + c$ $\int \sin ax \, dx = -\dfrac{1}{a} \cos ax + c$

These formulae are on page 26 of *Formulae and Tables*.

Worked Example 15.10

Find the following indefinite integrals:

(i) $\int \sin 3x \, dx$ (ii) $\int \cos 4x \, dx$ (iii) $\int (\cos 2x + \sin 5x) dx$

Solution

(i) $\int \sin 3x \, dx = -\dfrac{1}{3} \cos 3x + c$

(iii) $\int (\cos 2x + \sin 5x) \, dx = \dfrac{1}{2} \sin 2x - \dfrac{1}{5} \cos 5x + c$

(ii) $\int \cos 4x \, dx = \dfrac{1}{4} \sin 4x + c$

Worked Example 15.11

$f(\theta) = \sin\theta \cos\theta$

(i) Find $f'(\theta)$.

(ii) Hence, find $\int (\cos^2\theta - \sin^2\theta) \, d\theta$.

Solution

(i) $f'(\theta) = \sin\theta \, (-\sin\theta) + \cos\theta \, (\cos\theta)$ (Product Rule)

$= \cos^2\theta - \sin^2\theta$

(ii) $\int (\cos^2\theta - \sin^2\theta) \, d\theta = \sin\theta \cos\theta + c$ (Integration is the reverse process of differentiation.)

Exercise 15.3

1. Find the following indefinite integrals:

   (i) $\int e^{5x} \, dx$ (iv) $\int e^{\frac{x}{6}} \, dx$

   (ii) $\int e^{-3x} \, dx$ (v) $\int e^{-\frac{x}{7}} \, dx$

   (iii) $\int e^{4x} \, dx$ (vi) $\int (e^{4x} + e^{3x}) \, dx$

2. $f(x) = e^{2x + a}$, where a is a constant.

   (i) Write the function above in the form

   $$f(x) = e^c \, e^{g(x)}$$

   where $g(x)$ is a function of x and c is constant.

   (ii) Explain why

   $$\int e^c \, e^{g(x)} \, dx = e^c \int e^{g(x)} \, dx.$$

3. Using the results from Question 2, evaluate the following indefinite integrals:

   (i) $\int e^{x + 4} \, dx$ (iv) $\int e^{x - 6} \, dx$

   (ii) $\int e^{2x + 5} \, dx$ (v) $\int e^{5x - 2} \, dx$

   (iii) $\int e^{\frac{x}{4} + 10} \, dx$ (vi) $\int e^{\frac{x}{8} - 2} \, dx$

4. By expanding the brackets, find the following indefinite integrals:

   (i) $\int e^x \, (e^x + 1) \, dx$ (iii) $\int (e^x + e^{-x})(e^x - e^{-x}) \, dx$

   (ii) $\int e^{3x} \, (e^{2x} - 2) \, dx$ (iv) $\int (e^x + 2e^{2x})(e^x - 1) \, dx$

5. Find the following indefinite integrals:

   (i) $\int (e^x - e^{-x}) \, dx$

   (ii) $\int (e^x - e^{3x})(e^x + e^{3x}) \, dx$

   (iii) $\int (e^x + 1)(e^{2x} - e^x + 1) \, dx$

   (iv) $\int \dfrac{e^x - e^{-x}}{e^{-x} + 1} \, dx$

   Hint: Multiply numerator and denominator by e^x, then factorise.

6. Consider the function $y = a^x$, where a is some positive constant.

   (i) Show that $x = \dfrac{\ln y}{\ln a}$.

   (ii) Hence, find $\dfrac{dx}{dy}$.

(iii) Given that $\dfrac{dy}{dx} = \dfrac{1}{\left(\frac{dx}{dy}\right)}$, show that $\dfrac{dy}{dx} = (\ln a)a^x$.

(iv) Hence, find the indefinite integral $\displaystyle\int a^x \, dx$.

7. Find each of the following integrals:

(i) $\displaystyle\int 2^x \, dx$

(iv) $\displaystyle\int 7^x \, dx$

(ii) $\displaystyle\int 3^x \, dx$

(v) $\displaystyle\int 10e^{2x} \, dx$

(iii) $\displaystyle\int 5^x \, dx$

(vi) $\displaystyle\int (x^2 + 4^x) \, dx$

8. Find each of the following indefinite integrals:

(i) $\displaystyle\int 8^x \, dx$

(vi) $\displaystyle\int \left(\left(\frac{1}{10}\right)^x + 10^x\right) dx$

(ii) $\displaystyle\int 9^x \, dx$

(vii) $\displaystyle\int \frac{1}{2^x} \, dx$

(iii) $\displaystyle\int \left(\frac{1}{2}\right)^x dx$

(viii) $\displaystyle\int (e^{2x} + 2^x) \, dx$

(iv) $\displaystyle\int \left(\frac{1}{3}\right)^x dx$

(ix) $\displaystyle\int \frac{3}{5^x} \, dx$

(v) $\displaystyle\int \left(9^x + \left(\frac{1}{9}\right)^x\right) dx$

(x) $\displaystyle\int \left(\frac{2}{3^x} + \frac{5}{2^x}\right) dx$

9. Find each of the following indefinite integrals:

(i) $\displaystyle\int \frac{1}{x} \, dx$

(iv) $\displaystyle\int \frac{1}{5x} \, dx$

(ii) $\displaystyle\int \frac{3}{x} \, dx$

(v) $\displaystyle\int \frac{1}{8x} \, dx$

(iii) $\displaystyle\int -\frac{2}{x} \, dx$

(vi) $\displaystyle\int \left(\frac{3}{x} + \frac{2}{x}\right) dx$

10. f is the function $f\colon R \to R\colon t \to te^t - e^t$,
and g is the function $g\colon R \to R\colon t \to e^t$.

(i) Find $g'(t)$, the derivative of $g(t)$.

(ii) Find $f'(t)$, the derivative of $f(t)$.

(iii) Hence, find $\displaystyle\int te^t \, dt$.

11. Find each of the following indefinite integrals:

(i) $\displaystyle\int \sin 8x \, dx$

(iv) $\displaystyle\int 5 \cos 8x$

(ii) $\displaystyle\int \cos 4x \, dx$

(v) $\displaystyle\int \frac{\sin 3x}{2} \, dx$

(iii) $\displaystyle\int 2 \sin 6x \, dx$

(vi) $\displaystyle\int \frac{\cos 5x}{16} \, dx$

12. Find each of the following indefinite integrals:

(i) $\displaystyle\int (\sin 3x + \sin 2x) \, dx$

(ii) $\displaystyle\int (\cos 5x + \cos 3x) \, dx$

(iii) $\displaystyle\int (\sin 2x + \cos x) \, dx$

(iv) $\displaystyle\int (2 \sin 3x + 4 \cos 2x) \, dx$

(v) $\displaystyle\int (3 \sin 2x - 5 \cos 3x) \, dx$

(vi) $\displaystyle\int \left(5 \cos 4x - \frac{1}{2} \sin 2x\right) dx$

13. (a) Write the following products as sums
(see *Formulae and Tables*, p13):

(i) $2 \cos 2x \cos x$

(iii) $\sin 3x \sin x$

(ii) $2 \sin 5x \cos 3x$

(iv) $\cos 5x \sin 2x$

(b) Hence, find each of the following indefinite integrals:

(i) $\displaystyle\int 2 \cos 2x \cos x \, dx$

(iii) $\displaystyle\int \sin 3x \sin x \, dx$

(ii) $\displaystyle\int 2 \sin 5x \cos 3x \, dx$

(iv) $\displaystyle\int \cos 5x \sin 2x \, dx$

14. A particle is moving in a straight line so that its acceleration is given by $a = 5 + 3e^{-2t}$, where t is measured in seconds and a in ms^{-2}.

(i) Find the speed v after time t of the particle given that $v = 10$ ms^{-1} when $t = 0$.

(ii) Find the distance s travelled after time t given that $s = 0$ when $t = 0$.

15. An object moves in a straight line so that its acceleration at time t is given by $a = 17 - 5e^{-3t}$.

(i) Find the acceleration of the object when $t = 0$ and when $t = 5$.

(ii) How does the acceleration behave as time moves on?
i.e. What is $\displaystyle\lim_{t \to \infty} (17 - 5e^{-3t})$

(iii) Find the speed v after time t of the object given that $v = 15$ ms^{-1} when $t = 0$.

(iv) Find the distance s travelled after time t given that $s = 0$ when $t = 0$.

(v) Hence, find the distance travelled by the object after 20 seconds.

16. $y = e^{2x}, x \in R$

(i) What is $\dfrac{dy}{dx}$?

(ii) Find the indefinite integral $\int \dfrac{dy}{dx}\, dx$.

17. $y = e^{ax}, x \in R$ and a is constant.

(i) What is $\dfrac{dy}{dx}$?

(ii) Find the indefinite integral $\int \dfrac{dy}{dx}\, dx$.

18. Show that $y = e^{qx+r}, x \in R$ and q and r constants is a solution to the equation $\dfrac{dy}{dx} = qy$.

19. The rate of growth of the population P of a species of bacteria is given by

$$\frac{dP}{dt} = cP$$

where P is the population after t minutes and c is a positive constant.

(i) Given that $P = 2 \times 10^6$ when $t = 0$, find P in terms of c and t. (*Hint*: Use the result from Question 18.)

(ii) Find P when $t = 20$.

(iii) Given that $c = 2$, find the time to the nearest minute for the population to double.

20. (i) If $g(x) = \ln x$, find $g'(x)$, the derivative of $g(x)$ wrt x.

(ii) Hence, or otherwise, find the integral $\int \dfrac{1}{x}\, dx$.

(iii) Radioactive substances decay at a rate that is proportional to the amount of the substance present. That is, if $Q(t)$ is the amount of the substance at time t, then $\dfrac{d(Q(t))}{dt} = k(Q(t))$, where k is a negative constant of proportionality. This result leads to the equation:

$$\int \frac{d(Q(t))}{Q(t)} = \int k\, dt$$

By integrating on both sides of this equation, write $Q(t)$ in the form $Q(t) = Ae^{kt}$.

(iv) If a radioactive substance has a half-life of 421 years, and there currently exists 2.8×10^8 kg of the substance on Earth, then define the quantity function $Q(t)$ for this substance, where t is in years.

(v) The rate of change of another radioactive substance is calculated to be $Q'(t) = -1.5e^{-0.025t}$, where t is measured in years (from now) and $Q(t)$ is the quantity at time t, in kilograms.

If the current quantity on Earth is 60 kg, what will be the quantity in 10 years?

15.4 Definite Integrals

The indefinite integral $\int f(x)\, dx = F(x)$ is the general form of an antiderivative for a function f in x. For example:

If $f(x) = (x - 5)^2 = x^2 - 10x + 25$,

then $\int f(x)\, dx = F(x) = \dfrac{x^3}{3} - 5x^2 + 25x + c$, where c is an arbitrary constant.

The corresponding **definite integral** is defined as $\int_a^b f(x)\, dx = F(b) - F(a)$.

a and b are called the limits of integration. The significance of the definite integral will be examined later in this chapter in the context of signed area under a graph.

> If f is a continuous function defined on a closed interval $[a, b]$, then once an antiderivative F of f is known, the definite integral of f over that interval is given by:
>
> $$\int_a^b f(x)\, dx = F(x)\Big|_a^b$$
> $$= F(b) - F(a)$$

Worked Example 15.12

Evaluate each of the following definite integrals:

(i) $\int_1^4 5x^3\, dx$　　(ii) $\int_0^1 (x^4 - 2x^3 + 7)\, dx$　　(iii) $\int_1^4 \frac{3}{\sqrt{x}}\, dx$

Solution

(i) $\int_1^4 5x^3\, dx = \frac{5}{4}x^4 \Big|_1^4$

$= \frac{5}{4}(4)^4 - \frac{5}{4}(1)^4$

$= 320 - \frac{5}{4}$

$= \frac{1{,}275}{4}$

(ii) $\int_0^1 (x^4 - 2x^3 + 7)\, dx = \left[\frac{1}{5}x^5 - \frac{1}{2}x^4 + 7x\right]_0^1$

$= \left(\frac{1}{5}(1)^5 - \frac{1}{2}(1)^4 + 7(1)\right) - \left(\frac{1}{5}(0)^5 - \frac{1}{2}(0)^4 + 7(0)\right)$

$= \frac{1}{5} - \frac{1}{2} + 7$

$= \frac{67}{10}$

(iii) $\int_1^4 \frac{3}{\sqrt{x}}\, dx = \int_1^4 3x^{-\frac{1}{2}}\, dx$

$= 6x^{\frac{1}{2}} \Big|_1^4$

$= 6\sqrt{4} - 6\sqrt{1}$

$= 12 - 6$

$= 6$

Worked Example 15.13

Evaluate each of the following definite integrals:

(i) $\int_0^{\frac{\pi}{5}} \sin 5x\, dx$　　(ii) $\int_0^1 4e^{2x}$　　(iii) $\int_1^2 \frac{7}{x}\, dx$

Solution

(i) $\int_0^{\frac{\pi}{5}} \sin 5x\, dx = -\frac{1}{5}\cos 5x \Big|_0^{\frac{\pi}{5}}$

$= \left(-\frac{1}{5}\cos 5\left(\frac{\pi}{5}\right)\right) - \left(-\frac{1}{5}\cos 5(0)\right)$

$= -\frac{1}{5}\cos \pi + \frac{1}{5}\cos 0$

$= -\frac{1}{5}(-1) + \frac{1}{5}(1)$

$= \frac{2}{5}$

(ii) $\int_0^1 4e^{2x}\, dx = 2e^{2x} \Big|_0^1$

$= (2e^{2(1)}) - (2e^{2(0)})$

$= 2e^2 - 2e^0$

$= 2(e^2 - 1)$

(iii) $\int_1^2 \frac{7}{x}\, dx = 7\int_1^2 \frac{1}{x}\, dx$

$= 7 \ln x \Big|_1^2$

$= 7 \ln 2 - 7 \ln 1$

$= 7 \ln 2 - 7(0)$

$= 7 \ln 2$

Worked Example 15.14

(i) Find the derivative $F'(x)$ of the function $F(x) = \sin^2 x$.

(ii) Hence, find an antiderivative G of the function $g(x) = \sin 2x$.

(iii) Evaluate the definite integral $\int_{\frac{\pi}{4}}^{\frac{3\pi}{4}} \sin 2x\, dx$.

Solution

(i) $F(x) = \sin^2 x$

$\qquad = (\sin x)^2$

Let $u = \sin x.$ $\therefore y = u^2$

$\dfrac{du}{dx} = \cos x \qquad \dfrac{dy}{du} = 2u$

By the Chain Rule:

$\qquad F'(x) = \dfrac{dy}{du} \times \dfrac{du}{dx}$

$\qquad\qquad = 2u(\cos x)$

$\qquad\qquad = 2 \sin x \cos x$

$\therefore F'(x) = \sin 2x$ (*Formulae and Tables*, page 14)

(ii) The derivative of $\sin^2 x$ with respect to x is $\sin 2x$. Therefore, an antiderivative G of the function $g(x) = \sin 2x$ would be $G(x) = \sin^2 x + c$, where c is any constant.

(iii) $\int_{\frac{\pi}{4}}^{\frac{3\pi}{4}} \sin 2x\, dx = G\left(\dfrac{3\pi}{4}\right) - G\left(\dfrac{\pi}{4}\right)$

$\qquad\qquad = \sin^2 \dfrac{3\pi}{4} - \sin^2 \dfrac{\pi}{4}$

$\qquad\qquad = \left(\dfrac{1}{\sqrt{2}}\right)^2 - \left(\dfrac{1}{\sqrt{2}}\right)^2$

$\qquad\qquad = 0$

Exercise 15.4

1. Evaluate each of the following definite integrals:

   (i) $\int_{2}^{3} x\, dx$

   (ii) $\int_{1}^{8} x^2\, dx$

   (iii) $\int_{-1}^{4} x^5\, dx$

   (iv) $\int_{0}^{1} x^{10}\, dx$

2. Evaluate each of the following definite integrals:

   (i) $\int_{0}^{1} (x^3 + x^2 - x - 2)\, dx$

   (ii) $\int_{1}^{4} (x^4 + 8x + 2)\, dx$

   (iii) $\int_{-2}^{3} (x^5 - x^4 + x^3 - x^2 + x)\, dx$

   (iv) $\int_{-5}^{-3} (x^6 - 32)\, dx$

3. Evaluate these definite integrals:

   (i) $\int_{1}^{4} 2x(x - 3)\, dx$

   (ii) $\int_{1}^{9} 5x(x^2 - 2)\, dx$

   (iii) $\int_{0}^{1} (2x - 4)(3x - 2)\, dx$

   (iv) $\int_{-1}^{3} x(x^2 + 2x + 1)\, dx$

   (v) $\int_{-2}^{4} (x^2 - 1)(x + 1)\, dx$

   (vi) $\int_{-1}^{0} x(x + 1)(x - 1)\, dx$

4. Write the following expressions in their simplest form:

   (i) $\dfrac{x^2 + 2x + 1}{x + 1}$

   (ii) $\dfrac{2x^2 + x - 1}{2x - 1}$

   (iii) $\dfrac{x^2 - 16}{x - 4}$

   (iv) $\dfrac{9x^2 - 25}{3x + 5}$

   (v) $\dfrac{x^3 - 8}{x - 2}$

   (vi) $\dfrac{x^3 + 27}{x^2 - 3x + 9}$

5. Using your results from Question 4, evaluate the following definite integrals:

(i) $\int_1^5 \dfrac{x^2 + 2x + 1}{x + 1}\, dx$

(ii) $\int_2^4 \dfrac{2x^2 + x - 1}{2x - 1}\, dx$

(iii) $\int_5^7 \dfrac{x^2 - 16}{x - 4}\, dx$

(iv) $\int_0^3 \dfrac{9x^2 - 25}{3x + 5}\, dx$

(v) $\int_3^5 \dfrac{x^3 - 8}{x - 2}\, dx$

(vi) $\int_1^2 \dfrac{x^3 + 27}{x^2 - 3x + 9}\, dx$

6. Using page 25 of *Formulae and Tables* and your knowledge of antiderivatives, evaluate each of the following definite integrals:

(i) $\int_0^{\frac{\pi}{2}} \sin x\, dx$

(ii) $\int_{\frac{\pi}{2}}^{2\pi} \cos x\, dx$

(iii) $\int_0^{\frac{\pi}{3}} \sec^2 x\, dx$

(iv) $\int_0^{\frac{\pi}{3}} \cos x\, dx$

7. Evaluate each of the following definite integrals:

(i) $\int_1^2 e^x\, dx$

(ii) $\int_{-1}^4 e^{3x}\, dx$

(iii) $\int_0^5 e^{-2x}\, dx$

(iv) $\int_1^5 \dfrac{1}{e^{5x}}\, dx$

8. Using page 15 of *Formulae and Tables*, evaluate each of the following indefinite integrals:

(i) $\int_0^{\frac{\pi}{6}} \cos 2\theta \sin 4\theta\, d\theta$

(ii) $\int_0^{\frac{\pi}{2}} \cos 3\theta \cos 2\theta\, d\theta$

(iii) $\int_0^{\frac{\pi}{4}} \sin 3x \cos x\, dx$

(iv) $\int_0^{\frac{\pi}{6}} \sin 4x \cos 2x\, dx$

9. Using page 25 of *Formulae and Tables* and your knowledge of antiderivatives, evaluate each of the following definite integrals:

(i) $\int_0^3 \dfrac{dx}{\sqrt{9 - x^2}}$

(ii) $\int_0^4 \dfrac{dx}{\sqrt{16 - x^2}}$

(iii) $\int_0^{5\sqrt{3}} \dfrac{5\, dx}{25 + x^2}$

(iv) $6\int_0^6 \dfrac{dx}{36 + x^2}$

10. Evaluate each of the following definite integrals:

(i) $\int_0^1 (x^4 + x^2 - 8)\, dx$

(ii) $\int_2^3 (2x - 7)(x + 3)\, dx$

(iii) $\int_4^9 \sqrt{x}\, dx$

(iv) $\int_1^{16} \dfrac{1}{\sqrt{x}}\, dx$

(v) $\int_1^2 \dfrac{x^2 - 25}{x + 5}\, dx$

(vi) $\int_5^6 e^{3x + 2}\, dx$

11. Evaluate each of the following definite integrals:

(i) $\int_1^2 \dfrac{1}{x}\, dx$

(ii) $\int_3^4 \dfrac{5}{x}\, dx$

(iii) $\int_0^{\pi} \sin 4x\, dx$

(iv) $\int_0^{2\pi} \cos 4x\, dx$

(v) $\int_0^1 e^{2x}\, dx$

(vi) $\int_3^4 e^{5 - x}\, dx$

12. Evaluate each of the following definite integrals:

(i) $\int_0^{2\pi} (\sin 2x + \cos 4x)\, dx$

(ii) $\int_1^2 \left(x^2 + \dfrac{1}{x}\right) dx$

(iii) $\int_0^1 (e^{4x} + e^{-2x})\, dx$

(iv) $\int_1^4 \left(\sqrt{x} + \dfrac{1}{\sqrt{x}}\right) dx$

(v) $\int_0^{\pi} (\cos 5x - \sin 2x)\, dx$

(vi) $\int_1^4 \left(e^x + \dfrac{1}{x}\right) dx$

13. For each of the following equations, find the value of $k \in R^+$.

(i) $\int_0^k x\, dx = 18$

(ii) $\int_1^k \dfrac{2}{x}\, dx = 2$

(iii) $\int_0^k e^{3x}\, dx = \dfrac{1}{3}$

(iv) $\int_0^k 2\cos 2x\, dx = -1$

(v) $\int_0^9 \dfrac{k}{\sqrt{x}}\, dx = 30$

(vi) $\int_1^k \sqrt{t}\, dt = 42$

15.5 Area Under a Graph

Calculating the area under a graph is easy if the area can be divided into rectangles. If the graph is a smooth curve, then it is not possible to get a precise value for the area by dividing the area up into rectangles. However, it is possible to get good approximations for the area under a curve by fitting rectangles under the curve and summing the areas of the rectangles.

The accuracy of the approximations improves as the number of rectangles used increases while the width of each rectangle decreases.

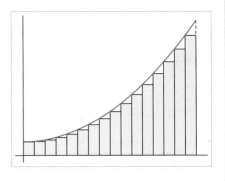

Worked Example 15.15

(i) Approximate the area under the graph of $f(x) = x^2 + 1$ and the x-axis over the interval $[0, 3]$ by fitting four rectangles of equal area under the graph and then adding.

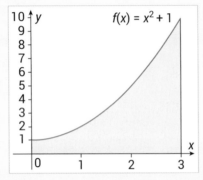

(ii) Approximate the area under the graph of $f(x) = x^2 + 1$ and the x-axis over the interval $[0, 3]$ by fitting eight rectangles of equal area under the graph and then adding. Explain why this approximation is better than that obtained in part (i).

Solution

(i)

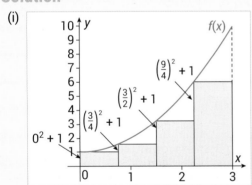

Step 1 Find the base length of the rectangles.

$$\text{Base length} = \frac{3 - 0}{4} = \frac{3}{4} = 0.75$$

Step 2 Find the height of each rectangle.

Rectangle	Height = $x^2 + 1$	Height
1	$0^2 + 1$	1
2	$\left(\frac{3}{4}\right)^2 + 1$	1.5625
3	$\left(\frac{3}{2}\right)^2 + 1$	3.25
4	$\left(\frac{9}{4}\right)^2 + 1$	6.0625

Step 3 Find the total area of the rectangles.

Area = 0.75(1) + 0.75(1.5625) +
0.75(3.25) + 0.75(6.0625)

Area of four rectangles = 8.90625 units^2

∴ Area under graph ≈ 8.90625 units^2

(ii) **Step 1** Find the base length of the rectangles.

$$\text{Base length} = \frac{3 - 0}{8} = \frac{3}{8} = 0.375$$

Step 2 Find the height of each rectangle.

Rectangle	Height = x^2 + 1	Height
1	$0^2 + 1$	1
2	$\left(\frac{3}{8}\right)^2 + 1$	1.140625
3	$\left(\frac{6}{8}\right)^2 + 1$	1.5625
4	$\left(\frac{9}{8}\right)^2 + 1$	2.265625
5	$\left(\frac{12}{8}\right)^2 + 1$	3.25
6	$\left(\frac{15}{8}\right)^2 + 1$	4.515625
7	$\left(\frac{18}{8}\right)^2 + 1$	6.0625
8	$\left(\frac{21}{8}\right)^2 + 1$	7.890625

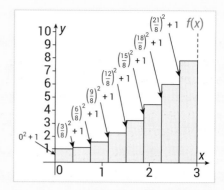

Step 3 Find the total area of the rectangles.

Area = 0.375(1 + 1.140625 + 1.5625 +
2.265625 + 3.25 + 4.515625 + 6.0625 +
7.890625)

= 0.375(27.6875)

Area = 10.3828125 units^2

∴ Area under graph ≈10.3828125 units^2

This is a better approximation than that used in part (i) because, by increasing the number of rectangles, we have reduced the area that was not calculated.

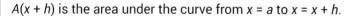

Theorem of Area

A curve $y = f(x)$ lies completely on or above the x-axis for x between a and b, as shown in the diagram.

The area between the curve, the x-axis and the lines $x = a$ and $x = b$ is given by:

$$\int_a^b f(x)\, dx$$

Proof

Consider the function $A(x)$, which we define to be the area under the curve from $x = a$ to $x = x$, where $x \leqslant b$.

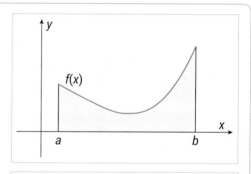

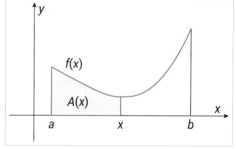

$A(x + h)$ is the area under the curve from $x = a$ to $x = x + h$.

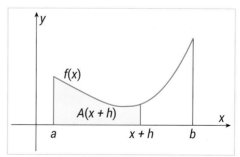

Consider the narrow strip between the two areas $A(x + h)$ and $A(x)$.

The area of this narrow strip may be written as $A(x + h) - A(x)$. However, the strip is approximately rectangular and, hence, its area is approximately $f(x) \times h$ (base × height).

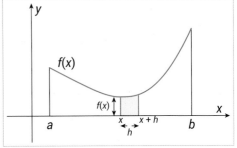

$$A(x + h) - A(x) \approx f(x) \times h$$

$$\frac{A(x + h) - A(x)}{h} \approx f(x)$$

As h becomes smaller, this approximation becomes more accurate:

$$\lim_{h \to 0} \frac{A(x + h) - A(x)}{h} = \lim_{h \to 0} f(x)$$

$$A'(x) = f(x)$$

$$\therefore A(x) + c = \int f(x)\, dx \quad \text{(c is the constant of integration)}$$

$$\therefore A(b) - A(a) = \int_a^b f(x)\, dx \quad \text{(definition of definite integral)}$$

$\therefore \int_a^b f(x)\, dx$ is the area between the curve, the x-axis and the lines $x = a$ and $x = b$.

Similarly, it can be proved that the area between $x = g(y)$ and the

y-axis from $y = p$ to $y = q$ is given by

$$\int_p^q g(y)\, dy$$

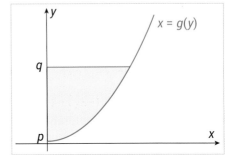

where x is a function of y ($x = g(y)$) and the curve $x = g(y)$ lies on or to the right of the y-axis on $p \leqslant y \leqslant q$.

If a region lies completely on or below the x-axis and we calculate the area of the region using the definite integral from $x = a$ to $x = b$, we will obtain a negative answer. Therefore, in this case:

$$\text{Area} = \left| \int_a^b f(x)\, dx \right| = -\int_a^b f(x)\, dx$$

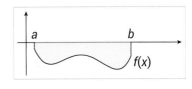

$$-\int_a^b f(x)\, dx = \int_b^a f(x)\, dx$$

If a region lies partially above and partially below the x-axis, we must use separate integrals when calculating the area of the region. In the case shown on the right, the shaded area is given by:

$$\text{Area} = \left| \int_a^b f(x)\, dx \right| + \int_b^c f(x)\, dx$$

$$= -\int_a^b f(x)\, dx + \int_b^c f(x)\, dx$$

$$\text{or} = \int_b^a f(x)\, dx + \int_b^c f(x)\, dx$$

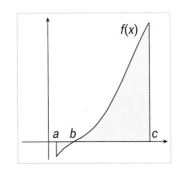

Worked Example 15.16

Find the area bounded by the curve $y = x^2 - 9$, the x-axis and the lines $x = 0$ and $x = 5$.

Solution

Step 1 Draw a sketch of the curve $y = x^2 - 9$.

x-intercepts

Let $y = 0$.

$x^2 - 9 = 0$

$(x - 3)(x + 3) = 0$

$x = \pm 3$

The x-intercepts are $(-3,0)$ and $(3,0)$.

The curve is quadratic and the coefficient of x^2 is positive. Therefore, the curve is $\cup$-shaped.

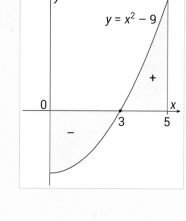

Step 2 Area $= \left| \int_0^3 (x^2 - 9)\, dx \right| + \int_3^5 (x^2 - 9)\, dx$

$= \left| \left[\tfrac{1}{3}x^3 - 9x \right]_0^3 \right| + \left[\tfrac{1}{3}x^3 - 9x \right]_3^5$

$= \left| \left[\tfrac{1}{3}(27) - 9(3) \right] - \left[\tfrac{1}{3}(0) - 9(0) \right] \right| + \left[\tfrac{1}{3}(125) - 9(5) \right] - \left[\tfrac{1}{3}(27) - 9(3) \right]$

$= \left| -18 \right| + \left(-3\tfrac{1}{3} \right) - (-18)$

$= 18 - 3\tfrac{1}{3} + 18$

$= 32\tfrac{2}{3}$ units^2

Exercise 15.5

1. (a) Approximate the area under the graph of $f(x) = x + 4$ over the interval $[2, 6]$ by computing the area of each rectangle and then adding.

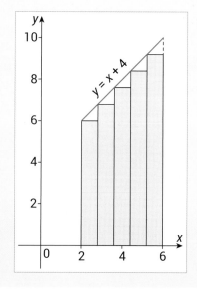

(b) Approximate the area under the graph of $f(x) = x + 4$ over the interval $[2, 6]$ by computing the area of each rectangle and then adding. Compare your answer to that for part (a).

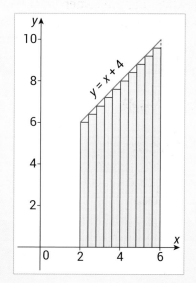

2. Approximate the area under the graph of $f(x) = 18 - 5x$ over the interval $[0, 3]$ by computing the area of each rectangle in the diagrams below and then adding.

(a)

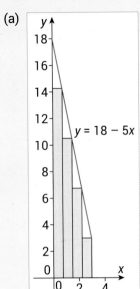

(b)

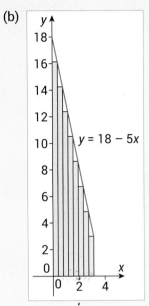

(c) Calculate the true area under the graph of $f(x) = 18 - 5x$.

3. (a) Approximate the area under the graph of $f(x) = x^2$ over the interval $[1, 6]$ by computing the area of each rectangle and then adding.

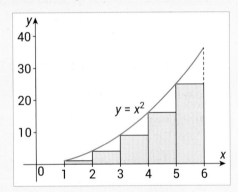

(b) Approximate the area under the graph of $f(x) = x^2$ over the interval $[1, 6]$ by computing the area of each rectangle to three decimal places and then adding. Compare your answer to that for part (a).

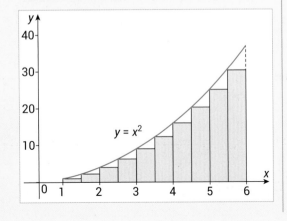

4. (a) Approximate the area under the graph of $f(x) = \frac{1}{x^2}$ over the interval $[1, 6]$ by computing the area of each rectangle and then adding.

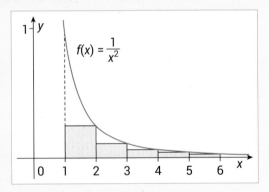

(b) Approximate the area under the graph of $f(x) = \frac{1}{x^2}$ over the interval $[1, 6]$ by computing the area of each rectangle to four decimal places and then adding. Compare your answer to that for part (a).

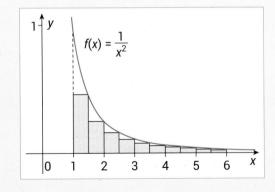

5. (a) Approximate the area under the graph of $f(x) = x^3$ over the interval [0, 1] by computing the area of each rectangle and then adding.

(b) The area under the graph of $f(x) = x^3$ is 0.25. Calculate the percentage error in taking the approximation in part (a) as the area under the graph.

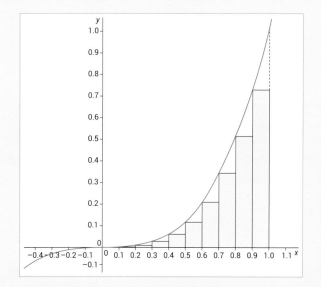

6. (a) Approximate the area under the graph of $f(x) = x^4 - x^2 + 1$ over the interval [0, 1] by computing the area of each rectangle and then adding.

(b) The area under the graph of $f(x) = x^4 - x^2 + 1$ is $\frac{13}{15}$. Calculate the percentage error in taking the approximation in (a) as the area under the graph.

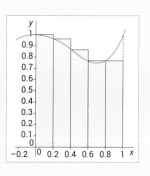

7. For each of the following identical rectangles constructed on the interval [0, 1] write down in fraction form the width of the rectangles:

(i)

(ii)

(iii)

(iv)   *n* rectangles

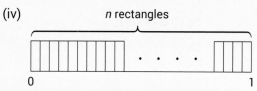

8. *n* rectangles of equal width are constructed under the curve $f(x) = x^2 + 3$ over the interval [0, 1].

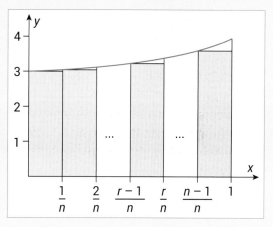

(i) What is the width of each rectangle?

(ii) Find in terms of *n*, $f\left(\frac{1}{n}\right)$.

(iii) Write down in terms of *n* the height of the 2nd rectangle.

(iv) Find A_2, the area of the second rectangle in terms of *n*.

(v) Find in terms of *r* and *n*, $f\left(\frac{r-1}{n}\right)$.

(vi) Show that the area of the rth rectangle is given by $A_r = \frac{1}{n}\left[\left(\frac{r-1}{n}\right)^2 + 3\right]$.

9. *n* rectangles of equal width are drawn under the graph of $f(x) = x^2 + 2,\ x \in R$ over the interval [0, 1].

(i) Explain why the width of each rectangle is $\frac{1}{n}$.

(ii) Show that the area of the *r*th rectangle is given by:

$$A_r = \frac{1}{n}\left(\left(\frac{r-1}{n}\right)^2 + 2\right)$$

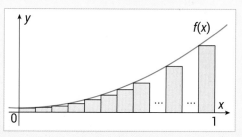

(iii) Hence, show that the sum of the areas of the *n* rectangles can be written as:

$$S_n = \frac{1}{n}\left\{[0^2 + 2] + \left[\left(\frac{1}{n}\right)^2 + 2\right] + \left[\left(\frac{2}{n}\right)^2 + 2\right] + \ldots + \left[\left(\frac{n-1}{n}\right)^2 + 2\right]\right\}$$

INTEGRAL CALCULUS

(iv) Show that the expression in part (iii) can be written as:

$$S_n = \frac{1}{n^3}[1^2 + 2^2 + 3^2 + \ldots + (n-1)^2 + 2n^3]$$

(v) Given that $\displaystyle\sum_{r=1}^{n} r^2 = \frac{n}{6}(2n+1)(n+1)$, find another expression for S_n.

(vi) Explain why $\displaystyle\lim_{n\to\infty} S_n$ is the area under the graph of $f(x)$.

(vii) Show that $\displaystyle\lim_{n\to\infty} S_n = \int_0^1 (x^2 + 2)\,dx$.

10. n rectangles are drawn under the graph of $f(x) = x^3 + 4$, $x \in R$ over the interval $[0, 1]$.

(i) Explain why the width of each rectangle is $\frac{1}{n}$.

(ii) Show that the area of the rth rectangle is given by:

$$A_r = \frac{1}{n}\left(\left(\frac{r-1}{n}\right)^3 + 4\right)$$

(iii) Hence, show that the sum of the areas of the n rectangles can be written as:

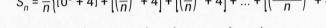

$$S_n = \frac{1}{n}\left\{[0^3 + 4] + \left[\left(\frac{1}{n}\right)^3 + 4\right] + \left[\left(\frac{2}{n}\right)^3 + 4\right] + \ldots + \left[\left(\frac{n-1}{n}\right)^3 + 4\right]\right\}$$

(iv) Show that the expression above can be written as:

$$S_n = \frac{1}{n^4}[1^3 + 2^3 + 3^3 + \ldots + (n-1)^3 + 4n^4]$$

(v) Given that $\displaystyle\sum_{r=1}^{n} r^3 = \left[\frac{n}{2}(n+1)\right]^2$, find another expression for S_n.

(vi) Show that $\displaystyle\lim_{n\to\infty} S_n = \int_0^1 (x^3 + 4)\,dx$.

In Questions 11–20, use definite integrals to find the indicated areas.

11. Find the area between the curve $y = x^2 + 2$, the x-axis and the lines $x = 2$ and $x = 4$.

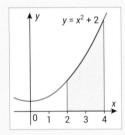

12. Find the area between the curve $y = x^2 - 1$ and the x-axis from $x = 1$ to $x = 4$.

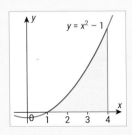

13. Find the area enclosed between the curve $y = \cos x$, the x-axis, the y-axis and the line $x = \frac{\pi}{3}$.

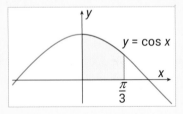

14. Find the area enclosed between the curve $y = e^x$, the x-axis, the y-axis and the line $x = \ln 5$.

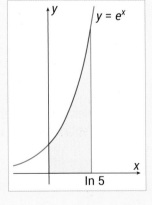

15. Find the area in the first quadrant between the curve $y = x^2$ and the y-axis, between the lines $y = 1$ and $y = 9$.

(*Hint:* Use $x = \sqrt{y}$ in first quadrant.)

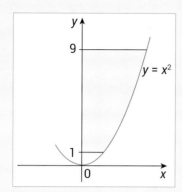

16. The diagram shows part of the graph of $y = x^3$. Find:

(i) The values of p and q

(ii) The area A_1, by integrating with respect to x

(iii) The area A_2

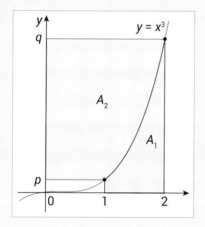

17. The diagram shows the curve $y = e^{-x}$.

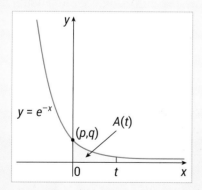

(i) Find the co-ordinates of the point (p,q) where this curve cuts the y-axis.

(ii) $A(t)$ is the area between this curve and the x-axis, $0 \leq x \leq t$.

Show that $A(t) = 1 - \dfrac{1}{e^t}$.

(iii) Find $\lim\limits_{t \to \infty} A(t)$.

18. (i) Find the area, as shown below, between the curve $y = \cos x$ and the x-axis, $0 \leq x \leq \dfrac{\pi}{2}$.

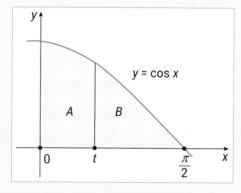

(ii) Find the value of t, if area of A = area of B.

19. The diagram shows the local maximum point, P, and the local minimum point, Q, of the curve $y = x^3 - 3x^2 - 9x$.

If O is the origin, show that the area of the shaded region is $50\frac{1}{2}$ square units.

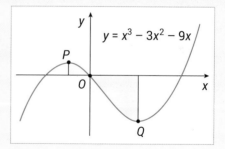

20. The sketch shows part of the graph of $y = (3x - 4)(3x + 4)$.

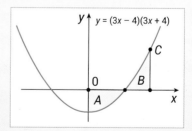

Find the co-ordinates of the point C such that the shaded regions A and B are equal in area.

15.6 Intersecting Curves and the Trapezoidal Rule

Worked Example 15.17

Find the area enclosed between the curve $y = x^2 - 2x + 2$ and the line $y = x$.

Solution

Step 1 Find where the line and the curve intersect.

$$y = x^2 - 2x + 2$$

$$y = x$$

Solve the pair of simultaneous equations.

$$x^2 - 2x + 2 = x$$

$$x^2 - 3x + 2 = 0$$

$$(x - 2)(x - 1) = 0$$

The line cuts the curve at $x = 1$ and $x = 2$.

Step 2 Draw a rough sketch of the line and the curve, and shade the required area.

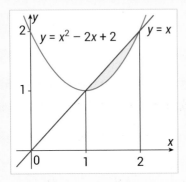

The area required =

(Area under $y = x$) − (Area under $y = x^2 - 2x + 2$) on the interval $[1, 2]$

$$\text{Area} = \int_1^2 x \, dx - \int_1^2 (x^2 - 2x + 2) \, dx$$

$$= \left[\frac{x^2}{2}\right]_1^2 - \left[\frac{x^3}{3} - x^2 + 2x\right]_1^2$$

$$= \left(2 - \frac{1}{2}\right) - \left[\left(\frac{8}{3} - 4 + 4\right) - \left(\frac{1}{3} - 1 + 2\right)\right]$$

$$= \frac{3}{2} - \frac{4}{3}$$

$$= \frac{1}{6} \text{ units squared}$$

Worked Example 15.18

(i) Use the Trapezoidal Rule with three trapezoids to approximate the area under the curve $y = e^{2x}$ and above the x-axis between $x = 1$ and $x = 4$. Give your answer correct to two decimal places.

(ii) Use a definite integral to find the true area and, hence, calculate the percentage error in using the Trapezoidal Rule to estimate the area.

(iii) Does the Trapezoidal Rule overestimate the true area? Explain.

Solution

(i) $A = \dfrac{h}{2}[y_1 + y_n + 2\,y_2 + y_3 + y_4 + \ldots + y_{n-1}]$

$$h = \frac{2 - 1}{3} = \frac{1}{3}$$

> The Trapezoidal Rule is found on page 12 of *Formulae and Tables*.

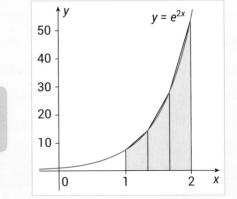

$$y_1 = e^2, \quad y_2 = e^{\frac{8}{3}}, \quad y_3 = e^{\frac{10}{3}}, \quad y_4 = e^4$$

$$A = \frac{1}{6}\left[e^2 + e^4 + 2\left(e^{\frac{8}{3}} + e^{\frac{10}{3}}\right)\right]$$

$$= 24.47 \text{ units}^2$$

(ii) Area $= \int_1^2 e^{2x}\, dx$

$= \left[\dfrac{e^{2x}}{2}\right]_1^2$

$= \dfrac{1}{2}[e^4 - e^2]$

$= 23.60$ (two decimal places)

Error $= 24.47 - 23.60$

$= 0.87$

% Error $= \dfrac{0.87}{23.60} \times 100$

$= 3.69\%$

(iii) The Trapezoidal Rule overestimates the true area, as $y = e^{2x}$ is an increasing function on $[1, 2]$ with $\dfrac{d^2y}{dx^2} > 0$.

Worked Example 15.19

Find the area enclosed between the curve $f(x) = x^2 + 5$ and the curve $g(x) = \dfrac{21}{16}x^2$.

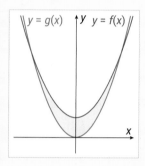

Solution

Step 1 Find where the two curves intersect.

$$x^2 + 5 = \dfrac{21}{16}x^2$$

$$16x^2 + 80 = 21x^2$$

$$5x^2 = 80$$

$$x^2 = 16$$

$$x = \pm 4$$

The curves intersect at $x = -4$ and at $x = 4$.

Step 2 Shaded area = Area under $y = f(x)$ – Area under $y = g(x)$ from $x = 4$ to $x = -4$

$$\int_{-4}^4 (x^2 + 5)\, dx - \int_{-4}^4 \dfrac{21}{16}x^2\, dx$$

$$= \left[\dfrac{x^3}{3} + 5x\right]_{-4}^4 - \left[\dfrac{7}{16}x^3\right]_{-4}^4$$

$$= \left[\left(\dfrac{64}{3} + 20\right) - \left(-\dfrac{64}{3} - 20\right)\right] - [(28) - (-28)]$$

$$= 26\dfrac{2}{3} \text{ units}^2$$

Exercise 15.6

1. Find the area enclosed between the curve $y = x - x^2$ and the line $y = \dfrac{x}{2}$.

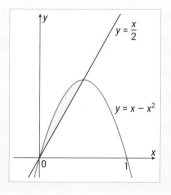

2. Find the area enclosed between the curve $y = 4x - x^2$ and the line $y = x$.

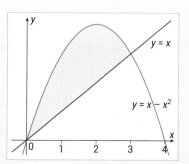

3. The diagram shows the curve $y = x(5 - x)$ and the line $y = 2x$.

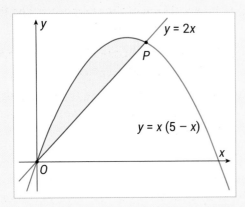

(i) Find the co-ordinates of P, the point where the curve and line intersect.

(ii) Find the area of the shaded region.

4. The diagram shows the curve $y = x^3$ and the line $y = 4x$.

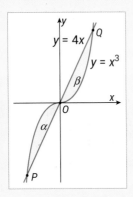

(i) Find the co-ordinates of P and Q.

(ii) The area labelled α is equal to the area labelled β. Find the total area bounded between the line and the curve.

5. The curves $y = x^2 - 4$ and $y = 8 - 2x^2$ are shown.

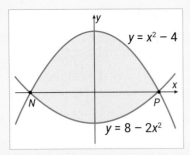

(i) Find the co-ordinates of the points N and P.

(ii) Hence, find the area bounded by the two curves.

6. The curves $y = x^3 - 9x^2 + 26x - 20$ and $y = x^2 - 5x + 10$ are shown.

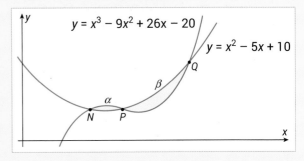

(i) Show that the co-ordinates of N, P and Q are $(2,4)$, $(3,4)$ and $(5,10)$ respectively.

(ii) Find the two finite areas, α and β, bounded by the two curves.

7. The shaded region R is bounded by the curve $y = -2x^2 + 4x$ and the line $y = \frac{3}{2}$.

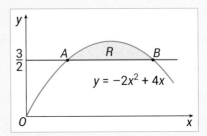

(i) Find the co-ordinates of A and B.

(ii) Hence, find the area of the region R.

8. Part of the curve with equation $y = 2x + \frac{8}{x^2} - 5$, $x > 0$ is shown. The points P and Q lie on the curve and have x co-ordinates 1 and 4.

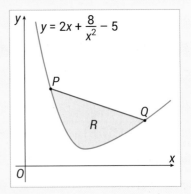

(i) Find the co-ordinates of P and Q.

(ii) Find the equation of the line PQ in the form $y = mx + c$.

(iii) Hence, find the area of the shaded region, labelled R.

9. Part of the graph of the cubic curve
$y = x^3 - 8x^2 + 20x$ is shown in the diagram.
The curve has a local maximum and local
minimum at A and B respectively.

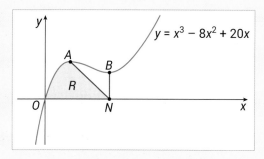

(i) Find the co-ordinates of A and B.

(ii) The line BN is parallel to the y-axis.
Find the co-ordinates of N.

(iii) The shaded region R is the area bounded by
the cubic curve, the x-axis and the line AN.
Find the area of R.

10. A sketch of part of the curve c with equation
$y = x(x - 1)(x - 5)$ is shown. Find the area
of the shaded region.

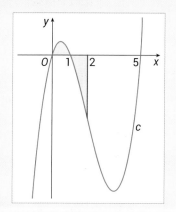

11. A graph of the function $f(x) = x^2 - 5x + 4$ is shown.

(i) Show that the
point $(1,0)$ is one
of the x-intercepts
of the curve and
find the other
x-intercept.

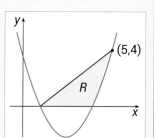

(ii) Show that the
point $(5,4)$ lies on
the curve.

(iii) Find the equation of the line containing
$(1,0)$ and $(5,4)$. Write the equation in the
form $y = mx + c$.

(iv) Hence, find the area of R, the region
bounded by the curve, the line and the
x-axis.

12. (i) Find the equation of the tangent to the
curve $y = x^2$ at the point $(4,16)$.

(ii) Draw a sketch of the curve $y = x^2$ and the
tangent found in part (i).

(iii) Find the area enclosed between the curve,
the tangent and the x-axis.

(iv) Hence, or otherwise, find the finite area
enclosed between the curve, the tangent
and the y-axis.

13. Find an approximate value for the area under
the curve $y = 16 - x^2$ and above the x-axis
between $x = 0$ and $x = 3$ by dividing the area
into three trapezoids of equal width.

Explain why use of the Trapezoidal Rule
underestimates the true area in this case.

14. (i) Use the Trapezoidal Rule to find an
approximation for the area under the
curve $y = 1 + 6x - x^2$ and above the x-axis
between $x = 0$ and $x = 6$. Divide the area
into six trapezoids.

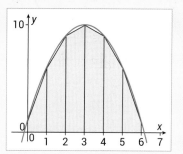

(ii) Approximate the area under the curve
$y = 1 + 6x - x^2$ and above the x-axis
between $x = 0$ and $x = 6$ by summing the
areas of the six rectangles constructed
using the curve.

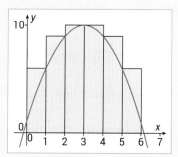

(iii) Find the exact area under the curve
$y = 1 + 6x - x^2$ and above the x-axis
between $x = 0$ and $x = 6$ by evaluating the
definite integral $\int_0^6 (1 + 6x - x^2)\, dx$.

INTEGRAL CALCULUS

15. The graph of the curve $y = \dfrac{16}{x^2} - \dfrac{x}{2} + 1$ is shown.

(i) Copy and complete the table.

(ii) Use the Trapezoidal Rule to find the approximate area of the region R.

(iii) Use integration to find the exact area of R.

(iv) Use the answers above to find the percentage error in the Trapezoidal Rule approximation of the area. Give your answer correct to one decimal place.

x	1	1.5	2	2.5	3	3.5	4
y	16.5	7.361			1.278	0.556	0

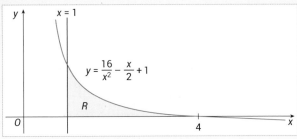

15.7 Average Value of a Function

The graph shown gives the temperature readings at a certain location over a 24-hour period.

How can we compute the average temperature reading during a day when infinitely many temperature readings are possible?

One approach is to take readings at, say, six-hour intervals and compute the mean of these.

So, $T_0 = 6$, $T_6 = 6$, $T_{12} = 3$, $T_{18} = 2$ and $T_{24} = 4$.

$$\text{Mean} = \frac{6+6+3+2+4}{5} = 4.2°C$$

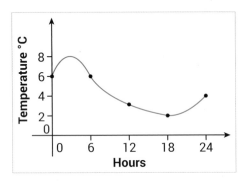

Taking readings over narrower intervals will improve the accuracy of our approximation of the average temperature during the day.

One such way in which this can be done is to use integration to find what is known as 'the **average value** of a function'.

Consider the graph of a function $y = f(x)$ on an interval $a \leqslant x \leqslant b$. We divide the interval $[a, b]$ into n equal subintervals.

If we call the width of each subinterval Δx, then $\Delta x = \dfrac{b-a}{n}$.

So, $n = \dfrac{b-a}{\Delta x}$.

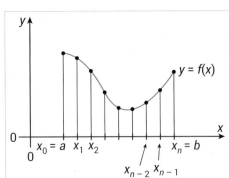

The average value of the numbers $f(x_0), f(x_1), \ldots, f(x_{n-1})$ is:

$$\frac{f(x_0) + f(x_1) + \ldots + f(x_{n-1})}{n}$$

$$= \frac{f(x_0) + f(x_1) + \ldots + f(x_{n-1})}{\dfrac{b-a}{\Delta x}}$$

$$= \frac{f(x_0)\Delta x + f(x_1)\Delta x + \ldots + f(x_{n-1})\Delta x}{b-a}$$

$$= \frac{1}{b-a}\left[f(x_0)\Delta x + f(x_1)\Delta x + \ldots + f(x_{n-1})\Delta x\right]$$

As $n \to \infty$, $f(x_0)\Delta x + f(x_1)\Delta x + \ldots + f(x_{n-1})\Delta x = \displaystyle\int_a^b f(x)\,dx$.

The **average value** of a function over the interval $[a, b]$ is:

$$\frac{1}{b-a}\int_a^b f(x)\,dx$$

Worked Example 15.20

(i) Find the average value of the function
$f: R \mapsto R: x \mapsto 2x^2 + x + 1$ on the interval $[1, 4]$.

(ii) Investigate the link between the area of region A and region B.

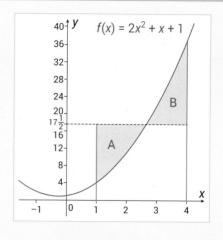

Solution

(i) Average value $= \dfrac{1}{4-1}\displaystyle\int_1^4 (2x^2 + x + 1)\,dx$

$= \dfrac{1}{3}\left[\dfrac{2}{3}x^3 + \dfrac{1}{2}x^2 + x\right]_1^4$

$= \dfrac{1}{3}\left(\left[\dfrac{2}{3}(4)^3 + \dfrac{1}{2}(4)^2 + 4\right] - \left[\dfrac{2}{3}(1)^3 + \dfrac{1}{2}(1)^2 + 1\right]\right)$

$= \dfrac{1}{3}\left(54\dfrac{2}{3} - 2\dfrac{1}{6}\right)$

$= 17\dfrac{1}{2}$

(ii) Area of rectangle $XYZW = 3\left(17\dfrac{1}{2}\right) = 52\dfrac{1}{2}$ units^2

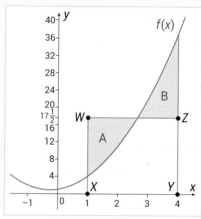

Area under $y = f(x)$ and above the x-axis on $[1, 4] = \displaystyle\int_1^4 (2x^2 + x + 1)\,dx$

$= \left[\dfrac{2x^3}{3} + \dfrac{x^2}{2} + x\right]_1^4$

$= 52\dfrac{1}{2}$ units^2

As these two values are the same,
area of region A = area of region B.

Note the following important result.

The diagram shows the graph of $y = f(x)$.
The average value of the function over the
interval $[a, b]$ is indicated on the diagram.

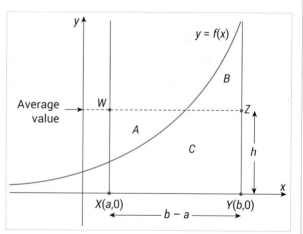

$B + C = \displaystyle\int_a^b f(x)\,dx$ (area under $f(x)$ between
$x = a$ and $x = b$)

Average value of $f(x)$ on the interval $[a, b] = h$

$= \dfrac{1}{b-a}\displaystyle\int_a^b f(x)\,dx$

$= \dfrac{1}{b-a}(B + C)$

The area of the rectangle $WXYZ = A + C$

$= (b - a)\dfrac{1}{b-a}(B + C)$

$= B + C$

$\therefore A = B$

(Average Value) × (Interval Width) = Signed Area

Worked Example 15.21

John's score on a test is given by $s(t) = t^2$, $0 \leqslant t \leqslant 10$, where $s(t)$ is his score after t hours of studying.

Marie's score on the same test is given by $q(t) = 10t$, $0 \leqslant t \leqslant 10$, where $q(t)$ is her score after t hours of studying.

(i) Find the average value of $s(t)$ over the interval [7, 10], and explain what it represents.

(ii) Find the average value of $q(t)$ over the interval [6, 10].

(iii) Assume that the students have the same study habits and are equally likely to study for any number of hours in the range [0, 10]. On average, how far apart will their test scores be?

Solution

(i) Average value $= \dfrac{1}{10 - 7} \displaystyle\int_7^{10} t^2 \, dt$

$= \dfrac{1}{3}\left[\dfrac{t^3}{3}\right]_7^{10}$

$= \dfrac{1}{3}\left[\dfrac{1{,}000}{3} - \dfrac{343}{3}\right]$

$= 73$

This represents the average mark John would get if he spent between 7 and 10 hours studying.

(ii) Average value $= \dfrac{1}{10 - 6} \displaystyle\int_6^{10} 10t \, dt$

$= \dfrac{1}{4}\left[5t^2\right]_6^{10}$

$= \dfrac{1}{4}[500 - 180]$

$= 80$

This represents the average mark Marie would get if she spent between 6 and 10 hours studying.

(iii) Difference $= \left| \dfrac{1}{10}\displaystyle\int_0^{10} 10t \, dt - \dfrac{1}{10}\displaystyle\int_0^{10} t^2 \, dt \right|$

$= \left| \dfrac{1}{10}\displaystyle\int_0^{10} (10t - t^2) \, dt \right|$

$= \left| \dfrac{1}{10}\left[5t^2 - \dfrac{t^3}{3}\right]_0^{10} \right|$

$= \left| \dfrac{1}{10}\left(500 - \dfrac{1{,}000}{3}\right) \right|$

$= 16\dfrac{2}{3}$

Exercise 15.7

1. The function f is defined by $f : R \mapsto R : x \mapsto x^2 + 1$.

(i) Use the graph to estimate the average value of f on the interval [1, 3].

(ii) Complete the table and hence find another estimate for the average value of f on the interval [1, 3].

x	1	1.25	1.5	1.75	2	2.25	2.5	2.75	3
f(x)									

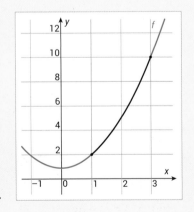

(iii) Use integration to find the average value of f on the interval [1, 3].

INTEGRAL CALCULUS

2. The function f is defined by $f: R \mapsto R: x \mapsto x^3$.

(i) Use the graph to estimate the average value of f on the interval [2, 4].

(ii) Complete the table and hence find another estimate for the average value of f on the interval [2, 4].

x	2	2.25	2.5	2.75	3	3.25	3.5	3.75	4
$f(x)$									

(iii) Use integration to find the average value of f on the interval [2, 4].

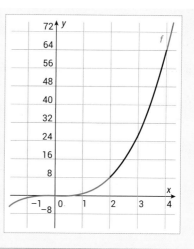

3. Find the average value of the function on the given interval.

(i) $f(x) = 8 - x^2$ [0, 2]

(ii) $g(t) = t^3 + t^2 - 8$ [0, 1]

(iii) $h(x) = x^4 + 2x^2$ [0, 3]

(iv) $s(t) = 2t^3 - 3t^2 + 4t$ [1, 4]

4. Find the average value of the function on the given interval.

(i) $g(x) = \sin x$ $\left[\pi, \dfrac{3\pi}{2}\right]$

(ii) $h(t) = \sqrt{t}$ [4, 9]

(iii) $f(t) = e^t$ [0, 4]

(iv) $g(x) = \sec^2 x$ $\left[0, \dfrac{\pi}{4}\right]$

5. Find the values of k such that the average value of $f(x) = 2 + 6x - 3x^2$ on the interval [0, k] is equal to 3.

6. In a certain town, the temperature in degrees Celsius t hours after 8 a.m. is modelled by the following function:

$$T(t) = 10 - 10 \sin \frac{\pi t}{12}$$

Find the average value of the function during the period from 8 a.m. to 8 p.m.

7. Find the average value of the following functions over the given interval:

(i) $f(x) = mx + 3$ [0, 3]

(ii) $p(x) = 3x^2 + 2$ [0, a]

(iii) $g(x) = x^n, n \neq -1$ [0, 2]

(iv) $h(x) = e^x + 5x$ [1, 4]

8. The population of a certain region can be approximated by $P(t) = 145e^{0.01t}$, where P is in thousands and t is the number of years since 2016.

Find the average size of the population from 2017 to 2020.

9. Eddie's speed in kilometres per hour, t minutes after entering a motorway, is given by:

$$v(t) = -\frac{1}{250}t^3 + \frac{1}{10}t^2 - \frac{5}{8}t + 50, \ t \leqslant 30$$

(i) Find Eddie's average speed on the time interval [6, 25].

(ii) Find the distance travelled by Eddie over the time interval [6, 25].

10. A typist's speed over a five-minute interval is given by $W(t) = -5t^2 + 11t + 70, \ t \in [0, 5]$.

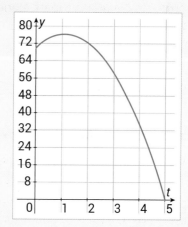

(i) Find the typist's speed at the beginning of the interval.

(ii) Find his maximum speed and when it occurs.

(iii) What was his average speed over the five-minute interval?

11. The acceleration of a race car in m/s^2 during the first 25 seconds of a road test is modelled by $a(t) = 0.02t^2 - 1.8t + 25$, $0 \leqslant t \leqslant 25$.

  (i) Calculate the average acceleration during the first 25 seconds of the road test.

  (ii) Find, in terms of t, the velocity of the car, $0 \leqslant t \leqslant 25$. Assume that the car starts from rest.

  (iii) Calculate the average velocity during the first 25 seconds of the road test.

  (iv) Find, in terms of t, the distance travelled, $0 \leqslant t \leqslant 25$.

  (v) What distance did the car travel in 25 seconds?

  (vi) If the car had travelled at its average velocity during the first 25 seconds, how far would it have travelled in that time?

Revision Exercises

1. **(a)** Find two antiderivatives of each of the following functions:

  (i) $f'(x) = 3$

  (ii) $f'(x) = 5x + 4$

  (iii) $f'(x) = 2x^2 - x - 3$

  (iv) $f'(x) = e^{2x}$

  (v) $f'(x) = 5e^{3x}$

  (vi) $f'(x) = 3e^{4 - 2x}$

(b) Find two antiderivatives of each of the following functions:

  (i) $f'(x) = \dfrac{7}{x}$

  (ii) $f'(x) = -\dfrac{3}{x}$

  (iii) $f'(x) = -\dfrac{7}{2x}$

  (iv) $f'(x) = 7^x$

  (v) $f'(x) = 2^x$

  (vi) $f'(x) = 10^x$

(c) Find the following indefinite integrals:

  (i) $\int (x^2 - 7x + 2)\, dx$

  (ii) $\int \dfrac{7}{x}\, dx$

  (iii) $\int e^{5x}\, dx$

  (iv) $\int (3x + 2)\, dx$

  (v) $\int -\dfrac{3}{2x}\, dx$

  (vi) $\int 3e^{7x - 2}\, dx$

2. **(a)** Find the following indefinite integrals:

  (i) $\int -2 \sin 2x\, dx$

  (ii) $\int 2 \cos 2x\, dx$

  (iii) $\int (\cos 2x - \sin 2x)\, dx$

  (iv) $\int (3 \cos 2x + \sin 2x)\, dx$

(b) Evaluate the following definite integrals:

  (i) $\int_0^{\pi} (5 \sin 2x - 3 \cos 2x)\, dx$

  (ii) $\int_0^{\frac{\pi}{4}} (2 \sin x \cos x)\, dx$

  (iii) $\int_0^{\pi} (\cos^2 x - \sin^2 x)\, dx$

3. Evaluate each of the following definite integrals:

  (i) $\int_2^3 (x^2 - 2x + 3)\, dx$

  (ii) $\int_1^8 (x^2 - 5x + 5)\, dx$

  (iii) $\int_{-1}^4 (x^5 + 4x^3 - 8x)\, dx$

  (iv) $\int_0^1 (x^{10} - x^5 + 1)\, dx$

4. **(a)** Find each of the following indefinite integrals:

  (i) $\int x^{\frac{1}{2}}\, dx$

  (ii) $\int \sqrt[3]{x}\, dx$

  (iii) $\int \dfrac{1}{x^{\frac{1}{2}}}\, dx$

  (iv) $\int \dfrac{1}{\sqrt[3]{x}}\, dx$

  (v) $\int x^{\frac{3}{2}}\, dx$

  (vi) $\int x^{-\frac{3}{2}}\, dx$

(b) By expanding the brackets find each of the following indefinite integrals:

  (i) $\int e^{2x} (e^x - e^{3x})\, dx$

  (ii) $\int (e^{2x} + e^x)(e^{3x} - e^x)\, dx$

  (iii) $\int x^{\frac{1}{2}} (x^{\frac{1}{4}} - x^{\frac{1}{3}})\, dx$

  (iv) $\int \left(\dfrac{1}{2x}\right)\left(\dfrac{1}{x} - \dfrac{1}{3x}\right) dx$

  (v) $\int \sin x\, (1 - 2 \cos x)\, dx$

  (vi) $\int \sin x\, (\sin x - \cos x \cot an\, x)\, dx$

5. Evaluate each of the following definite integrals:

  (i) $\int_1^2 e^x\, dx$

  (ii) $\int_{-1}^4 e^{5x}\, dx$

  (iii) $\int_0^5 e^{-3x}\, dx$

  (iv) $\int_1^5 \dfrac{1}{e^{2x}}\, dx$

6. (a) Find the derivatives of sin *ax*, cos *ax* and tan *ax*.

(b) Hence, evaluate each of the following definite integrals:

(i) $\int_0^{\frac{\pi}{2}} \sin 5x \, dx$ (iii) $\int_0^{\frac{\pi}{4}} \sec^2 x \, dx$

(ii) $\int_{\frac{\pi}{2}}^{2\pi} \cos 3x \, dx$ (iv) $\int_0^{\frac{\pi}{3}} \cos 9x \, dx$

7. Using page 25 of *Formulae and Tables* and your knowledge of antiderivatives, evaluate each of the following definite integrals:

(i) $\int_0^7 \frac{dx}{\sqrt{49 - x^2}}$ (iii) $\int_0^{5\sqrt{3}} \frac{15 \, dx}{225 + x^2}$

(ii) $\int_0^3 \frac{dx}{\sqrt{36 - x^2}}$ (iv) $6\int_0^8 \frac{dx}{64 + x^2}$

8. Find the average value of each function on the given interval.

(i) $g(x) = \sin 5x$ $\left[\pi, \frac{3\pi}{2}\right]$

(ii) $h(t) = \sqrt{2t}$ [9, 16]

(iii) $f(t) = e^t$ [1, 4]

(iv) $g(x) = \sec^2 x$ $\left[0, \frac{\pi}{4}\right]$

9. The temperature *T* (in °C) recorded during a day was modelled by the function $T = 0.001t^4 - 0.28t^2 + 20$, where *t* is the number of hours from noon.

What was the average temperature during the day?

10. *n* rectangles of equal width are drawn on the interval [0, 1] using the graph of $f(x) = x^2 + x + 1$, $x \in R$.

(i) Explain why the width of each rectangle is $\frac{1}{n}$.

(ii) Show that the area of the *r*th rectangle is given by:

$$A_r = \left[\frac{1}{n}\right]\left(\left[\frac{r}{n}\right]^2 + \frac{r}{n} + 1\right)$$

(iii) Hence, show that the sum of the areas of the *n* rectangles can be written as follows:

$$S_n = \frac{1}{n}\left(\left[\frac{1}{n}\right]^2 + \frac{1}{n} + 1 + \left[\frac{2}{n}\right]^2 + \frac{2}{n} + 1 + \left[\frac{3}{n}\right]^2 + \frac{3}{n} + 1 + \ldots + \left[\frac{n}{n}\right]^2 + \frac{n}{n} + 1\right)$$

(iv) Show that the expression above can be written as follows:

$$S_n = \frac{1}{n^3}[1^2 + 2^2 + \ldots + n^2] + \frac{1}{n^2}[1 + 2 + \ldots + n] + 1$$

(v) Given that $\sum_{r=1}^{n} r = \frac{n}{2}(n + 1)$ and $\sum_{r=1}^{n} r^2 = \frac{n}{6}(2n + 1)(n + 1)$, find another expression for S_n.

(vi) Show that $\lim_{n \to \infty} S_n = \int_0^1 (x^2 + x + 1) \, dx$.

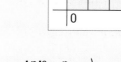

11. The gradient of a curve $y = f(x)$ is given by $\frac{dy}{dx} = Ax(1 - x)$, where *A* is a constant. The gradient of the curve at the point (2, -3) is -12.

(i) Find the value of *A*. (ii) Find the equation of the curve.

12. Let $f(x) = x^2 - 2x - 8$, $x \in R$.

(i) Show that the function has a local minimum at $x = 1$.

(ii) Show that the function is increasing on the interval (1, 5] and has an *x*-intercept at $x = 4$.

(iii) Hence, sketch a graph of the function over the interval (1, 5].

(iv) Find the area bounded between the curve $y = x^2 - 2x - 8$, the *x*-axis and the lines $x = 1$ and $x = 5$.

13. $f(x) = 4 - x^2$, $0 \leqslant x \leqslant 2$, and $g(x) = \dfrac{4 - x^2}{2}$,

$0 \leqslant x \leqslant 2$, are two real valued functions.

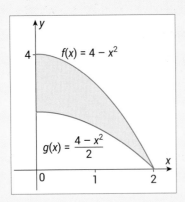

Find the area of the region bounded between f, g and the y-axis.

14.

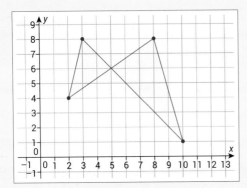

(i) Find the area of the shaded region in the diagram above.

(ii) Use integration methods to find the area of the same shaded area.

(*Hint:* Define four functions, one for each side, and integrate using suitable differences and limits of integration.)

15.

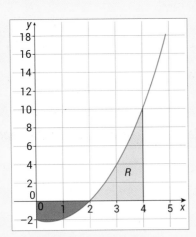

Part of the graph of the function
$f(x) = x^2 - x - 2$ is shown.

(i) Show that $x = 2$ is an x-intercept.

(ii) Use integration to find the area of the shaded region R.

(iii) Find the area of the region bounded by the graph, the x-axis and the y-axis.

(iv) Show that the area of R is 2.6 times the area found in part (iii).

16.

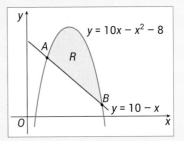

The region R is bounded by the curve
$y = 10x - x^2 - 8$ and the line $y = 10 - x$.

(i) Find the co-ordinates of the points A and B.

(ii) Hence, find the area R.

17. The stations of Liceu and Drassanes are consecutive stations on Line 3 of the Barcelona metro.

The metro trains on this line have been automated so that, under normal operating conditions, the velocity for a train travelling from Liceu to Drassanes is given by the piecewise function below:

$v(t) = 0$ on $[0, 0.5)$

$v(t) = (t - 0.5)^3$ on $[0.5, 2)$

$v(t) = 1.875t - 0.375$ on $[2, 5)$

$v(t) = 9$ on $[5, 11)$

$v(t) = 9 - (t - 11)^2$ on $[11, 14)$

where v is velocity (in ms⁻¹) and t is time (in seconds).

(i) Graph the velocity of the train against time over the 14-second journey from Liceu to Drassanes.

(ii) What is the average velocity of a metro train between Liceu and Drassanes?

(iii) How far apart are the two stations?

(iv) What is the rate of deceleration of the train 2 seconds before arriving at Drassanes station?

Exam Questions

1. (a) (i) Write down three distinct antiderivatives of the function $g: x \to x^3 - 3x^2 + 3$, $x \in R$.

   (ii) Explain what is meant by the indefinite integral of a function f.

   (iii) Write down the indefinite integral of g, the function in part (i).

   (b) (i) Let $h(x) = x \ln x$, for $x \in R$, $x > 0$.
       Find $h'(x)$.

   (ii) Hence, find $\int \ln x \, dx$.

   SEC Project Maths Leaving Certificate Higher Level, Sample Paper 1, 2012

2. (a) Let $f(x) = -0.5x^2 + 5x - 0.98$, where $x \in R$.

   (i) Find the value of $f(0.2)$.

   (ii) Show that f has a local maximum point at $(5, 11.52)$.

   (b) A sprinter's velocity over the course of a particular 100-metre race is approximated by the following model, where v is the velocity in metres per second and t is the time in seconds from the starting signal:

   $$v(t) = \begin{cases} 0, & \text{for } 0 \leq t < 0.2 \\ -0.5t^2 + 5t - 0.98, & \text{for } 0.2 \leq t < 5 \\ 11.52, & \text{for } t \geq 5 \end{cases}$$

   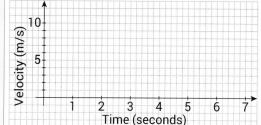

   Note that the function in part (a) is relevant to $v(t)$ above.

   (i) Sketch the graph of v as a function of t for the first 7 seconds of the race.

   (ii) Find the distance travelled by the sprinter in the first 5 seconds of the race.

   (iii) Find the sprinter's finishing time for the race.
       Give your answer correct to two decimal places.

   (c) A spherical snowball is melting at a rate proportional to its surface area. That is, the rate at which its volume is decreasing at any instant is proportional to its surface area at that instant.

   (i) Prove that the radius of the snowball is decreasing at a constant rate.

   (ii) If the snowball loses half of its volume in an hour, how long more will it take for it to melt completely?
       Give your answer correct to the nearest minute.

   SEC Project Maths Leaving Certificate Higher Level, Sample Paper 1, 2012

 Solutions and chapter summary available online

Answers

Chapter 1

Exercise 1.1

1. (i) −24   (ii) 27   (iii) $-\frac{1}{14}$ (iv) −100   (v) 6   **2.** (i) $10x - 2y$
(ii) $-2xy$ (iii) $pq - 3qr$ (iv) $2p^2 + 2p^3$ (v) $2xy^2 - 2x^2y$
(vi) $3m^2n - mn^2$ **3.** (i) $3x^2 + 27x - 10$ (ii) $3a^2 - a$
(iii) $36x^3 + 34x^2 - 8x$ (iv) $-2y^2 - xy$ (v) $b^3 + 4b^2 - 4a^2c - 3bc$
4. (i) (a) Degree: 2   (b) Constant: −6   (c) 3 terms   (d) −1
(ii) (a) Degree: 2   (b) Constant: −20   (c) 3 terms   (d) −7
(iii) (a) Degree: 5   (b) Constant: none   (c) 3 terms   (d) −9
(iv) (a) Degree: 5   (b) Constant: −12   (c) 6 terms   (d) 32
(v) (a) Degree: 5   (b) Constant: −7   (c) 6 terms   (d) 25
5. (i) $35x^2 + 12x + 1$ (ii) $p^2 - q^2$ (iii) $30st - 15s - 10t^2 + 5t$
(iv) $p^2 - 2pq + q^2$ (v) $32x^3 + 48x^2 + 18x$ (vi) $x^3 - x^2y - xy^2 + y^3$
(vii) $y^3 - 9y^2 + 27y - 27$ (viii) $8a^3 + 60a^2b + 150ab^2 + 125b^3$
(ix) $729x^3 - 486yx^2 + 108xy^2 - 8y^3$ **6.** (i) $a^4 + 4a^3 + 6a^2 + 4a + 1$
(ii) $b^3 - 9b^2 + 27b - 27$ (iii) $x^5 + 5x^4y + 10x^3y^2 + 10x^2y^3 + 5xy^4 + y^5$
(iv) $8a^3 + 36a^2b + 54ab^2 + 27b^3$ (v) $81y^4 - 432xy^3 +$
$864x^2y^2 - 768x^3y + 256x^4$ (vi) $243x^5 - 810x^4y + 1{,}080x^3y^2 -$
$720x^2y^3 + 240xy^4 - 32y^5$ **7.** (i) Area $= x^2 + 4x + 4$,
Perimeter $= 4x + 8$ (ii) Area $= 2x^2 - xy - 3y^2$,
Perimeter $= 6x - 4y$ **8.** Volume: $x^3 + 16x^2 + 83x + 140$,
Surface Area: $5x^2 + 53x + 138$ **9.** $11x - 4y + 20$ **10.** $5y + 3$
11. (i) $ax^2 + 10ax + 25a + bx^2 + 10bx + 25b$ (ii) $3p^3 - 3pq^2$
(iii) $z^4 - 2x^2z^2 + x^4$ (iv) $6a^3 + 21a^2b + 9ab^2 - 2a^2 - 7ab - 3b^2$
(v) $5x^3 + 30x^2y + 45xy^2 + 20y^3$ **12.** $n = 6, a = 3$

Exercise 1.2

1. $4ab^2(1 - 3b)$ **2.** $(7x + 2)(x + 1)$ **3.** $(3y - 7)(y + 1)$
4. $(5x + 2)(x + 2)$ **5.** $(x + 3)(x - 6)$ **6.** $(3x - 2)(x + 4)$
7. $(2y - 7)(y + 9)$ **8.** $(7x - 19)(x + 3)$ **9.** $(5a - 1)(5a + 1)$
10. $(2x - 1)(x - 4)$ **11.** $(3x - 2)(4y - 7)$ **12.** $(5x + 12)(x + 8)$
13. $(8a - 9b)(8a + 9b)$ **14.** $(2x + 1)(x - 12)$ **15.** $(4x + 3)(x + 1)$
16. $(2a - 5b)(3a + 2c)$ **17.** $(10y + 17)(y + 1)$ **18.** $(3x + 2)$
$(3x - 1)$ **19.** $(3x - 2)(3x - 5)$ **20.** $(4y + 19)(y + 1)$ **21.** $(x - 1)$
$(y - z)$ **22.** $(3x + 5)(2x + 9)$ **23.** $4(3p - 5q)(3p + 5q)$
24. $(4x - 7)(3x + 8)$ **25.** $(2x - 3)(4x - 5)$ **26.** $2(5x + 3)(x - 1)$
27. $6(2x + 1)(x - 2)$ **28.** $12y(2y + 1)(2y + 1)$ **29.** $4(2x - 5)$
$(2x + 5)$ **30.** $2x(x - 2)(x + 2)$ **31.** $p(3q + 4)(2q + 1)$
32. $x^2(x - 6)(x + 6)$ **33.** $(x - 3)(x^2 + 3x + 9)$ **34.** $(p + 2)$
$(p^2 - 2p + 4)$ **35.** $(x - y)(x^2 + xy + y^2)$ **36.** $(4a - 1)$
$(16a^2 + 4a + 1)$ **37.** $(2a + 3b)(4a^2 - 6ab + 9b^2)$ **38.** $(5p + 8q)$
$(25p^2 - 40pq + 64q^2)$ **39.** $(10x - 9)(100x^2 + 90x + 81)$
40. $(7c + d)(49c^2 - 7cd + d^2)$ **41.** $3(x - 6)(x^2 + 6x + 36)$
42. $16(2 + x)(4 - 2x + x^2)$ **43.** $54a(a + 2b)(a^2 - 2ab + 4b^2)$
44. $-2x - 5$ **45.** $(x + p)(x + p)$ **46.** $(ac - b)(ac + b)$
47. $(x^2 - 5)(x^2 + 5)$ **48.** $(ab - 1)(ab - 1)$ **49.** $(x^2 + y^2)(x - y)$
$(x + y)$ **50.** $(x - y + 3)(x - y - 3)$ **51.** $(4x - 3y)(2x - 3y)$
52. $a(a + 1)(a^2 - a + 1)$ **53.** $[a - (b + c)][a + (b + c)]$
54. $ab^2(b - 1)(b^2 + b + 1)$ **55.** $(x^2 + 2)(x - 3)(x + 3)$

Exercise 1.3

1. $\frac{8x - 11}{4}$ **2.** $-\frac{6x + 1}{6}$ **3.** $\frac{-3 + 8x}{4x - 5}$ **4.** $-\frac{3}{35x}$ **5.** $\frac{8 + x^2 + x}{x + 1}$
6. $\frac{2x - 5}{x^2 + 5x}$ **7.** $\frac{17x - 9}{3x^2 - 7x + 2}$ **8.** $\frac{11x + 14}{6x^2 + 7x - 5}$ **9.** $\frac{b^2}{a}$ **10.** $\frac{1}{x - y}$

11. $\frac{b}{a - b}$ **12.** −1   **13.** x **14.** $\frac{x}{x + 1}$ **15.** $x - 2$ **16.** $\frac{x^2 + 5x + 25}{2}$
17. $\frac{x^2 - xy + y^2}{x - y}$ **18.** $x^2 + y^2$ **19.** $\frac{p^2 - 2pq + q^2}{p + q}$ **20.** $\frac{x + 4}{x - 4}$
21. $\frac{3x}{x - 1}$ **22.** $\frac{2x + 1}{x^2 + x - 20}$ **23.** $\frac{-2x - 5}{(x + 2)(x - 3)}$ **24.** $\frac{x - 1}{x^2 + 3x + 2}$
25. $\frac{a^2 + 3}{a^2 - 1}$ **26.** $\frac{2a^2}{a^2 - b^2}$ **27.** $\frac{2a^2 + 12}{(a - 2)(a + 3)}$ **28.** $\frac{3n^2 + 6n + 2}{n(n + 1)(n + 2)}$
29. $\frac{2a}{a^2 - b^2}$ **30.** $\frac{2b}{(a - b)(a + b)}$ **31.** (i) $\frac{4}{x^2 - 1}$ (ii) $\frac{3}{x - 3}$

Exercise 1.4

1. $25ab$ **2.** $\frac{y}{x^2}$ **3.** $\frac{2x + 1}{2}$ **4.** $\frac{x + 2}{2x - 2}$ **5.** $\frac{4x^2}{x + 1}$ **6.** $\frac{y^2 + 8y}{y + 4}$
7. $\frac{(2x + 1)^2}{(x + 1)2}$ **8.** $\frac{3x}{2x + 9}$ **9.** $\frac{x + 3}{3x + 4}$ **10.** $\frac{1}{(x + 7)(4x - 3)}$ **11.** $\frac{x - y}{5}$
12. $(x - 5)^2$ **13.** $\frac{2x + 1}{3}$ **14.** $\frac{x}{2(x + 1)}$ **15.** $-\frac{x}{5}$ **16.** $\frac{ab - 1}{b - 1}$ **17.** pq
18. $-\frac{x + y}{x}$ **19.** $\frac{x - y}{x(x + y)}$ **20.** $\frac{R_1R_2}{R_1 + R_2}$

Exercise 1.5

1. (i) $x^5 + 5x^4y + 10x^3y^2 + 10x^2y^3 + 5xy^4 + y^5$
(ii) $x^6 + 6x^5y + 15x^4y^2 + 20x^3y^3 + 15x^2y^4 + 6xy^5 + y^6$
(iii) $x^7 + 7x^6y + 21x^5y^2 + 35x^4y^3 + 35x^3y^4 + 21x^2y^5 + 7xy^6 + y^7$
(iv) $a^8 + 8a^7b + 28a^6b^2 + 56a^5b^3 + 70a^4b^4 + 56a^3b^5 + 28a^2b^6 + 8ab^7 + b^8$
(v) $1 + 6x + 12x^2 + 8x^3$ (vi) $1 - 12x + 54x^2 - 108x^3 + 81x^4$
(vii) $1 + 12x + 60x^2 + 160x^3 + 240x^4 + 192x^5 + 64x^6$
(viii) $1 + 7k + 21k^2 + 35k^3 + 35k^4 + 21k^5 + 7k^6 + k^7$
2. (i) $1 + 4x + 6x^2 + 4x^3 + x^4$ (iii) 56   **3.** $1 + 9x + 27x^2 + 27x^3$
4. $1 - 10x + 40x^2 - 80x^3 + 80x^4 - 32x^5$ **5.** $338\sqrt{2}$
6. $1 + 6x^4 + 15x^2 + 20 + \frac{15}{x^2} + \frac{6}{x^4} + \frac{1}{x^6}$ **7.** (i) $2a^4 + 12a^2b^2 + 2b^4$
(ii) $16x^4 + 16x^2 + 2$ (iii) 66,562
8. (i) $a^5 + 5a^4b + 10a^3b^2 + 10a^2b^3 + 5ab^4 + b^5$
(ii) $2(10x + 80x^3 + 32x^5)$ (iii) 2,420

Exercise 1.6

1. (i) $28x^2$ (ii) $560x^4$ (iii) $84x^6y^3$ (iv) $112x^6$
(v) $20x^3y^3$ (vi) $-42xy^5$ (vii) $1{,}344x^6$ (viii) $-8{,}064x^5$
(ix) $5x^8$ (x) 2.2   **2.** (i) 210   (ii) 10   (iii) 15   (iv) 5,670
(v) 12   **3.** 10.5   **4.** 1.1045   **5.** $144b^2$ **6.** 14.4375
7. (i) −4,375   (ii) 35   **8.** (i) 6   (ii) −160   (iii) 210   (iv) $\frac{112}{729}$
(v) 455   **9.** (i) −70   (ii) 15,120   **10.** (i) 405   (ii) 45   **11.** 3
12. 3   **13.** 0.4   **14.** $\binom{12}{r}x^{12-2r}$, $-1.5 < x < 1.5$ **15.** $n = 6, a = 4$
16. $k = -2, n = 10, p = -960$ **17.** 168   **20.** $1 + 10x + 55x^2$, 55
21. 50   **22.** 70

Exercise 1.7

1. $x^2 + 4x + 1$ **2.** $x^2 + 3x - 10$ **3.** $2x^2 - 9x + 4$ **4.** $2x^2 + 5x$
5. $12x^2 + 8x - 4$ **6.** $3x^3 - 4x^2 - 13x + 14$ **7.** $(x - 4)(x + 3)$
9. $(2x - 5)(3x - 4)(2x + 5)(3x + 4)$ **10.** $x^3 - 8, (x - 3)(x + 2)$
$(x - 2)(x^2 + 2x + 4)$ **12.** $3x + 4$ is a factor, $5x + 4$ is not a factor

Revision Exercises

1. (a) (i) $4x^2 - 10x - 10$ (ii) $3a^3 + 3ab - 6ac - 2a^2b - 2b^2 + 4bc$
(iii) $x^2 + 6x + 1$ (iv) $15x^2 - 26x + 8$ (v) $121p^2 - 9q^2$
(b) (i) $9x^2 + 42x + 49$ (ii) $8x^3 - 12x^2 + 6x - 1$

(iii) $64x^3 - 240x^2 + 300x - 125$ (iv) $64p^4 + 16p^3 - 180p^2 - 189p - 54$
(c) (i) $32a^5 + 80a^4 + 80a^3 + 40a^2 + 10a + 1$
(ii) $256b^4 - 1{,}792b^3c + 4{,}704b^2c^2 - 5{,}488bc^3 + 2{,}401c^4$
(iii) $46{,}656x^6 - 233{,}280x^5 + 486{,}000x^4 - 540{,}000x^3 +$
$337{,}500x^2 - 112{,}500x + 15{,}625$ **2.** (a) (i) $(x + 9)(x - 10)$
(ii) $(3a - 2b)(5c - 4d)$ (iii) $(2x - 9)(2x + 9)$ (iv) $(2x + 1)(2x + 1)$
(b) (i) $(5x - 7y)(5x + 7y)$ (ii) $(11a - 12b)(11a + 12b)$
(iii) $(2m - 3x)(3m - 5b)$ (iv) $(5x + 2)(2x - 1)$ (v) $(7x - 4)(2x - 1)$
(c) (i) $(x + 3)(x^2 - 3x + 9)$ (ii) $2(b + 10)(b^2 - 10b + 100)$
(iii) $(y - 1)(y^2 + y + 1)$ (iv) $(2y - 1)(4y^2 + 2y + 1)$

3. (a) (i) $\frac{8x - 3}{(x - 3)(x + 4)}$ (ii) $\frac{2y - 13}{4y^2 - 1}$ (iii) $\frac{x - 2 - x^2}{x^2 - 1}$ (b) (i) $\frac{1}{2}$
(ii) $\frac{2}{4x + 5}$ (iii) $\frac{(a^2 + ab + b^2)}{6}$ (iv) $\frac{y + 1}{b^2 + b + 1}$ (v) $\frac{x}{x - 3}$ (c) (i) $\frac{4}{x - 2}$
(ii) $\frac{2}{2y - 1}$ (iii) 0 (iv) $\frac{13}{2x - 1}$ **4.** (a) (i) $\frac{x + 4}{x + 5}$ (ii) $\frac{a + b}{a^2 + ab + b^2}$
(iii) $-\frac{2}{3}$ (iv) $\frac{-1}{x + 3}$ (b) (i) $\frac{5x + 3}{(x - 3)(x + 3)}$ (ii) $\frac{10y + 8}{9y^2 - 4}$ (c) (i) $\frac{x - y + z}{x + y + z}$
(ii) $\frac{x(x + 5)}{x + 8}$ **5.** (a) (i) $4x^2 - x - 3$ (ii) $12x^2 - 2x - 4$
(iii) $8x^3 - 10x^2 + x + 1$ (iv) $x^3 + 5x^2 + 2x - 8$
(b) (i) $(3x + 5)(2x - 1)$ (c) $\frac{3}{x + 3}$ **6.** (a) (i) $(2x + 5)(4x^2 - 10x + 25)$
(ii) $(x - 6)(x^2 + 6x + 36)$ (iii) $(6x + 7y)(4x + 5y)$ (iv) $(a + b)(x + y)$
(v) $(3x - 2y)(3x - 2y)$ (b) (i) $-22{,}680$ (ii) 144
(c) $1 + 4x + 6x^2 + 4x^3 + x^4$ (d) (i) $\frac{(a - c)}{(a + c)}$ (ii) $\frac{y(3y + 1)}{y + 3}$
(iii) $\frac{a + b - c}{a - b - c}$ **7.** (a) (ii) $29, 21, 20$ (b) $153{,}090$
(c) (i) $3(x - 5)(x + 5)$ (ii) $x(3x - 5)(3x + 5)$
(iii) $(x^2 + y^2)(x - y)(x + y)$ (iv) $(x^2 + 9)(x - 3)(x + 3)$
(v) $(a - b)(x - y)(x + y)$ **8.** (a) (i) $(x + 3)(x + 17)$
(ii) $-1(x - 13)(x + 13)$ (iii) $(a - b)(a - b)$ (iv) $(a - b - c)$
$(a - b + c)$ (b) (i) Remainder exists $\therefore$ not a factor
(ii) $x - 2$ and $3x + 7$ (iii) $2x + 3$ and $2x - 1$
(c) (i) $(x + y)(x^2 - xy + y^2)$ (ii) $(x + y)^3$
(iii) $(x + y + z)(x^2 + y^2 + z^2 + 2xy - xz - yz)$ **9.** (a) (i) $2x - 5$
(ii) $3x - 1$ (b) $0 < x < 2$ (c) z **10.** (a) (i) $(x + y)(x^2 - xy + y^2 + 3)$
(ii) $x + y [x - y + 5]$ (iii) $(x - y - 2z)(x - y + 2z)$
(iv) $x - y(x^2 + xy + y^2 + x + y)$ (v) $(a - b - c)(a + b + c)$ (b) $\frac{55x^6}{2y^3}$, 3

Chapter 2

Exercise 2.1

1. -1 **2.** -5 **3.** 6 **4.** 5 **5.** $x = 4.5$ **6.** $x = 2$ **7.** $x = -5$
8. $x = -2\frac{2}{3}$ **9.** $x = \frac{7}{10}$ **10.** $a = \frac{1}{2}$ **11.** $x = \frac{3}{4}$ **12.** $x = 3$
13. $y = \frac{1}{2}$ **14.** 160 cm

Exercise 2.2

1. $x = 7, y = 0$ **2.** $x = 4, y = -1$ **3.** $x = 7, y = -3$ **4.** $x = 1, y = -2$
5. $x = 9, y = 8$ **6.** $x = 5, y = -4$ **7.** $p = -4, q = -5$ **8.** $x = 3$,
$y = -4$ **9.** $x = 7, y = 5$ **10.** $x = \frac{57}{41}, y = \frac{46}{41}$ **11.** $x = \frac{14}{5}, y = \frac{22}{5}$
12. $p = 0, q = -5$

Exercise 2.3

1. $x = 2, y = -1, z = 5$ **2.** $x = 1, y = 3, z = 5$ **3.** $a = 1, b = 3$,
$c = 0$ **4.** $z = 2, x = 4, y = 10$ **5.** $x = -1, y = 2, z = 5$
6. $p = \frac{1}{3}, q = -\frac{3}{4}, r = -5$ **7.** $x = 10, y = 0, z = 10$ **8.** $x = 2, y = 8$,
$z = 2$ **9.** $x = 2, y = -3, z = 1$ **10.** $x = \frac{1}{2}, y = \frac{1}{4}, z = \frac{3}{4}$ **11.** $x = 4$,
$y = 2, z = -1, a = 2, b = 2, c = -2, a = -2, b = 2, c = -2$

Exercise 2.4

1. (i) $x = 3$ **OR** -14 (ii) $x = 3$ (iii) $x = 7$ **OR** -9
2. (i) $x = -0.2, 2.9$ (ii) $x = -1.5, 1.5$ (iii) $x = -2.3$ (iv) $x = -2, 2$
3. $x = 2$ **4.** (i) $x = -0.63, 2.63$ (iv) $x = -1$ **OR** $x = 3$
5. (i) $x = 2$ **OR** $x = \frac{9}{2}$ (ii) $x = 2$ **OR** $x = -\frac{7}{3}$ (iii) $x = \frac{9}{5}$ **OR**
$x = -\frac{9}{5}$ (iv) $x = 0$ **OR** $x = 3\frac{6}{25}$ (v) $x = 4$ **OR** $x = -\frac{6}{7}$
(vi) $x = 4$ **OR** $x = -\frac{5}{4}$ (vii) $x = 2$ **OR** $x = -\frac{5}{8}$ (viii) $x = 2$ **OR**
$x = \frac{13}{16}$ **6.** $x = -3$ **OR** $x = -4$, Solution set for $y = \{-1, -2, -3\}$
7. $x = 5$ **OR** $x = \frac{7}{2}$, Solution set for $t = \left\{-2, \frac{5}{4}, 1, -\frac{7}{4}\right\}$
8. (i) $x^2 - 5x + 6 = 0$ (ii) $x^2 - 3x - 10 = 0$ (iii) $x^2 - 6x = 0$
(iv) $2x^2 + x - 15 = 0$ (v) $10x^2 - 7x + 1 = 0$ (vi) $16x^2 - 9 = 0$
(vii) $x^2 - 8x + 13 = 0$ (viii) $x^2 + 2x - 1 = 0$
9. (i) $x = 1.36$ **OR** $x = -5.86$ (ii) $x = 0.79$ **OR** $x = -1.42$
(iii) $x = 3.176$ **OR** $x = -2.676$ (iv) $x = 0.46$ **OR** $x = -2.71$
(v) $x = 3.122$ **OR** $x = -2.456$ (vi) $x = 0.658$ **OR** $x = -1.086$
10. (i) $x = \pm\sqrt{5}$ (ii) $x = -3 \pm \sqrt{2}$ (iii) $x = \frac{-4 \pm \sqrt{10}}{6}$
(iv) $x = \frac{-6 \pm \sqrt{33}}{3}$ **11.** (i) $x = \frac{5}{2}$ **OR** $x = 4$ (ii) $x = \frac{3}{5}$ **OR** $x = \frac{1}{2}$
(iii) $x = -\frac{3}{5}$ **OR** $x = 2$ (iv) $x = 10\frac{1}{2}$ **OR** $x = -1$
(v) $x = 0$ **OR** $x = -\frac{1}{3}$ (vi) $x = -6$ (vii) 3.56 or 0.56
(viii) 2.18 **OR** 0.57 **12.** $c = 16$, roots are 2 and 8
13. $d = 35$, roots are 5 and 7

Exercise 2.5

1. (i) $(-1,-3), (3,-1)$ (ii) $(-5,5), (5,0)$ (iii) $(0,-4), (5,1)$
(iv) $(-4,-1.5), (5,3)$ **2.** $x = 2, y = 3, x = 3, y = 2$ **3.** $x = -\frac{8}{3}$,
$y = -\frac{14}{3}, x = 4, y = 2$ **4.** $x = \frac{5}{2}, y = 4, x = 2, y = 5$ **5.** $x = -\frac{3}{5}$,
$y = \frac{3}{5}, x = -1, y = -1$ **6.** $x = 0, y = 1, x = \frac{2}{3}, y = 3$ **7.** $x = -6$,
$y = -3, x = 6, y = 3$ **8.** $b = \frac{2}{7}$ and $a = \frac{-11}{7}$ **OR** $b = -1$ and $a = 1$
9. $x = \frac{1}{3}, y = \frac{10}{3}, x = -9, y = 1$ **10.** $x = 6.4, y = -2.8, x = 8, y = -2$
11. $x = 10, y = 4, x = 6, y = -4$ **12.** $x = \frac{1}{2}, y = \frac{2}{3}, x = -\frac{15}{22}, y = -\frac{10}{11}$
13. $x = 0, y = 3, x = 10, y = -3$ **14.** $x = \frac{1}{2}, y = -1, x = -\frac{97}{86}$,
$y = -\frac{83}{43}$

Exercise 2.6

1. $x - 3$ and $x + 2$ **2.** $x = \frac{3}{2}, x = 6$ **3.** $x = 1, x = 2$ **4.** $x - 2, x + 5$
and $x - 4$ **5.** $3x - 5$ and $x - 2$ **6.** $x = -\frac{3}{2}, \frac{3}{4}, \frac{1}{2}$ **7.** $x = 0, 1, 4, 2$
8. (i) $x^3 - 6x^2 + 3x + 10 = 0$ (ii) $2x^3 + 7x^2 - 46x + 21 = 0$
(iii) $3x^3 + x^2 - 3x - 1 = 0$ (iv) $x^3 - 3x^2 - 10x = 0$
(v) $x^3 - 3x^2 + 3x - 1 = 0$ **9.** (b) (i) $(-3,0), (0,-6), (1,-8)$
10. (i) $x = \{1, 2, 3\}$ (ii) $x = \left\{3, \frac{1}{3}\right\}$ (iii) $x = \{-2, -3, 5\}$
(iv) $x = \left\{4, \frac{5 \pm \sqrt{41}}{2}\right\}$ (v) $x = 3, \left\{\frac{3 \pm \sqrt{65}}{4}\right\}$ **11.** $x = 1, x = 1 \pm 2\sqrt{3}$
12. (i) $f(x) = (x + 4)(x + 2)(x - 3)$ (ii) $f(x) = (x + 5)(x + 3)$
$(x - 1)^2$ (iii) $-x(x + 7)(x + 4)^2 (x - 3)$ (iv) $-(x + 2)(x + 1)^2$
$(x - 2)2(x - 4)$ (v) $x(x - 1)^2(x - 3)(x - 5)^2(x - 7)$
(vi) $x^2(x + 2)^2(x - 3)(x - 4)$ (vii) $x(x - 2)^2(x - 4)(x + 3)^3$
14. 12 **15.** $x^3 - 7x^2 + 13x - 3 = 0$ **16.** $k = 4$, Solution is: $x + 3$
and $x - 2$ **17.** $a = 2, b = 5$ **18.** $p = 4, q = 2$ **19.** $r = 1, s = 7$
20. $a = -1, b = 7, c = 13$ **21.** (b) $\frac{k + \sqrt{k^2 - 4}}{2}$ and $\frac{k - \sqrt{k^2 - 4}}{2}$
22. $a = 4, b = -11, c = -30, x = \{3, -2, -5\}$ **23.** $x = 6.208$
OR -1.208

Exercise 2.7

1. $b = \frac{a+d}{3c}$ **2.** $z = \frac{x-y}{3}$ **3.** $r = 10p - q$ **4.** $c = 2s - a - b$

5. $y = \frac{x}{z^2}$ **6.** $r = \pm\sqrt{\frac{S}{4\pi}}$ **7.** $a = \pm\sqrt{h^2 - b^2}$ **8.** $q = \pm\sqrt{\frac{s+r}{p}}$

9. $r = p^2 - pq + \frac{1}{4}q^2$ **10.** $a = \frac{R^3}{b}$ **11.** $x = \frac{(a-c)^2}{b^2}$

12. $u = \pm\sqrt{v^2 - 2as}$ **13.** $b = \frac{2a}{1+2c}$ **14.** $f = \frac{uv}{v+u}$ **15.** $p = \frac{ab}{1-a}$

16. $r = \frac{1+pq}{p}$ **17.** $x = \frac{1-a}{1+a}$ **19.** (i) 100π cm³ (ii) $h = \frac{3V}{\pi r^2}$

(iii) 5 cm (iv) $r = \sqrt{\frac{3V}{\pi h}}$ (v) 12 cm **20.** (i) 10 s

(ii) $l = \frac{T^2 g}{4\pi^2}$ (iii) 305 m (iv) $g = \frac{4\pi^2 l}{T^2}$ (v) 3.8 ms⁻²

21. (i) 84 m (ii) $u = \frac{2s - at^2}{2t}$ (iii) 2.5 ms⁻¹

(iv) $a = \frac{2s - 2ut}{t^2}$ (v) $\frac{-2}{3}$ ms⁻² (vi) 12 s

Exercise 2.8

1. $b = 3$, $q = 9$ **2.** $a = 1$, $b = 1$, $c = -12$ **3.** $q = 3$, $p = 5$
4. $a = 4$, $b = 2$ **5.** $p = 12$, $q = 48$ **6.** $a = 2$, $b = 2$, $c = 3$
7. $p = 1$, $q = 3$, $r = -2$ **8.** $r = 6$, $x = \{1, \frac{2}{3}, 3\}$ **9.** (i) $a = 1 - \frac{1}{2}b$
(ii) $-2 \pm \sqrt{6}$ **10.** (i) $b = a - 13$ (ii) $c = -12(b + 12)$

Exercise 2.9

1. Small 5 kg, Large 20 kg, Medium 15 kg **2.** (i) €200
(ii) €12,200, $x = 1{,}200$ units **3.** Karl is 40, Eddie is 25.
4. (i) €500,000 (ii) 2ⁿᵈ contract **5.** 1 hr 40 mins
6. €1,750 at high rate (9%), €1,250 at lower rate (5%)
7. 9 kg of 70% nickel alloy, 11 kg of 30% nickel alloy

8. 60 m, 240 m **9.** (i) -40°C or F (ii) $F = -12\frac{4}{13}°$,
$C = -24\frac{8}{13}°$ (iii) $C = 160°$, $F = 320°$ **10.** 1,928 cm, 2,428 cm
11. 21 **12.** 5, 7 **13.** $(3.8, -1.6)$ and $(1,4)$
14. Harry's speed = 10 kmh⁻¹, Cara's speed = 5 kmh⁻¹, Harry's
time = 5 hours, Cara's time = 7 hours **15.** (i) $350 - 25x$
(ii) $30 + 2x$ (iii) €225 **16.** (i) $(1, -4)$, $(-4, 1)$ (ii) $(-4,1)$ is
4 km west and 1 km north, $(1,-4)$ is 4 km south and 1 km
east (iii) 4.12 km **17.** (i) $39.2x = 284$ (ii) Gold = 7.24 g,
Silver = 12.76 g **18.** (a) (i) 16,000 (ii) 4,000 **19.** €1,500
20. 862 **21.** Simon: 5 hours, Peter: 20 hours **22.** Hot = 773
seconds, Cold = 673 seconds **23.** (a) (i) 18.78 ms⁻¹
(ii) 25.04 ms⁻¹ (b) (i) Minimum velocity increases by $\sqrt{2}$
(ii) $d = \frac{V_o^2}{19.6\,\mu}$ (c) 79.7 m **24.** (i) 348.71 ms⁻¹ (ii) $T = \frac{273}{109{,}561}$
$V^2 - 273$ (iii) 4°C (iv) 369 ms⁻¹

Revision Exercises

1. (a) (i) $x = 2$ (ii) $a = 0$ (iii) $y = 2.5$ (iv) $x = -5$ (b) (i) $x = 1$,
$y = -2$ (ii) $x = 2$, $y = 8$ (iii) $x = 7$, $y = \frac{3}{2}$ (c) (i) $x = -3$, $y = 3$, $z = 1$
(ii) $x = -1$, $y = -2$, $z = -3$ (iii) $x = 5$, $y = 1$, $z = 6$ (iv) $x = 5$, $y = -4$,
$z = 1$ **2.** (a) (i) $x = \frac{1}{2}$ (ii) $x = \frac{3}{2}$ OR $x = -\frac{3}{2}$
(iii) $x = 8$ OR $x = -3$ (iv) $x = \frac{11}{2}$ OR $x = 1$
(v) $x = \frac{-7}{17}$ OR $x = 5$ (b) (i) $x = \frac{3}{4}$ OR $x = 5$, $y = \frac{1}{2}$ OR $y = \frac{-3}{2}$ OR
$y = 1.79$ OR $y = -2.79$ (ii) $x = 3 \pm \sqrt{11}$, $t = \sqrt{11}$ OR $t = -\sqrt{11}$
(iii) $x = -4$, $\frac{2}{3}$, $-\frac{4}{5}$ (c) (i) $x = 3.71$ OR $x = -1.21$
(ii) $x = 1.86$ OR $x = 0.54$ (iii) $x = 3.27$ OR $x = -0.77$
(iv) $x = 1{\cdot}19$ OR $x = -1{\cdot}59$ (d) (i) $x = -1$, $y = -2$,
$x = 2$, $y = 1$ (ii) $x = \frac{1}{2}$, $y = 6$, $x = 3$, $y = 1$

(iii) $x = 1$, $y = 1$ **3.** (a) (i) $f(x) = x(x + 1)(x - 3)^2$
(ii) $f(x) = x(x + 3)(x + 1)(x - 2)(x - 3)$ (iii) $f(x) = x^2(x + 7)^2(x + 3)(x - 2)$
(iv) $f(x) = x^2(x + 7)(x + 6)(x + 4)^2(x + 1)$ (v) $f(x) = x(x + 1)$
$(x - 3)^3(x - 6)^2$ (c) (i) $x = \{1, 4, -2\}$ (ii) $x = \{-2, \frac{3}{2}\}$
(iv) $x = 3 - \sqrt{5}$, 3, $3 + \sqrt{5}$ (d) (i) $(3x + 1)(x + 2)$ (ii) $(x + 7)$ (iii) -2
4. (a) (i) $c = 2(b - a)$ (ii) $c = \frac{a - b}{d + 5}$ (iii) $p = \frac{q}{q + r}$ (iv) $r = \frac{A}{\pi l + 2\pi h}$
(v) $x = \pm\sqrt{\frac{y^2(1 - r)}{a}}$ (vi) $y = \sqrt[3]{\frac{3x + 1}{x - 1}}$ (b) (i) $a = 4$, $b = -5$
(ii) $p = -2$, $q = 14$ (iii) $p = 2$, $q = \frac{7}{4}$, $r = \frac{31}{8}$ (c) (i) $c = q(a - p)$
(ii) $c - q(a - p) = 0$ **5.** (a) (i) $h = \frac{9}{2}$ (ii) 10% (b) $x = 3$, $y = 7$
(c) 22, 45 (d) (i) $x + y + 26 = 60$, $x^2 + y^2 = 26^2$ (ii) $x = 24$ and $y = 10$
6. (a) 21 and 23 (b) (i) 40 mins (ii) Fiona: $56\frac{2}{3}$ km,
Gerry: $43\frac{1}{3}$ km (c) Planet and comet distance: 450.36 million km
Satellite and comet distance: 609.29 million km **OR** Satellite
and comet distance: 414.88 million km **7.** (a) 12 (rabbits),
18 (guinea pigs) (b) 8 people (c) (i) $g = \frac{2s}{t^2}$ (ii) 9.796 ms⁻²
(iii) 6.06 seconds **8.** (a) $x^2 - 5px + 4p^2 = 0$ (b) (i) $A(-2,0)$,
$B(1,0)$, $C(3,0)$, $D(5,0)$, $E(-1,-6)$ (ii) A, B and C are the roots
of the cubic function. A and D are the roots of the quadratic
function. B is the point of intersection of the line and the
x-axis, i.e. the root of the linear equation. B is also one point
of intersection between the linear function and the cubic
function. A is the point of intersection between the cubic
and the quadratic function. (iii) $3x - y - 3 = 0$, Quadratic:
$f(x) = (x + 2)(x - 5)$, Cubic: $g(x) = (x + 2)(x - 1)(x - 3)$
(c) (ii) The values of x for which $x^3 + 7x^2 + 14x + 8 = x^2 + 5x + 6$
9. (a) $\frac{x - 3}{2x^2 + 3x - 2}$, $x = 4$ (b) $a = -2$, $b = 6$, $c = -12$ (c) $a = -39$,
$b = 70$, $x = \{2, 5, -7\}$ **10.** (a) $t = 6$, $x = \{-2, 1, -5\}$
(c) (ii) $x^2 - 6x + 2 = 0$ (iii) $x^3 - 5x^2 - 4x + 2 = 0$
11. (a) $a = 1$, $b = -8$ (c) (ii) $\frac{3}{5}$

Exam Questions

1. (a) €4,279.50 (b) 7 g of 9-carat gold and 14 g of 18-carat
gold (c) (i) 6 g of copper (ii) 4 g of 9-carat gold, 38 g of
18-carat gold and 6 g of silver (d) (i) €$(20x - 40)(20 - x)$
(ii) €400 $\leqslant$ selling price $\leqslant$ €440 **3.** (a) $C(24, 7.488)$
(b) $D(10, 5)$, $E(38, 5)$

Chapter 3

Exercise 3.1

1. $x = 13$ **2.** $x = 9$ **3.** $x = 2\frac{5}{7}$ **4.** $x = 3$ **5.** $x = 2$
6. $x = 1$ **7.** $x = 1$ **8.** $x = 4$ **9.** $x = 2$ **10.** $x = 13$
11. $x = 7$ OR $x = 10$ **12.** $x = 0$ **13.** $x = 3$

Exercise 3.2

1. $x > -1$ **2.** $x > 3$ **3.** $x \geqslant 1$ **4.** $x < 2$ **5.** $x > \frac{1}{2}$ **6.** $x < 2$
7. $x > 2$ **8.** $x > -1$ **9.** (i) $2 < x \leqslant 4$ (ii) $x > -2$ (iii) $x > -3$
(iv) $x > \frac{1}{4}$ (v) $x \geqslant 7$ **10.** (iii) $-1 < x \leqslant 2$ **11.** (iii) $x \leqslant 1\frac{3}{4}$
12. (iii) $x \leqslant \frac{1}{3}$ and $x \geqslant 5$ **13.** 2,250 $\leqslant$ Calorie Intake $\leqslant$ 2,750
14. 9

Exercise 3.3

1. $x < -4$ OR $x > 3$ **2.** $\frac{-7}{2} < x < -2$ **3.** $\frac{2}{3} \leqslant x \leqslant 8$
4. $-\frac{3}{2} < x < 0$ **5.** $-\frac{5}{11} \leqslant x \leqslant \frac{5}{11}$ **6.** $x \leqslant -3$, $x \geqslant \frac{5}{2}$
7. $-2 < x < -1$ **8.** $x \leqslant \frac{-6}{5}$ OR $x \geqslant 12$ **9.** $-2 \leqslant x \leqslant -\frac{3}{5}$

10. $-3 < x < 2$ **11.** $-1 < x < 4$ **12.** $x < 3$ OR $x \geqslant 4\frac{1}{4}$
13. $2 < x < 4\frac{1}{3}$ **14.** $-2\frac{1}{5} \leqslant x < -2$ **15.** $1 \leqslant x < 1\frac{2}{3}$
16. $x \geqslant 5$ OR $x < 3$ **17.** (i) $x = 13.9$ OR $x = -0.9$ (ii) 14
18. $x \leqslant -3 - \sqrt{5}$ OR $x \geqslant -3 + \sqrt{5}$ **19.** (i) $15 \geqslant 20 - 5t^2 \geqslant 10$
(ii) Start filming at $t = 1.0$ second, Stop filming at $t = 1.4$
seconds **20.** (i) €1.59 $<$ Price $<$ €4.41 (ii) 17%
21. (i) $1.6x^2$ (ii) $1.6x^2 \leqslant 300$ (iii) $x \leqslant 13.69$
(iv) 811.2 cm³ $\leqslant$ Volume $\leqslant$ 1,124.864 cm³

Exercise 3.4

1. (i) 8 (ii) 3 (iii) 5 (iv) 5 (v) 11 (vi) 11 **2.** (i) 7 (ii) 1
(iii) 10 (iv) 100 (v) 1 (vi) 37 **4.** $x = -5$ OR $x = 5$
5. $x = -10$ OR $x = 10$ **6.** $x = -9$ OR $x = 7$ **7.** $x = 11$ OR
$x = 5$ **8.** $x = 4\frac{1}{2}$ OR $x = -3\frac{1}{2}$ **9.** $x = -16$ OR $x = 10$
10. $x = 7$ OR $x = -3$ **11.** $x \leqslant -2.5$ OR $x \geqslant 0.5$
12. $x = 2$ OR $x = 6$ **13.** (i) $x = -3$ **14.** (i) $x = -\frac{3}{2}$
15. $x = -\frac{1}{30}$ **16.** $-6 < x < 4$ **17.** $x < 1$ OR $x > 7$
18. (i) A(1, 2), B(5, 2), C(3, 0), D(0, 3) (ii) $1 < x < 5$
19. $-9 < x < -5$ OR $-1 < x < 3$ **20.** $-3 < x \leqslant 4$ OR
$10 \leqslant x < 17$ **21.** (i) $x = -1$ OR $x = 5$ (ii) $x = 1$ OR $x = 3$
(iii) $1 < x < 3$ (iv) $x \leqslant -1$ OR $x \geqslant 5$ (v) $-1 < x < 1$ OR
$3 < x < 5$

Exercise 3.5

10. (b) $x^2 + y^2 \geqslant 2xy$, $a^2 + x^2 \geqslant 2ax$, $b^2 + y^2 \geqslant 2by$
12. (i) $(a + b)(a - b)^2$

Exercise 3.6

1. (i) No real roots, discriminant < 0
(ii) Real distinct roots, discriminant > 0
(iii) Real distinct roots, discriminant > 0
(iv) No real roots, discriminant < 0
(v) Real, equal roots, discriminant $= 0$
2. (i) $16 \Rightarrow$ real distinct roots (ii) $0 \Rightarrow$ real equal roots
(iii) $-16 \Rightarrow$ no real roots (iv) $72 \Rightarrow$ real distinct roots
(v) $204 \Rightarrow$ real distinct roots (vi) $k^2 + 4a^2$, roots are real and
distinct if k, $a > 0$, roots are real and equal if k **and** $a = 0$
(vii) $0 \Rightarrow$ real equal roots (viii) $2,112 \Rightarrow$ real distinct roots
(ix) $(a - 1)^2 + 36 \Rightarrow$ real distinct roots **3.** Complex roots
4. $a \geqslant 8$ OR $a \leqslant -8$ **5.** -9 **6.** $c < -2$ **7.** $0 < q < 4$
8. $p \leqslant 0$ OR $p \geqslant 4$ **9.** $b = -\frac{2}{3}$ OR $b = -2$

Revision Exercises

1. (i) $x = 6$ (ii) $x = 4$ (iii) $x = 7$ (iv) $x = 1$ (v) $x = 0$ OR
$x = 5$ **2.** (a) (i) $x \geqslant 1$ (ii) $x < 2$ (iii) $x > -2\frac{1}{4}$
(b) (iii) $\frac{-3}{4} < x \leqslant 1$ **3.** (a) (i) $x = 5$ OR $x = 2$ (ii) $2 < x < 5$
(iii) $x = 3$ OR $x = 5$ (iv) $x \leqslant 3$ OR $x \geqslant 5$
(b) (i) $-2 < x < 4$ (ii) $x \leqslant -5$ OR $x \geqslant 4$
(iii) $-2 \leqslant x \leqslant 5$ (iv) $x < -2$ OR $x > 2$ (c) (i) $\frac{-5}{2} \leqslant x \leqslant 2$
(ii) $x < -\frac{1}{3}$ OR $x > \frac{1}{2}$ (iii) $-2 < x < 6$ **4.** (a) (i) $x = 7.1$ OR
$x = -1.6$ (ii) 7 (b) (i) $4 < x < \frac{15}{2}$ (ii) $x < -17$ OR $x > -7$
(iii) $3 < x \leqslant 8$ (iv) $x \leqslant -9$ OR $x \geqslant 11$ (c) 8 **5.** (b) (i) $x = 5$
OR $x = -5$ (ii) $x = 9$ OR $x = -11$ (iii) $x = 11$ OR $x = -9$
(iv) $x = -8$ OR $x = 10$ (c) (i) $x = -5$ OR $x = -1$ (ii) $x = 2$
OR $x = 10$ (iii) $x = -4$ (iv) $x = -\frac{3}{2}$ **6.** (b) (i) $-8 < x < 6$
(ii) $x \leqslant 3$ OR $x \geqslant 7$ **7.** (c) (i) $(q - p)(q^2 + pq + p^2)$ **8.** (a) 4
(c) $k = -2$ OR $k = 6$, $x = 1$, $x = -3$ **9.** (a) $k = -1$ OR $k = 2$,
$x = 1$, $x = -2$ (b) (i) $2(x + 3) < 5(x - 3)$, $3x < 27$ (ii) $x > 7$,
$x < 9$ (iii) He is eight years old. (c) (i) $-7 \leqslant x < -3$ OR
$7 < x \leqslant 11$ **10.** (a) $-1 < x < 19$ (c) Between one and two
hours **11.** (a) (i) $-6 < x < 0$ (c) 131 hours

Chapter 4

Exercise 4.1

1. (i) Area = 78.5 cm², Circumference = 31.4 cm
(ii) Area = 201.14 km², Circumference = 50.29 km
(iii) Area = 0.49π m², Circumference = 1.4π m
(iv) Area = 4.91 mm², Circumference = 7.85 mm
(v) Area = 63.64 cm², Circumference = 28.29 cm
(vi) Area = $3,969\pi$ mm², Circumference = 126π mm
2. (i) Area = 26.376 cm², Length of arc = 8.792 cm,
Perimeter = 20.792 cm (ii) Area = 203.66 mm²,
Length of arc = 33.94 mm, Perimeter = 57.94 mm
(iii) Area = 2,370.70 m², Length of arc = 158.05 m,
Perimeter = 218.05 m **4.** (i) Area = 256 cm²,
Perimeter = 67 cm (ii) Area = 20.77 cm²,
Perimeter = 21.49 cm (iii) Area = 68 cm²,
Perimeter = 51.45 cm **5.** (i) 2.114 cm (ii) 664.40 m
6. (i) 12 cm (ii) 224° (iii) 160° **7.** 58 m **8.** (i) 11,250 m²
(ii) 2,150 m² (iii) €7,793.75 **9.** 1,823 g **10.** Length: 10 m,
Width: 1.25 m **11.** (i) 63 cm² (ii) 32 cm **12.** €485 **13.** 28 cm
14. 40.5π cm² **15.** 30 m **16.** $y = 15.33$ m, $x = 72$ m OR
$y = 48$ m, $x = 23$ m **17.** $x\sqrt{2}$ **18.** (i) $2r^2$ (ii) $0.86r^2$
(iii) $1.14r^2$ **19.** (i) $\frac{\sqrt{2}y}{2}$ (ii) $\frac{1}{2}y$ (iii) $2 : 1$ **20.** Pink

Exercise 4.2

1. 1,956 cm² **2.** (i) Volume = 1,560 m³,
Surface area = 1,276 m² (ii) Volume = 612 m³,
Surface area = 424 m² (iii) Volume = 2,368 m³,
Surface area = 1,704 m² **3.** (a) (i) 960 m³ (ii) 171 m³
(iii) 162 m³ (c) (i) 740 m² (ii) 230 m² (iii) 220 m²
4. 186.04 cm² **5.** Volume = 6 m³, Surface area = 26.06 m²
6. $3\frac{1}{3}$ cm **7.** 295.84 cm³ **8.** $6 \cdot 32^{\frac{2}{3}} \cdot x^2$ **9.** (i) 1,774
(ii) 473,125 litres **10.** Volume = 21,283.44 cm³,
Surface Area = 4,608 cm² **11.** (ii) $12y + 2xy + 12x$
(iii) $x = 14$ cm, $y = 10$ cm **12.** (iii) 4 cm OR 1.78 cm

Exercise 4.3

1. (i) Volume = 1,808.64 cm³, CSA = 301.44 cm²,
TSA = 1,205.76 cm² (ii) Volume = 431.2 mm³,
CSA = 123.2 mm², TSA = 431.2 mm²
(iii) Volume = 320π m³, CSA = 160π m², TSA = 176π m²
(iv) Volume = 1,582.56 m³, CSA = 527.52 m²,
TSA = 640.56 m² **2.** (i) Volume = 401.92 cm³,
CSA = 251.2 cm², TSA = 452.16 cm²
(ii) Volume = 15,085.71 mm³, CSA = 5,154.29 mm²,
TSA = 10,182.86 mm² (iii) Volume = $27,648,000\pi$ mm³,
CSA = $288,000\pi$ mm², TSA = $518,000\pi$ mm²
(iv) Volume = 27,154,285.71 cm³, CSA = 384,685.71 cm²,
TSA = 565,714.29 cm² **3.** (i) Volume = 65,416.6 m³,
Surface area = 7,850 m² (ii) Volume = 11,498.67 mm³,
Surface area = 2,464 mm² (iii) Volume = $2,304\pi$ cm³,
Surface area = 576π cm² **4.** (i) Volume = 32,708.33 cm³,
CSA = 3,925 cm², TSA = 5,887.5 cm²
(ii) Volume = 6,387.6 mm³, CSA = 1,321.57 mm²,
TSA = 1,982.36 mm² (iii) Volume = 486π m³,
CSA = 162π m², TSA = 243π m² **5.** (ii) 96π cm³
6. 2 cm **7.** 38 mm **8.** 175 seconds
9. (i) 288π cm³ (ii) $10\frac{2}{3}$ cm **10.** (i) 18π cm³ (ii) 3 cm
(iii) 6 cm (iv) $(18 + 9\sqrt{2})\pi$ cm² **11.** $\sqrt{5} : 4$ **12.** Cylinder A
13. $h = \frac{32}{3}x$ **14.** $\left(\sqrt{\frac{3}{2}} - 1\right)x$ **15.** (i) 1,766.25 cm³ (ii) 8.42 cm
(iii) $16.84 \times 16.84 \times 16.84$ **16.** 261 mm × 90 mm

17. (i) $122.5\pi \text{ cm}^3$ (ii) 6 cm (iii) $110.25\pi \text{ cm}^3$ (iv) 9 cm
(vi) 335 cm² **18.** 3 cm **19.** 2,100 cm³
20. Volume = 3,315.84 cm³, TSA ≈ 1,510.97 cm²
21. $\pi\sqrt{3} : 2$ **22.** (a) (i) $\frac{4}{3}\pi r^3$ (ii) $\pi\left(\frac{4}{5} + 2\sqrt{\frac{129}{5}}\right)r^2$ (b) $\frac{Pr}{3}$

Exercise 4.4

1. 62 m² **2.** 912 cm² **3.** $302\frac{1}{2}$ m² **4.** 2,300 m²
5. 26 units² **6.** 173 m **7.** 18 m **8.** (i) 5.68 units² **9.** 175 m

Revision Exercises

1. (a) 10 cm (b) 446 cm³ (c) (i) Pink: r, Green: $\sqrt{2}r$
2. (a) $1,152\pi \text{ cm}^3$ (b) 21 cm (c) 800 seconds **3.** (a) 4 : 1
(b) Small jar: Radius 2.3 cm
Height 4.6 cm
Large jar: Radius 6.9 cm
Height 9.2 cm
4. (a) 28,662 (b) $V = \frac{\pi r^3}{6}$, TSA = $\pi\left(r^2 + r^2\sqrt{\frac{5}{4}}\right)$ **5.** (b) 4.67 cm
6. (a) (i) 5,640 m² (ii) 1,300 m² (b) (i) 14 units (ii) 5.8315 m
7. (a) (i) $\frac{5}{2}\pi x^2$ (ii) $\pi(5x)$ (b) p = 1.5 m, q = 2.4 m
8. (a) (i) 52.95 m² (ii) 22,239 m³ per minute
(b) (i) 1,432,200,000 km (ii) 691 days (iii) 4,500,000,000 km
(iv) 250 minutes **9.** (i) $l = 3r$ (ii) $\sqrt{8}r$ (iii) $\sqrt{2} : 1$

Exam Questions

1. (b) $h = 2$ **OR** $h = 7.83$ **2.** (a) Height = h cm,
Length = 20 – 2h cm, Width = (15 – h) cm
(b) $2h^3 - 50h^2 + 300h$ (d) 2.9 cm

Chapter 5

Exercise 5.1

1. (i) $2^5 \times 5$ (ii) $3 \times 7 \times 13$ (iii) 2^7 (iv) $3 \times 5 \times 7 \times 11$
(v) $2 \times 5 \times 11 \times 17$ (vi) $2^2 \times 3 \times 5^3 \times 7$ (vii) $2 \times 3 \times 17$
(viii) $2^3 \times 3^2 \times 17$ (ix) $2^7 \times 3^3 \times 11$ **2.** (a) (i) $102 = 2 \times 3 \times 17$,
$170 = 2 \times 5 \times 17$ (ii) $117 = 3^2 \times 13$, $130 = 2 \times 5 \times 13$
(iii) $2^4 \times 23$, $621 = 3^3 \times 23$ (iv) $58 = 2 \times 29$, $174 = 2 \times 3 \times 29$
(v) $60 = 2^2 \times 3 \times 5$, $765 = 3^2 \times 5 \times 17$ (vi) $123 = 3 \times 41$,
$615 = 3 \times 5 \times 41$ (vii) $69 = 3 \times 23$, $123 = 3 \times 41$ (viii) $20 = 2^2 \times 5$,
$30 = 2 \times 3 \times 5$, $60 = 2^2 \times 3 \times 5$ (ix) $8 = 2^3$, $10 = 2 \times 5$, $20 = 2^2 \times 5$
(x) $294 = 2 \times 3 \times 7^2$, $252 = 2^2 \times 3^2 \times 7$, $210 = 2 \times 3 \times 5 \times 7$
(b) (i) LCM = 510, HCF = 34 (ii) LCM = 1,170, HCF = 13
(iii) LCM = 9,936, HCF = 23 (iv) LCM = 174, HCF = 58
(v) LCM = 3,060, HCF = 15 (vi) LCM = 615, HCF = 123
(vii) LCM = 2,829, HCF = 3 (viii) LCM = 60, HCF = 10
(ix) LCM = 40, HCF = 2 (x) LCM = 8,820, HCF = 42 **3.** 18 cm
4. July 16 **5.** 10 students **6.** 1 cm width **7.** 700th **8.** (i) n
(ii) n **10.** (i) F (1) = 2, F (2) = 1 (iii) 6, 3, 5, 8, 4, 2, 1, 2, 1, 2, 1,
2, 1, 2, 1 10, 5, 8, 4, 2, 1, 2, 1, 2, 1, 2, 1, 2, 1, 2 15, 23, 35, 53,
80, 40, 20, 10, 5, 8, 4, 2, 1, 2, 1 32, 16, 8, 4, 2, 1, 2, 1, 2, 1, 2, 1,
1, 2 17, 26, 13, 20, 10, 5, 8, 4, 2, 1, 2, 1, 2, 1, 2 **11.** (ii) 1
(iii) ② (iv) ① **12.** (i) 9 (iii) 21! + 2, 21! + 3, 21! + 4, 21! + 5,
21! + 6, 21! + 7, 21! + 8, 21! + 9, 21! + 10, 21! + 11, 21! + 12, 21!
+ 13, 21! + 14, 21! + 15, 21! + 16, 21! + 17, 21! + 18, 21! + 19,
21! + 20, 21! + 21 (iv) Yes **13.** 3, 7, 31, 127 **14.** 14

Exercise 5.2

1. (i) 0 (ii) –6 (iii) 40 (iv) 0 **2.** (i) $\frac{7}{20}$ (ii) $12\frac{1}{2}$ (iii) $2\frac{11}{12}$
(iv) $\frac{3}{8}$ (v) $1\frac{1}{2}$ (vi) $\frac{125}{126}$ (vii) $\frac{57,498}{1,331}$ (viii) $5\frac{7}{100}$ **3.** $\frac{5}{9}$ units
4. $\frac{2}{5}$ units **5.** 36 **6.** $\frac{12}{17}$ **7.** 11 : 9 **8.** G **11.** (ii) 21 units
12. 2,301 **13.** (i) 90 (ii) 9,000 (iii) 3,124,213 **14.** 21

Exercise 5.3

2. (i) 3 (ii) 5 (iii) 3 divides p or 3 divides q
7. (a) (i) integer (ii) integer (iii) integer
(iv) rational number (b) (i) $\frac{ad - bc}{bd}$

Exercise 5.4

1. (i) 5.146 (ii) 7.298 (iii) 17.894 (iv) 62.124 (v) 23.765
(vi) 0.079 **2.** (a) (i) 0.0099 (ii) 0.0023 (iii) 0.013
(iv) 0.00085 (v) 0.24 (vi) 52 (b)(i) 30 (ii) 4 (iii) 20,000
(iv) 2,000 (v) 6,000 (vi) 1,000 **3.** (i) 3.4×10^7 (ii) 2.5×10^{-1}
(iii) 4.57×10^3 (iv) 3.2×10^{-5} (v) 5×10^6 (vi) 6.464×10^{-1}
4. (i) 265 (ii) 0.00453 (iii) 7,200,000 (iv) 0.04
(v) 26,400,000 (vi) 7,612 **5.** (i) 3,400 + 2,800 = 6,200
(ii) $8.7 \times 10^9 = 8,700,000,000$ **6.** (i) 2,000,000
(ii) 16,900 (iii) 2,480 (iv) 647,000 (v) 61.02 (vi) 943,000
7. (i) 0.0015 (ii) 0.000254 (iii) 0.000035 (iv) 0.00000667
8. (i) 7 (ii) 5 (iii) 5 (iv) 2 (v) 2

Revision Exercises

1. (i) 3 + 3 + 5 (ii) 7 + 13 + 13 (iii) 7 + 7 + 83 (iv) 3 + 7 + 7
(v) 5 + 95 + 97 **2.** 36 **3.** (i) $68 = 2^2 \times 17$, $102 = 2 \times 3 \times 17$,
HCF = 34, LCM = 204 (ii) $69 = 3 \times 23$, $123 = 3 \times 41$,
HCF = 3, LCM = 2,829 (iii) $104 = 2^3 \times 13$, $351 = 3^3 \times 13$,
HCF = 13, LCM = 2,808 (iv) $123 = 3 \times 41$, $615 = 3 \times 5 \times 41$,
HCF = 123, LCM = 615 **4.** (a) $\frac{1}{12}$ (b) (i) 3 children
(ii) 17, 19, 23 **7.** (i) 850,000 (ii) 0.13 (iii) 2.0
(iv) 0.000054 (v) 650,000 (vi) 0.00081
9. (i) $2,332 = 2^2 \times 11 \times 53$, $6,776 = 2^3 \times 7 \times 11^2$
(ii) HCF = 44, LCM = 359,128 **10.** 15
11. 24,153 and 42,153, 24,351 and 42,351, 12,354 and 21,354

Chapter 6

Exercise 6.1

1. a, b, d **2.** (a) f multiplies an input by 4 and then subtracts 1
(b) (i) 3 (ii) 1 (iii) $\frac{5}{2}$ (iv) $\frac{1}{3}$ **3.** 8 **4.** 4 **5.** (i) Yes
(ii) Domain = {1, 2, 3, 4}, Range = {8, 9, 10, 11} (iii) $x \rightarrow x + 7$
6. (i) $f(x) = x^2$ (ii) $f(x) = 4x + 6$ (iii) $f(x) = 98 - 3x$
(iv) $f(x) = 10 - 2x$ **7.** (i) $\frac{x}{2} + 3$ (ii) $f(4) = 5$, $f(18) = 12$, $f(-6) = 0$
(iii) 12 (iv) $\frac{x + 18}{4}$ (v) $\frac{x + 1}{2}$ (vi) $\frac{x + k}{2} + 3$ **9.** $a = 3$, $b = 2$
10. $a = 2$, $b = 3$ **11.** (i) $y = f(x) = 200 - x^2$ (ii) $10\sqrt{2}$ minutes
(iii) 10 minutes **12.** $y = 100x - x^2$, Domain is $\{x | x \in R, 0 < x < 100\}$
13. $l = 2\sqrt{25 - x^2}$, Domain = $\{x \mid x \in R, 0 \leq x < 5\}$ **14.** (a) (i) 6
(ii) 24 (iii) 38 (iv) 78 (v) 8 (vi) 14 (vii) 24 (viii) 78
15. (a) (i) $x^2 - 2$ (ii) $(x - 2)^2$ (iii) $(x + 1)^2$ (iv) $(x - 2)^2 + 1$
(v) $(x - 1)^2$ (vi) $(x^2 - 2)^2$ (vii) $(x + 1)^4$ (viii) $x - 3$
(b) $p = g \circ f \circ h$ **16.** (i) 2 **17.** 0 **19.** (a) (i) $f(x) = x^2 + 6$
(ii) $f(x) = 6(x - 2)^2$ (iii) $f(x) = (\sqrt{x} + 4)^3$ (iv) $f(x) = \frac{1}{4}\sin^2 x$
(b) (i) $f = h \circ g$ where $g(x) = x^2$, $h(x) = x + 6$ (ii) $f = k \circ h \circ g$
where $g(x) = x - 2$, $h(x) = x^2$, $k(x) = 6x$ (iii) $f = k \circ h \circ g$ where
$g(x) = \sqrt{x}$, $h(x) = x + 4$, $k(x) = x^3$ (iv) $f = k \circ h \circ g$ where
$g(x) = \sin x$, $h(x) = x^2$, $k(x) = \frac{x}{4}$ **20.** (i) $x = -\frac{1}{3}$ **OR** $x = -1$
(ii) $x = -\frac{3}{14}$ **21.** (ii) $a = 2$, $b = 3$ **OR** $a = -2$, $b = -3$ **23.** (i) $3x^2 + 8$
(ii) $9x^2 + 12x + 6$, No **24.** $g \circ f$

Exercise 6.2

1. (i) 7 (ii) $\frac{9}{4}$ (iii) –1 (iv) $x \geqslant 1$ **2.** (ii) 120 km
(iii) $87\frac{1}{2}$ miles (iv) [104 km, 120 km]

3. (i) −4.5 (ii) −1.45 **OR** 3.45 (iii) −1.45 ⩽ x ⩽ 3.45
(iv) $x = 1 ± \sqrt{6}$ **8.** (i) 16 (ii) 0.6 **OR** 6.9
(iii) 0.6 ⩽ x ⩽ 6.9 (iv) 0 ⩽ x ⩽ 0.6 **OR** 6.9 ⩽ x ⩽ 8
9. (i) $x = -2.6$ **OR** $x = 0.6$ (ii) −3 ⩽ x ⩽ −2.6 **OR** 0.6 ⩽ x ⩽ 2
10. (ii) 2 seconds or 4 seconds (iv) 0.2 seconds
(v) 1.3 metres **11.** (ii) 500 units (iii) €2,500 (iv) 400 units
or 600 units (v) 725 units (vi) P is a function of Q because
each value of Q is assigned to only one value of P.
12. (ii) 300 (iii) €90 (iv) No

Exercise 6.3

1. (i) $y = (x - 6)^2$ (ii) $x = 6$ (iii) (6,0); $x = 6$ **2.** (i) $f(x) = (x + 1)^2 - 7$
(ii) $x = -1 ± \sqrt{7}$ (iii) (−1,−7); $x = -1$ **3.** (i) $g(x) = (x - 3)^2 - 25$
(ii) $x = -2$ **OR** $x = 8$ (iii) (3,−25); $x = 3$ **4.** (i) $f(x) = 2(x + 1)^2 - 9$
(ii) $x = -1 ± \frac{3\sqrt{2}}{2}$ (iii) (−1,−9); $x = -1$ **5.** (i) $f(x) = 3(x + 2)^2 - 8$
(ii) $x = -2 ± \frac{2\sqrt{6}}{3}$ (iii) (−2,−8); $x = -2$ **6.** (i) $g(x) = (x + 1)^2 - 4$
(ii) $x = -3$ **OR** $x = 1$ (iii) (−1,−4); $x = -1$ **7.** (i) $y = 7 - (x + 2)^2$
(ii) $x = -2 ± \sqrt{7}$ (iii) (−2,7); $x = -2$ **8.** (i) $y = 13 - (x - 2)^2$
(ii) $x = 2 ± \sqrt{13}$ (iii) (2,13); $x = 2$ **9.** (i) $h(x) = 15 - 2(x + 1)^2$
(ii) $x = -1 ± \frac{\sqrt{30}}{2}$ (iii) (−1,15); $x = -1$ **10.** (i) $g(x) = 2 - (x - 2)^2$
(ii) $x = 2 ± \sqrt{2}$ (iii) (2,2); $x = 2$ **11.** (i) $g(x) = \frac{43}{3} - 3\left(x - \frac{7}{3}\right)^2$
(ii) $x = \frac{7 ± \sqrt{43}}{3}$ (iii) $\left(\frac{7}{3}, \frac{43}{3}\right)$; $x = \frac{7}{3}$ **12.** (i) $2(x - 2)^2 - 4$ (ii) −4
(iii) 0 **13.** (i) $-3(x + 1)^2 + 12$ (ii) 12 (iii) 11
14. (i) $(x - 6)^2 - 40$ (ii) −40 (iii) 32
15. (i) $-1(x - 6)^2 + 50$ (ii) 50 (iii) −22

Exercise 6.4

2. (i) $f(1.5) ≈ 4.9$ (ii) $x = -0.45, x = 0.6$ **OR** 2 (iii) $x ≈ -0.4, 1.15$
OR 1.45 **3.** $x = -1.55, x = -0.35, x = 1.9$ **7.** x^3 **8.** $(x - 2)^3 - 6$
9. (i) Shift four units to the left and three units downwards
(ii) $(x + 4)^3 - 3$ **10.** (i) 12,000 units (ii) 0.65 years
(iii) At time = 0 years and at time = 2 years (iv) 30,000 units
11. (i) 30°C (ii) 13°C (iii) [0.7 minutes, 1.3 minutes] **OR**
[3.95 minutes, 4 minutes] **12.** (ii) €10,480 (iii) €1,670 per year
(iv) Yes **13.** (ii) 495 cm (iii) 2.52 and 6.86 seconds

Exercise 6.5

9. $a = 6, b = 2$ **10.** $a = 4, b = \frac{1}{2}$ **11.** (iii) 5 days 18 hours
12. (iii) 60 cm^3 (iv) 3.3 hours **13.** (i) $P(x) = 15 (1.25)^{0.1x}$,
$P(x)$ in millions. (iii) 2035 **14.** (ii) 170 Wm^{-2}
(iii) 172.26 Wm^{-2} (iv) 1.22 mm **19.** (i) Shift two units to
the left (ii) $g(x) = 2^{x-2}$ **20.** 3^{x-3} **21.** $3(4^{x-3})$ **22.** $2^{x+2} + 3$

Exercise 6.6

7. (i) Multiply the function by 0.5 (ii) $0.5 \log_4 x$ **8.** $y = \log_5 (x - 5)$
9. $y = 3 \log_6 (x - 3) - 3$ **10.** (i) Domain $x > 1$; Range: no max.,
no min. (ii) Domain $x > -1$; Range: no max., no min.
(iii) Domain $x > 0$; Range: no max., no min. (iv) Domain $x > \frac{1}{3}$;
Range: no max., no min.

Exercise 6.7

1. (i) Surjective (ii) Surjective (iii) Not surjective
(iv) Not surjective (v) Not surjective (vi) Surjective
(vii) Not surjective (viii) Surjective (ix) Surjective
2. (i) Injective only (ii) Bijective (iii) Injective only
(iv) Bijective (v) Surjective only (vi) None of the above
(vii) Surjective only **3.** (iii) **4.** (i) (a) Range = {0, 4, 8, 16}
(b) One-to-one (ii) (a) Range = [2, ∞) (b) Not one-to-one

(iii) (a) Range = [−7, 5] (b) One-to-one (iv) (a) Range = $R \setminus \{0\}$
(b) One-to-one (v) (a) Range = [2, ∞) (b) Not one-to-one
(vi) (a) Range = R (b) One-to-one (vii) (a) Range = [−1, 1]
(b) Not one-to-one (viii) (a) Range = [0, ∞) (b) One-to-one
5. Yes **6.** No **7.** Yes **8.** No **9.** No **10.** No **11.** No
12. Yes **13.** (i) a (ii) b (iii) d **14.** (i) Is a function
(ii) Is not a function (iii) Is a function (iv) Is not a function
15. (i) (c) Bijective (ii) (d) None of the above
(iii) (b) Subjective only (iv) (a) Injective only **16.** (i) No
(ii) If $f: R \mapsto (-∞, 2]$ **17.** f is not injective **18.** f is not
injective **19.** f is injective **20.** $f: N \to E: x \to 2x$
21. $f: N \to 0: x \to 2x - 1$ **22.** $f: N \to M: x \to -2x$ **23.** (i) Yes
(ii) No **25.** (i) Is a bijection (ii) Not a bijection
(iii) Is a bijection **26.** Yes **27.** Yes **28.** (i) Yes (ii) Yes
(iii) Yes **29.** (i) No (ii) No (iii) No

Exercise 6.8

1. $\frac{x}{2}$ **2.** $\frac{x-1}{3}$ **3.** $\frac{x+4}{6}$ **4.** $+\sqrt{x - 6}$ **5.** $-\sqrt{-1 - x}$ **7.** f is
invertible **8.** f is invertible **9.** g is not invertible **10.** h is
invertible **11.** f is invertible **12.** g is not invertible
13. $\sqrt{\frac{x+5}{2}} + 3$ **14.** $\sqrt{\frac{x}{1-x}}$ **15.** $\ln x$ **16.** $\log_2 x$ **17.** $\frac{1}{3}\log_2(2x)$
18. $b^x - 1$

Revision Exercises

1. (i) −4 (ii) −3 (iii) 96 (iv) $3x^2 - 12x + 6$
2. (i) $bb: x \to \frac{x}{1 - 4x} - 4$ (ii) $ba: x \to \frac{1}{x^2 - 3} - 4$ (iii) $cc: x \to x + 6$
(iv) $acb: x \to \left(\frac{1-x}{x}\right)^2 - 3$ (v) $bac: x \to \frac{1}{x^2 + 6x + 6} - 4$
(vi) $cab: x \to \left(\frac{1}{x} - 4\right)^2$ **3.** (i) $x = 0.04$ **OR** −2.71 (ii) $x = ±0.41$
4. (ii) One (iii) $(x - 2)(x^2 + 3x + 5)$ **5.** (i) $\frac{x}{4} + 3$
(ii) $f(3) = 3.75, f(-2) = 2.5, f(-8) = 1$ (iii) 24 **6.** (i) 1-1 only
(ii) 1-1 only (iii) 1-1 and onto (iv) Onto only (v) 1-1 only
7. (i) 1-1 function (ii) Not a function (iii) Onto function
(iv) 1-1 and onto function **8.** (i) and (iv) **10.** $x = 0 ⇒ a = 2$,
$b = \frac{1}{4}$ **11.** Yes **12.** No **13.** No **14.** (i) Yes (ii) No
19. (i) $16\pi r^2$ (ii) $18\pi r^2$ (iii) 729π cm^3 **20.** $40,000(0.88)^t$ (in €)
21. $\frac{x+3}{3}$ **22.** $\frac{3x-1}{x}$ **23.** $\frac{1}{3}(12 - 8x)$ **24.** $-\frac{4}{x}$ **25.** $\frac{7x}{4}$
26. (i) $g^{-1}(x) = \frac{x}{3}, h^{-1}(x) = \frac{1}{x}, gh(x) = \frac{3}{x}$ **27.** (i) (a) [0, ∞) → [0, ∞)
OR (−∞, 0] → [0, ∞) (ii) (a) [−3, ∞) → [0, ∞) **OR** (−∞, −3] →
[0, ∞) (i) (b) $\sqrt{x}$ (ii) (b) $\sqrt{x} - 3$ **28.** (i) Not invertible
(ii) Not invertible (iii) Is invertible **29.** (iii) 220 (iv) 4.19 hours
(v) $A(1.18)^x$ (vi) $P(x) = 125(1.18)^x$ (vii) 223.1 **35.** (i) $x = -1$
OR $x = 1$ (ii) $x ⩽ -1$ **OR** $x ⩾ 1$ (iii) $-1 < x < 1$
36. $a = -1, b = -2, c = 4$ **37.** (i) $\frac{2}{3}$ (ii) $x = -2, -1$ **OR** 0
(iii) There is one real root **39.** (i) (a) $y = (x + 3)^2$ (b) $x = -3$
(c) (−3,0); $x = -3$ (ii) (a) $y = (x + 1)^2 - 9$ (b) $x = -4$ **OR** $x = 2$
(c) (−1,−9); $x = -1$ (iii) (a) $y = 2\left(x + \frac{1}{2}\right)^2 - \frac{19}{2}$ (b) $x = -\frac{1 ± \sqrt{19}}{2}$
(c) $\left(-\frac{1}{2}, -\frac{19}{2}\right)$; $x = -\frac{1}{2}$ (iv) (a) $y = (x + 1)^2 + 5$ (b) No real roots
(c) (−1,5); $x = -1$ (v) (a) $y = \frac{1}{3} - 3\left(x - \frac{2}{3}\right)^2$ (b) $x = \frac{1}{3}$ **OR**
$x = 1$ (c) $\left(\frac{2}{3}, \frac{1}{3}\right)$; $x = \frac{2}{3}$ (vi) (a) $y = 3\left(x - \frac{2}{3}\right)^2 - \frac{7}{3}$ (b) $x = \frac{2 ± \sqrt{7}}{3}$
(c) $\left(\frac{2}{3}, -\frac{7}{3}\right)$; $x = \frac{2}{3}$ **40.** (i) $x = 6 + 3\sqrt{5}$ (ii) $x = -5 ± \sqrt{29}$
41. (a) $(x + 1)^2 - 4$ (b) $x = 1, x = -3$ (c) (−1, −4), $x = -1$
(e) (i) Codomain = [−4, ∞), Range = [−4, ∞]
(iii) Domain = [−4, ∞), Range = [1, ∞] **42.** $2(3^x)$
43. (ii) Missile B (iii) fire Missile B seven minutes before
Missile A **45.** (i) 448, 501.76, 561.97, 629.41, 704.94
(iii) Exponent = t, Base = $(1 + i)$ (iv) €580 **46.** (i) $c(x) = 120(0.5^x)$,

(ii)+(iii) After roughly 1.25 days   **47.** (i) 9 billion   (ii) 2019
(iii) 0.4%   **48.** (i) 72°C   (ii) 5 mins   (iii) 32 mins
49. 2.4 (mol cm^{-3}) Over the first interval of 0–30 seconds
50. (ii) 1.27 tonnes   (iii) 22%   (iv) $F = -\frac{7}{75}w + 2.2$

Exam Questions

1. (a) maximum of $f = 20$, minimum of $f = -4$ (b) f is not injective

Chapter 7

Exercise 7.1

6. (i) 5.8 = 6 to the nearest whole number   (ii) 2.6   **7.** (i) 1
(ii) 3   **9.** (i) $x = 0$ (ii) An axial symmetry in the y-axis
10. (i) 10^9 (ii) 20^6 (iii) 7^8 (iv) e^5 (v) 4^5 (vi) e^{-3}
(vii) -5^7 (viii) 10^{36} (ix) e^4 (x) e^{25} **11.** (i) -3^3 (ii) 2^{20}
(iii) -5^{19} (iv) 3^3 (v) 4^{12} (vi) -1 (vii) -6^3 (viii) 6^3 **12.** (i) $\frac{1}{8}$
(ii) $\frac{1}{49}$ (iii) $\frac{1}{16}$ (iv) $\frac{1}{81}$ (v) $\frac{4}{81}$ (vi) $\frac{1}{8}$ (vii) $\frac{1}{32}$ (viii) $\frac{1}{200}$
(ix) $\frac{1}{10}$ (x) $\frac{1}{6}$ (xi) $\frac{1}{2}$ (xii) $\frac{1}{27}$ (xiii) $\frac{1}{4}$ (xiv) $\frac{1}{243}$ **13.** (i) 7
(ii) 3   (iii) 2   (iv) 2   (v) 1   (vi) 6   (vii) 3   (viii) 2   (ix) 11
14. (i) 2   (ii) 3   (iii) 10   (iv) 4   (v) 6   (vi) 4   **15.** (i) -2
(ii) -4 (iii) -10 (iv) 2   (v) 2   (vi) 2   **16.** (i) a^5 (ii) a^9 (iii) a^{14}
(iv) $a^{\frac{1}{2}}$ (v) $a^{\frac{7}{2}}$ (vi) a^{-3} (vii) $a^{-\frac{1}{2}}$ **17.** (i) 1,000   (ii) 25
(iii) 32   (iv) 27   (v) 27   (vi) 256   (vii) $\frac{1}{125}$ (viii) $\frac{32}{243}$
(ix) $\frac{9}{5}$ (x) $\frac{4}{9}$ **18.** (i) 3×5 (ii) $3^9 \times 5^9$ **19.** $2^2 \times 3^2$,
$2^{4,022} \times 3^{4,022}$ **20.** $2^2 \times 5^2$, $2^{3,202} \times 5^{3,202}$ **21.** 2

Exercise 7.2

1. (a) (i) 2^2 (ii) 2^3 (iii) 2^4 (iv) 2^0 (v) 2^{-1} (vi) 2^{-4}
(vii) 2^{-5} (viii) $2^{\frac{1}{2}}$ (ix) $2^{\frac{1}{3}}$ (x) 2   (b) (i) 3^0 (ii) 3^2 (iii) 3^{-1}
(iv) 3^{-3} (v) $3^{\frac{4}{3}}$ (vi) 3^6 (vii) $3^{\frac{5}{2}}$ (viii) $3^{\frac{9}{2}}$ (ix) 3^3
2. (i) $x = 4$ (ii) $x = 4$ (iii) $x = 3$ (iv) $x = 2$ (v) $x = 6$
(vi) $x = -5$ (vii) $x = -3$ (viii) $x = 0$ **3.** (i) $x = 3$ (ii) $x = 8$
(iii) $x = -1\frac{1}{2}$ (iv) $x = -3$ (v) $x = 10$ (vi) $x = -1$ **4.** (i) $x = 7\frac{1}{2}$
(ii) $x = 2\frac{1}{2}$ (iii) $x = 1\frac{1}{2}$ (iv) $x = 1\frac{2}{3}$ (v) $x = \frac{3}{4}$ (vi) $x = 1\frac{3}{10}$
5. (i) 2^4 (ii) 2^3 (iii) $2^{\frac{3}{2}}$ (iv) $2^{2\frac{1}{2}}$ (v) $x = 4\frac{1}{4}$ **6.** (i) $x = 4\frac{1}{2}$
(ii) $x = 7$ **7.** (b) 2^p (c) (i) $x = 8$ (ii) $x = 14$ **8.** (i) $x = 2$
(ii) $x = 1$ (iii) $x = 3$ (iv) $x = -1$ (v) $x = 1$ (vi) $x = 2$ OR
$x = 1$ **9.** (i) $x = 0$ OR $x = 2$ (ii) $x = 1$ OR $x = 0$
(iii) $x = -2$ OR $x = 2$ (iv) $x = 0$ (v) $x = -1$ OR $x = 0$
(vi) $x = 0$ **10.** (i) $x = 2$ (no solution for negative y)   (ii) $x = -1$
11. (ii) $x = 2$ OR $x = 1$

Exercise 7.3

1. (i) 28   (ii) 250   (iii) 20   (iv) 200   (v) 135   (vi) 400
2. (i) 4   (ii) 8   (iii) 10   (iv) 3   (v) 5   (vi) 5   **3.** (i) $2\sqrt{2}$
(ii) $3\sqrt{5}$ (iii) $10\sqrt{3}$ (iv) $2\sqrt{3}$ (v) $4\sqrt{2}$ (vi) $10\sqrt{5}$ (vii) $3\sqrt{3}$
(viii) $3\sqrt{6}$ (ix) $5\sqrt{3}$ (x) $7\sqrt{2}$ **4.** $\sqrt{50} + \sqrt{8} = 5\sqrt{2} + 2\sqrt{2} =$
$7\sqrt{2}$ **5.** $\sqrt{27} + \sqrt{12} = 3\sqrt{3} + 2\sqrt{3} = 5\sqrt{3}$ **6.** $\sqrt{125} + \sqrt{20} =$
$5\sqrt{5} + 2\sqrt{5} = 7\sqrt{5}$ **7.** $3\sqrt{11}$ ∴ $n = 3$ **8.** (i) $3\sqrt{2}$ (ii) $\sqrt{7}$
(iii) $\frac{1}{2}\sqrt{2}$ (iv) $\frac{3}{5}\sqrt{5}$ (v) $\frac{2}{11}\sqrt{11}$ (vi) $\frac{3}{5}\sqrt{15}$ (vii) $\sqrt{2}$
(viii) $-\frac{2}{3}\sqrt{15}$ (ix) $\frac{1}{5}\sqrt{5}$ **9.** (i) $2 + \sqrt{5}$ (ii) $\frac{1}{2} - \frac{1\sqrt{3}}{6}$
(iii) $20 + 5\sqrt{2}$ (iv) $\frac{7}{22} - \frac{3}{22}\sqrt{3}$ (v) $-\frac{26}{23} + \frac{7}{23}\sqrt{3}$ (vi) $-\frac{43}{74} + \frac{11}{74}\sqrt{11}$
(vii) $\frac{1}{5} + \frac{1}{10}\sqrt{2}$ (viii) $-4 + \sqrt{15}$ (ix) $\frac{101}{37} - \frac{22}{37}\sqrt{21}$

Exercise 7.4

1. (i) 3^9 (ii) 8   (iii) 27   (iv) 4^3 (v) 2^5 (vi) 5^2 **2.** (i) 4
(ii) x (iii) 2   (iv) 5   (v) 5   (vi) x **3.** (i) $\frac{1}{2}$ (ii) -2 (iii) $\frac{1}{2}$
(iv) 0   (v) $\frac{1}{3}$ (vi) 1   (vii) 2   (viii) 3   **4.** (i) 4   (ii) 4   (iii) 3
(iv) 3   (v) 3   (vi) $\frac{5}{3}$ (vii) -7 (viii) -4 **5.** (i) 7.39   (ii) 4.48
(iii) 1.11   (iv) 1.10   (v) -1.60 (vi) 2.73   (vii) 0.81
(viii) 2.40   **8.** (i) log 10   (ii) log 5   (iii) log 6   (iv) log 2
(v) $\log\frac{p}{\sqrt[3]{q}}$ (vi) $\log\frac{10a^3}{\sqrt[3]{b}}$ **9.** (i) $x = 1$ (ii) $x = 9$ (iii) $x = 5$
(iv) $x = 3$ **10.** (i) $x = 29$ (ii) $x = 2$ (iii) $x = 4$ (iv) $x = 2$
11. (i) $\frac{\log_{10}27}{\log_{10}4}$ (ii) $\frac{\log_{10}100}{\log_{10}2}$ (iii) $\frac{\log_{10}500}{\log_{10}4}$ **12.** (i) $\frac{\log_e20}{\log_e4}$
(ii) $\frac{\log_e30}{\log_e5}$ (iii) $\frac{\log_e40}{\log_e6}$ **13.** (i) $\frac{1}{4}\log_2 x$ (ii) $\frac{1}{2}\log_2(x + 4)$
(iii) $\frac{1}{3}\log_2(3x - 2)$ **14.** (i) $x = \frac{1}{2}$ (ii) $x = \frac{1}{2}(5^{12} - 1)$
(iii) $x = 4^6$, $= 4{,}096$ (iv) $x = 25$ (v) $x = -\frac{1}{2}$
15. (i) $x = 0$ OR $x = 5$ (ii) $x \approx 8.34$ (iii) $x \approx 7.03 \times 10^{16}$
(iv) $x \approx 1.53$ **16.** (i) $x = 2.32$ OR $x = 1.58$ (ii) $x = 1.00$
(iii) $x = 0.70$ (iv) $x = 0.18$ (v) $x = -1.00$ **17.** $x = 1$
18. (i) $x = 0.77$ OR $x = 0.63$ (ii) $x = -0.25$ (iii) $x = 0.58$
(iv) $x = 0.39$ OR $x = 0.90$ (v) $x = 0.30$ **19.** (i) $x = 1$
(ii) $x = e^2$ (iii) $x = -1$ (iv) $x = \frac{1}{3}$ **20.** (i) $x = 5$ (ii) $x = 4$
(iii) $x = 2$ (iv) $x = \sqrt{\frac{e}{7}}$ **21.** (i) $x = \frac{1}{2}\ln 3 = \ln\sqrt{3}$ (ii) $x = \frac{1}{3}e^2$
(iii) $x = e^{-5}$ (iv) $x = \frac{1}{7e^5}$ **22.** (i) $x = 2$ (ii) $x = \frac{7}{11}$
(iii) $x = 0$ (iv) $x \approx -0.34$

Exercise 7.5

1. (i) 600   (ii) 1,884   (iii) 20 minutes   **2.** (i) 136,000
(ii) 140,142   (iii) 19.63 years   **3.** (i) $a = 30$, $b = -\frac{1}{8}\log_e 2$
(ii) 5.30 g   (iii) 34.65 days   **4.** (ii) 0.6977 m   (iii) 5,776 years
5. (ii) €8,998.91   (iii) 17.67 years   **6.** (i) 4.8, an acid
(ii) 8.9, a base   (iii) 6.3×10^{-9} moles per litre   **7.** (i) 7.9
(ii) 1.0×10^{-7} moles per litre   **8.** Yes   **9.** (i) 14 years and
2 months   (ii) 10 years and 3 months   (iii) 7 years and
3 months   **10.** 12 years

Revision Exercises

1. (i) 5^{11} (ii) 3^6 (iii) 16^4 (iv) 7^{-5} (v) $17^{\frac{3}{5}}$ (vi) $5^{\frac{1}{2}}$
2. (i) a^{10} (ii) a^{24} (iii) $a^{\frac{3}{2}}$ (iv) a^2 **3.** (i) $5(\sqrt{5} + 3\sqrt{2})$
(ii) $20\sqrt{5}$ **4.** (i) $\frac{1}{8}$ (ii) (a) 2^7 (b) $2^{\frac{1}{2}}$ (iii) $x = 2\frac{3}{4}$ **5.** (i) $4a^4$, 2^6
(ii) $2^{\frac{9}{4}}$ (iii) $9a^5$, 3^7 (iv) 3^{11} **6.** (i) $\frac{5}{2}\sqrt{2}$ (ii) $2\sqrt{3}$ (iii) $\frac{1}{6}\sqrt{6}$
(iv) $-7 - 3\sqrt{6}$ (v) $\frac{1}{4} - \frac{1}{20}\sqrt{10}$ (vi) $2 - \frac{1}{2}\sqrt{14}$
(vii) $-\sqrt{15} - 2\sqrt{5}$ (viii) $\frac{7}{2} + \frac{1}{2}\sqrt{35}$ **7.** (i) $x = 6$ (ii) $x = 2$
(iii) $x = \frac{19}{4}$ (iv) $x = \frac{3}{5}$ (v) $x = 6$ **8.** (i) $x = 81$ (ii) $x = 25$
(iii) $x = -\frac{10}{3}$ (iv) $x = 3$ **9.** (a) 13   (b) 18   **10.** (i) $x = 3$
(ii) $x = 2$ (iii) $x = 0$ (iv) $x = \log_e\left(\frac{1}{3}\right)$ OR $x = \log_e 2$
(v) $x = 9$ OR $x = -3$ **11.** (i) $x = 3$, $y = 8$ (ii) $x = 2$, $y = 2.5$
(iii) $x = 4$, $y = -1$ **13.** (i) $a = 5$ (ii) 5^x **14.** (b) 5.25 years
(c) 0.132   (d) 17.4 years   **15.** 91.7%

Exam Questions

1. (i) $A = 2.920$, $b = 0.100$ (iv) 6.93   **2.** (i) 0.7851
(ii) 8,900 years   **3.** (i) $y = 77$, $A = 77$ (ii) -0.0339
(iii) 31 minutes

Chapter 8

Exercise 8.1

1. (i) triangle   (ii) square   (iii) square   **2.** (i) green triangle
(ii) purple hexagon   (iii) yellow hexagon   (iv) hexagon,
triangle   (v) $x = 2$ (vi) Purple as we are looking for T_2, T_6,
T_{10}, i.e. every 4th tile from T_2 **4.** (i) and (ii) First rule: The
number of lines in each figure is a prime number 2, 3, 5, 7,
11, 13, ..., Second rule: It is a repeating pattern 2, 3, 5, 7, 2,
3, 5, 7, ...   **5.** (ii) n such that $n \in N$ and HCF $(n, 14) = 1$
6. (i) $(10n - 3)^2$ (ii) $T_n = (10n)^2 - 6 \times 10n + 9$

Exercise 8.2

1. (iv) 30   (v) $3 + 3n$ **2.** (iv) 28   (v) $1 + 3n$ **3.** (iv) 18
(v) $4 + 2n$ (vi) $n - 1$ **4.** (i) $-7 - 4n$ (ii) -227 **5.** (i) $7n - 7$
(ii) 588   **6.** (ii) $-5 + 8n$ (ii) 763   **7.** (i) $37 - 6n$ (ii) -89
8. 35th term   **9.** -502 **10.** (i) $B_{100} = 200$ cm, $H_{100} = 100$ cm
(ii) n^2 (iii) 210th   (iv) 2   (v) 200th   **11.** (i) arithmetic
(ii) arithmetic   (iii) not arithmetic   (iv) not arithmetic
(v) arithmetic   (vi) not arithmetic   (vii) arithmetic
(viii) arithmetic   (ix) not arithmetic   (x) arithmetic
(xi) arithmetic   **12.** (i) arithmetic   (ii) arithmetic
(iii) not arithmetic   (iv) arithmetic   (v) not arithmetic
14. (i) C (ii) Sequence A: 2, 4, 8, 16, Sequence B: 1, 4, 9, 16,
Sequence C: 5, 9, 13, 17   (iii) 4   **15.** (i) $d_A = 6$, $d_B = 2$, $d_C = 3$
(ii) $m_A = 6$, $m_B = 2$, $m_C = 3$ **16.** (i) 7   (ii) -4 (iii) $T_4 = 7$, $T_5 = 3$
19. 46   **20.** 21   **21.** 34   **22.** (ii) 301   (iii) 298   (iv) column A,
Row 670   **24.** (i) 95 trees   (ii) 2025   **25.** (ii) 49th day
26. (ii) 1,800   (iii) 101

Exercise 8.3

1. (i) 1,425   (ii) 2,265   (iii) 2,895   (iv) 180   (v) 165
(vi) 2,115   (vii) 4,635   (viii) $-1,155$ (ix) $-1,455$ (x) $-4,650$
2. 3,240   **3.** 900   **4.** 40 terms, 1,640   **5.** (i) 1,560   (ii) 6,320
(iii) 4,760   **6.** (i) €395   (ii) €14,850   **7.** (i) 9.25 km   (ii) 33rd
(iii) 2,744 km   **8.** (i) 10 hours   (ii) 110 cm   **9.** (i) $d = -3$, $a = 21$
(ii) 3 terms or less **OR** 12 terms or more   **10.** 9   **11.** (i) 228
(ii) 34%   **16.** 4, $2n - 4$

Exercise 8.4

1. (iv) 28   (v) $0.5n^2 + 0.5n$ **2.** (iv) 64   (v) $n^2 + 2n + 1$
3. (i) quadratic   (ii) quadratic   (iii) quadratic
(iv) arithmetic   (v) quadratic   (vi) arithmetic   **4.** (i) (a) $a = 8$
(c) 56, 78, 104   (ii) (a) 1   (c) 15, 21, 28   (iii) (a) 15
(c) 95, 135, 183   (iv) (a) 5   (c) $-25, -43, -65$ (v) (a) 10
(c) 10, 19, 31   **5.** (i) $n^2 + n + 1$ (ii) $n^2 - n + 1$ (iii) $n^2 + 2n + 3$
(iv) $3n^2 - 7n + 17$ **6.** (i) $4n^2 - 4n + 20$ (ii) $-n^2 + 7n + 5$
(iii) $-2n^2 + 8n + 2$ (iv) $4 + 3n - n^2$ **7.** (i) $T_1 = 8$, $T_2 = 21$,
$T_3 = 40$ (ii) $3n^2 + 4n + 1$ (iii) 7,701   (iv) not a prime number
8. (i) 3   (ii) $T_1 = a + b + c$, $T_2 = 4a + 2b + c$, $T_3 = 9a + 3b + c$
(iii) $a + b + c = 12$, $4a + 2b + c = 16$, $9a + 3b + c = 23$
(iv) $1.5n^2 - 0.5n + 11$ (v) 1,346   **9.** (i) 125, 216, 343
10. (iii) 127   **11.** (i) T_4 (ii) $T_4 = 45$, $T_5 = 66$, $T_6 = 91$
(iv) quadratic

Exercise 8.5

1. (i) 2, 2^{n-1} (ii) 2, $5(2)^{n-1}$ (iii) 3, $7(3)^{n-1}$ (iv) $\frac{1}{2}$, $\frac{1}{2^n}$
(v) $\frac{1}{2}$, 2^{6-n} (vi) -2, $3(-2)^{n-1}$ **2.** (i) 3, 9, 27, 81   (ii) 6, 12, 24, 48
(iii) 20, 200, 2,000, 20,000   (iv) 1, 5, 25, 125   (v) 2, 6, 18, 54
3. (i) 2, 4, 8, 16, 32   (ii) 2   (iii) 24   **4.** (i) geometric

---

(ii) not geometric   (iii) geometric   (iv) geometric
(v) not geometric   **5.** (i) 765   (ii) 97,656   (iii) 1,275
(iv) 6,560   (v) $\frac{255}{256}$ **6.** (i) $\frac{3}{4,096}$, 4   (ii) 16,384   **7.** (i) $\frac{1}{4}$
(ii) 287.93   (iii) 0.06   **8.** (i) $x = 2$, $y = 4$ (ii) 438   **9.** 32,769
10. $r = 2$, $a = \frac{1}{2}$ **11.** $-\frac{1}{2}$ **12.** 24.67   **13.** $\frac{8}{3}\left(1 - \frac{1}{4^n}\right)$, 3
14. 8.49   **15.** 10 years   **16.** 15 years   **17.** $r = \pm\frac{3}{\sqrt{5}}$, $T_2 = \frac{10\sqrt{5}}{3}$
OR $-\frac{10\sqrt{5}}{3}$ **18.** (i) 1.4%   (ii) 2011 = 134,025, 2016 = 143,674
(iii) 1,241,000   **19.** (i) €18.06   (ii) €17.41   **20.** (i) 42.875 mg
(ii) 12 hours   (iii) 100 mg

Exercise 8.6

1. (a) (i) 3   (ii) $\frac{4}{3}$ (iii) $\frac{5}{6}$ (iv) $-\frac{1}{3}$ (v) $\frac{13}{15}$ (b) (i) 3   (ii) 2
(iii) $\frac{5}{2}$ (iv) 3   (v) 3   **2.** (i) $\frac{2}{5}$ (ii) 4   (iii) $\frac{-13}{15}$ (iv) undefined
(v) $\frac{4}{7}$ **3.** (i) 0   (ii) 0   (iii) 3   (iv) -1 (v) $\frac{8}{5}$ **4.** (i) $\frac{7}{6}$ (ii) $\frac{17}{25}$
(iii) $\frac{1}{12}$ (iv) 12   (v) 5   **5.** (i) 6   (ii) 3   (iii) $\frac{1}{6}$ (iv) 2
6. (i) $\frac{n^2 + n}{2}$ (ii) $\frac{1}{\sqrt{6}}$

Exercise 8.7

1. (i) 1   (ii) $\frac{9}{14}$ (iii) $\frac{25}{4}$ (iv) 6   (v) $\frac{16}{21}$ **2.** (i) 2   (ii) $\frac{16}{15}$
(iii) $\frac{21}{4}$ (iv) $\frac{1}{3}$ (v) $\frac{2}{5}$ **3.** (i) $\frac{5}{3}$ (ii) 2   (iii) $\frac{2}{3}$ **4.** $\frac{1}{2}$ **5.** 8, 4, 2, 1
OR 24, -12, 6, -3 **6.** $r = \frac{2 \pm \sqrt{2}}{4}$, $a = \frac{2}{2 + \sqrt{2}}$ **OR** $a = \frac{2}{2 - \sqrt{2}}$
7. (i) 1   (ii) $\frac{1}{3}$ (iii) $\frac{16}{9}$ (iv) $\frac{28}{9}$ (v) $\frac{697}{9}$ (vi) $\frac{226}{225}$ **8.** (i) $\frac{37}{30}$
(ii) $\frac{83}{18}$ (iii) $\frac{368}{45}$ (iv) $\frac{827}{90}$ (v) $\frac{311}{90}$ (vi) $\frac{8}{11}$ **9.** (i) $\frac{826}{99}$ (ii) $\frac{4}{33}$
(iii) $\frac{68}{11}$ (iv) $\frac{38}{11}$ (v) $\frac{65}{99}$ (vi) $\frac{977}{330}$ (vii) $\frac{137}{111}$ (viii) $\frac{5,251}{999}$
(ix) $\frac{43,463}{9,990}$ (x) $\frac{67,151}{9,990}$ **10.** (i) $|x| > 1$ (ii) $\frac{-1}{2} < x < \frac{1}{2}$
(iii) $-1 - a > x > 1 - a$ **12.** (i) $0 < x < 1$ (ii) $x > \sqrt{6}$ **OR** $x < -\sqrt{6}$

Revision Exercises

1. (i) 40   (ii) $\frac{1}{4}$ (iii) $\frac{37}{64}$ **2.** (i) 1 8 28 56 70 56 28 8 1,
1 9 36 84 126 126 84 36 9 1   (ii) arithmetic sequence,
$T_n = n$ (iii) quadratic, $T_n = 0.5n^2 + 0.5n$ **3.** (i) $-4, -1, 2, 5$
(ii) $\frac{n(3n - 11)}{2}$ **5.** (i) (a) 16   (c) $0.5n^2 - 0.5n + 16$ (d) 4,966
(ii) (a) 1   (c) $0.5n^2 + 0.5n$ (d) 5,050   (iii) (a) 12
(c) $0.5n^2 + 0.5n + 11$ (d) 5,061   (iv) (a) 1   (c) $2n^2 - n$
(d) 19,900   (v) (a) 8   (c) $5 + 4n - n^2$ (d) $-9,595$
6. (i) 1, 5, 25, 125, 625   (ii) 5   (iii) $\frac{1}{4}(5^n - 1)$ (iv) $4(5^{998})$
7. (i) $(2n - 1)\log_e 3$ (ii) 18   **8.** $\frac{22}{3}$, 9, $\frac{32}{3}$ **9.** (ii) $a = 2.5$,
$b = 4.5$, $c = -6$ **10.** $a^n r^{\frac{n^2}{2}}$ **11.** (i) quadratic   (ii) $4n^2 - 3n + 2$
(iii) 3,512   **12.** (i) 2   (ii) $a + b + c$, $4a + 2b + c$, $9a + 3b + c$
(iii) $a = 1$, $b = 1$, $c = 1$, $n^2 + n + 1$ (iv) $n^2 + n + 1$ (v) 931
13. (i) 3   (ii) $\frac{4}{7}$ (iii) $\sqrt{3}$ **14.** (i) $2n^2 + 2n$ (ii) $\sqrt{\frac{2}{3}}$
15. (i) $6\left(1 - \left(\frac{5}{6}\right)^n\right)$ (ii) 6   **16.** (i) $\frac{521}{99}$ (ii) $\frac{8}{9}$ (iii) $\frac{28}{11}$ (iv) $\frac{103}{33}$

Exam Questions

1. (a) the number of interior pieces is always less than the
number of edge pieces   (c) $n = 5$, $n = 6$, $n = 8$, $n = 12$
(d) $(n - 2)(m - 4) < 2m$ **2.** (b) n^2 (c) $3n$ (d) $a = \frac{3}{2}$, $b = \frac{3}{2}$
(e) 2,704   **3.** (b) $10\frac{13}{64}$ m   (c) 14 m   **4.** $\frac{172}{33}$

Chapter 9

Exercise 9.1

2. 1.08% **3.** 1.29% **4.** 1% **5.** 2.6% **6.** (i) 0.0394 (ii) 0.8%
7. 0.001 litre. **8.** 0.001 kg. **9.** (i) 0.05 (ii) 0.5% **10.** (i) €6,554
(ii) €6,555.6 (iii) €1.6 **11.** 54 ± 0.05 cm **12.** (i) 450 ± 2.5 g
(ii) Yes

Exercise 9.2

1. (i) Direct costs are costs directly linked to the production
of a product (e.g. cost of raw materials/labour), Indirect
costs are costs not directly linked to production (e.g. factory
rent/local authority waste collection charges) (ii) Fixed
costs are costs which don't change even as production levels
vary (e.g. factory rent/standing charge with a public utility
company), Variable costs vary as production varies (e.g.
labour costs, electricity costs) **2.** (i) €67,500 (ii) €6.75
3. (i) 150 (ii) €394 (iii) €2.92 (iv) €3.50 **4.** (i) 48,000 kg
(ii) 45,000 kg (iii) Product X: 6,000 × 8 × 3 = €144,000,
Product Y: 5,000 × 9 × 3 = €135,000 (iv) €305,000
5. (i) 40 m so for 60 units = 2,400 m
(ii) 120 m so for 60 units = 7,200 m (iii) €92,400
(iv) €29.52 **6.** (i) 58,500 kg (ii) 78,000 hours
(iii) €858,000 (iv) €1,778,000 (v) €397,000 (vi) €179,500

Exercise 9.3

1. €30,900 **2.** 21% **3.** (i) €7,600 (ii) 20% **4.** €73,500
5. (i) €28,550 (ii) €65,950 **6.** €44,190 **7.** €1,218.06
8. (i) €55.38 (ii) €148.85 (iii) €3,301.96 (iv) €899.59
9. (i) €8,800 (ii) €57,450 (iii) Eoin €2,452.81,
Sorcha €1,768.06

Exercise 9.4

1. €2.16 **2.** €1,087.79 **3.** €363 **4.** €250 **5.** €1,800
6. (i) €791 (ii) €87.50 (iii) €787.50 (iv) €819

Revision Exercises

1. (i) 145,000 kg (ii) 95,000 kg (iii) 80,000 hours
(iv) €600,000 (v) €1,449,000 (vi) €776,000 (vii) €998,500
2. €14,500 **3.** (i) €34.62 (ii) €93.03 (iii) €1,768.06
(iv) €623.69 **4.** (i) €26,450 (ii) €36,700 **5.** (i) €510.75
(ii) €60.75 (iii) €506.25 (iv) €517.50

Chapter 10

Exercise 10.1

1. (i) 2,000 (ii) 1,250 (iii) 25,000 (iv) 44,000 (v) 565,000
(vi) 10,000 (vii) 150,000 (viii) 250,000 (ix) 400,000,
(x) 45,000,000 **2.** €4,999.95 **3.** €12,244.47
4. €4,829.76 **5.** (i) €18,867.92 (Year 1), €17,799.93 (Year 2),
€16,792.39 (Year 3) (ii) −€1,539.76 (iii) No **6.** Yes
7. Project A **8.** (i) Restaurant Area (ii) Amusements
Area **9.** Invest **10.** €136,486·59 **11.** €8,891·91

Exercise 10.2

1. €27,204.19 **2.** €3,104.84 **3.** €137,130.62 **4.** €16,325.87
5. €35,573.69 **6.** €10,429.21 **7.** €173,830.60 **8.** €130,877.14
9. €1,418,299.58 **10.** €8,821.33 **11.** €1,958.82 **12.** €99,749.07
13. €14,002.66 **14.** €369,600.48 **15.** (i) €56,044.36

(ii) €58,764.46 **16.** €12,000 **17.** €16,177,050 **18.** €3,934
19. (i) €18,200 (ii) €231,065.97 (iii) €16,026.40
20. The first option **21.** €9,563.09 **22.** €6,333.85 **23.** 3.09%
24. 3.23% **25.** The 10-year bond **26.** 3.58% **27.** 25.89 years
28. 3 **29.** 4 **30.** 7.57 **31.** 6.07% **32.** 1.13% **33.** The 10 year
bond **34.** 1.47% **35.** (i) 3 (ii) The loan for €16,000 (iii) 0.63%
(iv) No **36.** € 202,298.44

Exercise 10.3

1. (i) €180,000 (ii) €783,009.38 (iii) €47,494.85
(iv) €19,555.73 (v) €15,372.14 (vi) €8,223.53 (vii) €8,785.13
2. (i) 15% (ii) 3.5% (iii) 25% **3.** €9,830.40 **4.** 150,859.81 m³
5. €60,000 **6.** €979,100 **7.** 5 **8.** 4 **9.** (i) €150,663.52 (ii) 5
(iii) 2007 **10.** The vehicle is **NOT** due for a change.
11. 6 months more **12.** 18% **13.** 24.34% **14.** 87.91% **15.** not

Exercise 10.4

1. €11,265.95 **2.** €8,941.42 **3.** €9,959.35 **4.** €8,488.89
5. (a) €43,942.09 (b) €3,577.36 **6.** (a) €862.74 **7.** Yes
8. €448.13 **9.** €3,544.66 **10.** €123.87 **11.** €122,077.73
12. $€\left(\frac{200}{i}\right)$, where i is the annual interest rate (in decimal form)
13. (i) €11,485.57 (ii) €944.22 (iii) €103.57
14. €226,423.91 **15.** €56.74 **16.** (a) 0.0846836%
(b) €333,408.52 (c) €1,968.08

Revision Exercises

1. (i) €194,444.44 (ii) €126,886.57 (iii) €25,215.42
(iv) €304,003.88 (v) €352,897.24 **2.** €12,879.37
3. (a) €113,207.55 (1ˢᵗ year), €106,799.57 (2ⁿᵈ year),
€100,754.31 (3ʳᵈ year) (b) €280,761.43 (c) Yes **4.** Project B
5. (a) €1,632,062.94 (b) €37,514.69 **6.** €190,426.99
7. €98,493.86 **8.** 6.536% **9.** 1.353% **11.** (i) €132,000
(ii) 13% (iii) 3% **12.** €67,704.07 **13.** €822,800 **14.** 6
15. 10 **16.** €28,164.88 **17.** €21,926.69 **18.** €17,584.58
19. (a) 0.2263% (b) €467.38 (c) €1,932 **20.** €1,536.42
21. (ii) €1,784.31

Exam Questions

1. (a) €19,417.48 (b) $€\left(\frac{20,000}{1.03^t}\right)$ (d) (i) 0.2466%,
(ii) $€[P(1.002466)^n]$ (iii) €390.12 (iv) 619.36
2. (a) Second: $A(1.04)$, Third: $A(1.04)^2$, Fourth: $A(1.04)^3$,
26ᵗʰ: $A(1.04)^{25}$ (b) $A\left(\frac{1.04^{26}-1}{0.04}\right)$ (c) $485,199
(d) (ii) $€\left(\frac{485,199(1.04)^{n-1}}{(1.0478)^{n-1}}\right)$ (iii) $11.5 million (e) 31.3%
3. (a) (i) 0.327% (ii) €392 (b) €487 **4.** (a) (i) 4.28%
(ii) 0.367% (b) €818

Chapter 11

Exercise 11.1

1. (i) 55 (ii) 385 (iii) 2,046 (iv) 20 **2.** (i) 20 (ii) 55
(iii) 873 (iv) 322 **3.** (i) $\sum_{r=1}^{6} r^3$ (ii) $\sum_{r=n}^{r=n+5} 5$ (iii) $\sum_{r=1}^{5} 3^r$
(iv) $\sum_{r=1}^{5} 5^r$ **4.** (i) $\sum_{r=1}^{n} r$ (ii) $\sum_{r=5}^{n} r^2$ (iii) $\sum_{r=3}^{n} r!$ (iv) $\sum_{r=1}^{n} 3r$
6. (i) $7x$ (ii) $x+y$ (iii) $y-x$ (iv) $3y+2x$

Exercise 11.4

15. (ii) 5   (iii) $n \geqslant 5, n \in N$ **16.** (ii) 5   (iii) $n \geqslant 5, n \in N$

Revision Exercises

1. (i) 180   (ii) 3,528   (iii) 46,230   (iv) 2,058   **2.** (i) 210
(iii) 8,200

Exam Questions

2. (b) $5\frac{7}{33}$.

Chapter 12

Exercise 12.1

1. (i) $10i$ (ii) $9i$ (iii) $5i$ (iv) $6i$ (v) $11i$ (vi) $8i$ **2.** (i) $4\sqrt{2}$
(ii) $4\sqrt{3}$ (iii) $5\sqrt{2}$ (iv) $5\sqrt{3}$ (v) $10\sqrt{2}$ (vi) $3\sqrt{3}$ (vii) $9\sqrt{2}$
(viii) $3\sqrt{6}$ **3.** (i) $2\sqrt{2}i$ (ii) $7\sqrt{2}i$ (iii) $3\sqrt{5}i$ (iv) $10\sqrt{3}i$
(v) $2\sqrt{3}i$ (vi) $5\sqrt{5}i$ **4.** (i) $\pm 3i$ (ii) $\pm 2i$ (iii) $\pm 5i$ (iv) $\pm 7i$
(v) $\pm\sqrt{7}i$ (vi) $\pm\sqrt{17}i$ (vii) $\pm\sqrt{14}i$ (viii) $\pm\frac{3}{2}i$ **5.** (i) -1 (ii) i
(iii) i (iv) 1   (v) i (vi) $-i$ **6.** (i) 7   (ii) 5   (iii) $6i$ (iv) $-8i$
(v) $-2i$ (vi) $-47i$ (vii) 1   (viii) -6 **8.** (i) $\frac{3}{8}$ (ii) $\frac{1}{8}$

Exercise 12.2

2. T, C, H, A, I, K, O, V, S, K, Y   **5.** (i) $\sqrt{5}$ (ii) $2\sqrt{2}$
(iii) $\sqrt{10}$ (iv) $\sqrt{13}$ (v) $\sqrt{65}$ (vi) 5   (vii) $\sqrt{2}$
(viii) $\sqrt{109}$ (ix) $\sqrt{53}$ (x) $\sqrt{34}$ **6.** (i) $\sqrt{11}$ (ii) 3
(iii) 7   (iv) 4   (v) 5   (vi) 7   (vii) 6   (viii) 3   **7.** (i) ± 4
(ii) ± 5 (iii) ± 24 (iv) $\pm\sqrt{2}$ (v) 20 **OR** -21 (vi) 5 **OR** -12
8. ± 3 **9.** ± 5 **11.** $-5 + 12i, 5 - 12i, -5 - 12i$ **12.** (a) (i) $\sqrt{37}$
(ii) $2\sqrt{5}$ (iii) $\sqrt{101}$ **13.** (a) (i) $\sqrt{5}$ (ii) $\sqrt{5}$ (iii) 5

Exercise 12.3

1. (i) $7 + 4i$ (ii) $11 + 5i$ (iii) $1 + 2i$ (iv) $13 + 2i$
(v) $7 - 5i$ (vi) $-4 - 5i$ (vii) $5 - 4i$ (viii) $33 - 36i$
(ix) 6   (x) $7 - 4i$ **2.** (i) $7 - i$ (ii) $-3 + 7i$ (iii) $3 - 7i$
(iv) $4 + 6i$ (v) $15 - 12i$ (vi) $19 - 6i$ (vii) $-20 + 39i$
(viii) $2 + \frac{7}{10}i$ **3.** (i) $5 + i$ (ii) $2 + 4i$ (iii) $-4 - 2i$
(iv) $14 + 7i$ (v) $7 - i$ (vi) $-8 - 3i$

5. (ii) Stretching of factor 2, dilation by factor 2
(iii) Stretching of factor 3, dilation by factor 3
(iv) Stretching of factor 4, dilation by factor 4
(v) Stretching of factor 5, dilation by factor 5
(vi) Stretching of factor -3, dilation by factor -3
(vii) Stretching of factor -4, dilation by factor -4
(viii) Stretching of factor -5, dilation by factor -5

6. (b) (ii) Dilation by factor $\frac{1}{2}$ (iii) Dilation by factor $\frac{1}{3}$
(iv) Dilation by factor $\frac{1}{4}$ (v) Dilation by factor $\frac{1}{6}$
7. (ii) $z_1 + \omega = 3 + 4i$, $z_2 + \omega = -1 + 6i$, $z_3 + \omega = 0 + 5i$
(iv) Translation of distance $\sqrt{2}$ units in north-east
direction   **8.** (ii) $4 + i = z_1 + \omega$, $0 + 3i = z_2 + \omega$, $-2 + 4i = z_3 + \omega$
(iv) Translation of distance $\sqrt{2}$ units in south-east direction
9. (ii) $3 + 3i$ (iv) $O\, z_1 z_3 z_2$ is a parallelogram.   **14.** -4 **15.** 6
17. $\omega = 1 - \frac{1}{2}i$ **OR** $\omega = 1 + 2i$

Exercise 12.4

1. (i) $-2 - 3i$ (iii) A 90° rotation anti-clockwise about the
origin   **2.** (i) $4 + 3i$ (iii) A 90° rotation clockwise about the
origin   **3.** (i) $-3 + 2i$ (iii) A 90° rotation clockwise about the
origin   **4.** (i) $41 + 11i$ (ii) $-18 + 13i$ (iii) $-15 + 16i$ (iv) 13
(v) 25   (vi) $-12 + 6i$ (vii) 2   (viii) $30 - 5i$ (ix) 8   (x) $9 + 17i$

5. (i) $\frac{5}{8} + \frac{5}{8}i$ (ii) $\frac{37}{1,760} - \frac{43}{220}i$ (iii) $\frac{43}{150} + \frac{73}{180}i$ (iv) 88   (v) 27
6. (i) $-1 + 3i$ (iii) A 90° rotation anti-clockwise about the origin
7. (i) $0 + i, -1.5 + i, -3 + i, -1.5 + 2i, -3 + 2.5i$ (iii) 90° rotation
anti-clockwise about the origin   **8.** (i) $0 - i, 2 - i, 4 - i, 0 - 2i,$
$2 - 2i, 4 - 2i$ (iii) 90° rotation clockwise about the origin

Exercise 12.5

1. (i) $3 - 4i$ (ii) $3 + 4i$ (iii) $-3 - 4i$ (iv) $-3 + 4i$ (v) $-\frac{1}{2} - 2i$
(vi) $3 + \frac{1}{3}i$ (vii) $-\frac{1}{4} + \frac{1}{4}i$ (viii) $-\frac{1}{5} - \frac{1}{5}i$ **2.** (i) $0 - 5i$
(ii) $5 - 0i$ (iii) $0 + 5i$ (iv) $-5 - 0i$ (v) $0 - 3i$ (vi) $3 + 0i$
(vii) $0 + 3i$ (viii) $-3 + 0i$ **3.** (i) $2 + 5i$ (ii) $4 + 2i$ (iii) $\frac{5}{2} + i$
(iv) $\frac{3}{2} + \frac{5}{2}i$ **4.** (i) $3 - 10i$ (ii) $2 - 5i$ (iii) $2 - 6i$ (iv) $5 - 3i$
5. (i) $8 - 8i$ (ii) $63 - 16i$ (iii) $3 - 4i$ (iv) $5 + 12i$ (v) $8 + 8i$
(vi) $63 + 16i$ **6.** (i) $2 - i$ (ii) $\frac{5}{7} + \frac{12}{7}i$ (iii) $-6 - 9i$
(iv) $-12 - 4i$ (v) $\frac{1}{5} - \frac{1}{5}i$ (vi) $0 - \frac{11}{4}i$ **7.** (i) $3 - i$ (ii) $3 - 2i$
(iii) $1 + 3i$ (iv) $1 - 2i$ (v) $2 + i$ **8.** (i) $1 - 3i$ (ii) $3 + 3i$
(iii) $\frac{1}{2} - \frac{1}{2}i$ (iv) $2 - \frac{1}{2}i$ (v) $5 - i$ (vi) $4 - 3i$ (vii) $-\frac{9}{2} - \frac{1}{2}i$
9. (i) $a - bi$ (ii) $c + di$ (iii) $(a + c) + (d - b)i$ (iv) $(a + c) +$
$(b - d)i$ (v) $(a + c) + (d - b)i$ **10.** $-\frac{4}{5} + \frac{3}{5}i$ **11.** $\overline{\left(\frac{z_1}{z_2}\right)} = \frac{\overline{z_1}}{\overline{z_2}}$
12. (i) $2 - 3i$ (ii) $|z_1| = \sqrt{221}$, $|z_2| = \sqrt{17}$ (iii) $\left|\frac{z_1}{z_2}\right| = \frac{|z_1|}{|z_2|}$
17. (i) -1 (ii) $-i$ (iii) $3i$ (iv) $3 + 2i$ (v) $15 - 10i$ (vi) $\frac{5}{2}$

Exercise 12.6

1. $-2 \pm 3i$ **2.** (i) $-2 \pm i$ (ii) $5 \pm i$ (iii) $3 \pm 4i$ (iv) $7 \pm i$
(v) $3 \pm i$ (vi) $8 \pm 2i$ **3.** (i) $-3 - 4i$ (ii) $-2 + 4i$ **5.** $4 \pm i$
7. (i) $48 - 14i$ (ii) $-98 + 14i$ **8.** $6 \pm 2i$ **9.** $-5 \pm 3i$
10. (i) $1 \pm i$ (ii) $4 \pm 3i$ (iii) $-1 \pm 4i$ (iv) $-2 \pm 6i$
11. (i) $z^2 - 4z + 13 = 0$ (ii) $z^2 - 10z + 26 = 0$ (iii) $z^2 - 6z + 13 = 0$
(iv) $z^2 - 12z + 52 = 0$ (v) $z^2 - 16z + 65 = 0$
(vi) $z^2 + 10z + 169 = 0$ (vii) $z^2 + 6z + 73 = 0$
(viii) $z^2 + 8z + 65 = 0$ **12.** (i) $2z^2 - 2z + 1 = 0$
(ii) $9z^2 - 6z + 2 = 0$ (iii) $36z^2 - 36z + 13 = 0$
(iv) $4z^2 - 4z + 17 = 0$ (v) $64z^2 + 48z + 13 = 0$
(vi) $20z^2 + 16z + 5 = 0$ (vii) $400z^2 + 600z + 369 = 0$
(viii) $225z^2 + 270z + 181 = 0$ **13.** (i) $\pm 4i$ (ii) $\frac{3}{2} \pm 2i$
(iii) $\frac{1}{3} \pm \frac{2}{3}i$ (iv) $2 \pm 7i$ **14.** (i) $3 + 2i$ (iii) $3 - 2i$

Exercise 12.7

1. (ii) $5 - i$ **2.** (ii) $-3 + 4i$ **3.** (ii) $-1 - i$ **5.** (i) $n = 3$ (ii) $1 + 3i$
(iii) $-\frac{1}{2}$ **6.** (i) 39   (ii) $2 - 3i$ **7.** (i) $a = 2, b = -10$ (ii) 2
(iii) 10   (iv) $z - 2$ (v) $-1 \pm 2i$ **8.** (i) -20 (iii) $z^2 + 4z + 5$
(iv) $z = 4, -2 + i, -2 - i$ **9.** (i) $-1, 3$ (iii) $\pm i$
11. (i) $z_1 = 1 + \sqrt{3}\,i, z_2 = 1 - \sqrt{3}\,i$ (ii) 4
(iii) $x^3 - 4x^2 - 4x + 16 = 0$ **12.** (ii) 2   (iii) 25
(iv) $z^2 - 8z + 400 = 0$ **13.** (i) $^-z_1$ is a root also   (ii) 3   (iii) 32
(iv) $z^2 + 3z + 32 = 0$ **14.** (i) $\overline{z}_1$ is a root also   (ii) 4   (iii) 64
(iv) $z^2 - z + 4 = 0$ **15.** (i) $b_0 = -b_1 = 2b_2$
(ii) $a_2 = -7a_3$ and $a_1 = 12a_3$ and $a_0 = -10a_3$

Exercise 12.8

1. (i) $3\sqrt{2}\left(\cos\frac{\pi}{4} + i\sin\frac{\pi}{4}\right)$ (ii) $\sqrt{2}\left(\cos\frac{\pi}{4} + i\sin\frac{\pi}{4}\right)$
(iii) $4\left(\cos\frac{\pi}{3} + i\sin\frac{\pi}{3}\right)$ (iv) $2\left(\cos\frac{\pi}{6} + i\sin\frac{\pi}{6}\right)$
2. (i) $4\sqrt{2}\left(\cos\frac{3\pi}{4} + i\sin\frac{3\pi}{4}\right)$ (ii) $3\sqrt{2}\left(\cos\frac{3\pi}{4} + i\sin\frac{3\pi}{4}\right)$

(iii) $10\left(\cos\frac{2\pi}{3} + i\sin\frac{2\pi}{3}\right)$　(iv) $2\left(\cos\frac{5\pi}{6} + i\sin\frac{5\pi}{6}\right)$

3. (i) $2\left(\cos\left(-\frac{5\pi}{6}\right) + i\sin\left(-\frac{5\pi}{6}\right)\right)$

(ii) $7\sqrt{2}\left(\cos\left(-\frac{3\pi}{4}\right) + i\sin\left(-\frac{3\pi}{4}\right)\right)$

(iii) $2\left(\cos\left(-\frac{2\pi}{3}\right) + i\sin\left(-\frac{2\pi}{3}\right)\right)$　(iv) $4\left(\cos\left(-\frac{5\pi}{6}\right) + i\sin\left(-\frac{5\pi}{6}\right)\right)$

4. (i) $2\sqrt{2}\left(\cos\left(-\frac{\pi}{4}\right) + i\sin\left(-\frac{\pi}{4}\right)\right)$　(ii) $3\sqrt{2}\left(\cos\left(-\frac{\pi}{4}\right) + i\sin\left(-\frac{\pi}{4}\right)\right)$

(iii) $2\left(\cos\left(-\frac{\pi}{3}\right) + i\sin\left(-\frac{\pi}{3}\right)\right)$　(iv) $4\left(\cos\left(-\frac{\pi}{3}\right) + i\sin\left(-\frac{\pi}{3}\right)\right)$

5. (i) $2\left(\cos\frac{\pi}{3} + i\sin\frac{\pi}{3}\right)$　(ii) $2\sqrt{2}\left(\cos\frac{\pi}{4} + i\sin\frac{\pi}{4}\right)$

(iii) $\sqrt{2}\left(\cos\frac{3\pi}{4} + i\sin\frac{3\pi}{4}\right)$　(iv) $4\left(\cos\frac{11\pi}{6} + i\sin\frac{11\pi}{6}\right)$

6. (i) $1 + i$　(ii) $\frac{3}{2} + \frac{\sqrt{3}}{2}i$　(iii) $\frac{\sqrt{3}}{2} + \frac{3}{2}i$　(iv) $-1 + i$

(v) $-\frac{3}{2} - \frac{\sqrt{3}}{2}i$　(vi) $\frac{\sqrt{3}}{2} - \frac{3}{2}i$　**7.** (i) $4 + 4i$　(ii) $-3 + 0i$　(iii) $0 + 2i$

(iv) $\sqrt{3} - i$　(v) $-100 + 0i$　**8.** (i) $\frac{3\pi}{4}$　(ii) $-\frac{3\pi}{4}$　(iii) $-\frac{5\pi}{4}$

10. (i) $10\left[\cos\frac{\pi}{2} + i\sin\frac{\pi}{2}\right]$　(ii) $15\left[\cos\frac{16\pi}{63} + i\sin\frac{16\pi}{63}\right]$

(iii) $14\left[\cos\frac{3\pi}{8} + i\sin\frac{3\pi}{8}\right]$　(iv) $63\left[\cos\frac{11\pi}{24} + i\sin\frac{11\pi}{24}\right]$

(v) $27\left[\cos\frac{7\pi}{10} + i\sin\frac{7\pi}{10}\right]$　**11.** (i) $2\left[\cos\frac{\pi}{6} + i\sin\frac{\pi}{6}\right]$

(ii) $2\left[\cos\frac{\pi}{4} + i\sin\frac{\pi}{4}\right]$　(iii) $2\left[\cos\frac{\pi}{10} + i\sin\frac{\pi}{10}\right]$

(iv) $3\left[\cos\left(-\frac{\pi}{6}\right) + i\sin\left(-\frac{\pi}{6}\right)\right]$　(v) $11\left[\cos\left(-\frac{9\pi}{20}\right) + i\sin\left(-\frac{9\pi}{20}\right)\right]$

12. (i) $6\left(\cos\frac{5\pi}{24} + i\sin\frac{5\pi}{24}\right)$　(ii) $50\left(\cos\frac{3\pi}{10} + i\sin\frac{3\pi}{10}\right)$

(iii) $3\left(\cos\frac{\pi}{16} + i\sin\frac{\pi}{16}\right)$　(iv) $3\left(\cos\frac{\pi}{14} + i\sin\frac{\pi}{14}\right)$

13. (ii) $-2\sqrt{3} + 2i$　**14.** (i) $r = 4$, $\theta = \frac{\pi}{4}$　(ii) $r = \frac{18}{5}$, $\theta = -\frac{\pi}{24}$

(iii) $r = 10$, $\theta = -\frac{11\pi}{15}$　(iv) $r = 2$, $\theta = -\frac{13\pi}{24}$

15. (i) $2\left[\cos\left(-\frac{\pi}{6}\right) + i\sin\left(-\frac{\pi}{6}\right)\right]$　(ii) $2\sqrt{2}\left[\cos\frac{\pi}{4} + i\sin\frac{\pi}{4}\right]$

(iii) $\sqrt{2}\left(\cos\left(-\frac{3\pi}{4}\right) + i\sin\left(-\frac{3\pi}{4}\right)\right)$　**16.** (i) $\sqrt{2}\left(\cos\frac{\pi}{4} + i\sin\frac{\pi}{4}\right)$,

$\sqrt{2}\left(\cos\left(-\frac{\pi}{4}\right) + i\sin\left(-\frac{\pi}{4}\right)\right)$　(ii) $2\left[\cos\frac{2\pi}{3} + i\sin\frac{2\pi}{3}\right]$,

$2\left[\cos\left(-\frac{2\pi}{3}\right) + i\sin\left(-\frac{2\pi}{3}\right)\right]$　(iii) $2\left(\cos\frac{5\pi}{6} + i\sin\frac{5\pi}{6}\right)$,

$2\left(\cos\left(-\frac{5\pi}{6}\right) + i\sin\left(-\frac{5\pi}{6}\right)\right)$　(iv) $2\sqrt{2}\left(\cos\frac{\pi}{4} + i\sin\frac{\pi}{4}\right)$,

$2\sqrt{2}\left(\cos\left(-\frac{\pi}{4}\right) + i\sin\left(-\frac{\pi}{4}\right)\right)$　**17.** (i) $\frac{23\sqrt{3} - 14}{2} + \left(-\frac{23 + 14\sqrt{3}}{2}\right)i$

(iii) $\arg(z) = \frac{2\pi}{3}$, $|z| = 1$　(iv) $\cos\frac{2\pi}{3} + i\sin\frac{2\pi}{3}$

(v) an anti-clockwise, 120°　**19.** (i) $1\left(\cos\frac{\pi}{4} + i\sin\frac{\pi}{4}\right)$

(ii) $1(\cos\pi + i\sin\pi)$　(iii) $a = -\frac{1}{\sqrt{2}}$, $b = -\frac{1}{\sqrt{2}}$

Exercise 12.9

1. (i) $\frac{1}{\sqrt{2}} + \frac{1}{\sqrt{2}}i$　(ii) $\frac{1}{\sqrt{2}} + \frac{1}{\sqrt{2}}i$　(iii) $\frac{1}{2} + \frac{\sqrt{3}}{2}i$　(iv) $1 + 0i$

(v) $\frac{1}{2} - \frac{\sqrt{3}}{2}i$　(vi) $15,625 + 0i$　(vii) $-4 + 0i$　(viii) $-\frac{81}{2} + \frac{81\sqrt{3}}{2}i$

2. (i) $\frac{\pi}{6}$　(ii) 2　(iii) $2\cos\left(\frac{\pi}{6} + i\sin\frac{\pi}{6}\right)$　(iv) $512 - 512\sqrt{3}i$

3. (ii) $\arg(z) = \frac{7\pi}{4}$, $|z| = \sqrt{2}$　(iii) $\sqrt{2}\left(\cos\frac{7\pi}{4} + i\sin\frac{7\pi}{4}\right)$

(iv) $16\sqrt{2}\left(\cos\frac{7\pi}{4} + i\sin\frac{7\pi}{4}\right)$　**4.** (i) $\frac{3\pi}{4}$　(ii) $\sqrt{2}$

(iii) $\sqrt{2}\left(\cos\frac{3\pi}{4} + i\sin\frac{3\pi}{4}\right)$　(iv) $z^5 = 4\sqrt{2}\left(\cos\frac{7\pi}{4} + i\sin\frac{7\pi}{4}\right)$,

$z^9 = 16\sqrt{2}\left(\cos\frac{3\pi}{4} + i\sin\frac{3\pi}{4}\right)$　**5.** (i) $4,096 + 0i$　(ii) $256 + 0i$

(iii) $\frac{1}{2} + \frac{\sqrt{3}}{2}i$　(iv) $-\frac{1}{\sqrt{2}} + \frac{1}{\sqrt{2}}i$　(v) $1 + 0i$　(vi) $-1 + 0i$

(vii) $-8,192 - 8,192i$　(viii) $64 - 64i$　**6.** (ii) $\arg(z) = \frac{\pi}{4}$, $|z| = 1$

(iii) $\cos\frac{\pi}{4} + i\sin\frac{\pi}{4}$　(iv) $0 - i$　(v) 9　**7.** (i) $\cos 3\theta + i\sin 3\theta$

(ii) $\cos^3\theta + 3\cos^2\theta\sin\theta i - 3\cos\theta\sin^2\theta - \sin^3\theta i$

(iv) Period $= \frac{2\pi}{3}$, Range $= [-1, 1]$　**8.** (i) $B = 4A$　(ii) $\cos^4 A - 6$

$\cos^2 A\sin^2 A + \sin^4 A + 4(\cos^3 A\sin A - \cos A\sin^3 A)i$

(iv) $\frac{\pi}{8} + \frac{n\pi}{4}$　**12.** (i) $243\left[-\frac{\sqrt{3}}{2} - \frac{1}{2}i\right]$　(ii) $-512 + 512\sqrt{3}i$

(iii) $125\left(\frac{1}{\sqrt{2}} + \frac{1}{\sqrt{2}}i\right)$

Exercise 12.10

1. (ii) $\arg(\omega) = \frac{5\pi}{3}$, $|\omega| = 2$

(iii) $2\left(\cos\frac{5\pi}{3} + 2n\pi\right) + i\sin\left(\frac{5\pi}{3} + 2n\pi\right)$　(iv) Two

(v) $-\frac{\sqrt{6}}{2} + \frac{\sqrt{2}}{2}i$, $\frac{\sqrt{6}}{2} - \frac{\sqrt{2}}{2}i$　**2.** (i) $\sqrt{2} + \sqrt{2}i$, $-\sqrt{2} - \sqrt{2}i$

(ii) $-\frac{\sqrt{2}}{2} + \frac{\sqrt{6}}{2}i$, $\frac{\sqrt{2}}{2} - \frac{\sqrt{6}}{2}i$　(iii) $\frac{\sqrt{6}}{2} + \frac{\sqrt{2}}{2}i$, $-\frac{\sqrt{6}}{2} - \frac{\sqrt{2}}{2}i$

(iv) $-\frac{\sqrt{3}}{2} + \frac{1}{2}i$, $\frac{\sqrt{3}}{2} - \frac{1}{2}i$　(v) 2, $-1 + \sqrt{3}i$, $-1 - \sqrt{3}i$

(vi) $\frac{1}{2} + \frac{\sqrt{3}}{2}i$, $-1 + 10i$, $\frac{1}{2} - \frac{\sqrt{3}}{2}i$　(vii) $\sqrt{2}\left(\frac{\sqrt{3}}{2} - \frac{1}{2}i\right)$, $\sqrt{2}\left(\frac{1}{2} + \frac{\sqrt{3}}{2}i\right)$,

$\sqrt{2}\left(-\frac{\sqrt{3}}{2} + \frac{1}{2}i\right)$, $\sqrt{2}\left(-\frac{1}{2} - \frac{\sqrt{3}}{2}i\right)$　(viii) $0 + 4i$, $-2\sqrt{3} - 2i$, $2\sqrt{3} - 2i$

3. (i) $64\left(\cos\left(-\frac{\pi}{2} + 2n\pi\right) + i\sin\left(-\frac{\pi}{2} + 2n\pi\right)\right)$

(ii) $2\left[\cos\frac{\pi}{12} - i\sin\frac{\pi}{12}\right]$, $2\left[\cos\frac{\pi}{4} + i\sin\frac{\pi}{4}\right]$, $2\left[\cos\frac{7\pi}{12} + i\sin\frac{7\pi}{12}\right]$,

$2\left[\cos\frac{11\pi}{12} + i\sin\frac{11\pi}{12}\right]$, $2\left[\cos\frac{5\pi}{4} + i\sin\frac{5\pi}{4}\right]$,

$2\left[\cos\frac{19\pi}{12} + i\sin\frac{19\pi}{12}\right]$　(iv) 60°　(v) hexagon　**4.** (i) z_3 is

found by rotating z_2 120° anti-clockwise about the origin.
Or, equivalently, by finding the reflection of z_2 under an axial
symmetry in the real axis.　(ii) $z_2 = -1 + \sqrt{3}i$, $z_3 = -1 - \sqrt{3}i$

5. (i) $2^{\frac{1}{4}}$　(ii) $z_2 = 2^{\frac{1}{4}}\left(\cos\frac{7\pi}{12} + i\sin\frac{7\pi}{12}\right)$, $z_3 = 2^{\frac{1}{4}}\left(\cos\frac{13\pi}{12} + i\sin\frac{13\pi}{12}\right)$,

$z_4 = 2^{\frac{1}{4}}\left(\cos\frac{19\pi}{12} + i\sin\frac{19\pi}{12}\right)$, by rotation of preceding root 90°
anti-clockwise about the origin　**7.** (iii) Three other
roots　(v) Since $i\omega$ is the reflection of ω following a 90°
anti-clockwise rotation about the origin. Since $f(z)$ is of
degree 4, any 90° anti-clockwise rotation about the origin of
a root will yield another root since $90° = \frac{1}{4} \times 360°$.

8. $z_2 = \cos\frac{2\pi}{5} + i\sin\frac{2\pi}{5}$, $z_3 = \cos\frac{4\pi}{5} + i\sin\frac{4\pi}{5}$,

$z_4 = \cos\frac{6\pi}{5} + i\sin\frac{6\pi}{5}$, $z_5 = \cos\frac{8\pi}{5} + i\sin\frac{8\pi}{5}$, $z^5 - 1 = (z - 1)$

$(z - z_2)(z - z_3)(z - z_4)(z - z_5)$　**9.** (i) $1 + 0i$, $-\frac{1}{2} + \frac{\sqrt{3}}{2}i$, $-\frac{1}{2} - \frac{\sqrt{3}}{2}i$

(iii) 0　(iv) ω is the cube root of 1　**10.** (i) $1 + 0i$, $0 + i$,
$-1 + 0i$, $0 - i$　(iv) ω is the cube root of 1.

Revision Exercises

1. (a) (i) $-1 + 0i$　(ii) $-1 - 2i$　(iii) $3 + 6i$　(iv) $3 + 4i$
(v) $-1 + 3i$　(vi) $-1 + 3i$　(vii) $8 + 11i$　(viii) $-3 - 5i$
(d) The quadrilateral is a parallelogram.　**2.** (a) (i) $12i$
(ii) i　(iii) 1　(iv) $-i$　(v) $2 + 3i$　(b) (i) $17 - i$　(ii) $10 + 3i$
(iii) $\frac{13}{5} - \frac{9}{5}i$　**3.** (ii) $z_1 + \theta = 3 + 2i$, $z_2 + \theta = -2 + 3i$,
$z_3 + \theta = -4 + 3i$　(iv) A translation of $\sqrt{2}$ units in length in the
direction north-east　**4.** (i) $\frac{11}{37} - \frac{8}{37}i$　(ii) $|z_1| = \sqrt{5}$, $|z_2| = \sqrt{37}$
(iii) $\left|\frac{z_1}{z_2}\right| = \frac{|z_1|}{|z_2|}$　**5.** (i) $\{1, -6 \pm 5i\}$　(ii) $\{3, 1 \pm 3i\}$　(iii) $\{-2, -3 \pm 7i\}$
(iv) $\{-2, 1 \pm i\}$　**6.** (i) $-5 + 4i$　(iii) A 90° clockwise rotation
about the origin　**7.** (i) $6\left(\cos\frac{3\pi}{20} + i\sin\frac{3\pi}{20}\right)$
(ii) $30\left(\cos\frac{20\pi}{99} + i\sin\frac{20\pi}{99}\right)$　(iii) $5\left(\cos\frac{5\pi}{72} + i\sin\frac{5\pi}{72}\right)$
(iv) $2\left(\cos\frac{8\pi}{27} + i\sin\frac{8\pi}{27}\right)$　**11.** (i) $\frac{2}{\sqrt{3}}\left(\cos\frac{\pi}{3} + i\sin\frac{\pi}{3}\right)$
(ii) $-\frac{1}{2}\left(\frac{4}{3}\right)^{10} + \frac{\sqrt{3}}{2}\left(\frac{4}{3}\right)^{10} \cdot i$　**12.** (i) $2 + 2\sqrt{3}i$, -4, $2 - 2\sqrt{3}i$
(ii) $2 + i$　**OR**　$2 - 3i$

Exam Questions

1. (ii) $\pm\sqrt{3}$　(iii) $2\left(\cos\frac{2\pi}{3} + i\sin\frac{2\pi}{3}\right)$　**OR**　$2\left(\cos\frac{4\pi}{3} + i\sin\frac{4\pi}{3}\right)$

2. (a) (i) $2\left(\cos\frac{2\pi}{3} + i\sin\frac{2\pi}{3}\right)$　(ii) $\frac{\sqrt{2}}{2} + \frac{\sqrt{6}}{2}i$, $\frac{-\sqrt{2}}{2} - \frac{\sqrt{6}}{2}i$

(b) (ii) $\frac{1}{2}$　**4.** (a) $5 + i$　(b) 0

Chapter 13

Exercise 13.1

1. (i) 2 (ii) 2 **2.** (i) –1 (ii) –1 **3.** Yes, $\lim_{x\to4} f(x)$ exists as $\lim_{x\to4^-} f(x) = \lim_{x\to4^+} f(x) = 5$ **4.** Yes, $\lim_{x\to1} f(x)$ exists as $\lim_{x\to1^-} f(x) = \lim_{x\to1^+} f(x) = 0$ **5.** (i) 3 (ii) $\lim_{x\to1} H(x)$ does not exist

6. (i) 4 (ii) $\lim_{x\to0} f(x)$ does not exist **7.** (i) 83.6 (ii) 80

8. (b) (i) 0 (ii) 11.52 (iii) 11.52 **9.** (i) 7 (ii) 25 (iii) 8

(iv) 10 (v) 12 **10.** (i) $\frac{4}{3}$ (ii) $\frac{6}{7}$ (iii) $\frac{2}{15}$ (iv) $\frac{2}{5}$ (v) $\frac{3}{4}$

Exercise 13.2

1. (ii) 3 (iii) $f(x)$ is a linear function so has a constant slope
2. (ii) –6 **3.** (i) $2x$ (ii) $2x + 2$ (iii) $2x + 2$ (iv) $-2x$ (v) $2 - 2x$
(vi) $2 - 2x$ (vii) $-4x$ (viii) $-4x$ (ix) $-3 - 4x$ **4.** (i) $6x$ (ii) 6
(iii) $y = 6x - 3$ **5.** (i) $2x + 2$ (ii) $6x - y - 4 = 0$ **6.** (i) $3 - 2x$
(ii) 1 (iii) $x - y + 3 = 0$ **9.** (i) $6 - 4x$ (ii) $(-2,-19)$

Exercise 13.3

1. (i) $8x + 2$ (ii) $12x^{11} + 9$ (iii) $9x^2 + 8x - 3$ (iv) 3 (v) –2
(vi) –1 (vii) 0 (viii) 0 (ix) 0 **2.** (i) $2x - 2$ (ii) 198
3. (i) $3x^2 - 2x$ (ii) 85 **4.** (i) $96x^7 + 48x^3 + 24x$ (ii) 168
5. (i) $3ax^2 + 2bx + c$ (ii) $3a + 2b + c$ **6.** (i) $3ax^2 + 2ax$
7. (i) $px^{p-1} + 2(p-1)x^{p-2}$ **8.** (i) $qax^{q-1} + 2a(1-q)x$
9. (i) $2 - 4x$ (ii) –6 (iii) $y = -6x + 13$ (iv) $(0,13)$ **10.** (i) $2x + 2$
(ii) 2 (iii) $y = 2x + 1$ (iv) $\left(-\frac{1}{2}, 0\right)$ **11.** (i) $y = -2x + 1$
(ii) $y = 7x - 4$ (iii) $y = -5x + 9$ (iv) $y = 5x$ **12.** (i) $3x^2 + 10x + 5$
(ii) 5 (iii) $y = 5x + 1$ (iv) $\left(-\frac{1}{5}, 0\right)$ (v) $\frac{1}{10}$ units^2

13. (i) $2 + 6x - 3x^2$ (ii) 2 (iii) $y = 2x + 1$ (iv) $\left(-\frac{1}{2}, 0\right)$

(v) $\frac{1}{4}$ units^2 **15.** (3,2) **16.** (i) $\frac{1}{2\sqrt{x}}$ (ii) $\frac{1}{3\sqrt[3]{x^2}}$ (iii) $\frac{1}{4\sqrt[4]{x^3}}$

(iv) $\frac{3}{2}\sqrt{x}$ (v) $-\frac{1}{2\sqrt{x^3}}$ (vi) $-\frac{1}{3\sqrt[3]{x^4}}$ (vii) $-\frac{2}{5\sqrt[5]{x^7}}$ (viii) $\frac{1}{\sqrt{x}}$

(ix) $\frac{1}{\sqrt[3]{x^2}}$ (x) $-\frac{1}{\sqrt{x^3}}$ (xi) $\frac{1}{\sqrt[3]{x^4}}$ (xii) $\frac{2}{\sqrt[5]{x^3}}$ **17.** (i) $\frac{1}{2\sqrt{x}}$ (ii) $\frac{1}{4\sqrt[4]{x^3}}$

(iii) $-\frac{1}{5\sqrt[5]{x^4}}$ (iv) $\frac{1}{6\sqrt[6]{x^5}}$ (v) $\frac{1}{9\sqrt[9]{x^8}}$ (vi) $-\frac{5}{x^6}$ (vii) $-\frac{7}{x^8}$ (viii) $-\frac{9}{x^{10}}$

(ix) $-\frac{10}{x^{11}}$ (x) $\frac{7}{10x^{\frac{3}{10}}}$ (xi) $\frac{14}{45x^{\frac{31}{45}}}$ (xii) $\frac{1}{p}x^{\frac{1-p}{p}}$ (xiii) $-\frac{9}{x^4}$

(xiv) $-\frac{4}{x^3}$ (xv) $-\frac{3}{2\sqrt{x^3}}$ (xvi) $-\frac{2}{3\sqrt[3]{x^4}}$ (xvii) $-\frac{5}{2\sqrt{x^7}}$ **18.** (i) $3 + x$

(ii) $\frac{3\sqrt{x}}{2} + \frac{1}{2\sqrt{x}}$ (iii) $-\frac{2}{3x^{\frac{5}{3}}} - \frac{1}{2x^{\frac{3}{2}}}$ (iv) $\frac{2}{3x^{\frac{1}{3}}} - \frac{1}{3x^{\frac{4}{3}}}$ **19.** (i) 1

(ii) $2x + 1$ (iii) $2x - 1$ (iv) $3x^2 + 4x + 4$ **20.** $a = 3, b = -4$

21. $c = 4, d = -\frac{1}{2}$

Exercise 13.4

2. (i) $9(3x+1)^2$ (ii) $6x(x^2+7)^2$ (iii) $45x^2(3x^3-8)^4$
(iv) $24(8x+3)^2$ (v) $6x^2(x^3-25)$ (vi) $(6x^2-12x)(x^3-3x^2+2)$
3. (i) $14(7x+1)$ (ii) $-4(3-x)^3$ (iii) $20(4x-5)^4$ (iv) $6x(x^2+1)^2$
(v) $21(2+3x)^6$ (vi) $-54x(9-3x^2)$ **4.** (i) $\frac{x+1}{\sqrt{x^2+2x}}$

(ii) $\frac{4x+1}{2\sqrt{2x^2+x}}$ (iii) $\frac{2x+2}{3(x^2-2x+4)^{\frac{2}{3}}}$ (iv) $\frac{x+1}{2\sqrt[4]{(x^2+2x)^3}}$ (v) $\frac{x}{\sqrt{x^2-8}}$

(vi) $\frac{4x}{3\sqrt[3]{(2x^2+4)^2}}$ (vii) $\frac{x+4}{2\sqrt{(x^2+8x)^3}}$ **5.** (i) $\frac{2x+2}{5(x^2+2x+4)^{\frac{4}{5}}}$

(ii) $\frac{-(2x+2)}{(x^2+2x+1)^2}$ (iii) $\frac{6-8x}{(2x^2-3x+4)^3}$ (iv) $\frac{-(40x+12)}{(5x^2+3x+8)^5}$

(v) $-\frac{1}{(x+2)^2}$ (vi) $\frac{-2}{(x+2)^3}$ (vii) $-\frac{3}{(x+2)^4}$ (viii) $-\frac{(10x+10)}{(x^2+2x+3)^6}$

6. (i) $-18(2-6x)^2$ (ii) $\frac{4x^3}{\sqrt{2x^4-5}}$ (iii) $-\frac{2x}{(x^2+3)^2}$ (iv) $\frac{6x^2}{\sqrt{4x^3-5}}$

(v) $-\frac{1+14\sqrt{x}}{2\sqrt{x}(\sqrt{x}+7x)^2}$ **7.** (i) $\frac{6x}{(8-x^2)^{\frac{3}{2}}}$ (ii) $\frac{3x^2+6}{(x^3+6x)^{\frac{4}{3}}}$ (iii) $\frac{3x}{2(2+x^2)^{\frac{1}{4}}}$

(iv) $\frac{6x}{(4-x^2)^4}$ (v) $-\frac{7x^6}{2(x^7-6)^{\frac{3}{2}}}$ **8.** (i) $-\frac{1}{8\sqrt{x}(6-\sqrt{x})^{\frac{3}{4}}}$ (ii) $-\frac{1}{2x^2\sqrt{1+\frac{1}{x}}}$

(iii) $\frac{2(x^4-1)}{3x^3\left(x^2+\frac{1}{x^2}\right)^{\frac{2}{3}}}$ (iv) $-\frac{x+2}{2x^2\sqrt{x+1}}$ (v) $-\frac{(2x+7)}{(x^2+7x)^{\frac{3}{2}}}$

(vi) $\frac{4x-3}{\sqrt{4x^2-6x+9}}$ **9.** (i) 2 (ii) $y = 2x - 1$ (iii) x-intercept: $\left(\frac{1}{2}, 0\right)$,
y intercept: $(0, -1)$ (iv) $\frac{1}{4}$ units^2 **10.** (i) $\frac{15}{32}$

(ii) $15x - 32y + 34 = 0$ **11.** (i) $y = -10x + 11$ (ii) 1

(iii) $y = -10x + 1$ (iv) $\frac{10\sqrt{101}}{101}$ units (v) 6 units^2

12. –0.32 **13.** $\frac{25}{4}$ **14.** (i) –1 (ii) 1 (iii) –1.6875

Exercise 13.5

1. (i) (a) $15x^{14}$ (ii) (a) $15x^{14}$ (iii) (a) $24x - 7$ (iv) (a) $2x$

(v) (a) $5x^4 + 10x$ **2.** (i) (a) $10x^{\frac{3}{2}} + 6x$ (ii) (a) $\frac{35}{2}x^{\frac{5}{2}} + 9x^2$

(iii) (a) $18x^2 - 10x + 4$ (iv) (a) $\frac{9}{2}x^{\frac{1}{2}} + x^{-\frac{1}{2}} + 7$

(v) (a) $3x^{\frac{1}{2}} + \frac{17}{2}x^{-\frac{1}{2}} + 11$ **3.** (i) (a) $6x^5$ (ii) (a) 1 (iii) (a) $12x^3 + 1$

(iv) (a) 1 (v) (a) $15x^4 - 1$ (vi) (a) $2x - 3$ **4.** (i) $30x + 11$

(ii) $15x^2 - 4x - 5$ (iii) $-4x^3 - 15x^2 - 4x + 5$ (iv) $3\sqrt{x} + \frac{2}{\sqrt{x}}$

5. (i) $\frac{1}{(7x+2)^2}$ (ii) $-\frac{13}{(9x+1)^2}$ (iii) $\frac{1-x^2}{(x^2+1)^2}$ (iv) $\frac{-2(x^2+x+5)}{(x^2-5)^2}$

(v) $-\frac{1}{(x+2)^2}$ **6.** 16 **7.** 142 **8.** $\frac{4}{9}$ **9.** $-\frac{7}{9}$

10. (i) $40x^3 - 21x^2 - 26x + 13$ (ii) 5.8125

(iii) $y = 5.8125x - 2.0859375$ **11.** (i) 5 (ii) 5 (iii) $y = 5x$

12. (i) $\frac{3}{2}\left(\sqrt{x} + \frac{1}{\sqrt{x}}\right)$ (ii) $\frac{x^{\frac{5}{2}} + 9x^{\frac{3}{2}} + 3\sqrt{x} + \frac{3}{\sqrt{x}}}{2x(x+3)^2}$ (iii) $\frac{1}{2}$

13. (i) $15x^4 - 68x^3 + 93x^2 - 42x$ (ii) $\frac{3}{8}$

14. (i) $(90x^2 - 20x)(3x^3 - x^2)^9$ (ii) $\frac{-84x^4 + 18x^3 - 360x^2 + 80x}{(3x^3 - x^2)^{11}}$

Exercise 13.6

1. (i) $\cos x - \sin x$ (ii) $-3\sin\theta$ (iii) $\cos\theta$ (iv) $4\cos\theta$
(v) $-2\sin x - 3\cos x$ (vi) $3\sec^2\theta$ **2.** (i) 0 (ii) 1 (iii) 0
(iv) $-\sqrt{2}$ (v) 1 **3.** $y = -\theta + \left(3 + \frac{\pi}{2}\right)$ **4.** (i) $x\cos x + \sin x$

(ii) $\cos x - x\sin x$ (iii) $x(x\sec^2 x + 2\tan x)$
(iv) $(x^2+1)\cos x + 2x\sin x$ (v) $3x^2\cos x - (x^3+1)\sin x$
(vi) $\cos 2x$ (vii) $\tan x\sec x + \sin x$ (viii) $\sec x - \sin x\tan x$
(ix) $\cos 2x - x\sin x + \cos x$ **5.** (i) $\frac{2(\sin x - x\cos x)}{\sin^2 x}$ (ii) $\frac{\cos x + x\sin x}{\cos^2 x}$

(iii) $\frac{\tan x - x\sec^2 x}{\tan^2 x}$ (iv) $\frac{2x\sin x - (x^2+1)\cos x}{\sin^2 x}$

(v) $-\frac{[(x+1)\sin x + \cos x]}{(x+1)^2}$ (vi) $\frac{(x^2+1)\sec^2 x - 2x\tan x}{(x^2+1)^2}$

(vii) $\frac{\tan x(\sec x - \cos x)}{\sin^2 x}$ (viii) $\sec^2 x$ (ix) $\frac{-(\sin x\tan x + \sec x)}{\tan^2 x}$

6. (i) $2[\cos x - x\sin x]$ (ii) $x(x\cos x + 2\sin x)$

(iii) $x\sec^2 x + \tan x$ (iv) $\frac{\sin x - x\cos x}{\sin^2 x}$ (v) $\frac{4(\cos x + x\sin x)}{\cos^2 x}$

7. (i) $3\cos 3x$ (ii) $-4\sin 4x$ (iii) $5\sec^2 5x$ (iv) $3\cos(3x+4)$
(v) $-8\sin(8x-2)$ (vi) $3\sec^2(3x+4)$ (vii) $10\cos 5x$
(viii) $-12\sin 4x$ **8.** (i) $5\cos 5x$ (ii) $-9\sin 3x$ (iii) $35\sec^2 5x$
(iv) $6\cos 3x - 10\sin 2x$ (v) $2\sec^2 2x + 3\sec^2 3x$

9. (i) $3\sin^2 x \cos x$ (ii) $-\sin 2x$ (iii) $4\tan^3 x \sec^2 x$
(iv) $5\sin^4 x \cos x$ (v) $-6\cos^5 x \sin x$ (vi) $7\tan^6 x \sec^2 x$
10. (i) $6\sin^2 2x \cos 2x$ (ii) $-3\cos 6x$ (iii) $20\tan^3 5x \sec^2 5x$
(iv) $15\sin^4 3x \cos 3x$ (v) $-24\cos^5 4x \sin 4x$
(vi) $16\tan^7 2x \sec^2 2x$ **11.** (i) $2\sin x \cos x$ (ii) $2\tan x \sec^2 x$
(iii) $-15\cos^2 5x \sin 5x$ (iv) $2\sin 4x - 3\sin 6x$
(v) $12\tan^3 3x \sec^2 3x + 20\tan^4 4x \sec^2 4x$ **12.** (i) $\cos x - x \sin x$
(ii) $y = \left(\frac{3\pi}{2}x\right) - \left(\frac{3\pi}{2}\right)^2$ **13.** (i) $\sec x \tan x$ (ii) $\cot x \operatorname{cosec} x$
(iii) $-\operatorname{cosec}^2 x$ **14.** (ii) $y = -\frac{1}{\sqrt{2}}x + \frac{1}{\sqrt{2}}\left(\frac{11\pi}{8} + \frac{1}{2}\right)$
(iii) $y = \frac{1}{2\sqrt{2}}\left(1 - \frac{11\pi}{4}\right)x + \frac{(11\pi)^2}{64\sqrt{2}}$ **15.** (i) $\cos 3\theta + 3\cos\theta$
(ii) $a = 4$ and $b = 3$ **16.** $\cos 2\theta$

Exercise 13.7

1. (i) $\frac{1}{\sqrt{9-x^2}}$ (ii) $-\frac{1}{\sqrt{16-x^2}}$ (iii) $\frac{5}{25+x^2}$
(iv) $\frac{1}{\sqrt{49-x^2}} + \frac{1}{\sqrt{81-x^2}}$ (v) $\frac{1}{\sqrt{64-x^2}} - \frac{1}{\sqrt{121-x^2}}$
2. (i) $\frac{2x}{\sqrt{16-x^2}} + 2\sin^{-1}\frac{x}{4}$ (ii) $\cos^{-1}\frac{x}{3} - \frac{x}{\sqrt{9-x^2}}$
(iii) $\frac{8x}{16+x^2} + 2\tan^{-1}\frac{x}{4}$ (iv) $\frac{x+2}{\sqrt{9-x^2}} + \sin^{-1}\frac{x}{3}$
(v) $(2x+2)\cos^{-1}\frac{x}{5} - \frac{x^2+2x}{\sqrt{25-x^2}}$ (vi) $\frac{3x^3}{9+x^2} + 3x^2\tan^{-1}\frac{x}{3}$
3. (i) $\frac{\sqrt{4-x^2}\sin^{-1}\frac{x}{2} - x}{\sqrt{4-x^2}\left(\sin^{-1}\frac{x}{2}\right)^2}$ (ii) $\frac{x^2 + 2x\sqrt{9-x^2}\cos^{-1}\frac{x}{3}}{\sqrt{9-x^2}\left(\cos^{-1}\frac{x}{3}\right)^2}$
(iii) $\frac{(16+x^2)\tan^{-1}\frac{x}{4} - 4x}{(16+x^2)\left(\tan^{-1}\frac{x}{4}\right)^2}$ (iv) $\frac{3x^2\sqrt{(9-x^2)}\frac{\sin^{-1}x}{3} - x^3}{\sqrt{(9-x^2)\left(\sin^{-1}\frac{x}{3}\right)^2}}$
(v) $\frac{(x+1) - \sqrt{4-x^2}\sin^{-1}\frac{x}{2}}{\sqrt{4-x^2}(x+1)^2}$ (vi) $\frac{3x - 3(9+x^2)\tan^{-1}\frac{x}{3}}{x^4(9+x^2)}$
4. (i) $\frac{x}{\sqrt{1-x^2}} + \sin^{-1}x$ (ii) $-\frac{x+4}{\sqrt{9-x^2}} + \cos^{-1}\frac{x}{3}$
(iii) $\frac{4(x^3+1)}{x(16+x^2)} + \frac{2x^3-1}{x^2}\cdot\tan^{-1}\frac{x}{4}$ (iv) $\frac{1}{x\sqrt{4-x^2}} - \frac{1}{x^2}\cdot\sin^{-1}\frac{x}{2}$
5. (i) $\frac{1}{x^2\sqrt{1-x^2}} - \frac{2\sin^{-1}x}{x^3}$ (ii) $-\frac{1}{(x-1)\sqrt{4-x^2}} - \frac{\cos^{-1}\frac{x}{2}}{(x-1)^2}$
(iii) $\frac{1}{(x^4-1)(1+x^2)} - \frac{4x^3\tan^{-1}x}{(x^4-1)^2}$ (iv) $-\frac{1}{(x^2+1)\sqrt{9-x^2}} - \frac{2x\cos^{-1}\frac{x}{3}}{(x^2+1)^2}$
6. (i) $\frac{4}{\sqrt{1-16x^2}}$ (ii) $\frac{5}{\sqrt{1-25x^2}}$ (iii) $\frac{2x}{\sqrt{1-x^4}}$ (iv) $\frac{2x}{\sqrt{1-(x^2+1)^2}}$
(v) $\frac{2}{1+4x^2}$ (vi) $\frac{3x^2}{1+x^6}$ (vii) $-\frac{3x^2}{\sqrt{1-(x^3+3)^2}}$
(viii) $-\frac{2}{x\sqrt{x^2-4}}$ **7.** (i) $\frac{2}{\sqrt{1-4x^2}}$ (ii) $\frac{3x^2}{\sqrt{1-x^6}}$ (iii) $\frac{2}{1+(2x-\pi)^2}$
(iv) $-\frac{5}{\sqrt{1-\left(5x+\frac{\pi}{2}\right)^2}}$ **8.** (i) $\frac{4\sqrt{455}}{455}$ (ii) $\frac{75}{34}$ (iii) $-\frac{8\sqrt{7}}{7}$
(iv) $-\frac{3\sqrt{5}}{10}$ **9.** (i) $\frac{1}{\sqrt{x}(1+x)}$ (ii) $y = \frac{1}{2}x - \frac{1}{2}(1-\pi)$
10. (i) $\frac{3}{\sqrt{1-(3x-1)^2}}$ (ii) $y = 4.2x - 1.2$ **11.** (i) $\frac{\pi}{3}$
(ii) $\frac{1}{\sqrt{1-\left(x+\frac{\sqrt{3}}{2}\right)^2}}$ (iii) 2 (iv) $y = 2x + \frac{\pi}{3}$ **12.** $y = \frac{\pi}{4}$
14. (i) $[-9, -7]$ (ii) $[1, 2]$ (iii) $[0, 1]$ (iv) $(-\infty, -1] \cup [1, \infty)$
15. (i) $\tan^{-1}\left(\frac{x}{1+x}\right)$ (ii) $\frac{1}{(1+x)^2}$ **16.** (ii) $-\frac{1}{x\sqrt{x^2-1}}$
(iii) $-\frac{1}{x^2\sqrt{x^2-1}} - \frac{1}{x^2}\sin^{-1}\frac{1}{x}$ **17.** (i) $f'(x) = -\frac{2}{4+x^2}$,
$g'(x) = -\frac{2}{4+x^2}$ (iii) $\frac{\pi}{2}$

Exercise 13.8

1. (i) $2e^{2x}$ (ii) $5e^{5x}$ (iii) $4e^{4x}$ (iv) $-2e^{-2x}$ (v) $-e^{\cos x}\cdot\sin x$
(vi) $5e^{5x-4}$ (vii) $2(x+1)e^{(x+1)^2}$ (viii) $\sec^2 x\cdot e^{\tan x}$
2. (i) $\frac{3}{3x+2}$ (ii) $\frac{2x}{x^2-8}$ (iii) $\frac{4}{4x-5}$ (iv) $\cot x$ (v) $\frac{4x^3}{x^4-5}$
(vi) $\frac{2}{x-1}$ (vii) $\frac{2}{\sin 2x}$ (viii) $-\frac{4}{1-4x}$ (ix) $-\frac{3x^2}{3-x^3}$ (x) $\frac{1}{x}$
3. (i) $1 + \ln x$ (ii) $e^{2x}(1+2x)$ (iii) $x^2(1+3\ln x)$
(iv) $x(x+2)e^x$ (v) $x^3(3x+4)e^{3x}$ (vi) $3x^2$ **4.** (i) $\frac{(2x-1)e^{2x}}{x^2}$
(ii) $\frac{2(1-x\ln x)}{xe^x}$ (iii) $\frac{e^x - 3e^{2x}}{e^x+1}$ (iv) 0 (v) $\frac{e^{x^2}(2x^2-3)}{x^4}$ (vi) $\frac{1-x}{e^x}$
5. (i) $-\frac{1}{x}$ (ii) $\frac{1}{5x}$ (iii) $\frac{3}{x+3}$ (iv) $\frac{3}{3x+2} - \frac{2}{2x-3}$
(v) $\frac{5}{2(5x+2)}$ (vi) 5 **6.** (i) $3^x\cdot\ln 3$ (ii) $2^x\cdot\ln 8$ (iii) $\frac{4^x\ln 4}{8}$
(iv) $\frac{5^x\ln 5}{2}$ (v) $\left(\frac{7}{8}\right)^x\ln\left(\frac{7}{8}\right)$ (vi) $15^x\ln 15$ **7.** (i) $\frac{108}{155}$ (ii) 0
(iii) 0 (iv) 3 (v) $-\frac{1}{e}$ (vi) 2 **10.** 0

Exercise 13.9

1. (i) $-\frac{x}{y}$ (ii) $-\frac{x}{y}$ (iii) $-\frac{x}{y}$ (iv) $-\frac{x}{y}$ (v) $-\frac{x}{y}$ **2.** (i) $\frac{-(x+1)}{y-1}$
(ii) $\frac{-(x+2)}{y-3}$ (iii) $\frac{1-2x}{2y-4}$ (iv) $\frac{-(5x+1)}{(5y-1)}$ (v) $\frac{-(7x+1)}{7y-1}$
3. (i) $\frac{3-x}{y+2}$ (ii) $\frac{8-x}{y-2}$ (iii) $\frac{-(x+3)}{(y-9)}$ (iv) $\frac{5-x}{y+3}$ (v) $\frac{7-x}{y+6}$
4. $-\frac{3}{4}$ **5.** $\frac{2}{3}$ **6.** $2x - y - 9 = 0$ **7.** (i) 2 (ii) $2x - y - 3 = 0$
(iii) $(0,-3)$ **8.** (i) 1 (ii) $x - y + 2 = 0$ (iv) $E(7,9)$ (vi) $11°$

Revision Exercises

1. $\lim\limits_{x\to4^-} f(x) = 22$ and $\lim\limits_{x\to4^+} f(x) = 22$, $\lim\limits_{x\to4} f(x)$ exists **2.** (i) 6
(ii) 4 (iii) does not exist **3.** (i) 42 (ii) $\frac{1}{5}$ (iii) 6 (iv) -3
4. (i) continuous (ii) continuous (iii) not continuous
(iv) not continuous **5.** (i) 2 (ii) $2x$ (iii) $-2x$ (iv) $4x + 3$
(v) $-3 - 10x$ **6.** (i) $2x - 3$ (ii) 1 (iii) $y = x - 4$ **7.** (i) $4x + 12$
(ii) $30x + 10$ (iii) $4x^3 - 19$ (iv) $21x^6 - 24x - 4$ (v) $12x^2$
8. $y = 5.75x - 25$ **9.** (i) $12x + 2$ (ii) $9x^2 - 4x - 16$
(iii) $15x^2 + 4x - 11$ (iv) $4x^3 - 3x^2 - 1$ **10.** (i) $\frac{9}{(x+8)^2}$
(ii) $\frac{x^2+18x+1}{(x+9)^2}$ (iii) $\frac{-12x}{(x^2-2)^2}$ (iv) 1 **11.** (i) $10(x+2)^9$
(ii) $\frac{x}{\sqrt{x^2+2}}$ (iii) $\frac{3x^2}{\sqrt{(x^3+1)}}$ (iv) $\frac{x}{2\sqrt[4]{x^2-8^3}}$ **12.** (i) $24x + 18$
(ii) $\frac{9}{(5x+2)^2}$ (iii) $\frac{21(x-4)^2}{(x+3)^4}$ (iv) $9x^2 - 4x - 15$
13. (i) $\cos x$ (ii) $-\sin x$ (iii) $\sec^2 x$ (iv) $2\cos x$
14. (i) $2x(2\cos x - x\sin x)$ (ii) $2x\sin x + (x^2+1)(\cos x)$
(iii) $2\cos 2x$ (iv) $\frac{\cos x + x\sin x}{\cos^2 x}$ **15.** (i) 0 (ii) 0 (iii) 0
(iv) 0 **16.** (i) $\frac{9\sqrt{x}}{2} - \frac{11}{2\sqrt{x}}$ (ii) $-\frac{2}{(2x-3)^2}$ (iii) $\frac{2t-1}{5(t^2-t+1)^{\frac{4}{5}}}$
(iv) $\frac{2}{(x^2+1)^{\frac{3}{2}}}$ **17.** (i) $10e^{10x}$ (ii) $18xe^{9x^2-4}$
(iii) $(45x^2 - 6x)e^{15x^3-3x^2}$ (iv) $\frac{1}{x}$ (v) $\frac{6x+4}{3x^2+4x-2}$
(vi) $\frac{3x-16}{x(x-8)}$ **18.** (i) $\frac{1}{\sqrt{81-x^2}}$ (ii) $-\frac{1}{\sqrt{25-x^2}}$ (iii) $\frac{15}{225+x^2}$

(iv) $\frac{2}{\sqrt{1-4x^2}}$ (v) $\frac{-7}{\sqrt{1-49x^2}}$ (vi) $\frac{9}{1+81x^2}$

19. (i) $\frac{3}{3x+1} - \frac{2}{2x-5}$ (ii) $\frac{-17}{80}$ **20.** (i) 4.0000

(ii) −1.5271 (iii) 0 (iv) −0.05 **21.** (i) $\frac{2}{1+\cos 2\theta}$

22. (i) $x^2 + y^2 - 6x - 6y + 13 = 0$ (ii) $\frac{-2x+6}{2y-6}$

(iii) 2 (iv) 0 (v) $D\left(\frac{11+\sqrt{5}}{2}, 3+\sqrt{5}\right)$ (vi) $r = \sqrt{5}$, 8.09 units^2

23. (ii) $-\frac{1}{\sqrt{3}}$ (v) 17.26 units^2

Exam Questions

1. (a) 4 (b) (2,1), (−6,3)

Chapter 14

Exercise 14.1

1. (i) 2 (ii) 2 (iii) $6x - 6$ (iv) $4e^{2x}$ (v) $16e^{4x+2}$ (vi) $-\cos x$
(vii) $-3\sin x$ (viii) $2\cos x$ (ix) $2 + 4e^{2x} - \cos x$
(x) $2 + 4e^{2x-3} - 3\sin x$ **2.** (i) 2 (ii) 6 (iii) 2 (iv) $6x - 6$
(v) $18x + 12$ (vi) $6x + 4$ **3.** (i) $\frac{6}{(x+2)^3}$ (ii) $\frac{4}{(x+4)^3}$ (iii) $\frac{-6}{(x-2)^3}$

(iv) $\frac{10}{(x+5)^3}$ (v) $\frac{-6}{(x+2)^3}$ (vi) $\frac{64x^2 - 16(x^2-3)}{(x^2-3)^3}$ **4.** (i) $\frac{-1}{(x+5)^2}$

(ii) $\frac{-9}{(3x-2)^2}$ (iii) $\frac{-25}{(5x+4)^2}$ (iv) $\frac{-4}{(2x+3)^2}$ (v) $\frac{2x^2+8}{(-x^2+4)^2}$

(vi) $\frac{-2x^2-16}{(x^2-8)^2}$ **5.** (i) $-9\sin 3x$ (ii) $-9\cos 3x$ (iii) $-4\sin(2x+4)$
(iv) $-4\cos(2x-8)$ (v) $-8x^2\sin(\sqrt{2}x^2-8) + 2\sqrt{2}\cos(\sqrt{2}x^2-8)$
(vi) $-12x^2\cos(\sqrt{3}x^2-9) - 2\sqrt{3}\sin(\sqrt{3}x^2-9)$ **6.** (i) $-\sin t$
(ii) $-\frac{4x}{(4+x^2)^2}$ (iii) $\frac{4\pi}{3}$ (iv) $-\frac{1}{t^2}$ (v) $2e^x\cos x$ **11.** −3

12. (iii) $\frac{\ln 32}{60}$ **13.** (iv) $\frac{\sqrt{3}}{2}$ metres

Exercise 14.2

1. (i) (a) [0.1, 1.1] (b) (0.1, 1.1] (c) N/A (ii) (a) [0, 2]
(b) N/A (c) (0, 2) (iii) (a) $R\setminus\{2\}$ (b) N/A (c) $R\setminus\{2\}$
(iv) (a) $R\setminus\{3\}$ (b) $R\setminus\{3\}$ (c) N/A **2.** (i) (a) [−4, 3.6]
(b) [−4, −2), (2, 4] (c) (−2, 2) (ii) (a) [0.1, 2.1] (b) (0.1, 1.5)
(c) (1.5, 2.1] (iii) (a) R (b) (−∞, 0) (c) (0, ∞) (iv) (a) R
(b) $\left(\frac{5}{3}, 5\right)$ (c) $\left(-\infty, \frac{5}{3}\right)$, (5, ∞) **3.** (i) $3x^2 - 12x$ (ii) $x = 0$ or $x = 4$
(iv) $0 \leqslant x \leqslant 4$ (v) A function is decreasing on an interval if
$f'(x) \leqslant 0$ for all values of x on that interval (vi) $0 \leqslant x \leqslant 4$
4. (i) $6x - 6x^2$ (ii) $x = 0$ OR $x = 1$ (iv) $0 \leqslant x \leqslant 1$
(v) A function is increasing on an interval if $f'(x) \geqslant 0$ for all
values of x on that interval (vi) $0 \leqslant x \leqslant 1$ **5.** (i) $6x^2 - 6x - 36$
(ii) $x = -2$ OR $x = 3$ (iv) $-2 < x < 3$ (v) $x < -2$ and $x > 3$
(vi) $-2 < x < 3$ (vii) $x < -2$ and $x > 3$ **6.** (i) Increasing:
$x \leqslant -\frac{1}{3}$ OR $x \geqslant 1$ Decreasing: $-\frac{1}{3} \leqslant x \leqslant 1$ (ii) Increasing:
$x \leqslant -\frac{1}{3}$ OR $x \geqslant 1$ Decreasing: $-\frac{1}{3} \leqslant x \leqslant 1$ (iii) Increasing:
$0 \leqslant x \leqslant 1\frac{1}{3}$ Decreasing: $x \leqslant 0$ and $x \geqslant 1\frac{1}{3}$ (iv) Increasing:
$0 \leqslant x \leqslant 5\frac{1}{3}$ Decreasing: $x \leqslant 0$ OR $x \geqslant 5\frac{1}{3}$
7. (i) $f': A \to R: x \to 6x^2 - 90x + 216$ (ii) $x = 3$ OR $x = 12$
(iii) $3 < x > 12$ (iv) f is not injective You can draw a
horizontal line that cuts the graph of f more than once
8. (i) $f': B \to R: x \to 3x^2 - 10x + 3$ (ii) $\frac{1}{3} < x < 3$
(iii) $\left[0, \frac{1}{3}\right)$, (3, 5] **9.** (i) (a) (3, 9] (b) [1, 3) (ii) (a) [0, 3)
(b) (3, 5] (iii) (a) [1, 5) (b) (5, 6] (iv) (a) [1, 6] (b) N/A
10. (i) (a) (4, 7) (b) [3, 4), (7, 8] (ii) (a) [3, 5), (8, 9]
(b) (5, 8) (iii) (a) (−∞, −1), (2, ∞) (b) (−1, 2) (iv) (a) (−2, 1)
(b) (−∞, −2), (1, ∞) **12.** (i) $f': R \to R: x \to 3x^2 + 12x + 15$
$f': R \to R: x \to 3[(x+2)^2 + 1]$ (ii) f is an increasing function

Exercise 14.3

1. (i) (a) $2x + 2$ (b) $x = -1$ (c) (−1,−4) (ii) (a) $4x + 3$
(b) $x = -\frac{3}{4}$ (c) $\left(-\frac{3}{4}, -6\frac{1}{8}\right)$ (iii) (a) $2x - 1$ (b) $x = \frac{1}{2}$
(c) $\left(\frac{1}{2}, -12\frac{1}{4}\right)$ (iv) (a) $6x + 4$ (b) $x = -\frac{2}{3}$ (c) $\left(-\frac{2}{3}, -6\frac{1}{3}\right)$
(v) (a) $6x - 1$ (b) $x = \frac{1}{6}$ (c) $\left(\frac{1}{6}, -1\frac{1}{12}\right)$ **2.** (i) (a) $3x^2 - 2x - 5$
(b) $x = \frac{5}{3}$ OR $x = -1$ (c) $\left(\frac{5}{3}, 10\frac{14}{27}\right)$, (−1,20)
(ii) (a) $6x^2 - 4x - 2$ (b) $x = -\frac{1}{3}$ OR $x = 1$ (c) $\left(-\frac{1}{3}, 3\frac{10}{27}\right)$,
(−1,5) (iii) (a) $9x^2 - 4x - 5$ (b) $x = -\frac{5}{9}$ OR $x = 1$
(c) $\left(-\frac{5}{9}, -4\frac{77}{81}\right)$, (1,−11) (iv) (a) $6x^2 - 10x - 4$ (b) $x = -\frac{1}{3}$, $x = 2$
(c) $\left(-\frac{1}{3}, 9\frac{19}{27}\right)$, (2,−3) (v) (a) $3x^2 - 4x - 4$ (b) $x = -\frac{2}{3}$ OR $x = 2$
(c) $\left(-\frac{2}{3}, 2\frac{13}{27}\right)$, (2,−7) **3.** (i) (−1,−9) (ii) (−4,−4) (iii) (3,63),
(−3,−45) (iv) (1,2) **4.** (ii) −0.2 (iii) 0.2 **5.** (ii) −0.2
(iii) 0.04 (iv) give s **6.** (ii) 0.6 (iii) −0.6 **8.** (iii) (2.5,−8.25)
9. (iv) Maximum (−5,250) Minimum (5,−250) **10.** (i) 3
(iii) (3,8) **11.** (i) 5 (iii) (5,28) **12.** (i) $x = \pm 2$
(iii) A(−2,16), B(2,−16) **13.** (3,−71) Minimum,
(−2,54) Maximum **14.** (i) Minimum (−1,0),
Maximum (1,4) (ii) (−1,0), (2,0), (0,2) (iii) (0,2) (v) (−1,1)
15. (i) $\left(\frac{\pi}{3}, -0.685\right)$ Minimum, $\left(\frac{5\pi}{3}, 6.968\right)$ Maximum,
$\left(\frac{7\pi}{3}, 5.598\right)$ Minimum (ii) 9.4 (iii) ≈ 9.425 **16.** (ii) $\left(\frac{1}{e}, -\frac{1}{e}\right)$ is
Minimum **17.** A **18.** D **19.** (ii) Maximum at $x = 0$,
Minimum at $x = 8$, Point of inflection at $x = 4$
(iii) minimum points (0,0) and $\left(\frac{2b}{3a}, \frac{-4b^3}{27a^2}\right)$,
point of inflection $\left(\frac{b}{3a}, \frac{-2b^2}{27a^2}\right)$ (iv) $a = 1$, $b = 12$
(v) (0,0) Maximum, (4,−128) Point of inflection,
(8,−256) Minimum **20.** (ii) local minimum
22. (i) $f'(x) = 2xe^{x^2}$, $f''(x) = 2e^{x^2}(1 + 2x^2)$ (ii) (0,1)
(iii) local minimum **23.** (iii) $\pi^e < e^\pi$

Exercise 14.4

1. (i) $50 - x$ (ii) $50x - x^2$ (iii) 25 m (iv) 625 cm^2
2. (i) $100 - 2x$ (ii) $100x - 2x^2$ (iii) 25 m (iv) 1,250 m^2
3. (iii) $5\sqrt{2}$ (iv) $20\sqrt{2}$ m **4.** (ii) $100x - x^2$ (iii) 50 m
(iv) 31.83 m (v) 3,183 m^2 (vi) circular **5.** (ii) $150x - \frac{3}{2}x^2$
(iii) 50 m (iv) 7,500 m^2 **6.** (iii) $\frac{1}{2}x\left[4 - \frac{12}{3-x}\right]$ (iv) $-\frac{12}{(3-x)^2}$
(v) 24 units^2 **7.** (ii) $8x - 3.57x^2$ m^2 (iii) $\frac{400}{357}$ m, $\frac{400}{357}$ m
8. (i) $x + y = 64$ (ii) $y = 64 - x$ (iv) 32 (v) So the two
numbers are 32 and 32 **9.** $x = y = 50$ **10.** (i) $440x - 0.3x^2$
(ii) $-0.8x^2 + 440x - 6,000$ (iii) 275 (iv) €54,500 **11.** (i) 2 g
(ii) 2.25 g (iii) 1.9375 g **12.** (i) $1,200x - x^2$
(ii) $-3,500 + 1,180x - x^2$ (iii) 590 units (iv) €344,600
(v) €610 **13.** (i) $h = \left(\frac{1,000}{\pi r^2}\right)$ (ii) $2\pi r^2 + 2,000r^{-1}$
(iii) $r = \left(\frac{500}{\pi}\right)^{\frac{1}{3}}$ cm, $h = 2\left(\frac{500}{\pi}\right)^{\frac{1}{3}}$ cm **14.** (iv) 10 cm
15. (i) $2\sqrt{3}$ (iii) $4\sqrt{3}x - 2\sqrt{3}x^2$ cm^2 (iv) $2\sqrt{3}$ cm^2 (v) 50%

Exercise 14.5

1. (i) $f'(x)$ is the rate of change in weight with respect to the
height (of the tree) (ii) $f'(x) > 0$ (iii) kg/m
2. (i) $T(5)$ is the temperature of the bread 5 minutes out of the
oven. (ii) $T'(t) < 0$ (iii) °C/minute **3.** (i) 16 m (ii) 25 m
(iii) $2t$ ms^{-1} (iv) 8 ms^{-1} (v) 2 ms^{-2} **4.** (i) 35 m
(iii) $40 - 10t$ ms^{-1} (iv) 0 ms^{-1} (v) 4 seconds (vi) 80 m
5. (i) $-1.2t + 0.67$ (ii) −2.93 °C/day (iii) 13 hours
6. (i) $8\pi r$ (ii) 64π(cm^2 s^{-1}) **7.** (i) 3 (ii) $m = 6$, $n = 2$

(iv) 1,200 cm³/min   (v) 480 cm²/min   **8.** (i) $V = \frac{4}{3}\pi r^3$
(ii) $S = 4\pi r^2$ (iv) 576π cm³ s⁻¹   (v) 96π cm² s⁻¹   **9.** (i) 2π
(ii) $2\pi r$ (iii) $\frac{1}{r}$ (iv) 2 cm/s   **10.** (i) $\frac{dA}{dx} = 4x$, $\frac{dP}{dx} = 6$ (ii) $\left(\frac{3}{2x}\right)$,
(iii) 12 cm s⁻¹   **11.** (i) 32 m³   (ii) −10 m³ h⁻¹   (iii) 24.5 hours
12. (b) (i) $\frac{4}{\pi}$ m/min   (ii) 2 m²/min

Revision Exercises

1. (i) $f'(x) = 9x^2 + 4x + 1$, $f''(-3) = -50$ (ii) $f'(x) = 16x^3 - 6x + 1$,
$f''(-3) = 426$ (iii) $f'(x) = 35x^6 - 15x^4 + 12x^2$, $f''(-3) = -49,482$
(iv) $f'(x) = 30x^5 + 16x^3 - 6x$, $f''(-3) = 12,576$ **2.** (i) $-4\cos 2x$
(ii) $-25\sin 5x$ (iii) $16e^{4x+2}$ (iv) $\frac{-16x}{(64+x^2)^2}$ (v) $-162\cos 18x$
(vi) $\frac{-2}{(x+1)^2}$ **4.** (i) $3x^2 - 14x + 16$ (iii) $x < 2$ and $x > \frac{8}{3}$
(iv) $2 < x < \frac{8}{3}$ **5.** (ii) −0.2   (iii) 0.2   **7.** (i) $r^2 = 676 - h^2$
(ii) $\frac{1}{3}\pi(676h - h^3)$ (iii) $2,255\pi$ **8.** (iii) $3\sqrt{2}$ (iv) $108\sqrt{2}\pi$
9. (i) cm³ s⁻¹   (ii) a cm   (iii) $33\frac{1}{3}\%$ (iv) $\frac{4a^3c}{27}$ cm³ s⁻¹
10. (i) 13.197 cm   (ii) 30 cm   **11.** (ii) N/m   (iii) 10 N
(iv) −2 N/m   **12.** (i) πr^2 (ii) $2\pi r$ (iii) 10   (v) 500π cm² s⁻¹
13. (i) $a(t) = 0.001190547t^2 - 0.055040784t + 7.1963$
(ii) $v(10) = 70.55$ ms⁻¹, $a(10) = 6.76$ ms⁻²
(iii) maximum 19.16 ms⁻², minimum 6.56 ms⁻²

Exam Questions

2. (a) $x = 3$ (b) $1 - \frac{1}{2\sqrt{(x+6)}}$ (c) $\left(-5\frac{1}{4}, -6\frac{1}{4}\right)$
3. (b)(i) −0.0288   (ii) 2°   (d) (ii) (x,y)
4. (a)(iii) $V(t) = (4 \times 10^6)$ (b)(i) $0.1\,\pi r^2$ cm³
(ii) 1273.3 cm/min   (d) 13 hours

Chapter 15

Exercise 15.1

1. (i) 4   (ii) $2x + 2$ (iii) $4x - 3$ (iv) $3x^2 + 4x + 5$
(v) $16x^3$ (vi) $25x^4 - 16x^3$ **3.** (i) $45x^2 + 36x + 20$ (ii) $4x$
(iii) $-\frac{5}{(x-3)^2}$ (iv) $\frac{3}{(x+4)^2}$ (v) $60(3x-2)^{19}$ (vi) $60(x-2)^{11}$
5. (i) $\cos x$ (ii) $-\sin x$ (iii) $\sec^2 t$ (iv) $\frac{1}{t}$ (v) e^x
7. (i) $-2\sin 2x$ (ii) $9\cos 3x$ (iii) $2x\,e^{x^2}$ (iv) $\frac{2}{x}$ (v) $2^x \ln 2$
9. (i) $-\frac{1}{\sqrt{16-x^2}}$ (ii) $\frac{1}{\sqrt{25-x^2}}$ (iii) $\frac{6}{36+x^2}$ (iv) $-\frac{3}{\sqrt{1-9x^2}}$
(v) $\frac{4}{1+16x^2}$ **11.** (i) $f'(x) = x^4$ (ii) $f'(x) = x^5$ (iii) $f'(x) = x^9$
(iv) $f'(x) = x^{499}$ (v) $f'(x) = x^{r-1}$ **13.** (i) $f'(x) = x^2$
(ii) $f'(x) = x^3$ (iii) $f'(x) = x$ (iv) $f'(x) = x^{\frac{1}{2}}$ (v) $f'(x) = x^{\frac{3}{2}}$
14. (i) $\frac{x^3}{3} + c$ (ii) $\frac{x^4}{4} + c$ (iii) $\frac{x^2}{2} + c$ (iv) $\frac{2x^{\frac{3}{2}}}{3} + c$ (v) $\frac{2x^{\frac{5}{2}}}{5} + c$

Exercise 15.2

1. (i) $\frac{x^3}{3} + c$ (ii) $\frac{x^4}{4} + c$ (iii) $\frac{x^2}{2} + c$ (iv) $4x + c$ **2.** (i) $\frac{x^5}{5} + c$
(ii) $\frac{x^6}{6} + c$ (iii) $\frac{x^9}{9} + c$ (iv) $\frac{x^{n+1}}{n+1} + c$ (v) $\frac{-1}{x} + c$ (vi) $\frac{-1}{3x} + c$
3. (i) $\frac{5x^3}{3} + c$ (ii) $\frac{3x^2}{2} + c$ (iii) $2x + c$ (iv) $\frac{ax^4}{4} + c$
4. (i) $\frac{x^3}{3} + x^2 + x + c$ (ii) $\frac{x^5}{5} - 6x + c$ (iii) $\frac{x^4}{4} + x + c$
(iv) $\frac{x^4}{4} + x^3 - \frac{x^2}{2} + 2x + c$ **5.** (i) $\frac{1}{6}x^6 + \frac{3}{5}x^5 + x^2 + c$
(ii) $\frac{1}{11}x^{11} + 9x + c$ (iii) $\frac{1}{9}x^9 + \frac{1}{7}x^7 + \frac{1}{5}x^5 + \frac{1}{3}x^3 + x + c$
(iv) $\frac{9}{10}x^{10} + \frac{7}{8}x^8 + \frac{5}{6}x^6 + \frac{3}{4}x^4 + \frac{1}{2}x^2 + c$ (v) $x^{100} + c$ **6.** (ii) $\frac{1}{7}x^7 + $
$\frac{1}{3}x^3 + c$ **7.** (i) $4x^4 + 20x^3 + 25x^2$ (ii) $4x^3 + 20x^2 + 25x$

(iii) $x^4 + \frac{20}{3}x^3 + \frac{25}{2}x^2 + c$ **8.** (i) $2x^6 - 2x^3 + 3x^5 - 3x^2$
(ii) $2x^4 + 3x^3 - 2x - 3$ (iii) $\frac{2}{5}x^5 + \frac{3}{4}x^4 - x^2 - 3x + c$
9. (i) $\frac{x^2}{2} + \frac{x^3}{3} + c$ (ii) $\frac{x^4}{4} + \frac{8x^3}{3} + 8x^2 + c$ (iii) $x^4 - \frac{9x^2}{4} + c$
(iv) $\frac{x^5}{5} + \frac{x^4}{4} - \frac{x^3}{3} - \frac{x^2}{2} + c$ **10.** (i) $\frac{25t^6}{6} + 6t^5 + \frac{9t^4}{4} + c$
(ii) $\frac{y^4}{4} + y^3 + \frac{3y^2}{2} + y + c$ (iii) $2x^3 + x^2 - 4x - 3$, $\frac{x^4}{2} + \frac{x^3}{3} - 2x^2 -$
$3x + c$ (iv) $\frac{x^2}{2} - x + c$ **11.** (i) $\frac{2}{3}x^{\frac{3}{2}} + c$ (ii) $\frac{1}{3}x^3 - \frac{1}{x} + c$
(iii) $\frac{2}{3}\sqrt{x^3} + 2\sqrt{x} + c$ (iv) $\frac{3}{4}\sqrt[3]{x^4} + c$ (v) $\frac{4}{5}x^{\frac{5}{4}} + c$
(vi) $\frac{1}{6}x^6 + \frac{5}{4}x^{\frac{4}{5}} + c$ **12.** (i) $2\sqrt{x^3} + c$ (ii) $8x + \frac{15}{4}\sqrt[3]{x^4} + c$
(iii) $2\sqrt{x^3} + \frac{2}{3}\sqrt{x} + c$ (iv) $\frac{5}{7}x^{\frac{7}{5}} + c$ (v) $\frac{6}{5}\sqrt{x^5} + \frac{10}{3}\sqrt{x^3} + c$
(vi) $\frac{3}{7}x^7 + \frac{1}{5}x^{\frac{5}{6}} + c$ **13.** (i) $\frac{3}{2}x^2 - \frac{2}{x} + 3$ (ii) $\frac{5}{2}$ **14.** $x^2 - 8x + 5$
15. (i) 19 ms⁻¹   (ii) 10s   (iii) $10t + \frac{3}{2}t^2$ (iv) 291.5 m
16. (i) −15 ms⁻²   (ii) $-t^3 + t^2 + 6t - 5$ (iii) −845 ms⁻¹
17. (i) $3 + 5t + 2t^2 - \frac{2t^3}{3}$ ms⁻¹, $413\frac{2}{3}$ ms⁻¹
(ii) $s(t) = 10 + 3t + \frac{5t^2}{2} + \frac{2t^3}{3} - \frac{t^4}{6}$, $20,263\frac{1}{3}$ m
18. (i) If up is the positive direction then the acceleration
of the ball is towards the earth (negative direction) and of
magnitude 9.8 ms⁻²   (ii) $16 - 9.8t$ (ms⁻¹)   (iii) 0 ms⁻¹
(iv) $\frac{80}{49}$ seconds   (v) $16t - 4.9t^2$ m   (vi) 7.294 seconds
19. (i) $y = 4x^2 - x^3$ (ii) $(0,0)$ and $(4,0)$
20. (i) $10 + 9t - 0.45t^2$ ms⁻¹   (ii) 55 ms⁻¹
(iii) $10t + 4.5t^2 - 0.15t^3$ m   (iv) 11.81 seconds
21. $y = \frac{3x^2}{2} - 5x - 1$

Exercise 15.3

1. (i) $\frac{1}{5}e^{5x} + c$ (ii) $-\frac{1}{3}e^{-3x} + c$ (iii) $\frac{1}{4}e^{4x} + c$ (iv) $6e^{\frac{x}{6}} + c$
(v) $-7e^{-\frac{x}{7}} + c$ (vi) $\frac{1}{4}e^{4x} + \frac{1}{3}e^{3x} + c$ **2.** (i) $e^a\,e^{2x}$
3. (i) $e^{x+4} + c$ (ii) $\frac{1}{2}e^{2x+5} + c$ (iii) $4e^{\frac{x}{4}+10} + c$ (iv) $e^{x-6} + c$
(v) $\frac{1}{5}e^{5x-2} + c$ (vi) $8e^{\frac{x}{8}-2} + c$ **4.** (i) $\frac{1}{2}e^{2x} + e^x + c$
(ii) $\frac{1}{5}e^{5x} - \frac{2}{3}e^{3x} + c$ (iii) $\frac{1}{2}e^{2x} + \frac{1}{2}e^{-2x} + c$ (iv) $\frac{2}{3}e^{3x} - \frac{1}{2}e^{2x} -$
$e^x + c$ **5.** (i) $e^x + e^{-x} + c$ (ii) $\frac{1}{2}e^{2x} - \frac{1}{6}e^{6x} + c$ (iii) $\frac{1}{3}e^{3x} + x + c$
(iv) $e^x - x + c$ **6.** (ii) $\frac{1}{y \ln a}$ (iv) $\frac{1}{\ln a} \cdot a^x + c$ **7.** (i) $\frac{2^x}{\ln 2} + c$
(ii) $\frac{3^x}{\ln 3} + c$ (iii) $\frac{5^x}{\ln 5} + c$ (iv) $\frac{7^x}{\ln 7} + c$ (v) $5e^{2x} + c$
(vi) $\frac{1}{3}x^3 + \frac{4^x}{\ln 4} + c$ **8.** (i) $\frac{8^x}{\ln 8} + c$ (ii) $\frac{9^x}{\ln 9} + c$ (iii) $\frac{-1}{(\ln 2)2^x} + c$
(iv) $\frac{-1}{(\ln 3)3^x} + c$ (v) $\frac{(9^{2x}-1)}{(\ln 9)9^x} + c$ (vi) $\frac{(10^{2x}-1)}{(\ln 10)10^x} + c$ (vii) $\frac{-1}{(\ln 2)2^x} + c$
(viii) $\frac{\frac{1}{2}e^{2x} + 2^x}{\ln 2} + c$ (ix) $\frac{-3}{(\ln 5)5^x} + c$ (x) $\frac{-2}{(\ln 3)3^x} - \frac{5}{(\ln 2)2^x} + c$
9. (i) $\ln x + c$ (ii) $3\ln x + c$ (iii) $-2\ln x + c$ (iv) $\frac{1}{5}\ln x + c$
(v) $\frac{1}{8}\ln x + c$ (vi) $5\ln x + c$ **10.** (i) e^t (ii) $t\,e^t$
(iii) $t\,e^t - e^t + c$ **11.** (i) $-\frac{1}{8}\cos(8x) + c$ (ii) $\frac{1}{4}\sin 4x + c$
(iii) $-\frac{1}{3}\cos 6x + c$ (iv) $\frac{5}{8}\sin(8x) + c$ (v) $-\frac{1}{6}\cos 3x + c$
(vi) $\frac{1}{80}\sin 5x + c$ **12.** (i) $-\frac{1}{3}\cos 3x - \frac{1}{2}\cos 2x + c$
(ii) $\frac{1}{5}\sin 5x + \frac{1}{3}\cos 3x + c$ (iii) $-\frac{1}{2}\cos 2x - \sin x + c$
(iv) $-\frac{2}{3}\cos 3x + 2\sin 2x + c$ (v) $-\frac{3}{2}\cos 2x - \frac{5}{3}\sin 3x + c$
(vi) $\frac{5}{4}\sin 4x + \frac{1}{4}\cos 2x + c$ **13.** (a) (i) $\cos 3x + \cos x$

(ii) $\sin 8x + \sin 2x$ (iii) $\frac{1}{2}(\cos 2x - \cos 4x)$

(iv) $\frac{1}{2}(\sin 7x - \sin 3x)$ (b) (i) $\frac{\sin 3x}{3} + \sin x + c$

(ii) $\frac{-\cos 8x}{8} - \frac{\sin 2x}{2} + c$ (iii) $\frac{\sin 2x}{4} - \frac{\sin 4x}{8} + c$

(iv) $\frac{\cos 3x}{6} - \frac{\cos 7x}{14} + c$ 14. (i) $5t - \frac{3}{2}e^{-2t} + \frac{23}{2}$

(ii) $\frac{5}{2}t^2 + \frac{3}{4}e^{-2t} + \frac{23}{2}t - \frac{3}{4}$ 15. (i) $a(0) = 12$ ms^{-2},

$a(5) = 16.999998$ ms^{-2} (ii) 17 ms^{-2} (iii) $17t + \frac{5}{3}e^{-3t} + \frac{40}{3}$

(iv) $\frac{17}{2}t^2 - \frac{5}{9}e^{-3t} + \frac{40}{3}t + \frac{5}{9}$ (v) 3,667.22 m 16. (i) $2e^{2x}$

(ii) $e^{2x} + c$ 17. (i) ae^{ax} (ii) $e^{ax} + c$ 19. (i) $P = (2 \times 10^6)e^{ct}$

(ii) $(2 \times 10^6)e^{20c}$ 20. (i) $\frac{1}{x}$ (ii) $\ln x + c$ (iii) $Q(t) = Ae^{kt}$

(iv) $2.8 \times 108 \times 0.99835e^t$ (v) 46.728 kg

Exercise 15.4

1. (i) $2\frac{1}{2}$ (ii) $170\frac{1}{3}$ (iii) $682\frac{1}{2}$ (iv) $\frac{1}{11}$ 2. (i) $-\frac{23}{12}$

(ii) $270\frac{3}{5}$ (iii) $62\frac{11}{12}$ (iv) $10,784\frac{2}{7}$ 3. (i) -3 (ii) 7,790

(iii) 2 (iv) $42\frac{2}{3}$ (v) 72 (vi) $\frac{1}{4}$ 4. (i) $x + 1$ (ii) $x + 1$

(iii) $x + 4$ (iv) $3x - 5$ (v) $x^2 + 2x + 4$ (vi) $x + 3$

5. (i) 16 (ii) 8 (iii) 20 (iv) $28\frac{1}{2}$ (v) $56\frac{2}{3}$ (vi) $4\frac{1}{2}$

6. (i) 1 (ii) -1 (iii) $\sqrt{3}$ (iv) $\frac{\sqrt{3}}{2}$ 7. (i) $e^2 - e$

(ii) $\frac{1}{3}\left(e^{12} - \frac{1}{e^3}\right)$ (iii) $\frac{1}{2}\left(1 - \frac{1}{e^{10}}\right)$ (iv) $\frac{1}{5}\left(\frac{1}{e^5} - \frac{1}{e^{25}}\right)$ 8. (i) 1

(ii) -1 (iii) $\sqrt{3}$ (iv) $\frac{1}{2}\sqrt{3}$ 9. (i) $\frac{\pi}{2}$ (ii) $\frac{\pi}{2}$ (iii) $\frac{\pi}{3}$ (iv) $\frac{\pi}{4}$

10. (i) $-7\frac{7}{15}$ (ii) $-10\frac{5}{6}$ (iii) $12\frac{2}{3}$ (iv) 6 (v) $-3\frac{1}{2}$

(vi) $\frac{e^{17}}{3}(e^3 - 1)$ 11. (i) $\ln 2$ (ii) $5\ln\left(\frac{4}{3}\right)$ (iii) 0

(iv) 0 (v) $\frac{1}{2}(e^2 - 1)$ (vi) $e(e - 1)$ 12. (i) 0 (ii) $\frac{7}{3} + \ln 2$

(iii) $\frac{e^6 + e^2 - 2}{4e^2}$ (iv) $6\frac{2}{3}$ (v) 0 (vi) $e^4 - \ln 4 - e$ 13. (i) 6

(ii) e (iii) $\frac{1}{3}\ln 2$ (iv) $\frac{3\pi}{4} + n\pi$ (v) 5 (vi) 16

Exercise 15.5

1. (a) 30.4 (b) 31.2 2. (a) 25.875 (b) 28.6875 (c) 31.5

3. (a) 55 units^2 (b) 63.125 units^2 4. (a) 0.4914 units^2

(b) 0.63 units^2 5. (a) 0.2025 (b) 19% 6. (a) 0.87328

(b) 0.763% 7. (i) $\frac{1}{4}$ (ii) $\frac{1}{6}$ (iii) $\frac{1}{8}$ (iv) $\frac{1}{n}$ 8. (i) $\frac{1}{n}$

(ii) $\frac{1}{n^2} + 3$ (iii) $\frac{1}{n^2} + 3$ (iv) $\frac{1}{n}\left(\frac{1}{n^2} + 3\right)$ (v) $\left(\frac{r-1}{n}\right)^2 + 3$

9. (v) $\frac{1}{6}\left(14 - \frac{3}{n} + \frac{1}{n^2}\right)$ 10. (v) $\frac{1}{4}\left(17 - \frac{2}{n} + \frac{1}{n^2}\right)$ 11. $22\frac{2}{3}$ units^2

12. 18 units^2 13. $\frac{\sqrt{3}}{2}$ units^2 14. 4 units^2 15. $17\frac{1}{3}$ units^2

16. (i) $p = 1, q = 8$ (ii) $3\frac{3}{4}$ units^2 (iii) $11\frac{1}{4}$ units^2

17. (i) (0,1) (iii) 1 unit^2 18. (i) 1 unit^2 (ii) $\frac{\pi}{6}$ 20. $C\left(\frac{4}{\sqrt{3}}, 32\right)$

Exercise 15.6

1. $\frac{1}{48}$ units^2 2. 4.5 units^2 3. (i) $P(3,6)$ (ii) 4.5 units^2

4. (i) $P(-2,-8)$; $Q(2,8)$ (ii) 8 units^2 5. (i) $P(2,0)$; $N(-2,0)$

(ii) 32 units^2 6. (ii) $\alpha = 0.41\dot{6}$ units^2, $\beta = 2.\dot{6}$ units^2

7. (i) $A\left(\frac{1}{2}, \frac{3}{2}\right) B\left(\frac{3}{2}, \frac{3}{2}\right)$ (ii) $\frac{1}{3}$ units^2 8. (i) $P(1,5)$, $Q\left(4, 3\frac{1}{2}\right)$

(ii) $y = -\frac{1}{2}x + \frac{11}{2}$ (iii) $17\frac{3}{4}$ units^2 9. (i) $A(2,16)$, $B\left(\frac{10}{3}, \frac{400}{27}\right)$

(ii) $N\left(\frac{10}{3}, 0\right)$ (iii) $33\frac{1}{3}$ units^2 10. $3\frac{1}{2}$ units^2 11. (i) (4,0)

(iii) $y = x - 1$ (iv) $6\frac{1}{6}$ units^2 12. (i) $y = 8x - 16$

(iii) $5\frac{1}{3}$ units^2 (iv) $\frac{64}{3}$ units^2 13. $38\frac{1}{2}$ units^2

14. (i) 41 units^2 (ii) 50 units^2 (iii) 42 units^2

15. (ii) 11.8775 units^2 (iii) 11.25 units^2 (iv) 5.6%

Exercise 15.7

1. (i) $5\frac{2}{3}$ (ii) $5\frac{5}{12}$ (iii) $5\frac{1}{3}$ 2. (i) 33 (ii) $30\frac{3}{4}$ (iii) 30

3. (i) $6\frac{2}{3}$ (ii) $-7\frac{5}{12}$ (iii) $22\frac{1}{5}$ (iv) $31\frac{1}{2}$ 4. (i) $\frac{2}{\pi}$ (ii) $2\frac{8}{15}$

(iii) $\frac{1}{4}(e^4 - 1)$ (iv) $\frac{4}{\pi}$ 5. $\frac{3 \pm \sqrt{5}}{2}$ 6. 3.634 °C 7. (i) $\frac{3m}{2} + 3$

(ii) $\frac{1}{a}[a^3 + 2a] = a^2 + 2$ (iii) $\frac{2n}{n+1}$ (iv) $\frac{e^4}{3} - \frac{e}{3} + \frac{25}{2}$ 8. 149,426

9. (i) 46.855 kmh^{-1} (ii) 247.29 m 10. (i) 70 (ii) $t = 1.1$,

76.05 (iii) $55\frac{5}{6}$ 11. (i) $6\frac{2}{3}$ (ms^{-2}) (ii) $\frac{t^3}{150} - 0.9t^2 + 25t$ (ms^{-1})

(iii) $151\frac{1}{24}$ (ms^{-1}) (iv) $\frac{t^4}{600} - 0.3t^3 + \frac{25t^2}{2}$ (v) $3,776\frac{1}{24}$

(vi) $3,776\frac{1}{24}$

Revision Exercises

1. (c) (i) $\frac{1}{3}x^3 - \frac{7}{2}x^2 + 2x + c$ (ii) $7\ln x + c$ (iii) $\frac{1}{5}e^{5x} + c$

(iv) $\frac{3}{2}x^2 + 2x + c$ (v) $-\frac{3}{2}\ln x + c$ (vi) $\frac{3}{7}e^{7x-2} + c$

2. (a) (i) $\cos 2x + c$ (ii) $\sin 2x + c$ (iii) $\frac{\sin 2x}{2} + \frac{\cos 2x}{2} + c$

(iv) $\frac{3}{2}\sin 2x - \frac{1}{2}\cos 2x + c$ (b) (i) 0 (ii) $\frac{1}{2}$ (iii) 0 3. (i) $4\frac{1}{3}$

(ii) $47\frac{5}{6}$ (iii) $877\frac{1}{2}$ (iv) $\frac{61}{66}$ 4. (a) (i) $\frac{2}{3}x^{\frac{3}{2}} + c$ (ii) $\frac{3}{4}x^{\frac{4}{3}} + c$

(iii) $2\sqrt{x} + c$ (iv) $\frac{3}{2}x^{\frac{2}{3}} + c$ (v) $\frac{2}{5}x^{\frac{5}{2}} + c$ (vi) $-\frac{2}{\sqrt{x}} + c$

(b) (i) $\frac{1}{3}e^{3x} - \frac{1}{5}e^{5x} + c$ (ii) $\frac{1}{5}e^{5x} + \frac{1}{4}e^{4x} - \frac{1}{3}e^{3x} - \frac{1}{2}e^{2x} + c$

(iii) $\frac{4}{3}x^{\frac{3}{4}} - \frac{6}{7}x^{\frac{7}{6}} + c$ (iv) $-\frac{1}{3}x + c$ (v) $\frac{1}{2}\cos 2x - \cos x + c$

(vi) $-\frac{1}{2}\sin 2x + c$ 5. (i) $e^2 - e$ (ii) $\frac{1}{5}\left(e^{20} - \frac{1}{e^5}\right)$ (iii) $\frac{1}{3}\left(-1\frac{1}{e^{15}}\right)$

(iv) $\frac{1}{2}\left(\frac{1}{e^2} - \frac{1}{e^{10}}\right)$ 6. (a) $a\cos ax, -a\sin ax, a\sec^2 ax$

(b) (i) $\frac{1}{5}$ (ii) $\frac{1}{3}$ (iii) 1 (iv) 0 7. (i) $\frac{\pi}{2}$ (ii) $\frac{\pi}{6}$ (iii) $\frac{\pi}{6}$ (iv) $\frac{3\pi}{16}$

8. (i) $\frac{2}{5\pi}$ (ii) $\frac{74\sqrt{2}}{21}$ (iii) $\frac{1}{3}(e^4 - e)$ (iv) $\frac{4}{\pi}$ 9. 10.7072 °C

10. (v) $\frac{1}{6}\left(2 + \frac{3}{n} + \frac{1}{n^2}\right) + \frac{1}{2}\left(1 + \frac{1}{n}\right) + 1$ 11. (i) 6

(ii) $y = 3x^2 - 2x^3 + 1$ 12. (iv) $21\frac{1}{3}$ units^2 13. $2\frac{2}{3}$ units^2

14. (i) 17.5 units^2 (ii) 17.5 units^2 15. (ii) $8\frac{2}{3}$ units^2

(iii) $3\frac{1}{3}$ units^2 16. (i) $A(2,8)$ $B(9,1)$ (ii) $57\frac{1}{6}$ units^2

17. (ii) 6.559 ms^{-1} (iii) 91.828 metres (iv) 2 ms^{-2}

Exam Questions

1. (a) (iii) $\frac{x^4}{4} - x^2 + 3x + c$ (b) (i) $1 + \ln x$ (ii) $x\ln x - x + c$

2. (a) (i) 0 (b) (ii) 36.864 m (iii) 10.48 seconds

(c) (ii) 3 hours 51 minutes

This anti-bullying campaign is supported by the Department of Education and Skills with the co-operation of the Irish Educational Publishers Association

Stand Up!
Show Your Support
For Your Lesbian Gay Bisexual & Transgender Friends

Don't Stand For Homophobic or Transphobic Bullying

For information and advice contact
BeLonG To - Ireland's national LGBT Youth Services
www.belongto.org

Celebrating 10 Years

BeLonG To Youth Services
For Lesbian, Gay, Bisexual &
Transgender Young People

AN ROINN OIDEACHAIS AGUS SCILEANNA
DEPARTMENT OF EDUCATION AND SKILLS